P9-AEW-000

THE BROADMAN HYMNAL

The
BROADMAN HYMNAL

Great Standard Hymns and Choice Gospel Songs New and Old, for Use in all Religious Services, such as the Worship Hour, Sunday School, Young People's Meetings, Assemblies, and Evangelistic Services.

B. B. McKinney, *Music Editor*

●

EDITIONS

Cloth Board (Obtainable in Round or Shaped Notes)
Deluxe Pulpit Edition (Round Notes Only, with Special Topical Index)
Pianist's and Organist's Edition (Loose-leaf, Round Notes Only)

BROADMAN PRESS
NASHVILLE, TENNESSEE

451.001

FOREWORD

With something akin to a proper appreciation of the value of music in group and public worship, we have genuine happiness in presenting *The Broadman Hymnal*. If music is the universal language, and it is, hymns of confession, of praise, of petition, of hope, of comfort, of adoration, of consecration easily become the mediums through which all devout souls may join in giving expression to their deepest emotions.

This volume is distinguished for its contents, for its facilities for the ready use of its contents, and for its substantial and beautiful workmanship. Here we have the stately, soul-stirring hymns dear to the hearts of all Christians, the best of more recent hymns, some of which make their initial appearance, and a number of very popular choruses. The indexes are so complete that a desired number may be located without inconvenience or delay. In size, paper, type, and binding, it meets the requirements of solidity and dignity.

As we visualize multitudes of Christians of all names joining in soulful worship through the use of *The Broadman Hymnal,* it is not difficult to understand the satisfaction that is ours in having such a worthy bearer of our press name.

BROADMAN PRESS
The Editor

451–001
PRINTED AND BOUND IN THE U.S.A.
100.S66KSP

The Broadman Hymnal

1 All Hail the Power

CORONATION

EDWARD PERRONET — OLIVER HOLDEN

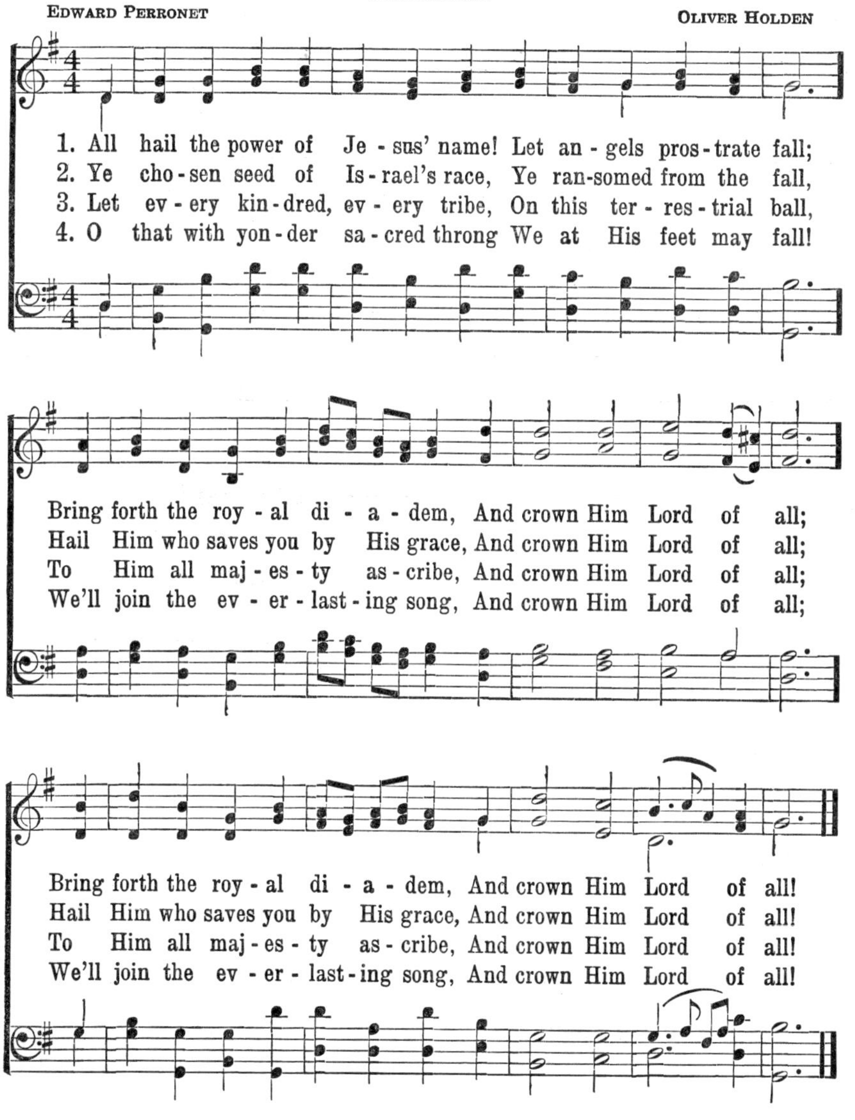

1. All hail the power of Je - sus' name! Let an - gels pros - trate fall;
2. Ye cho - sen seed of Is - rael's race, Ye ran-somed from the fall,
3. Let ev - ery kin - dred, ev - ery tribe, On this ter - res - trial ball,
4. O that with yon - der sa - cred throng We at His feet may fall!
Bring forth the roy - al di - a - dem, And crown Him Lord of all;
Hail Him who saves you by His grace, And crown Him Lord of all;
To Him all maj - es - ty as - cribe, And crown Him Lord of all;
We'll join the ev - er - last - ing song, And crown Him Lord of all;
Bring forth the roy - al di - a - dem, And crown Him Lord of all!
Hail Him who saves you by His grace, And crown Him Lord of all!
To Him all maj - es - ty as - cribe, And crown Him Lord of all!
We'll join the ev - er - last - ing song, And crown Him Lord of all!

2 O Worship the King

ROBERT GRANT — LYONS — J. MICHAEL HAYDN

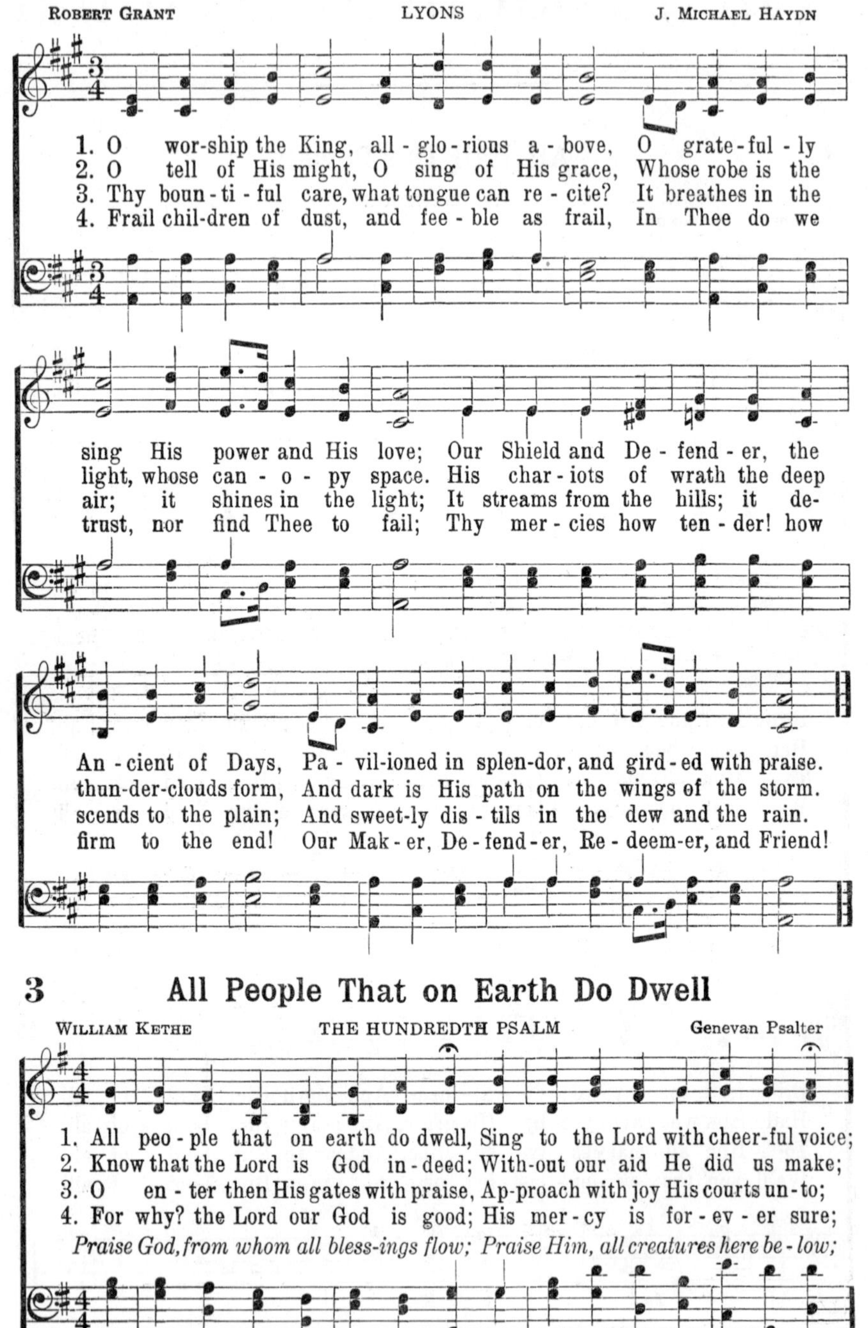
1. O worship the King, all-glorious above, O gratefully sing His power and His love; Our Shield and Defender, the Ancient of Days, Pavilioned in splendor, and girded with praise.
2. O tell of His might, O sing of His grace, Whose robe is the light, whose canopy space. His chariots of wrath the deep thunder-clouds form, And dark is His path on the wings of the storm.
3. Thy bountiful care, what tongue can recite? It breathes in the air; it shines in the light; It streams from the hills; it descends to the plain; And sweetly distils in the dew and the rain.
4. Frail children of dust, and feeble as frail, In Thee do we trust, nor find Thee to fail; Thy mercies how tender! how firm to the end! Our Maker, Defender, Redeemer, and Friend!
3 All People That on Earth Do Dwell
WILLIAM KETHE
THE HUNDREDTH PSALM
Genevan Psalter
1. All people that on earth do dwell, Sing to the Lord with cheerful voice;
2. Know that the Lord is God indeed; Without our aid He did us make;
3. O enter then His gates with praise, Approach with joy His courts unto;
4. For why? the Lord our God is good; His mercy is forever sure;
Praise God, from whom all blessings flow; Praise Him, all creatures here below;

All People That on Earth Do Dwell

Him serve with fear, His praise forth tell; Come ye be - fore Him and re - joice.
We are His flock, He doth us feed, And for His sheep He doth us take.
Praise, laud, and bless His name al-ways, For it is seem - ly so to do.
His truth at all times firm - ly stood, And shall from age to age en-dure.
Praise Him a - bove, ye heaven-ly host; Praise Fa-ther, Son, and Ho - ly Ghost.
4
Come, Thou Almighty King
Anonymous
ITALIAN HYMN
FELICE DE GIARDINI
1. Come, Thou Al - might - y King, Help us Thy name to sing,
2. Come, Thou In - car - nate Word, Gird on Thy might - y sword,
3. Come, Ho - ly Com - fort - er, Thy sa - cred wit - ness bear
4. To the great One in Three E - ter - nal prais - es be
Help us to praise: Fa - ther, all - glo - ri - ous, O'er all vic-
Our prayer at - tend: Come, and Thy peo - ple bless, And give Thy
In this glad hour: Thou who al - might - y art, Now rule in
Hence ev - er - more. His sov-ereign maj - es - ty May we in
to - ri - ous, Come, and reign o - ver us, An - cient of Days.
Word suc - cess; Spir - it of ho - li - ness, On us de - scend.
ev - ery heart, And ne'er from us de - part, Spir - it of power.
glo - ry see, And to e - ter - ni - ty Love and a - dore.

5
O For a Thousand Tongues
AZMON
Charles Wesley
Carl G. Glaser
Arr. by Lowell Mason
1. O for a thou-sand tongues to sing My great Re-deem-er's praise,
2. My gra-cious Mas-ter and my God, As-sist me to pro-claim,
3. Je-sus! the name that charms our fears, That bids our sor-rows cease;
4. He breaks the power of can-celed sin, He sets the pris-oner free;
The glo-ries of my God and King, The tri-umphs of His grace.
To spread through all the earth a-broad The hon-ors of Thy name.
'Tis mu-sic in the sin-ner's ears, 'Tis life, and health, and peace.
His blood can make the foul-est clean; His blood a-vailed for me.
6
Holy, Holy, Holy
Reginald Heber
NICAEA
Rev. John B. Dykes
1. Ho-ly, Ho-ly, Ho-ly, Lord God Al-might-y! Ear-ly in the
2. Ho-ly, Ho-ly, Ho-ly! All the saints a-dore Thee, Cast-ing down their
3. Ho-ly, Ho-ly, Ho-ly! Tho' the dark-ness hide Thee, Tho' the eye of
4. Ho-ly, Ho-ly, Ho-ly, Lord God Al-might-y! All Thy works shall
morn-ing our song shall rise to Thee; Ho-ly, Ho-ly, Ho-ly!
gold-en crowns a-round the glass-y sea; Cher-u-bim and ser-a-phim
sin-ful man Thy glo-ry may not see, On-ly Thou art ho-ly;
praise Thy name, in earth, and sky, and sea; Ho-ly, Ho-ly, Ho-ly!

Holy, Holy, Holy

7 When Morning Gilds the Skies

Mer-ci-ful and Might-y! God in Three per-sons, bless-ed Trin-i-ty!
fall-ing down be-fore Thee, Who wert, and art, and ev-er-more shalt be.
there is none be-side Thee Per-fect in power, in love, and pu-ri-ty.
Mer-ci-ful and Might-y! God in Three per-sons, bless-ed Trin-i-ty!
7
When Morning Gilds the Skies
From the German
Tr. by EDWARD CASWALL
LAUDES DOMINI
JOSEPH BARNBY
1. When morn-ing gilds the skies, My heart a-wak-ing cries:
2. Does sad-ness fill my mind, A sol-ace here I find:
3. In heaven's e-ter-nal bliss The love-liest strain is this,
4. Be this, while life is mine, My can-ti-cle di-vine,
May Je-sus Christ be praised! A-like at work and prayer
May Je-sus Christ be praised! Or fades my earth-ly bliss,
May Je-sus Christ be praised! The powers of dark-ness fear,
May Je-sus Christ be praised! Be this th' e-ter-nal song,
To Je-sus I re-pair: May Je-sus Christ be praised!
My com-fort still is this: May Je-sus Christ be praised!
When this sweet chant they hear: May Je-sus Christ be praised!
Through all the a-ges long: May Je-sus Christ be praised!

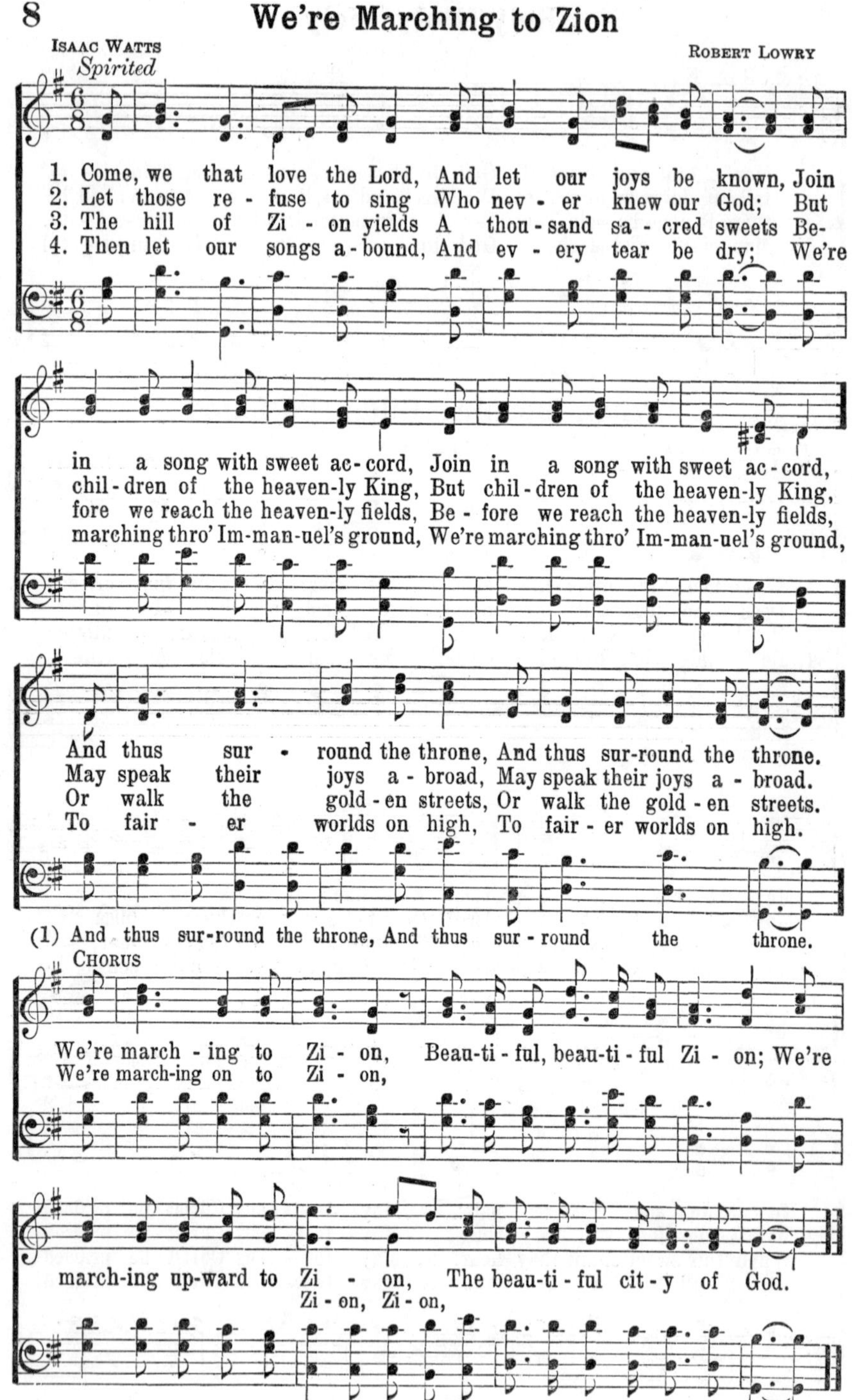
8
We're Marching to Zion
Isaac Watts
Robert Lowry
Spirited
1. Come, we that love the Lord, And let our joys be known, Join in a song with sweet ac-cord, Join in a song with sweet ac-cord, And thus sur - round the throne, And thus sur-round the throne.
2. Let those re - fuse to sing Who nev - er knew our God; But chil-dren of the heaven-ly King, But chil-dren of the heaven-ly King, May speak their joys a - broad, May speak their joys a - broad.
3. The hill of Zi - on yields A thou-sand sa - cred sweets Be-fore we reach the heaven-ly fields, Be - fore we reach the heaven-ly fields, Or walk the gold - en streets, Or walk the gold - en streets.
4. Then let our songs a-bound, And ev - ery tear be dry; We're marching thro' Im-man-uel's ground, We're marching thro' Im-man-uel's ground, To fair - er worlds on high, To fair - er worlds on high.
(1) And thus sur-round the throne, And thus sur - round the throne.
Chorus
We're march - ing to Zi - on, Beau-ti - ful, beau-ti - ful Zi - on; We're
We're march-ing on to Zi - on,
march-ing up-ward to Zi - on, The beau-ti - ful cit - y of God.
Zi - on, Zi - on,

9 Whiter Than Snow

JAMES NICHOLSON — WILLIAM G. FISCHER

1. Lord Je-sus, I long to be per-fect-ly whole; I want Thee for-ev-er to live in my soul; Break down ev-ery i-dol, cast out ev-ery foe; Now wash me, and I shall be whit-er than snow.
2. Lord Je-sus, look down from Thy throne in the skies, And help me to make a com-plete sac-ri-fice; I give up my-self, and what-ev-er I know—Now wash me, and I shall be whit-er than snow.
3. Lord Je-sus, for this I most hum-bly en-treat, I wait, bless-ed Lord, at Thy cru-ci-fied feet; By faith, for my cleans-ing, I see Thy blood flow—Now wash me, and I shall be whit-er than snow.
4. Lord Je-sus, Thou see-est I pa-tient-ly wait, Come now, and with-in me a new heart cre-ate; To those who have sought Thee, Thou nev-er saidst No— Now wash me, and I shall be whit-er than snow.
CHORUS
Whiter than snow, yes, whiter than snow; Now wash me, and I shall be whiter than snow.

10 Safely Through Another Week

JOHN NEWTON — SABBATH — LOWELL MASON

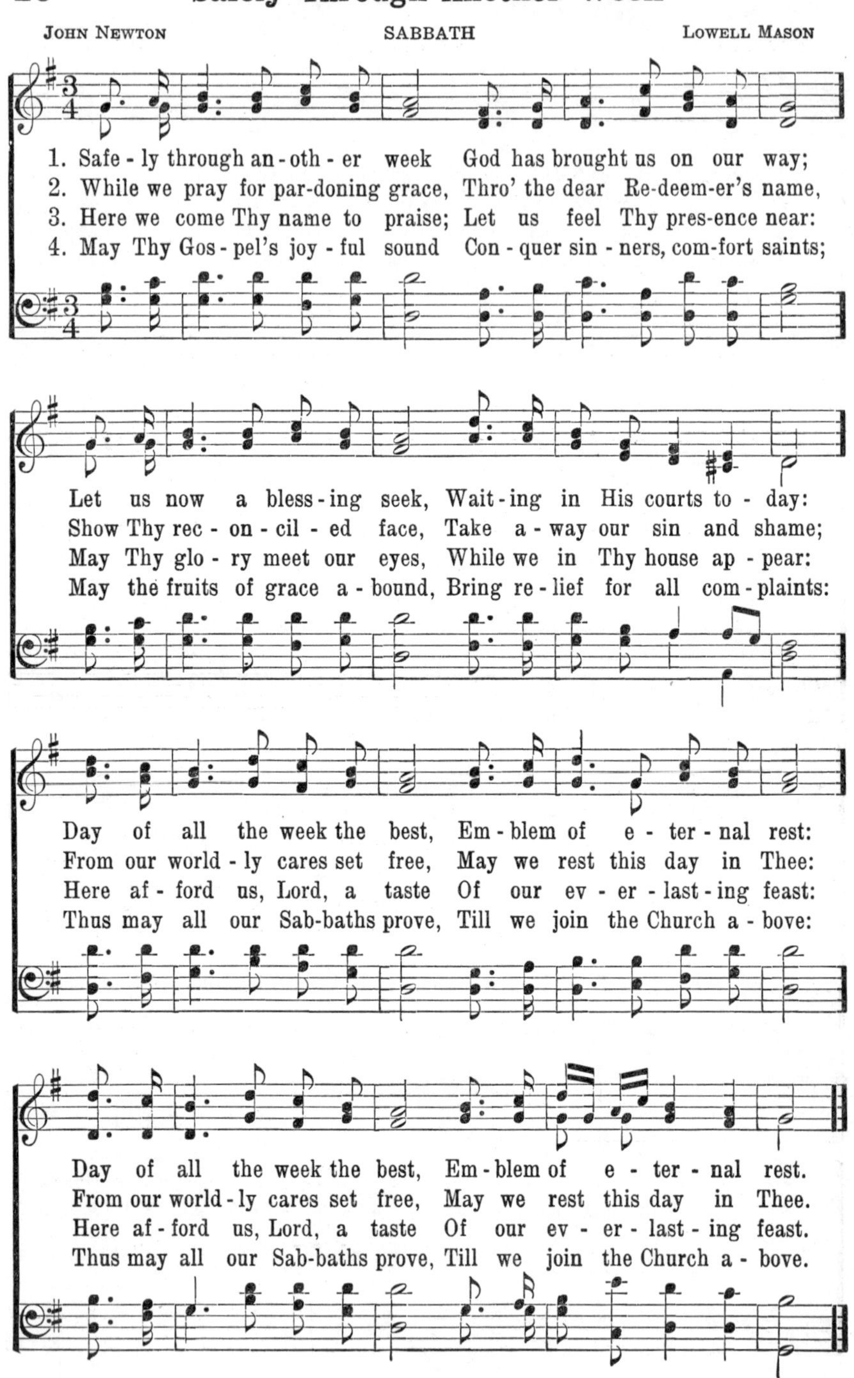
1. Safe - ly through an - oth - er week God has brought us on our way;
2. While we pray for par-doning grace, Thro' the dear Re-deem-er's name,
3. Here we come Thy name to praise; Let us feel Thy pres-ence near:
4. May Thy Gos - pel's joy - ful sound Con - quer sin - ners, com-fort saints;
Let us now a bless - ing seek, Wait - ing in His courts to - day:
Show Thy rec - on - cil - ed face, Take a - way our sin and shame;
May Thy glo - ry meet our eyes, While we in Thy house ap - pear:
May the fruits of grace a - bound, Bring re - lief for all com - plaints:
Day of all the week the best, Em - blem of e - ter - nal rest:
From our world - ly cares set free, May we rest this day in Thee:
Here af - ford us, Lord, a taste Of our ev - er - last - ing feast:
Thus may all our Sab-baths prove, Till we join the Church a - bove:
Day of all the week the best, Em - blem of e - ter - nal rest.
From our world - ly cares set free, May we rest this day in Thee.
Here af - ford us, Lord, a taste Of our ev - er - last - ing feast.
Thus may all our Sab-baths prove, Till we join the Church a - bove.

11 O Day of Rest and Gladness

C. WORDSWORTH — MENDEBRAS — Arr. by L. MASON

1. O day of rest and glad - ness, O day of joy and light,
2. On thee, at the cre - a - tion, The light first had its birth;
3. To - day on wea - ry na - tions The heaven-ly man - na falls;
4. New grac - es ev - er gain - ing From this our day of rest,
O balm of care and sad - ness, Most beau - ti - ful, most bright;
On thee, for our sal - va - tion, Christ rose from depths of earth;
To ho - ly con - vo - ca - tions The sil - ver trump-et calls,
We reach the rest re - main - ing To spir - its of the blest.
On thee, the high and low - ly, Bend - ing be - fore the throne,
On thee, our Lord, vic - to - rious, The Spir - it sent from heaven;
Where Gos - pel light is glow - ing With pure and ra - diant beams,
To Ho - ly Ghost be prais - es, To Fa - ther, and to Son;
Sing "Ho - ly, Ho - ly, Ho - ly," To the great Three in One.
And thus on thee, most glo - rious, A tri - ple light was given.
And liv - ing wa - ter flow - ing With soul - re - fresh-ing streams.
The Church her voice up - rais - es To Thee, blest Three in One.

12 The Morning Light Is Breaking

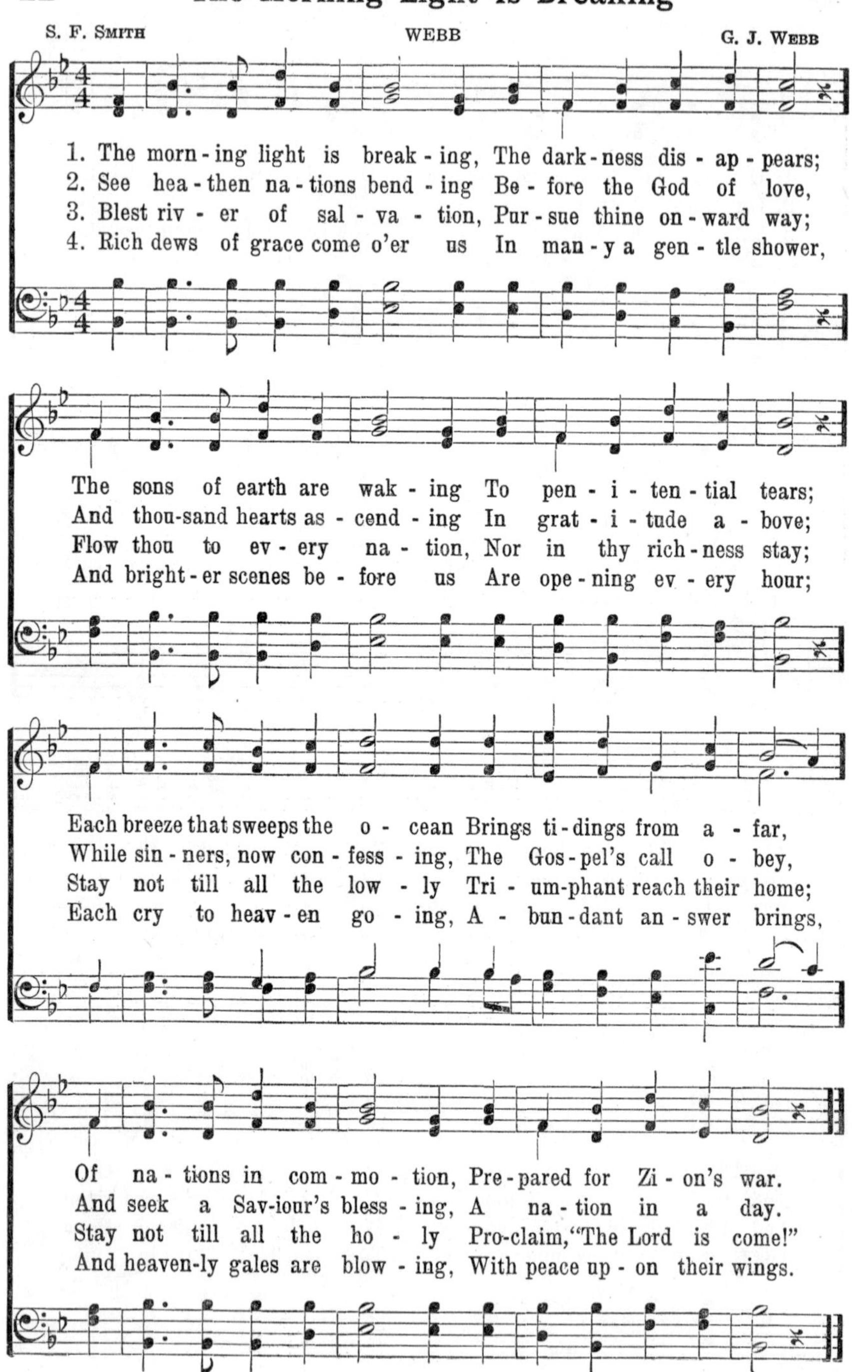
S. F. SMITH
WEBB
G. J. WEBB
1. The morn-ing light is break-ing, The dark-ness dis-ap-pears;
2. See hea-then na-tions bend-ing Be-fore the God of love,
3. Blest riv-er of sal-va-tion, Pur-sue thine on-ward way;
4. Rich dews of grace come o'er us In man-y a gen-tle shower,
The sons of earth are wak-ing To pen-i-ten-tial tears;
And thou-sand hearts as-cend-ing In grat-i-tude a-bove;
Flow thou to ev-ery na-tion, Nor in thy rich-ness stay;
And bright-er scenes be-fore us Are ope-ning ev-ery hour;
Each breeze that sweeps the o-cean Brings ti-dings from a-far,
While sin-ners, now con-fess-ing, The Gos-pel's call o-bey,
Stay not till all the low-ly Tri-um-phant reach their home;
Each cry to heav-en go-ing, A-bun-dant an-swer brings,
Of na-tions in com-mo-tion, Pre-pared for Zi-on's war.
And seek a Sav-iour's bless-ing, A na-tion in a day.
Stay not till all the ho-ly Pro-claim, "The Lord is come!"
And heaven-ly gales are blow-ing, With peace up-on their wings.

13
Saviour, Like a Shepherd Lead Us
Dorothy A. Thrupp
SHEPHERD
William B. Bradbury
1. Sav - iour, like a shep-herd lead us, Much we need Thy ten-der care;
2. We are Thine; do Thou be - friend us, Be the Guard-ian of our way;
3. Thou hast prom-ised to re - ceive us, Poor and sin - ful though we be;
4. Ear - ly let us seek Thy fa - vor; Ear - ly let us do Thy will;
In Thy pleas-ant pas-tures feed us, For our use Thy folds pre-pare:
Keep Thy flock, from sin de - fend us, Seek us when we go a - stray:
Thou hast mer-cy to re - lieve us, Grace to cleanse, and power to free:
Bless-ed Lord and on - ly Sav - iour, With Thy love our bos-oms fill:
Bless-ed Je - sus, Bless-ed Je - sus, Thou hast bought us, Thine we are;
Bless-ed Je - sus, Bless-ed Je - sus, Hear, O hear us when we pray;
Bless-ed Je - sus, Bless-ed Je - sus, Ear - ly let us turn to Thee;
Bless-ed Je - sus, Bless-ed Je - sus, Thou hast loved us, love us still;
Bless-ed Je - sus, Bless-ed Je - sus, Thou hast bought us, Thine we are.
Bless-ed Je - sus, Bless-ed Je - sus, Hear, O hear us when we pray.
Bless-ed Je - sus, Bless-ed Je - sus, Ear - ly let us turn to Thee.
Bless-ed Je - sus, Bless-ed Je - sus, Thou hast loved us, love us still.

14 Seeking for Me

E. E. Hasty

1. Je - sus, my Sav-iour, to Beth - le-hem came, Laid in a man - ger to
2. Je - sus, my Sav-iour, in mer - cy and love, Came from the man-sions of
3. Je - sus, my Sav-iour, the same as of old, While I did wan - der a-
4. Je - sus, my Sav-iour, shall come from on high, Sweet is the prom - ise as
sorrow and shame; Oh, it was won-der-ful, blest be His name, Seek-ing for me, for
heav-en a-bove, Ten-der-ly pleading for sin-ners like me, Pleading for me, for
far from the fold, Gently and long He hath pled with my soul, Call-ing for me, for
wea-ry years fly; Oh, I shall see Him de-scend-ing the sky, Com-ing for me, for
for me, ...
for me, ...
me: Seek-ing for me, Seek-ing for me, Seek-ing for me, Seek-ing for me;
me: Pleading for me, Pleading for me, Pleading for me, Pleading for me;
me: Call-ing for me, Call-ing for me, Call-ing for me, Call-ing for me;
me: Com-ing for me, Com-ing for me, Com-ing for me, Com-ing for me;
Oh, it was won-der-ful, blest be His name, Seek-ing for me, for me.
Ten-der - ly plead-ing for sin-ners like me, Pleading for me, for me.
Gen-tly and long He hath pled with my soul, Call - ing for me, for me.
Oh, I shall see Him de-scend-ing the sky, Com-ing for me, for me.

15 Jesus Saves

PRISCILLA J. OWENS
WM. J. KIRKPATRICK
1. We have heard the joy - ful sound: Je - sus saves! Je - sus saves!
2. Waft it on the roll - ing tide; Je - sus saves! Je - sus saves!
3. Sing a - bove the bat - tle strife, Je - sus saves! Je - sus saves!
4. Give the winds a might - y voice, Je - sus saves! Je - sus saves!
Spread the ti - dings all a - round: Je - sus saves! Je - sus saves!
Tell to sin - ners far and wide: Je - sus saves! Je - sus saves!
By His death and end - less life, Je - sus saves! Je - sus saves!
Let the na - tions now re - joice,— Je - sus saves! Je - sus saves!
Bear the news to ev - ery land, Climb the steeps and cross the waves;
Sing, ye is - lands of the sea; Ech - o back, ye o - cean caves;
Sing it soft - ly through the gloom, When the heart for mer - cy craves;
Shout sal - va - tion full and free; High - est hills and deep - est caves;
On - ward!—'tis our Lord's com - mand; Je - sus saves! Je - sus saves!
Earth shall keep her ju - bi - lee: Je - sus saves! Je - sus saves!
Sing in tri - umph o'er the tomb,—Je - sus saves! Je - sus saves!
This our song of vic - to - ry,— Je - sus saves! Je - sus saves!

16 When I Can Read My Title Clear

ISAAC WATTS — PISGAH — J. C. LOWRY

1. When I can read my ti - tle clear To man-sions in the skies,
2. Should earth a - gainst my soul en - gage, And fi - ery darts be hurled,
3. Let cares, like a wild del - uge come, And storms of sor-row fall!
4. There shall I bathe my wea - ry soul In seas of heaven-ly rest,
I'll bid fare-well to ev - ery fear, And wipe my weep - ing eyes.
Then I can smile at Sa - tan's rage, And face a frown - ing world.
May I but safe - ly reach my home, My God, my heaven, my all.
And not a wave of trou - ble roll, A - cross my peace - ful breast.
And wipe my weep-ing eyes, And wipe my weep - ing eyes,
And face a frown-ing world, And face a frown - ing world,
My God, my heaven, my all, My God, my heaven, my all,
A - cross my peace-ful breast, A - cross my peace - ful breast,
I'll bid fare-well to ev - ery fear, And wipe my weep - ing eyes.
Then I can smile at Sa - tan's rage, And face a frown - ing world.
May I but safe - ly reach my home, My God, my heaven, my all.
And not a wave of trou - ble roll, A - cross my peace - ful breast.

17

O Could I Speak

SAMUEL MEDLEY — ARIEL — DR. LOWELL MASON

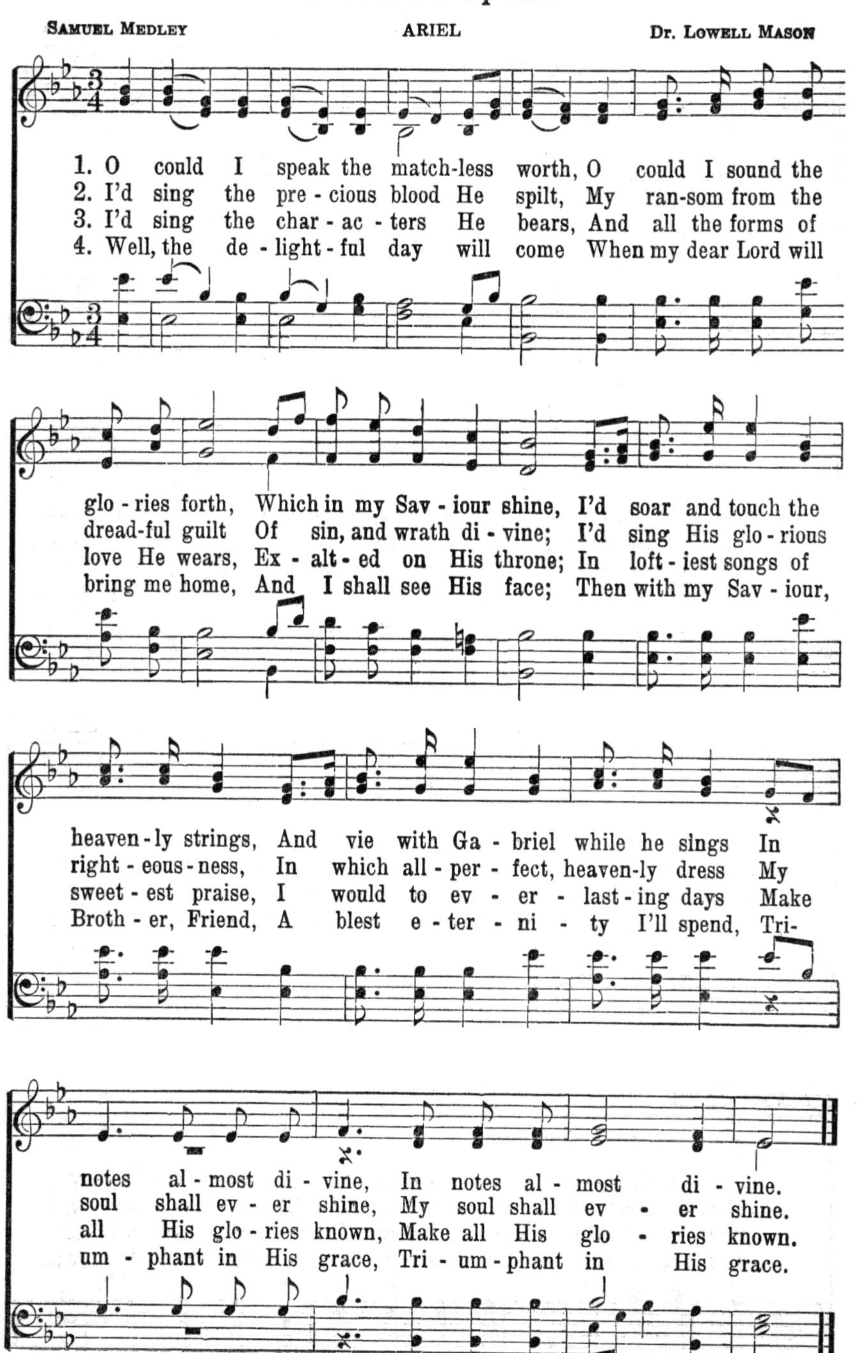
1. O could I speak the match-less worth, O could I sound the
2. I'd sing the pre - cious blood He spilt, My ran-som from the
3. I'd sing the char - ac - ters He bears, And all the forms of
4. Well, the de - light - ful day will come When my dear Lord will
glo - ries forth, Which in my Sav - iour shine, I'd soar and touch the
dread-ful guilt Of sin, and wrath di - vine; I'd sing His glo - rious
love He wears, Ex - alt - ed on His throne; In loft - iest songs of
bring me home, And I shall see His face; Then with my Sav - iour,
heaven - ly strings, And vie with Ga - briel while he sings In
right - eous - ness, In which all - per - fect, heaven-ly dress My
sweet - est praise, I would to ev - er - last - ing days Make
Broth - er, Friend, A blest e - ter - ni - ty I'll spend, Tri-
notes al - most di - vine, In notes al - most di - vine.
soul shall ev - er shine, My soul shall ev - er shine.
all His glo - ries known, Make all His glo - ries known.
um - phant in His grace, Tri - um - phant in His grace.

18 Crown Him with Many Crowns

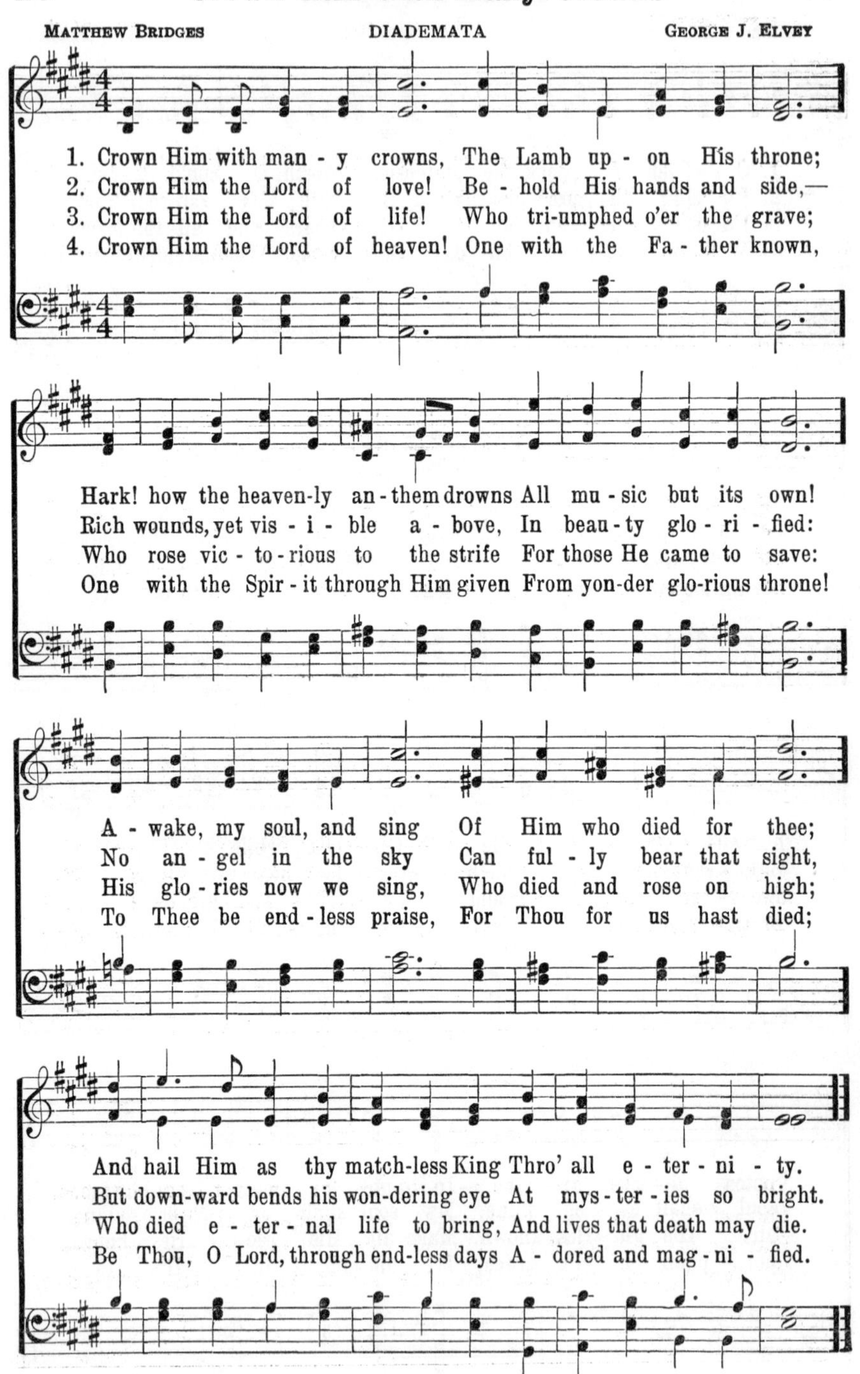
MATTHEW BRIDGES
DIADEMATA
GEORGE J. ELVEY
1. Crown Him with man - y crowns, The Lamb up - on His throne;
2. Crown Him the Lord of love! Be - hold His hands and side,—
3. Crown Him the Lord of life! Who tri-umphed o'er the grave;
4. Crown Him the Lord of heaven! One with the Fa - ther known,
Hark! how the heaven-ly an - them drowns All mu - sic but its own!
Rich wounds, yet vis - i - ble a - bove, In beau - ty glo - ri - fied:
Who rose vic - to - rious to the strife For those He came to save:
One with the Spir - it through Him given From yon-der glo-rious throne!
A - wake, my soul, and sing Of Him who died for thee;
No an - gel in the sky Can ful - ly bear that sight,
His glo - ries now we sing, Who died and rose on high;
To Thee be end - less praise, For Thou for us hast died;
And hail Him as thy match-less King Thro' all e - ter - ni - ty.
But down-ward bends his won-dering eye At mys - ter - ies so bright.
Who died e - ter - nal life to bring, And lives that death may die.
Be Thou, O Lord, through end-less days A - dored and mag - ni - fied.

19

Love Divine

Charles Wesley
LOVE DIVINE
John Zundel
1. Love di - vine, all love ex - cel-ling, Joy of heaven, to earth come down!
2. Breathe, O breathe Thy lov-ing Spir - it In - to ev - ery trou - bled breast!
3. Come, Al-might - y to de - liv - er, Let us all Thy life re - ceive;
4. Fin - ish then Thy new cre - a - tion; Pure and spot-less let us be;
Fix in us Thy hum - ble dwell-ing; All Thy faith - ful mer - cies crown.
Let us all in Thee in - her - it, Let us find that sec - ond rest.
Sud - den - ly re - turn, and nev - er, Nev - er - more Thy tem - ples leave:
Let us see Thy great sal - va - tion, Per - fect - ly re - stored in Thee:
Je - sus, Thou art all com - pas - sion, Pure, un-bound-ed love Thou art;
Take a - way our bent to sin - ning; Al - pha and O - me - ga be;
Thee we would be al - ways bless-ing, Serve Thee as Thy hosts a - bove,
Changed from glo-ry in - to glo - ry, Till in heaven we take our place,
Vis - it us with Thy sal - va - tion; En - ter ev - ery trem-bling heart.
End of faith, as its be - gin-ning, Set our hearts at lib - er - ty.
Pray, and praise Thee with-out ceas - ing, Glo - ry in Thy per - fect love.
Till we cast our crowns be - fore Thee, Lost in won - der, love, and praise.

20 I Saw the Cross of Jesus

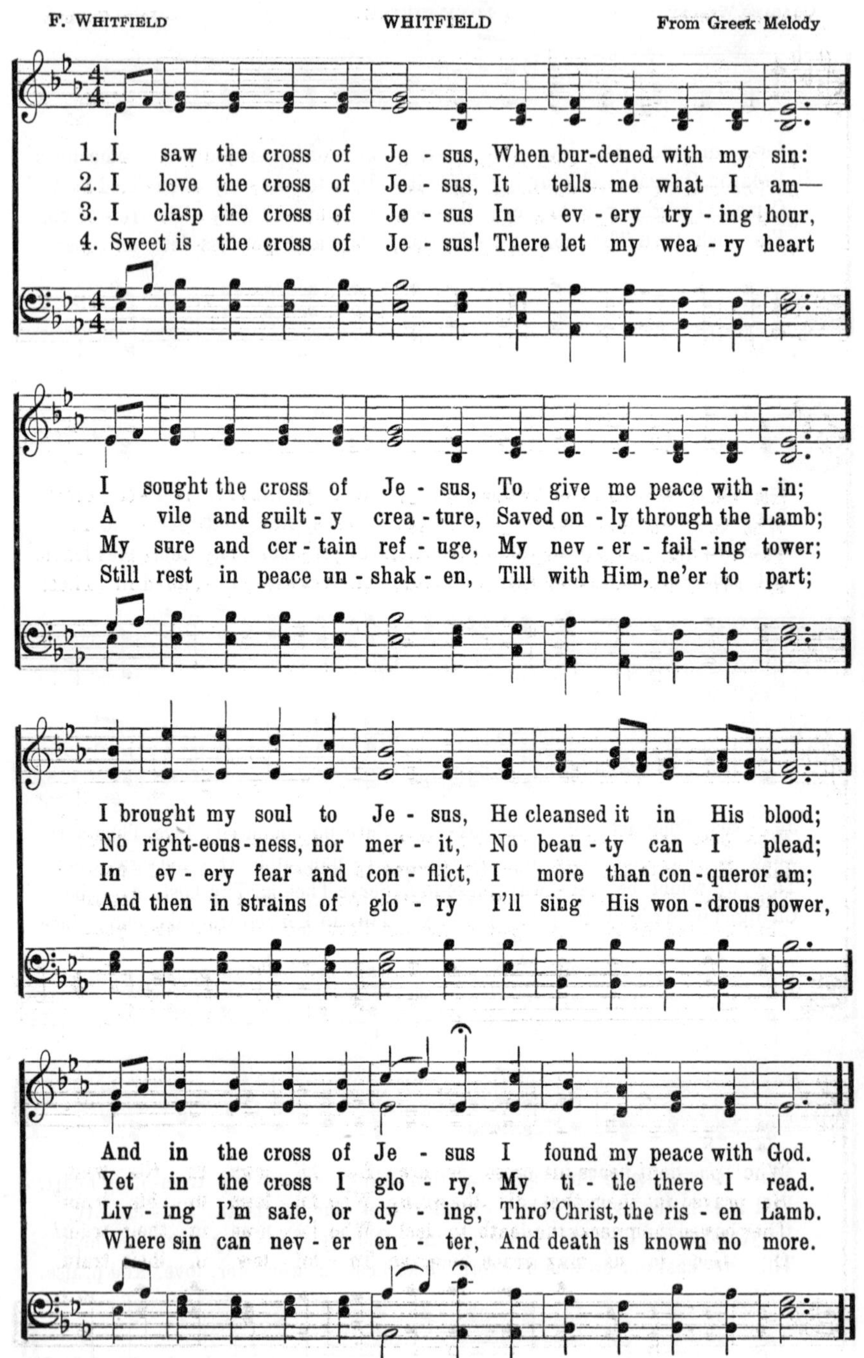
F. WHITFIELD
WHITFIELD
From Greek Melody
1. I saw the cross of Je - sus, When bur-dened with my sin:
2. I love the cross of Je - sus, It tells me what I am—
3. I clasp the cross of Je - sus In ev - ery try - ing hour,
4. Sweet is the cross of Je - sus! There let my wea - ry heart
I sought the cross of Je - sus, To give me peace with - in;
A vile and guilt - y crea - ture, Saved on - ly through the Lamb;
My sure and cer - tain ref - uge, My nev - er - fail - ing tower;
Still rest in peace un - shak - en, Till with Him, ne'er to part;
I brought my soul to Je - sus, He cleansed it in His blood;
No right-eous - ness, nor mer - it, No beau - ty can I plead;
In ev - ery fear and con - flict, I more than con - queror am;
And then in strains of glo - ry I'll sing His won - drous power,
And in the cross of Je - sus I found my peace with God.
Yet in the cross I glo - ry, My ti - tle there I read.
Liv - ing I'm safe, or dy - ing, Thro' Christ, the ris - en Lamb.
Where sin can nev - er en - ter, And death is known no more.

21 The Son of God Goes Forth to War

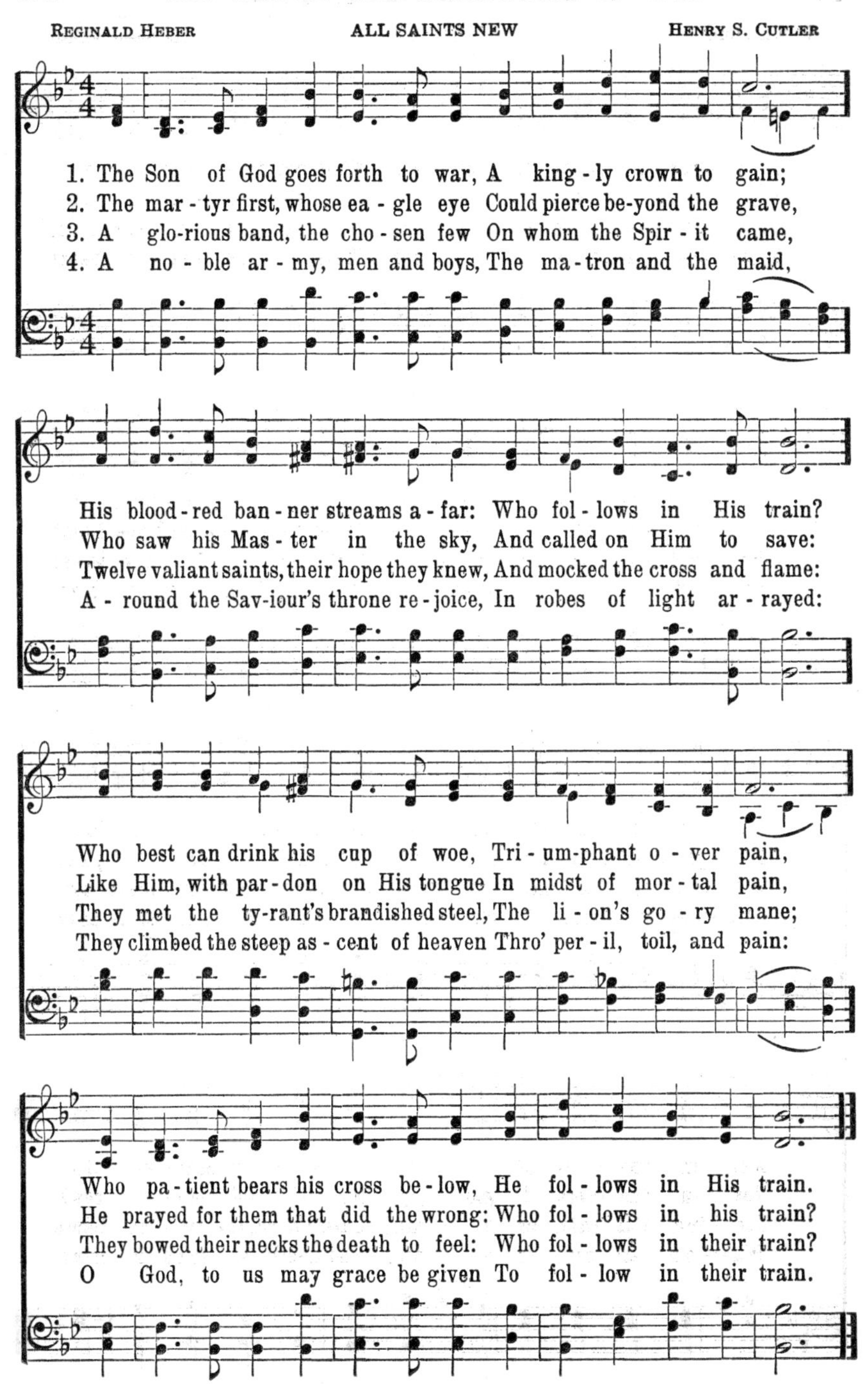
REGINALD HEBER
ALL SAINTS NEW
HENRY S. CUTLER
1. The Son of God goes forth to war, A king - ly crown to gain;
2. The mar - tyr first, whose ea - gle eye Could pierce be-yond the grave,
3. A glo-rious band, the cho - sen few On whom the Spir - it came,
4. A no - ble ar - my, men and boys, The ma-tron and the maid,
His blood-red ban - ner streams a - far: Who fol - lows in His train?
Who saw his Mas - ter in the sky, And called on Him to save:
Twelve valiant saints, their hope they knew, And mocked the cross and flame:
A - round the Sav-iour's throne re - joice, In robes of light ar - rayed:
Who best can drink his cup of woe, Tri - um-phant o - ver pain,
Like Him, with par - don on His tongue In midst of mor - tal pain,
They met the ty-rant's brandished steel, The li - on's go - ry mane;
They climbed the steep as - cent of heaven Thro' per - il, toil, and pain:
Who pa - tient bears his cross be - low, He fol - lows in His train.
He prayed for them that did the wrong: Who fol - lows in his train?
They bowed their necks the death to feel: Who fol - lows in their train?
O God, to us may grace be given To fol - low in their train.

22 The Lord Is My Shepherd

JAMES MONTGOMERY
THOMAS KOSCHAT
1. The Lord is my Shep-herd, no want shall I know; I feed in green
2. Thro' the val-ley and shad-ow of death though I stray, Since Thou art my
3. In the midst of af - flic - tion my ta - ble is spread; With blessings un-
4. Let good-ness and mer - cy, my boun - ti - ful God, Still fol - low my
pas - tures, safe-fold - ed I rest; He lead - eth my soul where the
Guard-ian, no e - vil I fear; Thy rod shall de - fend me, Thy
meas-ured my cup run - neth o'er; With per-fume and oil Thou a-
steps till I meet Thee a - bove: I seek by the path which my
still wa - ters flow, Re - stores me when wan-dering, re-deems when op-
staff be my stay; No harm can be - fall, with my Com - fort - er
noint-est my head; O what shall I ask of Thy prov - i - dence
fore - fa-thers trod, Thro' the land of their so - journ, Thy king - dom of
pressed; Re - stores me when wan-dering, re - deems when op - pressed.
near; No harm can be - fall, with my Com - fort - er near.
more? O what shall I ask of Thy prov - i - dence more?
love; Thro' the land of their so - journ, Thy king - dom of love.

23 The Sheltering Rock

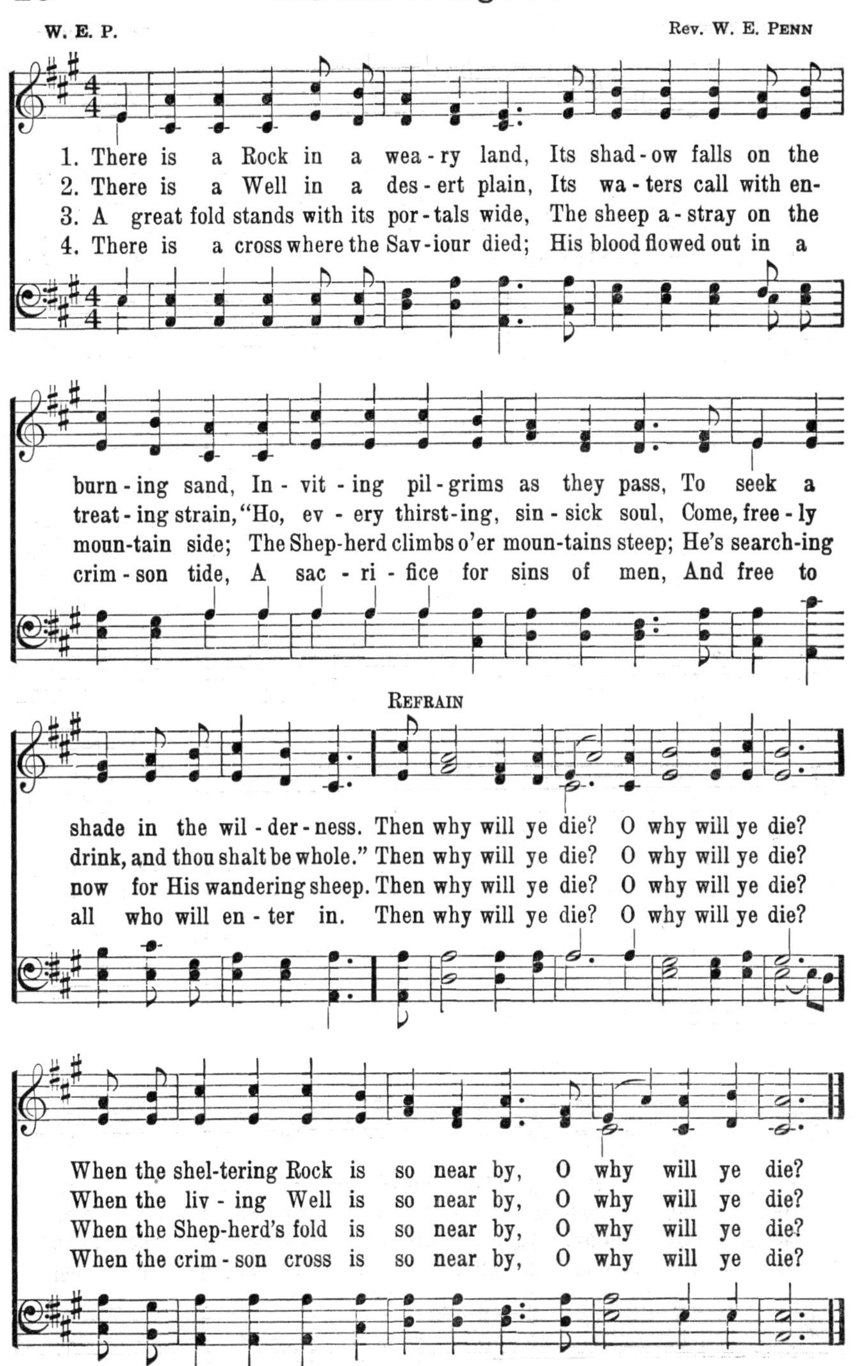

W. E. P.
Rev. W. E. Penn
1. There is a Rock in a wea-ry land, Its shad-ow falls on the
2. There is a Well in a des-ert plain, Its wa-ters call with en-
3. A great fold stands with its por-tals wide, The sheep a-stray on the
4. There is a cross where the Sav-iour died; His blood flowed out in a
burn-ing sand, In-vit-ing pil-grims as they pass, To seek a
treat-ing strain, "Ho, ev-ery thirst-ing, sin-sick soul, Come, free-ly
moun-tain side; The Shep-herd climbs o'er moun-tains steep; He's search-ing
crim-son tide, A sac-ri-fice for sins of men, And free to
Refrain
shade in the wil-der-ness. Then why will ye die? O why will ye die?
drink, and thou shalt be whole." Then why will ye die? O why will ye die?
now for His wandering sheep. Then why will ye die? O why will ye die?
all who will en-ter in. Then why will ye die? O why will ye die?
When the shel-tering Rock is so near by, O why will ye die?
When the liv-ing Well is so near by, O why will ye die?
When the Shep-herd's fold is so near by, O why will ye die?
When the crim-son cross is so near by, O why will ye die?

24 How Tedious and Tasteless the Hours

JOHN NEWTON — DE FLEURY — LEWIS EDSON

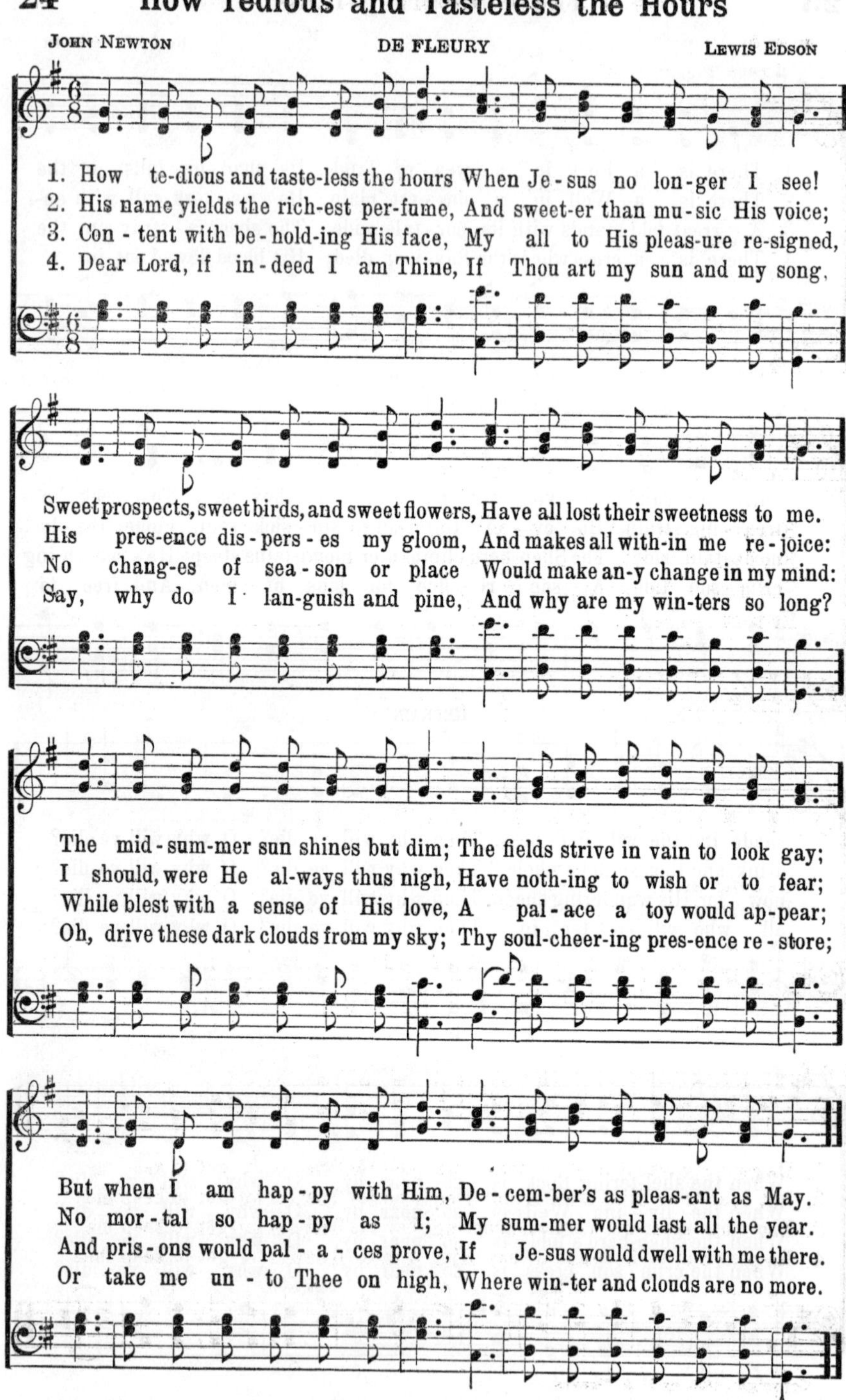

1. How te-dious and taste-less the hours When Je-sus no lon-ger I see!
2. His name yields the rich-est per-fume, And sweet-er than mu-sic His voice;
3. Con-tent with be-hold-ing His face, My all to His pleas-ure re-signed,
4. Dear Lord, if in-deed I am Thine, If Thou art my sun and my song,
Sweet prospects, sweet birds, and sweet flowers, Have all lost their sweetness to me.
His pres-ence dis-pers-es my gloom, And makes all with-in me re-joice:
No chang-es of sea-son or place Would make an-y change in my mind:
Say, why do I lan-guish and pine, And why are my win-ters so long?
The mid-sum-mer sun shines but dim; The fields strive in vain to look gay;
I should, were He al-ways thus nigh, Have noth-ing to wish or to fear;
While blest with a sense of His love, A pal-ace a toy would ap-pear;
Oh, drive these dark clouds from my sky; Thy soul-cheer-ing pres-ence re-store;
But when I am hap-py with Him, De-cem-ber's as pleas-ant as May.
No mor-tal so hap-py as I; My sum-mer would last all the year.
And pris-ons would pal-a-ces prove, If Je-sus would dwell with me there.
Or take me un-to Thee on high, Where win-ter and clouds are no more.

25

He'll Never Forget to Keep Me

F. A. G. — F. A. Graves

Tenor & Alto Duet

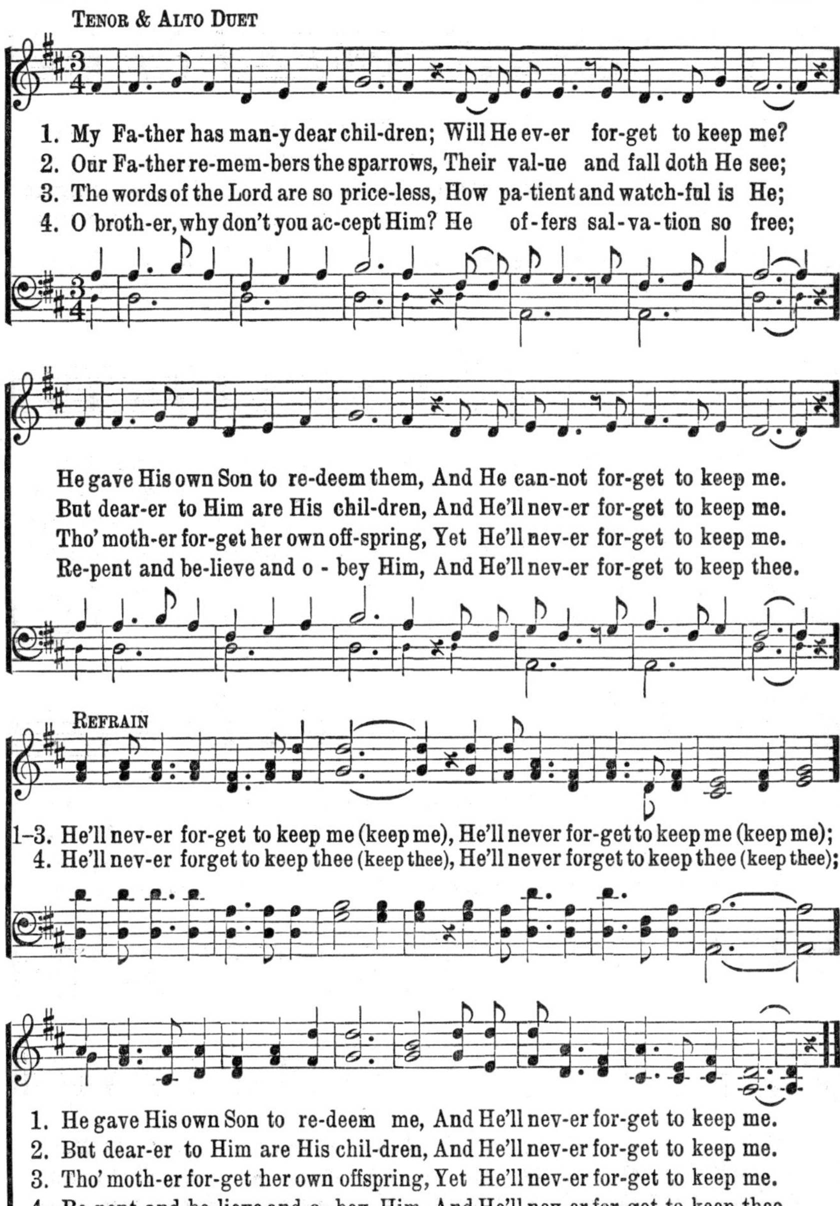
1. My Fa-ther has man-y dear chil-dren; Will He ev-er for-get to keep me?
2. Our Fa-ther re-mem-bers the sparrows, Their val-ue and fall doth He see;
3. The words of the Lord are so price-less, How pa-tient and watch-ful is He;
4. O broth-er, why don't you ac-cept Him? He of-fers sal-va-tion so free;
He gave His own Son to re-deem them, And He can-not for-get to keep me.
But dear-er to Him are His chil-dren, And He'll nev-er for-get to keep me.
Tho' moth-er for-get her own off-spring, Yet He'll nev-er for-get to keep me.
Re-pent and be-lieve and o - bey Him, And He'll nev-er for-get to keep thee.
Refrain
1–3. He'll nev-er for-get to keep me (keep me), He'll never for-get to keep me (keep me);
4. He'll nev-er forget to keep thee (keep thee), He'll never forget to keep thee (keep thee);
1. He gave His own Son to re-deem me, And He'll nev-er for-get to keep me.
2. But dear-er to Him are His chil-dren, And He'll nev-er for-get to keep me.
3. Tho' moth-er for-get her own offspring, Yet He'll nev-er for-get to keep me.
4. Re-pent and be-lieve and o - bey Him, And He'll nev-er for-get to keep thee.

26 When I Get to the End of the Way

CHARLIE D. TILLMAN
1. The sands have been washed in the foot - prints Of the Stran-ger on
2. There are so man - y hills to climb up - ward, I oft - en am
3. He loves me too well to for - sake me, Or give me a
4. When the last fee - ble steps have been tak - en, And the gates of that
D. S.— toils of the road will seem noth - ing, When I get to the
Gal - i - lee's shore— And the voice that sub-dued the rough bil - lows
long-ing for rest; But He who ap-points me my path-way,
tri - al too much; All His peo - ple have been dear - ly pur - chased,
cit - y ap - pear, And the beau - ti - ful songs of the an - gels
end of the way; And the toils of the road will seem noth - ing,
4. Then the
FINE
Will be heard in Ju - de - a no more. But the path of that lone Gal - i-
Knows just what is need-ful and best. I know in His Word He hath
And Sa - tan can nev - er claim such. By and by I shall see Him and
Float out on my lis - ten - ing ear; When all that now seems so mys-
When I get to the end of the way.
D. S.
le - an With joy I will fol - low to - day; And the
prom-ised That my strength "it shall be as my day;" And the
praise Him, In the cit - y of un - end - ing day; And the
te - rious Will be bright and as clear as the day; Then the

27 Is Not This the Land of Beulah?

Anonymous
Arranged
1. I am dwell-ing on the moun-tain, Where the gold - en sun-light gleams,
2. I can see far down the moun-tain, Where I wan-dered wea-ry years,
3. I am drink-ing at the foun-tain, Where I ev - er would a - bide,
4. Tell me not of heav - y cross - es, Nor the bur - dens hard to bear,
5. Oh, the cross has won-drous glo - ry! Oft I've proved this to be true,
O'er a land of won-drous beau-ty, Far ex - ceeds my fond - est dreams;
Oft - en hin-dered in my jour-ney By the ghosts of doubts and fears,
For I've tast - ed life's pure riv - er, And my soul is sat - is - fied;
For I've found this great sal - va - tion Makes each bur-den light ap - pear;
When I'm in the way so nar - row, I can see a path-way through;
Where the air is pure, e - the - real, La - den with the breath of flowers,
Bro - ken vows and dis - ap - point-ments Thick-ly sprin - kled all the way;
There's no thirst-ing for life's pleas-ures, Nor a - dorn - ing rich and gay,
And I love to fol - low Je - sus, Glad - ly count - ing all but dross,
And how sweet - ly Je - sus whis - pers, "Take the cross, thou need'st not fear,
CHO.—Is not this the land of Beu - lah, Bless - ed, bless - ed land of light,
D. S. for Chorus.
They are bloom-ing by the foun-tain, 'Neath the am - a - ran-thine bowers.
But the Spir - it led un - er - ring To the land I hold to - day.
For I've found a rich - er treas - ure, One that fad - eth not a - way.
World-ly hon - ors all for - sak - ing For the glo - ry of the cross.
For I've trod the way be - fore thee, And the glo - ry lin - gers near."
Where the flow - ers bloom for - ev - er, And the sun is al - ways bright?

I've Found a Friend

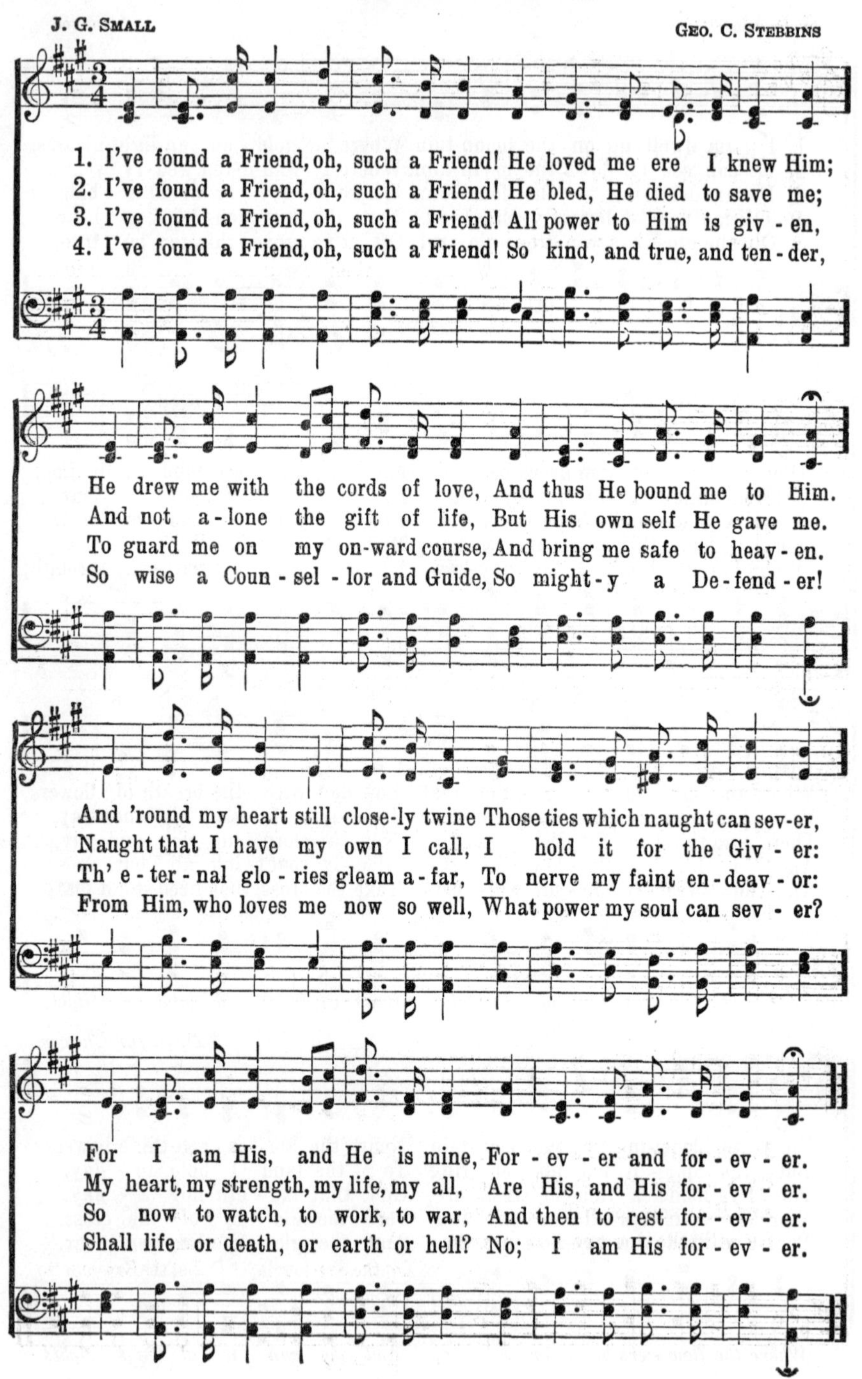
J. G. SMALL
GEO. C. STEBBINS
1. I've found a Friend, oh, such a Friend! He loved me ere I knew Him;
2. I've found a Friend, oh, such a Friend! He bled, He died to save me;
3. I've found a Friend, oh, such a Friend! All power to Him is giv - en,
4. I've found a Friend, oh, such a Friend! So kind, and true, and ten - der,
He drew me with the cords of love, And thus He bound me to Him.
And not a - lone the gift of life, But His own self He gave me.
To guard me on my on-ward course, And bring me safe to heav - en.
So wise a Coun - sel - lor and Guide, So might - y a De - fend - er!
And 'round my heart still close-ly twine Those ties which naught can sev-er,
Naught that I have my own I call, I hold it for the Giv - er:
Th' e - ter - nal glo - ries gleam a - far, To nerve my faint en - deav - or:
From Him, who loves me now so well, What power my soul can sev - er?
For I am His, and He is mine, For - ev - er and for - ev - er.
My heart, my strength, my life, my all, Are His, and His for - ev - er.
So now to watch, to work, to war, And then to rest for - ev - er.
Shall life or death, or earth or hell? No; I am His for - ev - er.

29

Let Him In

J. B. ATCHINSON
E. O. EXCELL
1. There's a Stran-ger at the door, Let Him in;
2. O - pen now to Him your heart, Let Him in;
3. Hear you now His lov - ing voice? Let Him in;
4. Now ad-mit the heaven-ly Guest, Let Him in;
Let the Sav-iour in, Let the Sav-iour in;
He has been there oft be - fore, Let Him in;
If you wait He will de - part, Let Him in;
Now, oh, now make Him your choice, Let Him in;
He will make for you a feast, Let Him in;
Let the Sav-iour in, Let the Sav-iour in;
Let Him in, ere He is gone, Let Him in, the Ho - ly One,
Let Him in, He is your Friend, He your soul will sure de - fend,
He is stand-ing at your door, Joy to you He will re - store,
He will speak your sins for - given, And when earth ties all are riven,
Je - sus Christ, the Fa-ther's Son, Let Him in.
He will keep you to the end, Let Him in.
And His name you will a - dore, Let Him in.
He will take you home to heaven, Let Him in.
Let the Sav-iour in, Let the Sav-iour in.

30 Stand By Me

C. A. T. — C. A. Tindley, Arr. by F. A. Clark

1. When the storms of life are rag - ing, Stand by me (stand by me); When the
2. In the midst of trib - u - la - tions, In the
3. In the midst of faults and fail-ures, In the
4. In the midst of per - se - cu - tion, In the
5. When I'm grow-ing old and fee - ble, (by me); When I'm
storms of life are rag - ing, Stand by me; . . . . When the
midst of trib - u - la - tions, When the
midst of faults and fail - ures, When I
midst of per - se - cu - tion, When my
grow - ing old and fee - ble, stand by me; When my
world is toss - ing me Like a ship up - on the sea;
hosts of hell as - sail, And my strength be - gins to fail,
do the best I can, And my friends mis - un - der-stand,
foes in bat - tle ar - ray Un - der - take to stop my way,
life be - comes a bur - den, And I'm near - ing chill - y Jor - dan,
Thou who rul - est wind and wa - ter, Stand by me (stand by me).
Thou who nev - er lost a bat - tle,
Thou who know - est all a - bout me,
Thou who saved Paul and Si - las,
O Thou "Lil - y of the Val - ley," (by me).

31 Stand Up, Stand Up for Jesus

WEBB
GEORGE DUFFIELD
GEORGE J. WEBB
1. Stand up, stand up for Je - sus, Ye sol - diers of the cross!
2. Stand up, stand up for Je - sus, The trump - et call o - bey;
3. Stand up, stand up for Je - sus, Stand in His strength a - lone;
4. Stand up, stand up for Je - sus, The strife will not be long;
Lift high His roy - al ban - ner, It must not suf - fer loss:
Forth to the might - y con - flict, In this His glo - rious day:
The arm of flesh will fail you, Ye dare not trust your own:
This day, the noise of bat - tle, The next, the vic - tor's song:
From vic - tory un - to vic - tory, His ar - my shall He lead,
Ye that are men, now serve Him, A - gainst un - num-bered foes;
Put on the gos - pel ar - mor, And, watch-ing un - to prayer,
To him that o - ver - com - eth, A crown of life shall be;
Till ev - ery foe is van-quished And Christ is Lord in - deed.
Your cour - age rise with dan - ger, And strength to strength op-pose.
Where du - ty calls, or dan - ger, Be nev - er want - ing there.
He with the King of Glo - ry Shall reign e - ter - nal - ly!

32

Jesus Christ Is Risen Today

14th Century Latin Hymn
4th Stanza, CHARLES WESLEY
LLANFAIR
ROBERT WILLIAMS
1. Je - sus Christ is risen to - day, Al - - - le - lu - ia!
2. Hymns of praise then let us sing, Al - - - le - lu - ia!
3. But the pains which He en - dured, Al - - - le - lu - ia!
4. Sing we to our God a - bove, Al - - - le - lu - ia!
Our tri - um - phant ho - ly day, Al - - le - lu - ia!
Un - to Christ, our heaven-ly King, Al - - le - lu - ia!
Our sal - va - tion have pro-cured; Al - - le - lu - ia!
Praise e - ter - nal as His love; Al - - le - lu - ia!
Who did once, up - on the cross, Al - - le - lu - ia!
Who en - dured the cross and grave, Al - - le - lu - ia!
Now a - bove the sky He's King, Al - - le - lu - ia!
Praise Him, all ye heaven-ly host, Al - - le - lu - ia!
Suf - fer to re - deem our loss. Al - - le - lu - ia!
Sin - ners to re - deem and save. Al - - le - lu - ia!
Where the an - gels ev - er sing: Al - - le - lu - ia!
Fa - ther, Son, and Ho - ly Ghost. Al - - le - lu - ia!

33 Christ the Lord Is Risen Today

CHARLES WESLEY — WORGAN — From "Lyra Davidica"

1. Christ the Lord is risen to - day, Al - - - le - lu - ia!
2. Lives a - gain our glo - rious King: Al - - - le - lu - ia!
3. Love's re - deem-ing work is done, Al - - - le - lu - ia!
4. Soar we now, where Christ has led, Al - - - le - lu - ia!
Sons of men and an - gels say: Al - - - le - lu - ia!
Where, O death, is now thy sting? Al - - - le - lu - ia!
Fought the fight, the bat - tle won; Al - - - le - lu - ia!
Fol - lowing our ex - alt - ed Head; Al - - - le - lu - ia!
Raise your joys and tri - umphs high, Al - - - le - lu - ia!
Dy - ing once, He all doth save: Al - - - le - lu - ia!
Death in vain for - bids Him rise; Al - - - le - lu - ia!
Made like Him, like Him we rise; Al - - - le - lu - ia!
Sing, ye heavens, and earth, re - ply, Al - - - le - lu - ia!
Where thy vic - to - ry, O grave? Al - - - le - lu - ia!
Christ has o - pened Par - a - dise. Al - - - le - lu - ia!
Ours the cross, the grave, the skies. Al - - - le - lu - ia!

34 Jesus, I My Cross Have Taken

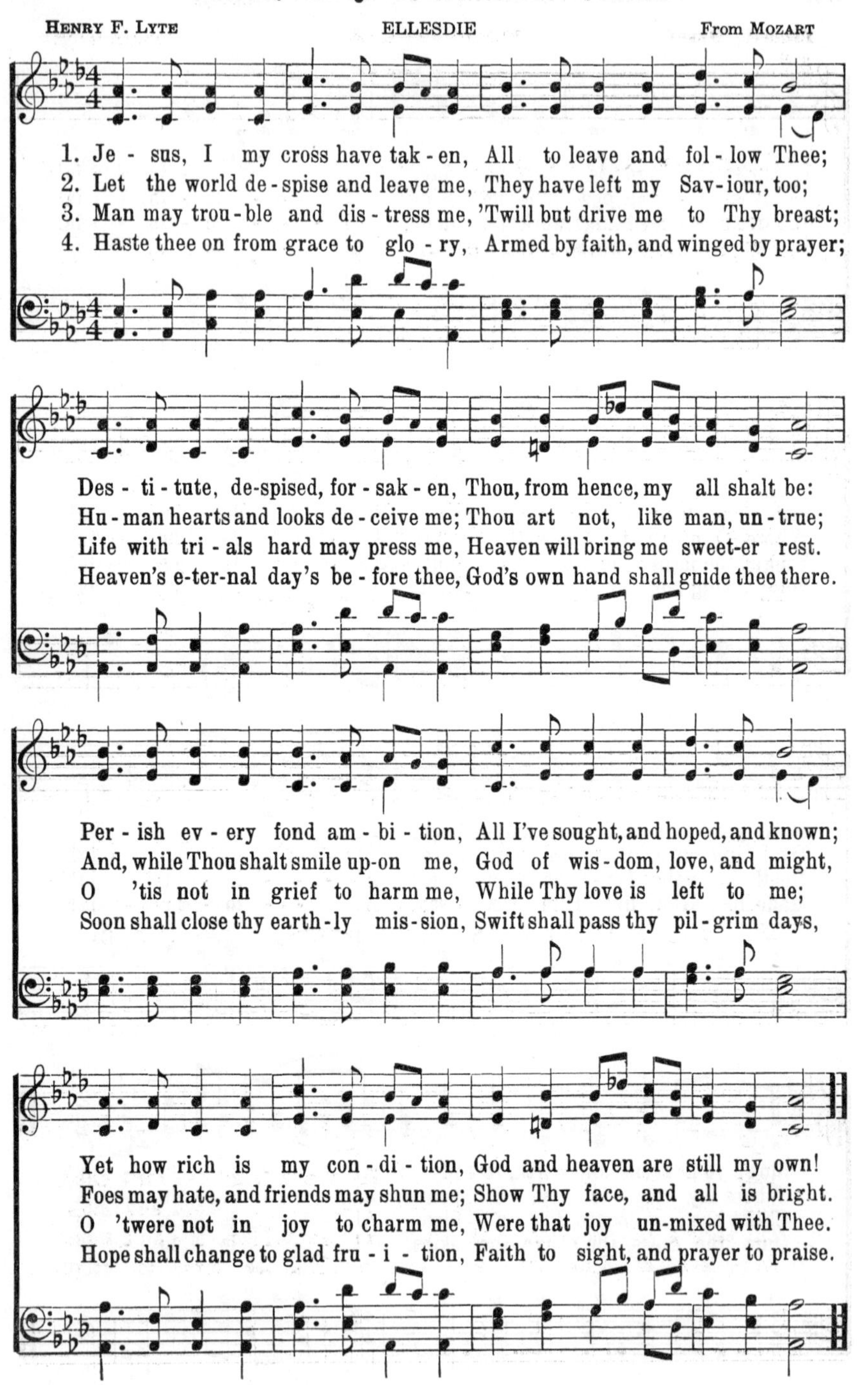
HENRY F. LYTE
ELLESDIE
From MOZART
1. Je - sus, I my cross have tak - en, All to leave and fol - low Thee;
2. Let the world de - spise and leave me, They have left my Sav - iour, too;
3. Man may trou - ble and dis - tress me, 'Twill but drive me to Thy breast;
4. Haste thee on from grace to glo - ry, Armed by faith, and winged by prayer;
Des - ti - tute, de-spised, for - sak - en, Thou, from hence, my all shalt be:
Hu - man hearts and looks de - ceive me; Thou art not, like man, un - true;
Life with tri - als hard may press me, Heaven will bring me sweet-er rest.
Heaven's e-ter-nal day's be - fore thee, God's own hand shall guide thee there.
Per - ish ev - ery fond am - bi - tion, All I've sought, and hoped, and known;
And, while Thou shalt smile up-on me, God of wis - dom, love, and might,
O 'tis not in grief to harm me, While Thy love is left to me;
Soon shall close thy earth - ly mis - sion, Swift shall pass thy pil - grim days,
Yet how rich is my con - di - tion, God and heaven are still my own!
Foes may hate, and friends may shun me; Show Thy face, and all is bright.
O 'twere not in joy to charm me, Were that joy un-mixed with Thee.
Hope shall change to glad fru - i - tion, Faith to sight, and prayer to praise.

35 From Greenland's Icy Mountains

REGINALD HEBER — MISSIONARY HYMN — LOWELL MASON

1. From Green-land's i - cy moun - tains, From In - dia's cor - al strand;
2. What though the spi - cy breez - es Blow soft o'er Cey-lon's isle;
3. Shall we, whose souls are light - ed With wis-dom from on high,
4. Waft, waft, ye winds, His sto - ry, And you, ye wa - ters, roll,
Where Af - ric's sun - ny foun - tains Roll down their gold - en sand:
Though ev - ery pros - pect pleas - es, And on - ly man is vile?
Shall we to men be - night - ed The lamp of life de - ny?
Till, like a sea of glo - ry, It spreads from pole to pole:
From man-y an an - cient riv - er, From man-y a palm - y plain,
In vain with lav - ish kind - ness The gifts of God are strown;
Sal - va - tion! O sal - va - tion! The joy - ful sound pro - claim,
Till o'er our ran-somed na - ture The Lamb for sin - ners slain,
They call us to de - liv - er Their land from er - ror's chain.
The hea - then in his blind - ness Bows down to wood and stone.
Till earth's re - mot - est na - tion Has learned Mes - si - ah's name.
Re - deem - er, King, Cre - a - tor, In bliss re - turns to reign.

The Ninety and Nine

ELIZABETH C. CLEPHANE — IRA D. SANKEY

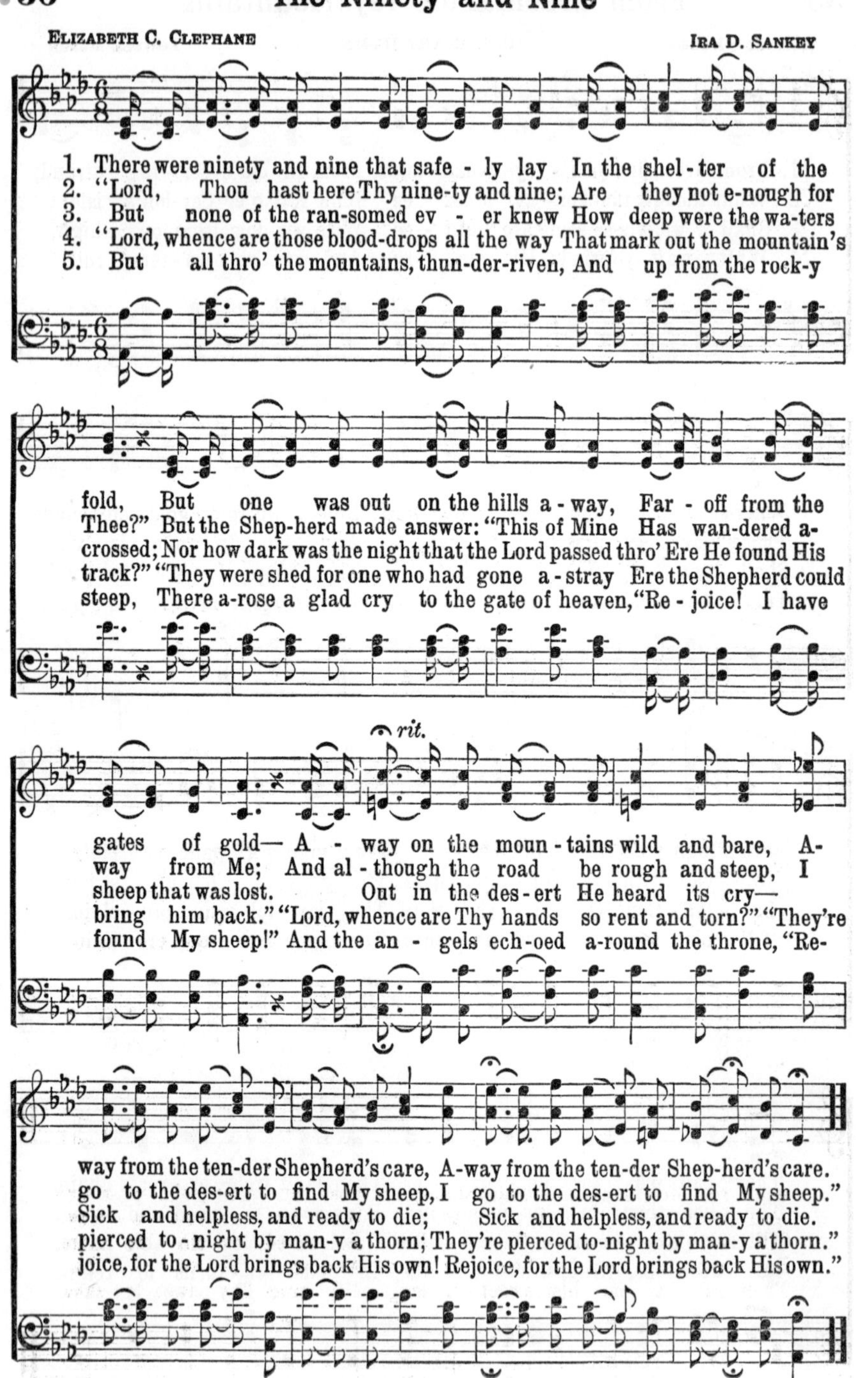
1. There were ninety and nine that safe - ly lay In the shel - ter of the
2. "Lord, Thou hast here Thy nine-ty and nine; Are they not e-nough for
3. But none of the ran-somed ev - er knew How deep were the wa-ters
4. "Lord, whence are those blood-drops all the way That mark out the mountain's
5. But all thro' the mountains, thun-der-riven, And up from the rock-y
fold, But one was out on the hills a - way, Far - off from the
Thee?" But the Shep-herd made answer: "This of Mine Has wan-dered a-
crossed; Nor how dark was the night that the Lord passed thro' Ere He found His
track?" "They were shed for one who had gone a - stray Ere the Shepherd could
steep, There a-rose a glad cry to the gate of heaven, "Re - joice! I have
rit.
gates of gold— A - way on the moun - tains wild and bare, A-
way from Me; And al - though the road be rough and steep, I
sheep that was lost. Out in the des - ert He heard its cry—
bring him back." "Lord, whence are Thy hands so rent and torn?" "They're
found My sheep!" And the an - gels ech-oed a-round the throne, "Re-
way from the ten-der Shepherd's care, A-way from the ten-der Shep-herd's care.
go to the des-ert to find My sheep, I go to the des-ert to find My sheep."
Sick and helpless, and ready to die; Sick and helpless, and ready to die.
pierced to - night by man-y a thorn; They're pierced to-night by man-y a thorn."
joice, for the Lord brings back His own! Rejoice, for the Lord brings back His own."

37 There Is a Fountain

William Cowper — CLEANSING FOUNTAIN — Lowell Mason

1. There is a foun-tain filled with blood Drawn from Im-man-uel's veins;
2. The dy-ing thief re-joiced to see That foun-tain in his day;
3. Dear dy-ing Lamb, Thy pre-cious blood Shall nev-er lose its power,
4. E'er since by faith I saw the stream Thy flow-ing wounds sup-ply,
5. When this poor lisp-ing, stammering tongue Lies si-lent in the grave,
And sin-ners, plunged be-neath that flood, Lose all their guilt-y stains:
And there may I, though vile as he, Wash all my sins a-way:
Till all the ran-somed Church of God Be saved, to sin no more:
Re-deem-ing love has been my theme, And shall be till I die:
Then in a no-bler, sweet-er song, I'll sing Thy power to save:
Lose all their guilt-y stains, Lose all their guilt-y stains;
Wash all my sins a-way, Wash all my sins a-way;
Be saved, to sin no more, Be saved, to sin no more;
And shall be till I die, And shall be till I die;
I'll sing Thy power to save, I'll sing Thy power to save;
And sin-ners, plunged be-neath that flood, Lose all their guilt-y stains.
And there may I, though vile as he, Wash all my sins a-way.
Till all the ran-somed Church of God Be saved, to sin no more.
Re-deem-ing love has been my theme, And shall be till I die.
Then in a no-bler, sweet-er song I'll sing Thy power to save.

A Mighty Fortress

M. L. EIN' FESTE BURG MARTIN LUTHER

1. A might-y for-tress is our God, A bul-wark nev-er fail - ing;
2. Did we in our own strength confide, Our striv-ing would be los - ing,
3. And though this world, with devils filled, Should threaten to un - do us,
4. That word a - bove all earthly powers—No thanks to them—a - bid - eth;
Our help-er He, a - mid the flood Of mor-tal ills pre - vail - ing.
Were not the right Man on our side, The Man of God's own choos - ing.
We will not fear, for God hath willed His truth to tri-umph through us.
The Spir-it and the gifts are ours Thro' Him who with us sid - eth.
For still our an-cient foe Doth seek to work us woe; His craft and power
Dost ask who that may be? Christ Je-sus, it is He; Lord Sab-aoth is
The prince of darkness grim—We trem-ble not for him; His rage we can
Let goods and kin-dred go, This mor-tal life al - so; The bod - y they
are great, And, armed with cru-el hate, On earth is not his e - qual.
His name, From age to age the same, And He must win the bat - tle.
en-dure, For lo! his doom is sure: One lit-tle word shall fell him.
may kill; God's truth a - bid-eth still, His king-dom is for - ev - er.

39 America the Beautiful

KATHARINE LEE BATES — MATERNA — SAMUEL A. WARD

1. O beau - ti - ful for spa-cious skies, For am - ber waves of grain,
2. O beau - ti - ful for pil - grim feet, Whose stern, im-pas-sioned stress
3. O beau - ti - ful for he - roes proved In lib - er - at - ing strife,
4. O beau - ti - ful for pa - triot dream That sees be - yond the years
For pur - ple moun-tain maj - es - ties A - bove the fruit - ed plain!
A thor - ough-fare for free - dom beat A - cross the wil - der - ness!
Who more than self their coun - try loved, And mer - cy more than life!
Thine al - a - bas - ter cit - ies gleam, Un-dimmed by hu - man tears!
A - mer - i - ca! A - mer - i - ca! God shed His grace on thee,
A - mer - i - ca! A - mer - i - ca! God mend thine ev - ery flaw,
A - mer - i - ca! A - mer - i - ca! May God thy gold re - fine,
A - mer - i - ca! A - mer - i - ca! God shed His grace on thee,
And crown thy good with broth - er-hood From sea to shin - ing sea.
Con - firm thy soul in self - con-trol, Thy lib - er - ty in law.
Till all suc - cess be no - ble-ness, And ev - ery gain di - vine.
And crown thy good with broth - er-hood From sea to shin - ing sea.

Mother Knows

Anonymous — FLORA HAMILTON CASSEL

SOLO OR DUET
1. No-bod-y knows of the work it makes To keep the home to-geth-er,
2. No-bod-y knows of the sleep-less care Be-stowed on ba-by broth-er,
3. No-bod-y knows of the anx-ious fears Lest dar-lings may not weath-er
4. No-bod-y clings to the way-ward child, Tho' scorned by ev-ery oth-er,
No-bod-y knows of the steps it takes, No-bod-y knows but moth-er;
No-bod-y knows of the ten-der prayer, No-bod-y knows but moth-er;
Storms of this life in the com-ing years, No-bod-y knows but moth-er;
Leads it so gen-tly from path-ways wild, No-bod-y can but moth-er;
No-bod-y lis-tens to child-ish woes, Which kiss-es on-ly smoth-er,
No-bod-y knows of the les-sons taught, Of lov-ing one an-oth-er;
No-bod-y knows of the tears that start, The grief she'll glad-ly smoth-er,
No-bod-y knows of the hour-ly prayer For him, our err-ing broth-er,
No-bod-y's pained by the might-y blow, No-bod-y,—on-ly moth-er.
No-bod-y knows of the patience sought, No-bod-y,—on-ly moth-er.
No-bod-y knows of the breaking heart, No-bod-y,—on-ly moth-er.
Pride of her heart, once so pure and fair, No-bod-y,—on-ly moth-er.

41 O Blessed Day of Motherhood!

ERNEST F. MCGREGOR
MATER
ARTHUR DEPEW
1. O bless - ed day of Moth - er-hood! We lift our hearts in praise,
2. O sa - cred day of Moth - er-hood! Our faith by Thee in-creased,
3. O pre - cious day of Moth - er-hood! Teach us in Thee to find
4. O won-drous day of Moth - er-hood! Thy love to all a - bound;
To thank Thee, Source of ev - ery good; Thy joy crowns all our days. O
Hath each al - lur - ing foe with-stood; Our souls Thou hast re-leased. O
The great - er gifts of broth - er - hood; Bring peace to all man-kind. O
Be - side the cross once Ma - ry stood; A - gain let love be crowned. O
God, our Fa - ther, bless this day, En - rich its gold - en store
Of bless - ed Moth-er love, and may Thy chil-dren Thee a - dore.
Of sa - cred Moth-er love, and may Thy chil-dren Thee a - dore.
Of pre-cious Moth-er love, and may Thy chil-dren Thee a - dore.
Of won-drous Moth-er love, and may Thy chil-dren Thee a - dore.
Organ

I Will Sing You a Song

ELLEN H. GATES PHILIP PHILLIPS

1. I will sing you a song of that beau-ti-ful land, The far - a-way home of the
2. Oh, that home of the soul! In my visions and dreams Its bright, jasper walls I can
3. That unchangeable home is for you and for me, Where Je-sus of Naz-a-reth
4. Oh, how sweet it will be in that beau-ti - ful land, So free from all sor-row and
soul, Where no storms ev-er beat on the glit-ter-ing strand, While the years of e-
see; Till I fan - cy but thin - ly the veil in-ter-venes Be - tween the fair
stands; The King of all kingdoms for-ev - er is He, And He hold-eth our
pain, With songs on our lips and with harps in our hands, To meet one an-
ter - ni-ty roll, While the years of e - ter - ni-ty roll; Where no storms ev-er
cit - y and me, Be - tween the fair cit - y and me; Till I fan-cy but
crowns in His hands, And He holdeth our crowns in His hands; The King of all
oth - er a - gain, To meet one an - oth - er a-gain; With songs on our
beat on the glit - ter-ing strand, While the years of e - ter - ni - ty roll.
thin - ly the veil in - ter-venes Be - tween the fair cit - y and me.
king-doms for - ev - er is He, And He hold-eth our crowns in His hands.
lips and with harps in our hands, To meet one an - oth - er a - gain.

43 The Home Over There

D. W. C. Huntington
Tullius C. O'Kane
1. O think of the home o-ver there, By the side of the riv - er of light,
2. O think of the friends over there, Who be-fore us the journey have trod,
3. My Sav-iour is now o-ver there, There my kindreds and friends are at rest,
4. I'll soon be at home o-ver there, For the end of my jour-ney I see;
o-ver there,
Where the saints, all immortal and fair, Are robed in their garments of white.
Of the songs that they breathe on the air, In their home in the palace of God.
Then a-way from my sor-row and care, Let me fly to the land of the blest.
Man - y dear to my heart, o-ver there, Are watching and waiting for me.
over there.
Refrain
O-ver there, o-ver there, O think of the home o - ver there,
O think of the friends o-ver there,
My Sav-iour is now o - ver there,
O-ver there, o-ver there, I'll soon be at home o - ver there,
over there,
O-ver there, o-ver there, o-ver there, O think of the home o - ver there.
O think of the friends o-ver there.
My Sav-iour is now o - ver there.
O-ver there, o-ver there, I'll soon be at home o - ver there.

Jesus Is Coming

James M. Gray
J. C. Trowbridge
1. The Sav - iour who loves me and suf - fered the loss Of heav - en - ly glo - ry to die on the cross, The Babe of the man - ger, though born with-out stain, This Je - sus is com-ing, is com - ing a - gain!
2. The an - gels, re - joic - ing and sing - ing His praise To Beth - le - hem shep-herds of ear - li - er days, Will come in the glo - ry, at-tend - ing His train, When Je - sus, my Sav-iour, is com - ing a - gain!
3. The saints will be with Him, O heav - en - ly bliss! How tear - ful the part - ing from fac - es we miss! But clouds are de - scend-ing, and we who re - main Are caught up to meet them with Je - sus a - gain!
4. O hearts that are wea - ry, and sin - ful, and sad, We car - ry the ti - dings that make us so glad; We pub - lish the Sav - iour o'er moun-tain and plain; The Lord who re-deemed us is com - ing a - gain!
Chorus
Je - sus is com-ing, is com-ing, is com-ing! Je - sus is com-ing a - gain!
My heart is so hap-py, my soul is so glad, For Je-sus is com-ing a - gain!
rit.

45 Launch Out Into the Deep

A. B. Simpson and
B. B. McKinney

Kelso Carter
Arr. by B. B. McKinney

1. The mer - cy of God is an o - cean di - vine, A
2. But man - y, a - las! on - ly stand on the shore And
3. Oh, let us launch out on this o - cean so broad, Where
4. Launch out, oh, launch out where the break - ers are high, Where

bound-less and fath - om - less flood; Launch out in the deep, cut a-
gaze on the o - cean so wide; They nev - er have ven-tured its
floods of sal - va - tion e'er flow; Oh, let us be lost in the
souls sink be-neath the dark wave; Launch out in the deep ere they

way the shore - line, And be lost in the full - ness of God.
depths to ex-plore, Or to launch on the fath - om - less tide.
mer - cy of God, Till the depths of His full - ness we know.
lan-guish and die— Bring them safe - ly to Christ who can save.

CHORUS

Launch out (Launch out) in-to the deep (in-to the deep), Oh, let the shore-line go;

Launch out, launch out in the o - cean di-vine, Out where the full tides flow.

Onward, Christian Soldiers

SABINE BARING-GOULD
ST. GERTRUDE
ARTHUR SULLIVAN
1. On-ward, Christian sol-diers, Marching as to war, With the cross of Je - sus
2. At the sign of tri-umph Satan's host doth flee; On then, Christian sol-diers,
3. Like a might-y ar - my Moves the Church of God; Brothers, we are treading
4. On-ward, then, ye peo - ple, Join our happy throng, Blend with ours your voices
Go - ing on be - fore! Christ, the roy - al Mas - ter, Leads a-gainst the foe;
On to vic - to - ry! Hell's foun-da-tions quiv - er At the shout of praise;
Where the saints have trod; We are not di - vid - ed; All one bod - y we,
In the tri-umph song; Glo - ry, laud, and hon - or, Un - to Christ the King:
REFRAIN
For-ward in - to bat - tle, See, His ban-ners go!
Brothers, lift your voic - es, Loud your anthems raise! Onward, Christian sol-diers,
One in hope and doc-trine, One in char - i - ty.
This thro' countless a - ges Men and an-gels sing.
March-ing as to war, With the cross of Je - sus Go-ing on be - fore!

47 A Child of the King

HATTIE E. BUELL — REV. JOHN B. SUMMER, arr.

1. My Fa-ther is rich in hous-es and lands, He hold-eth the
2. My Fa-ther's own Son, the Sav-iour of men, Once wan-dered on
3. I once was an out-cast stran-ger on earth, A sin-ner by
4. A tent or a cot-tage, why should I care? They're build-ing a
wealth of the world in His hands! Of ru-bies and dia-monds, of
earth as the poor-est of them; But now He is plead-ing our
choice, and an al-ien by birth; But I've been a-dopt-ed, my
pal-ace for me o-ver there; Tho' ex-iled from home, yet,
sil-ver and gold, His cof-fers are full, He has rich-es un-told.
par-don on high, That we may be His when He comes by and by.
name's writ-ten down, An heir to a man-sion, a robe, and a crown.
still I may sing: All glo-ry to God, I'm a child of the King.
CHORUS
I'm a child of the King, A child of the King:
With Je-sus my Sav-iour I'm a child of the King.

The Crowning Day

EL NATHAN
JAMES MCGRANAHAN
1. Our Lord is now re-ject-ed, And by the world dis-owned, By the man-y
2. The heavens shall glow with splendor, But brighter far than they The saints shall
3. Our pain shall then be o-ver, We'll sin and sigh no more, Be-hind us
4. Let all that look for, has-ten The com-ing joy-ful day, By ear-nest
still neg-lect-ed, And by the few enthroned; But soon He'll come in glo-ry,
shine in glo-ry, As Christ shall them ar-ray; The beau-ty of the Sav-iour
all of sor-row, And naught but joy be-fore; A joy in our Re-deem-er,
con-se-cra-tion, To walk the nar-row way, By gathering in the lost ones,
FINE
The hour is draw-ing nigh, For the crowning day is com-ing by and by.
Shall daz-zle ev-ery eye, In the crowning day that's com-ing by and by.
As we to Him are nigh, In the crowning day that's com-ing by and by.
For whom our Lord did die, For the crowning day that's com-ing by and by.
D.S.—Each wait-ing, watch-ful eye, In the crown-ing day that's com-ing by and by.
CHORUS
Oh, the crowning day is com-ing, Is com-ing by and by, When our Lord shall
D. S.
come in "pow-er," And "glo-ry" from on high. Oh, the glorious sight will gladden

49 Christ Returneth

H. L. Turner
James McGranahan
1. It may be at morn, when the day is a-wak-ing, When sunlight thro' dark-ness and shad-ow is break-ing, That Je-sus will come in the full-ness of glo-ry, To re-ceive from the world "His own."
2. It may be at mid-day, it may be at twi-light, It may be, per-chance, that the black-ness of mid-night Will burst in-to light in the blaze of His glo-ry, When Je-sus re-ceives "His own."
3. While its hosts cry Ho-sanna, from heav-en de-scend-ing, With glo-ri-fied saints and the an-gels at-tend-ing, With grace on His brow, like a ha-lo of glo-ry, Will Je-sus re-ceive "His own."
4. Oh, joy! oh, de-light! should we go with-out dy-ing, No sick-ness, no sad-ness, no dread and no cry-ing, Caught up thro' the clouds with our Lord in-to glo-ry, When Je-sus re-ceives "His own."
Chorus
O Lord Je-sus, how long, how long Ere we shout the glad song, Christ re-turn-eth! Hal-le-lu-jah! hal-le-lu-jah! A-men, Hal-le-lu-jah! A-men.
rit.

He Brought Me Out

Rev. H. J. Zelley
Cho. by H. L. G.

H. L. Gilmour

1. My heart was distressed 'neath Je-ho-vah's dread frown, And low in the pit where my sins dragged me down; I cried to the Lord from the deep mir-y clay, Who ten-der-ly brought me out to gold-en day.
2. He placed me up-on the strong Rock by His side, My steps were es-tab-lished and here I'll a-bide; No dan-ger of fall-ing while here I re-main, But stand by His grace un-til the crown I gain.
3. He gave me a song, 'twas a new song of praise; By day and by night its sweet notes I will raise; My heart's o-ver-flow-ing, I'm hap-py and free, I'll praise my Re-deem-er, who has res-cued me.
4. I'll sing of His won-der-ful mer-cy to me, I'll praise Him till all men His good-ness shall see; I'll sing of sal-va-tion at home and a-broad, Till man-y shall hear the truth and trust in God.
Chorus
He bro't me out of the mir-y clay, He set my feet on the Rock to stay; He puts a song in my soul to-day, A song of praise, hal-le-lu-jah!

51 Saved to the Uttermost

W. J. K. | Wm. J. Kirkpatrick

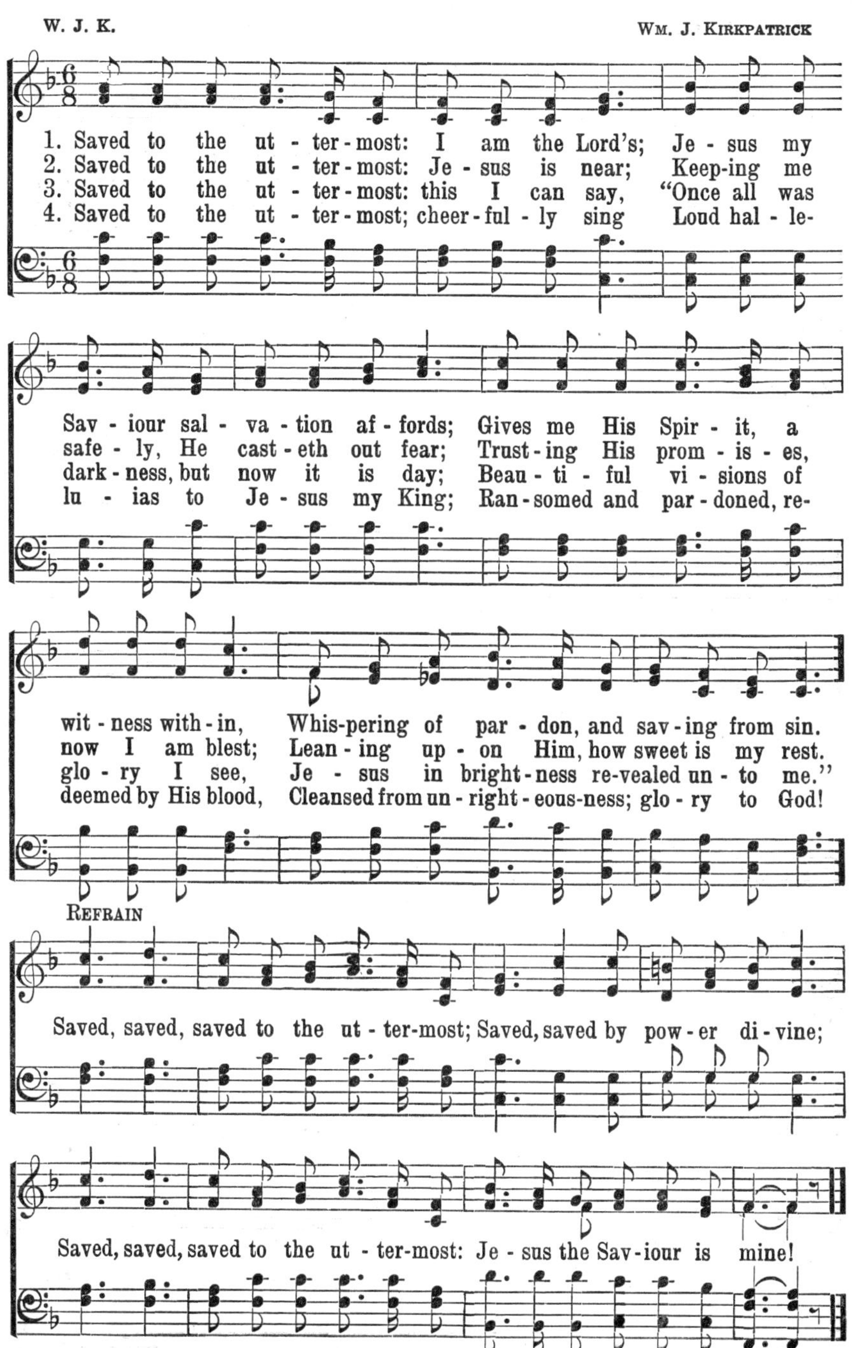

1. Saved to the ut - ter - most: I am the Lord's; Je - sus my Sav - iour sal - va - tion af - fords; Gives me His Spir - it, a wit - ness with - in, Whis-pering of par - don, and sav - ing from sin.
2. Saved to the ut - ter - most: Je - sus is near; Keep-ing me safe - ly, He cast - eth out fear; Trust - ing His prom - is - es, now I am blest; Lean - ing up - on Him, how sweet is my rest.
3. Saved to the ut - ter - most: this I can say, "Once all was dark - ness, but now it is day; Beau - ti - ful vi - sions of glo - ry I see, Je - sus in bright - ness re-vealed un - to me."
4. Saved to the ut - ter - most; cheer - ful - ly sing Loud hal - le - lu - ias to Je - sus my King; Ran - somed and par - doned, re - deemed by His blood, Cleansed from un - right - eous-ness; glo - ry to God!
Refrain
Saved, saved, saved to the ut - ter-most; Saved, saved by pow - er di - vine;
Saved, saved, saved to the ut - ter-most: Je - sus the Sav - iour is mine!

Have Faith In God

B. B. McK.
B. B. McKinney
1. Have faith in God when your path - way is lone - ly, He sees and
2. Have faith in God when your prayers are un - an-swered, Your ear - nest
3. Have faith in God in your pain and your sor - row, His heart is
4. Have faith in God though all else fail a - bout you; Have faith in
knows all the way you have trod; Nev - er a - lone are the
plea He will nev - er for - get; Wait on the Lord, trust His
touched with your grief and de - spair; Cast all your cares and your
God, He pro - vides for His own; He can - not fail though all
least of His chil - dren; Have faith in God, have faith in God.
Word and be pa - tient; Have faith in God, He'll an - swer yet.
bur - dens up - on Him, And leave them there, oh, leave them there.
king - doms shall per - ish, He rules, He reigns up - on His throne.
Chorus
Have faith in God, He's on His throne; Have faith in God, He watcheth o'er His own;
rit.
He can-not fail, He must pre-vail; Have faith in God, have faith in God.

53 My Latest Sun Is Sinking Fast

J. Hascall
Wm. B. Bradbury
1. My lat-est sun is sink-ing fast, My race is near-ly run;
2. I know I'm nearing the ho-ly ranks Of friends and kin-dred dear,
3. I've al-most gained my heaven-ly home, My spir-it loud-ly sings;
4. O bear my long-ing heart to Him, Who bled and died for me;
My strong-est tri-als now are past, My tri-umph is be-gun.
For I brush the dews on Jor-dan's banks, The cross-ing must be near.
Thy ho-ly ones, be-hold, they come! I hear the noise of wings.
Whose blood now cleans-es from all sin, And gives me vic-to-ry.
f Chorus
O come, an-gel band, Come and a-round me stand; O bear me a-
way on your snow-y wings To my im-mor-tal home; O
bear me a-way on your snow-y wings To my im-mor-tal home.

54 Is Your All on the Altar?

E. A. H.
Elisha A. Hoffman
1. You have longed for sweet peace, and for faith to in-crease, And have ear-nest-ly,
2. Would you walk with the Lord, in the light of His Word, And have peace and con-
3. Oh, we nev - er can know what the Lord will be-stow Of the bless-ings for
4. Who can tell all the love He will send from a - bove, And how hap - py our
fer - vent-ly prayed; But you can-not have rest or be per - fect-ly blest
tent-ment al - way, You must do His sweet will, to be free from all ill,
which we have prayed, Till our bod - y and soul He doth ful - ly con - trol,
hearts will be made, Of the fel - low-ship sweet we shall share at His feet,
Un - til all on the al - tar is laid.
On the al - tar your all you must lay.
And our all on the al - tar is laid.
When our all on the al - tar is laid.
Chorus
Is your all on the al - tar of
sac - ri - fice laid? Your heart, does the Spir-it con - trol? . . . You can on - ly be
blest and have peace and sweet rest, As you yield Him your bod - y and soul.

55 One More Day's Work For Jesus

ANNA B. WARNER
ROBERT LOWRY
1. One more day's work for Je - sus, One less of life for me!
2. One more day's work for Je - sus! How sweet the work has been,
3. One more day's work for Je - sus! O yes, a wea - ry day;
4. O bless - ed work for Je - sus! O rest at Je - sus' feet!
But heaven is near - er, And Christ is dear - er Than
To tell the sto - ry, To show the glo - ry, Where
But heaven shines clear - er And rest comes near - er, At
There toil seems pleas - ure, My wants are treas - ure, And
yes - ter-day, to me; His love and light Fill all my soul to-night.
Christ's flock en-ter in! How it did shine In this poor heart of mine!
each step of the way; And Christ in all, Be-fore His face I fall.
pain for Him is sweet. Lord, if I may, I'll serve an-oth - er day!
REFRAIN
One more day's work for Je - sus, One more day's work for Je - sus,
One more day's work for Je - sus, One less of life for me!

56 I Am Thine, O Lord

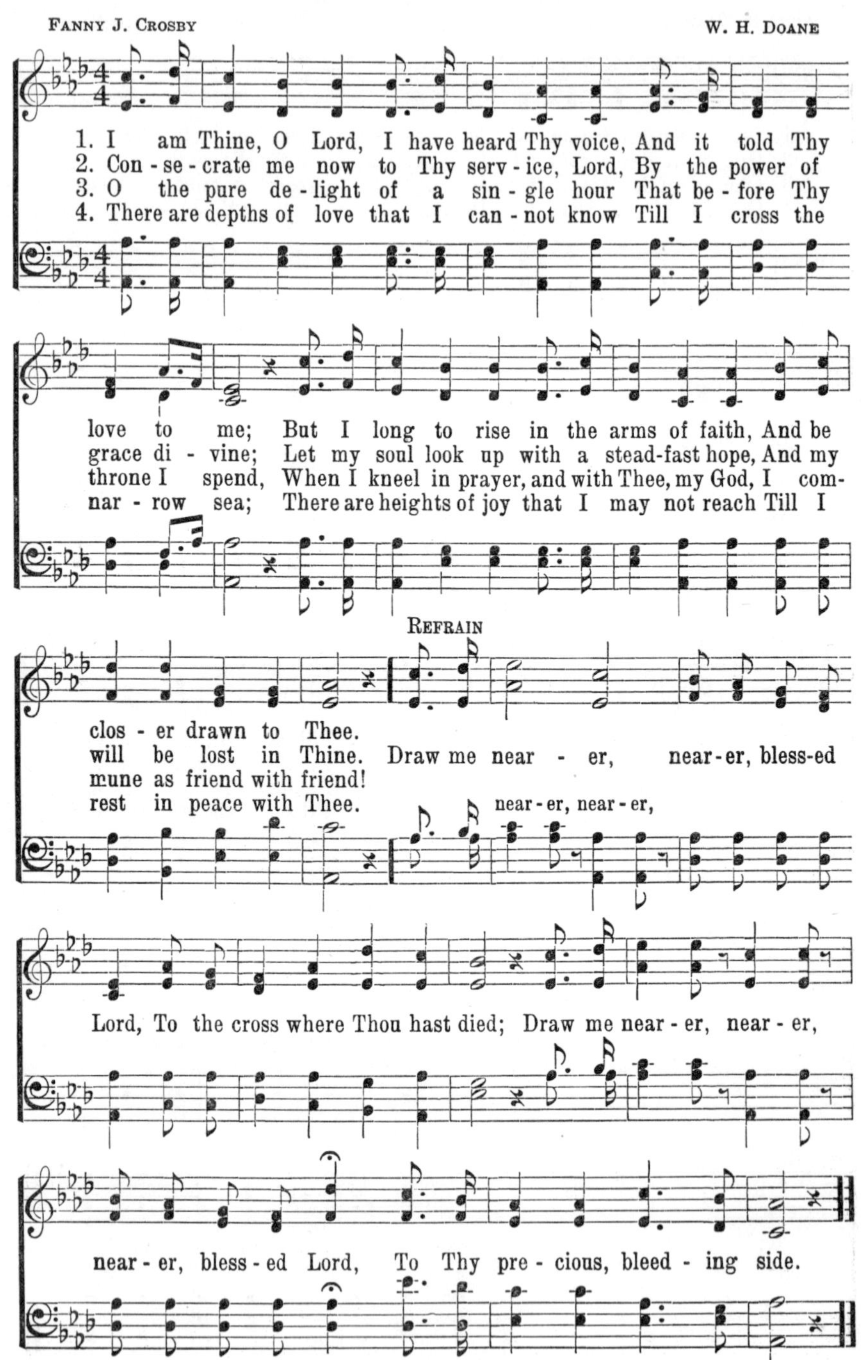

Fanny J. Crosby
W. H. Doane
1. I am Thine, O Lord, I have heard Thy voice, And it told Thy love to me; But I long to rise in the arms of faith, And be closer drawn to Thee.
2. Con - se - crate me now to Thy serv - ice, Lord, By the power of grace di - vine; Let my soul look up with a stead-fast hope, And my will be lost in Thine.
3. O the pure de - light of a sin - gle hour That be - fore Thy throne I spend, When I kneel in prayer, and with Thee, my God, I com-mune as friend with friend!
4. There are depths of love that I can - not know Till I cross the nar - row sea; There are heights of joy that I may not reach Till I rest in peace with Thee.
Refrain
Draw me near - er, near - er, bless-ed Lord, To the cross where Thou hast died; Draw me near - er, near - er, near - er, bless - ed Lord, To Thy pre - cious, bleed - ing side.
near - er, near - er,

57 Jesus Is Calling

FANNY J. CROSBY GEO. C. STEBBINS

1. Je - sus is ten - der - ly call - ing thee home— Call - ing to - day,
2. Je - sus is call - ing the wea - ry to rest— Call - ing to - day,
3. Je - sus is wait - ing; O come to Him now— Wait-ing to - day,
4. Je - sus is plead - ing; O list to His voice: Hear Him to - day,
call - ing to - day; Why from the sun - shine of love wilt thou roam
call - ing to - day; Bring Him thy bur - den and thou shalt be blest;
wait - ing to - day; Come with thy sins; at His feet low - ly bow;
hear Him to - day; They who be - lieve on His name shall re - joice;
Far-ther and far-ther a - way?
He will not turn thee a - way.
Come, and no lon - ger de - lay.
Quick-ly a - rise and a - way.
REFRAIN
Call - - ing to - day, ...
Call - ing, call - ing to - day, to - day,
Call - - - ing to - day, ... Je - - - - sus is
Call - ing, call - ing to - day, to - day; Je - sus is ten - der - ly
call - - - - ing, Is ten - der - ly call - ing to - day.
call - ing to - day,

58 Moment By Moment

D. W. Whittle — May Whittle Moody

1. Dy-ing with Je-sus, by death reckoned mine; Liv-ing with Je-sus, a
2. Nev-er a tri-al that He is not there, Nev-er a bur-den that
3. Nev-er a heart-ache and nev-er a groan; Nev-er a tear-drop and
4. Nev-er a weak-ness that He doth not feel, Nev-er a sick-ness that
new life di-vine; Look-ing to Je-sus till glo-ry doth shine, Mo-ment by
He doth not bear, Nev-er a sor-row that He doth not share, Mo-ment by
nev-er a moan; Nev-er a dan-ger but there on the throne, Mo-ment by
He can-not heal; Mo-ment by mo-ment, in woe or in weal, Je-sus my
Chorus
mo-ment, O Lord, I am Thine.
mo-ment, I'm un-der His care. Mo-ment by mo-ment I'm kept in His love;
mo-ment He thinks of His own.
Sav-iour a-bides with me still.
Mo-ment by mo-ment I've life from a-bove; Look-ing to Je-sus till
glo-ry doth shine; Mo-ment by mo-ment, O Lord, I am Thine.

59 The Banner of the Cross

D. W. WHITTLE JAMES McGRANAHAN

1. There's a roy - al ban - ner giv - en for dis-play To the sol - diers
2. Though the foe may rage and gath - er as the flood, Let the stand-ard
3. O - ver land and sea, wher-ev - er man may dwell, Make the glo - rious
4. When the glo - ry dawns—'tis draw-ing ver - y near—It is has-tening
of the King; As an en - sign fair we lift it up to - day,
be dis - played; And be-neath its folds, as sol-diers of the Lord,
ti - dings known; Of the crim - son ban - ner now the sto - ry tell,
day by day— Then be-fore our King the foe shall dis - ap-pear,
While as ran-somed ones we sing.
For the truth be not dis-mayed!
While the Lord shall claim His own!
And the cross the world shall sway!
CHORUS
March-ing on, . . . march-ing
on, on,
on, . . . For Christ count ev - ery-thing but loss! . . . . . . And to
on, on, ev - ery - thing, ev - ery-thing but loss!
crown Him King, toil and sing 'Neath the ban-ner of the cross!
we'll Be - neath

Lift Him Up

JOHNSON OATMAN, JR.
B. B. BEALL
1. How to reach the mass-es, men of ev - ery birth, For an an-swer
2. Oh! the world is hun-gry for the liv - ing bread, Lift the Sav - iour
3. Don't ex - alt the preach-er, don't ex - alt the pew, Preach the Gos-pel
4. Lift Him up by liv - ing as a Chris-tian ought, Let the world in
Je - sus gave the key: "And I, if I be lift - ed up from the
up for them to see; Trust Him, and do not doubt the words that He
sim-ple, full and free; Prove Him and you will find that prom - ise is
you the Sav-iour see; Then men will glad - ly fol - low Him who once
earth, Will draw all men un - to Me."
said, "I'll draw all men un - to Me."
true, "I'll draw all men un - to Me."
taught,"I'll draw all men un - to Me."
REFRAIN
Lift Him up, ...
Lift the pre-cious Sav - iour up,
Lift Him up, ... Still He speaks from e - ter - ni - ty: "And
Lift the pre-cious Sav-iour up,
I, if I be lift - ed up from the earth, Will draw all men un - to Me."

61 Make Me a Channel of Blessing

H. G. S.
H. G. Smyth
1. Is your life a chan-nel of bless-ing? Is the love of God flow-ing thro' you? Are you tell-ing the lost of the Sav-iour? Are you read-y His serv-ice to do?
2. Is your life a chan-nel of bless-ing? Are you bur-dened for those that are lost? Have you urged up-on those who are stray-ing, The Sav-iour who died on the cross?
3. Is your life a chan-nel of bless-ing? Is it dai - ly tell-ing for Him? Have you spo-ken the word of sal-va-tion To those who are dy-ing in sin?
4. We can-not be chan-nels of bless-ing If our lives are not free from known sin; We will bar-ri-ers be and a hin-drance To those we are try-ing to win.
Chorus
Make me a chan-nel of bless-ing to-day, Make me a chan-nel of bless-ing, I pray; My life pos-sess-ing, my serv-ice bless-ing, Make me a chan-nel of bless-ing to-day.
rit.

62 Hark, Hark, My Soul!

FREDERICK W. FABER
VOX ANGELICA
HENRY SMART
1. Hark, hark, my soul! an - gel - ic songs are swell-ing O'er earth's green fields and
2. Far, far a - way, like bells at eve-ning peal-ing, The voice of Je - sus
3. On - ward we go, for still we hear them singing, "Come, wea-ry souls, for
4. An - gels, sing on! your faith-ful watches keep-ing; Sing us sweet frag-ments
o-cean's wave-beat shore; How sweet the truth those blessed strains are tell - ing
sounds o'er land and sea, And la - den souls by thou-sands meek-ly steal-ing,
Je - sus bids you come;" And thro' the dark, its ech - oes sweet-ly ring - ing,
of the songs a - bove; Till morn-ing's joy shall end the night of weep - ing,
Of that new life when sin shall be no more!
Kind Shep-herd, turn their wea - ry steps to Thee.
The mu - sic of the gos - pel leads us home.
And life's long shad-ows break in cloud - less love.
REFRAIN
An - gels of Je - sus,
an - gels of light, Sing - ing to wel - come the pil-grims of the night!

63 Who Is On the Lord's Side?

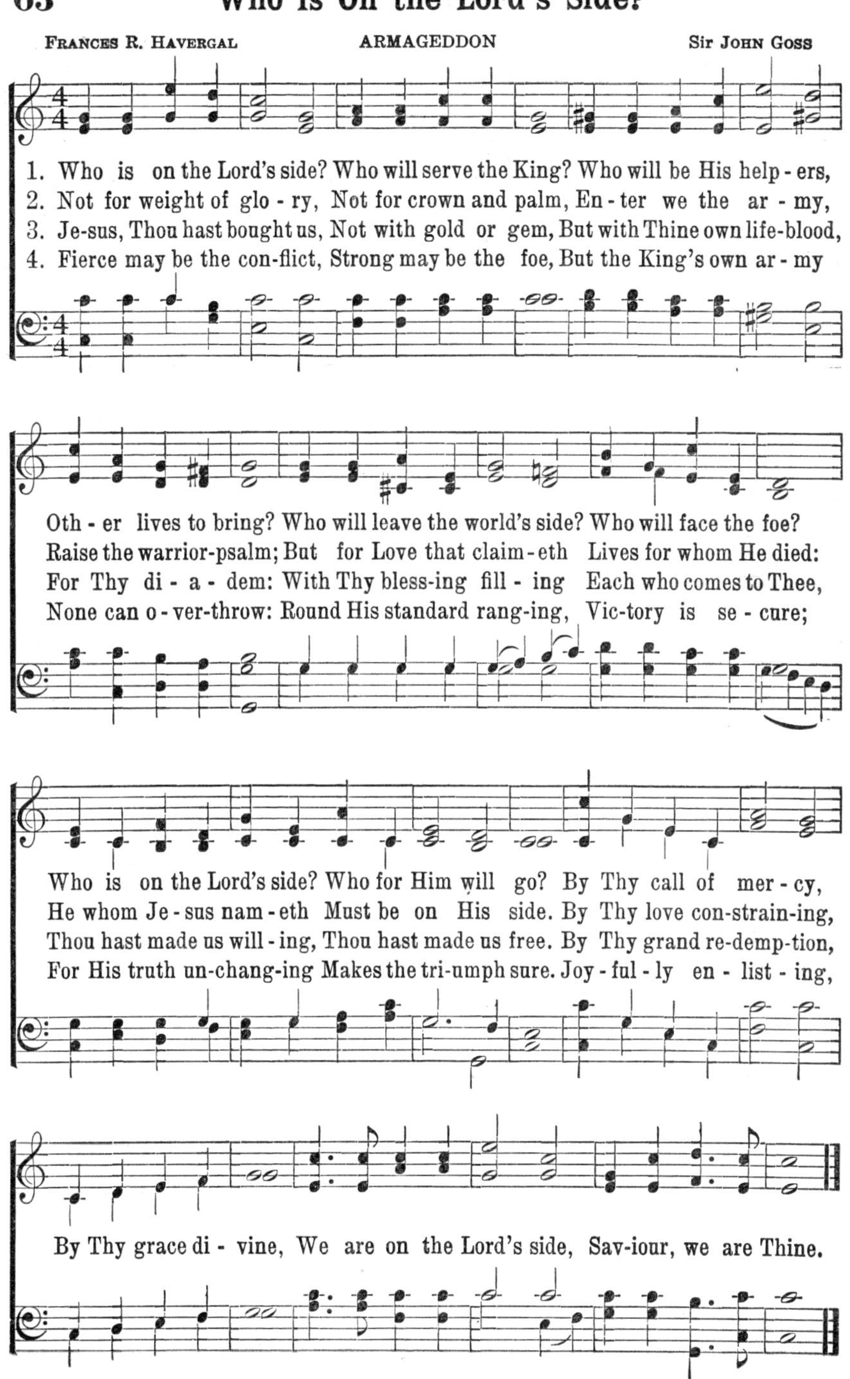
FRANCES R. HAVERGAL
ARMAGEDDON
Sir JOHN GOSS
1. Who is on the Lord's side? Who will serve the King? Who will be His help - ers,
2. Not for weight of glo - ry, Not for crown and palm, En - ter we the ar - my,
3. Je-sus, Thou hast bought us, Not with gold or gem, But with Thine own life-blood,
4. Fierce may be the con-flict, Strong may be the foe, But the King's own ar - my
Oth - er lives to bring? Who will leave the world's side? Who will face the foe?
Raise the warrior-psalm; But for Love that claim - eth Lives for whom He died:
For Thy di - a - dem: With Thy bless-ing fill - ing Each who comes to Thee,
None can o - ver-throw: Round His standard rang-ing, Vic-tory is se - cure;
Who is on the Lord's side? Who for Him will go? By Thy call of mer - cy,
He whom Je - sus nam - eth Must be on His side. By Thy love con-strain-ing,
Thou hast made us will - ing, Thou hast made us free. By Thy grand re-demp-tion,
For His truth un-chang-ing Makes the tri-umph sure. Joy - ful - ly en - list - ing,
By Thy grace di - vine, We are on the Lord's side, Sav-iour, we are Thine.

To the Work

FANNY J. CROSBY
W. H. DOANE
1. To the work! to the work! we are serv - ants of God, Let us fol - low the path that our Mas - ter has trod; With the balm of His coun - sel our strength to re - new, Let us do with our might what our hands find to do.
2. To the work! to the work! let the hun - gry be fed; To the foun-tain of life let the wea - ry be led; In the cross and its ban - ner our glo - ry shall be, While we her - ald the ti - dings, "Sal-va - tion is free!"
3. To the work! to the work! there is la - bor for all; For the king-dom of dark - ness and er - ror shall fall; And the name of Je - ho - vah ex - alt - ed shall be, In the loud swell-ing cho - rus, "Sal-va - tion is free!"
4. To the work! to the work! in the strength of the Lord, And a robe and a crown shall our la - bor re - ward, When the home of the faith - ful our dwell - ing shall be, And we shout with the ransomed, "Sal-va - tion is free!"
CHORUS
Toil-ing on, toil-ing on, Toil-ing on, toil-ing on;
Toil-ing on, toil-ing on, Toil-ing on, toil-ing on;
Let us hope, let us watch, And la - bor till the Mas-ter comes.
and trust, and pray,

65 In Tenderness He Sought Me

W. SPENCER WALTON A. J. GORDON

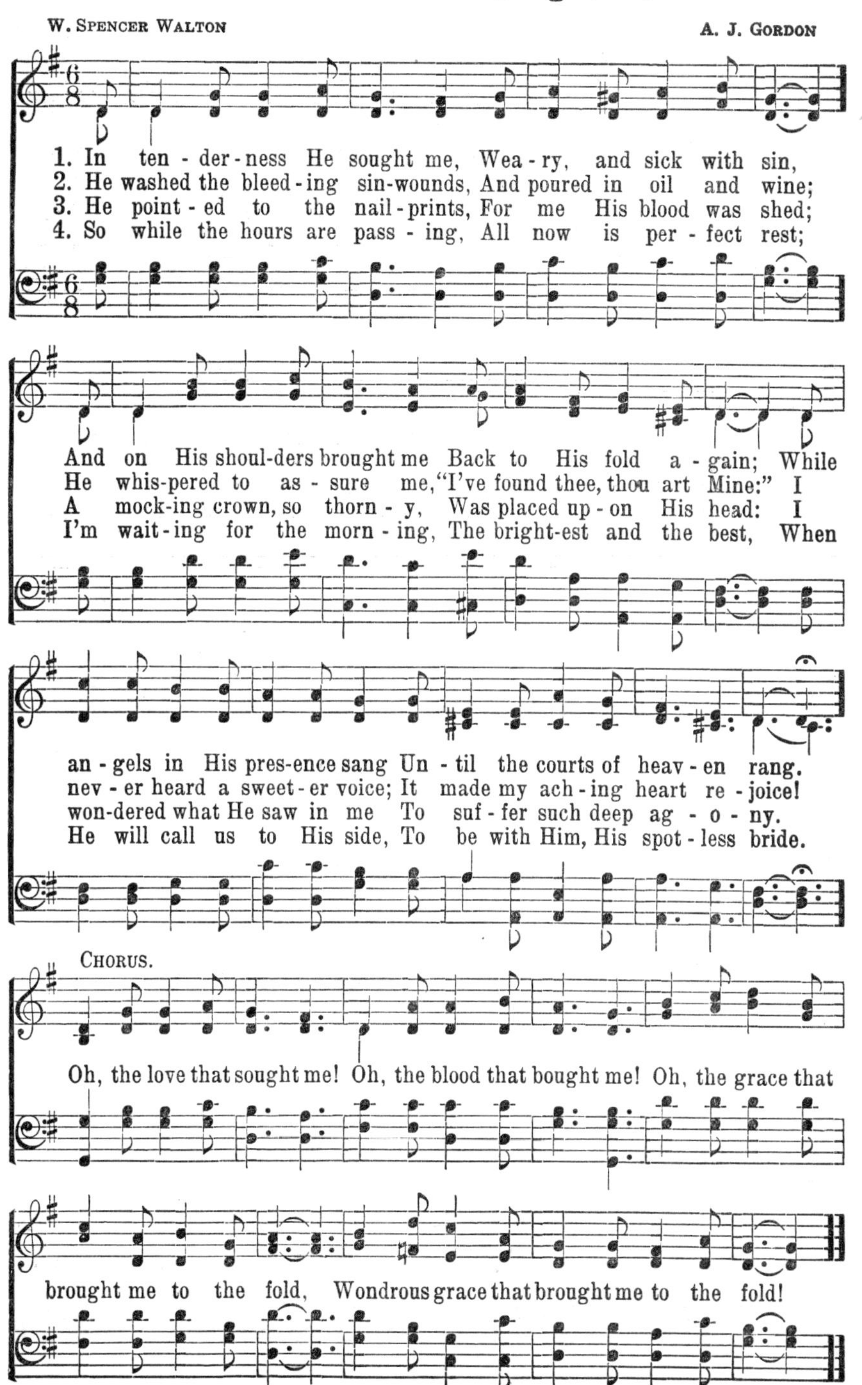

1. In ten - der - ness He sought me, Wea - ry, and sick with sin,
2. He washed the bleed - ing sin-wounds, And poured in oil and wine;
3. He point - ed to the nail - prints, For me His blood was shed;
4. So while the hours are pass - ing, All now is per - fect rest;
And on His shoul-ders brought me Back to His fold a - gain; While
He whis-pered to as - sure me, "I've found thee, thou art Mine:" I
A mock-ing crown, so thorn - y, Was placed up - on His head: I
I'm wait-ing for the morn - ing, The bright-est and the best, When
an - gels in His pres-ence sang Un - til the courts of heav - en rang.
nev - er heard a sweet - er voice; It made my ach - ing heart re - joice!
won-dered what He saw in me To suf - fer such deep ag - o - ny.
He will call us to His side, To be with Him, His spot - less bride.
CHORUS.
Oh, the love that sought me! Oh, the blood that bought me! Oh, the grace that
brought me to the fold, Wondrous grace that brought me to the fold!

Nothing Between

Words and Music by C. A. Tindley
Arr. by F. A. Clark
1. Noth-ing be-tween my soul and the Sav-iour, Naught of this world's de-
2. Noth-ing be-tween like world - ly pleas-ure; Hab-its of life, though
3. Noth-ing be-tween, like pride or sta-tion; Self or friends shall
4. Noth-ing be-tween, e'en man-y hard tri - als, Tho' the whole world a-
lu - sive dream: I have re-nounced all sin - ful pleas-ure,
harmless they seem, Must not my heart from Him ev - er sev - er,—
not in-ter-vene; Tho' it may cost me much trib-u - la - tion,
gainst me con-vene; Watching with prayer and much self-de - ni - al, I'll
Chorus
Je-sus is mine, there's nothing be-tween.
He is my all, there's nothing be-tween.
I am re-solved, there's nothing be-tween.
tri-umph at last, with nothing be-tween.
Noth-ing be-tween my soul and the
Sav-iour, So that His bless-ed face may be seen; Noth-ing pre-vent-ing the
least of His fa - vor, Keep the way clear! Let noth-ing be-tween.

67 Will Jesus Find Us Watching?

FANNY J. CROSBY — W. H. DOANE

1. When Jesus comes to reward His servants, Whether it be noon or night, Faithful to Him will He find us watching, With our lamps all trimmed and bright?
2. If, at the dawn of the early morning, He shall call us one by one, When to the Lord we restore our talents, Will He answer thee—Well done?
3. Have we been true to the trust He left us? Do we seek to do our best? If in our hearts there is naught condemns us, We shall have a glorious rest.
4. Blessed are those whom the Lord finds watching, In His glory they shall share; If He shall come at the dawn or midnight, Will He find us watching there?
rit.
CHORUS
O can we say we are ready, brother? Ready for the soul's bright home? Say, will He find you and me still watching, Waiting, waiting when the Lord shall come?

Ye Must Be Born Again

W. T. Sleeper — George C. Stebbins

1. A rul - er once came to Je - sus by night To ask Him the way of sal - va-tion and light; The Master made answer in words true and plain,
2. Ye chil-dren of men, at - tend to the word So sol-emn - ly ut - tered by Je - sus the Lord; And let not this message to you be in vain,
3. O ye who would en-ter that glo - ri - ous rest, And sing with the ransomed the song of the blest; The life ev - er-last-ing if ye would ob - tain,
4. A dear one in heav-en thy heart yearns to see, At the beau - ti - ful gate may be watch-ing for thee; Then list to the note of this sol - emn re - frain,
"Ye must be born a - gain." . . a - gain.
Chorus
"Ye must be born a- gain, . . . a - gain, Ye must be born a - gain; . . . a - gain;
I ver - i - ly, ver - i - ly say un - to thee, Ye must be born a - gain." . . a - gain.

69 Wonderful, Wonderful Jesus

Annie B. Russell — Ernest O. Sellers

1. There is nev - er a day so drear - y, There is nev - er a
2. There is nev - er a cross so heav - y, There is nev - er a
3. There is nev - er a care or bur - den, There is nev - er a
4. There is nev - er a guilt - y sin - ner, There is nev - er a
night so long (so long), But the soul that is trust-ing Je - sus Will
weight of woe (of woe), But that Je - sus will help to car - ry Be-
grief or loss (or loss), But that Je - sus in love will light - en When
wan-dering one (not one), But that God can in mer - cy par - don Thro'
some-where find a song (a song).
cause He lov - eth so (loves so).
car - ried to the cross (the cross).
Je - sus Christ, His Son (His Son).
Chorus
Won-der-ful, won-der - ful Je - sus,
In the heart He im-plant-eth a song: . . . A song of de-liverance, of
He plant-eth a song:
cour - age, of strength, In the heart He im - plant-eth a song (a song).

70 When I See the Blood

John
J. G. F.
1. Christ our Re-deem-er died on the cross, Died for the sin-ner, paid all his due; All who re-ceive Him need nev-er fear, Yes, He will pass, will pass o-ver you.
2. Chief-est of sin-ners, Je-sus can save, As He has prom-ised, so will He do; Oh, sin-ner, hear Him, trust in His Word, Then He will pass, will pass o-ver you.
3. Judg-ment is com-ing, all will be there, Who have re-ject-ed, who have re-fused? Oh, sin-ner, has-ten, let Je-sus in, Then God will pass, will pass o-ver you.
4. Oh, what com-pas-sion, oh, bound-less love! Je-sus hath pow-er, Je-sus is true; All who be-lieve are safe from the storm, Oh, He will pass, will pass o-ver you.
Chorus
When I see the blood, When I see the blood, When I see the blood, I will pass, I will pass o-ver you.
When I see the blood, When I see the blood, When I see the blood, o-ver you.
rit.

71 The Old Rugged Cross

Rev. G. B.
Rev. Geo. Bennard
1. On a hill far a-way stood an old rug-ged cross, The em-blem of
2. Oh, that old rug-ged cross so de-spised by the world, Has a won-drous at-
3. In the old rug-ged cross, stained with blood so di-vine, A won - drous
4. To the old rug-ged cross I will ev - er be true, Its shame and re-
suf-fering and shame; And I love that old cross where the dear-est and best
trac-tion for me; For the dear Lamb of God left His glo - ry a - bove,
beau - ty I see; For 'twas on that old cross Je - sus suf-fered and died,
proach glad-ly bear; Then He'll call me some day to my home far a - way,
For a world of lost sin-ners was slain.
To bear it to dark Cal - va - ry.
To par-don and sanc-ti - fy me.
Where His glo-ry for - ev - er I'll share.
Chorus
So I'll cher-ish the old rug-ged
cross, the
cross, . . . Till my tro-phies at last I lay down; I will cling to the
old rug-ged cross,
old rug-ged cross, . . . And ex-change it some day for a crown.
cross, the old rug-ged cross,

Throw Out the Life-Line

EDWARD S. UFFORD — E. S. UFFORD
Arr. by GEORGE C. STEBBINS

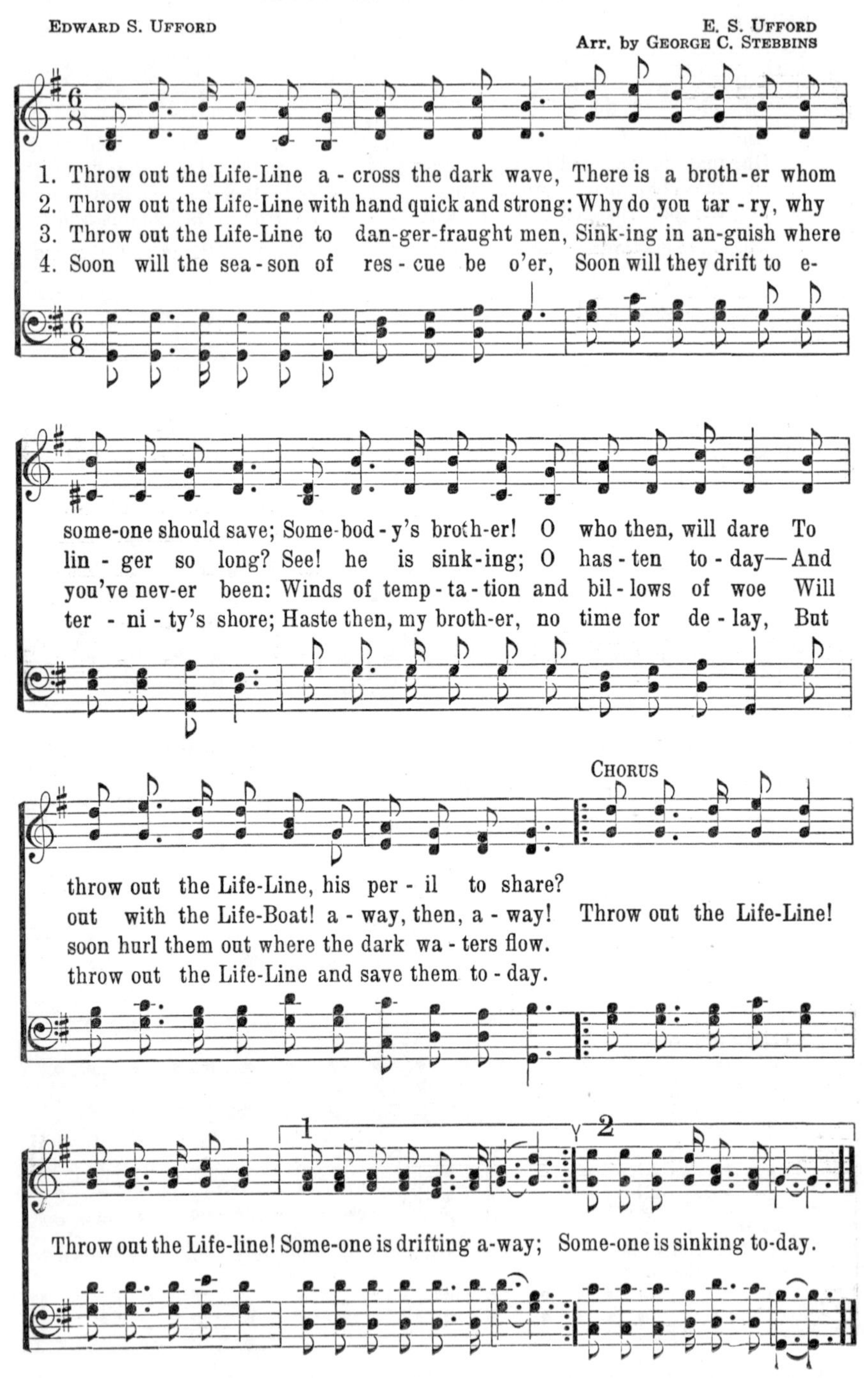
1. Throw out the Life-Line a - cross the dark wave, There is a broth-er whom
2. Throw out the Life-Line with hand quick and strong: Why do you tar - ry, why
3. Throw out the Life-Line to dan-ger-fraught men, Sink-ing in an-guish where
4. Soon will the sea - son of res - cue be o'er, Soon will they drift to e-
some-one should save; Some-bod - y's broth-er! O who then, will dare To
lin - ger so long? See! he is sink-ing; O has - ten to - day— And
you've nev-er been: Winds of temp - ta - tion and bil - lows of woe Will
ter - ni - ty's shore; Haste then, my broth-er, no time for de - lay, But
throw out the Life-Line, his per - il to share?
out with the Life-Boat! a - way, then, a - way!
soon hurl them out where the dark wa - ters flow.
throw out the Life-Line and save them to - day.
CHORUS
Throw out the Life-Line!
1
2
Throw out the Life-line! Some-one is drifting a-way; Some-one is sinking to-day.

73 It Is Well with My Soul

H. G. Spafford
P. P. Bliss
1. When peace, like a riv - er, at - tend-eth my way, When sor-rows like
2. Though Sa-tan should buf-fet, tho' tri - als should come, Let this blest as-
3. My sin—oh, the bliss of this glo - ri - ous tho't—My sin—not in
4. And, Lord, haste the day when the faith shall be sight, The clouds be rolled
sea - bil - lows roll; What-ev - er my lot, Thou hast taught me to say,
sur - ance con - trol, That Christ has re - gard - ed my help - less es - tate,
part, but the whole—Is nailed to the cross and I bear it no more,
back as a scroll, The trump shall re-sound and the Lord shall de-scend,
It is well, it is well with my soul.
And hath shed His own blood for my soul.
Praise the Lord, praise the Lord, O my soul!
"E - ven so"— it is well with my soul.
Chorus
It is well . . . . with my
It is well
soul, ... It is well, it is well with my soul.
with my soul,

The Wayfaring Stranger

Words arr.

Arr. from an old Southern Melody

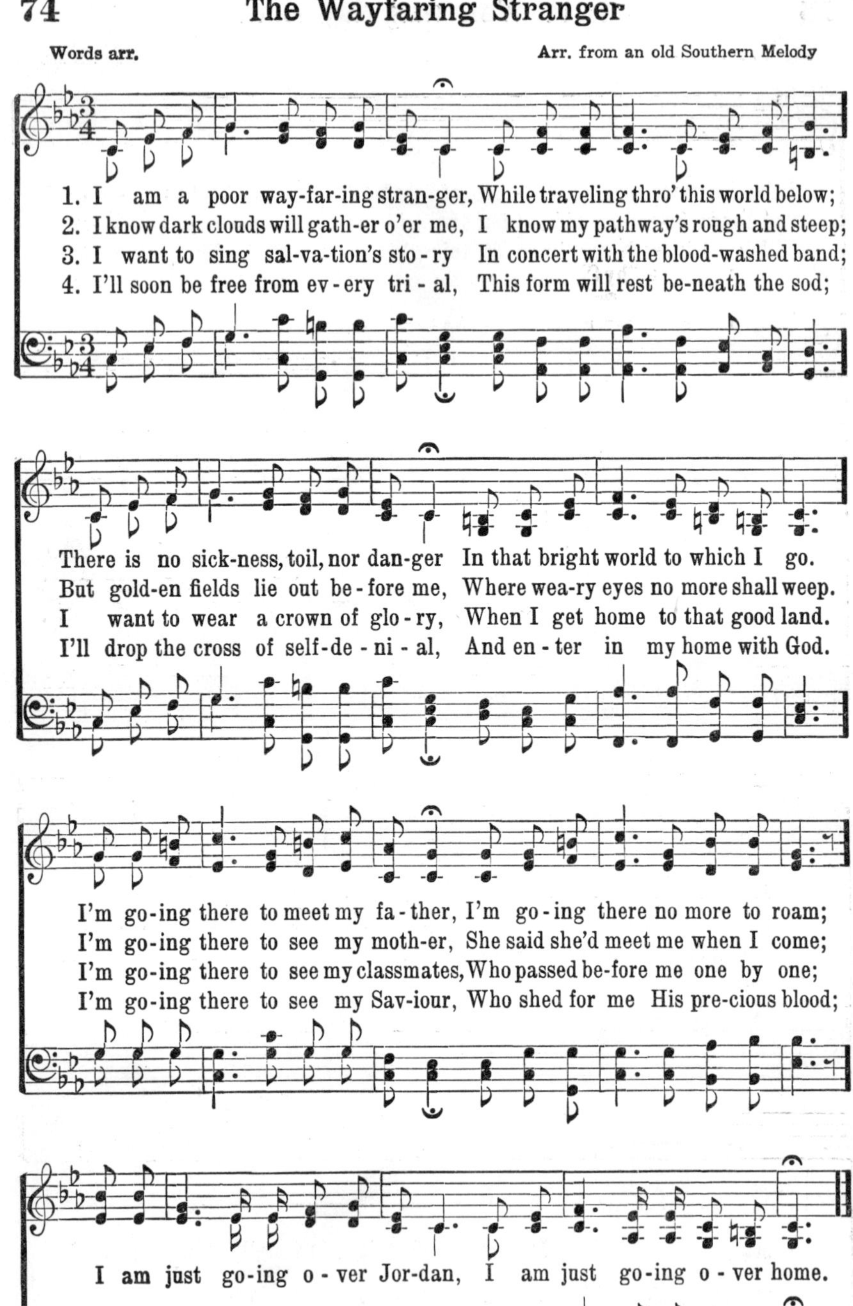
1. I am a poor way-far-ing stran-ger, While traveling thro' this world below;
2. I know dark clouds will gath-er o'er me, I know my pathway's rough and steep;
3. I want to sing sal-va-tion's sto - ry In concert with the blood-washed band;
4. I'll soon be free from ev - ery tri - al, This form will rest be-neath the sod;
There is no sick-ness, toil, nor dan-ger In that bright world to which I go.
But gold-en fields lie out be - fore me, Where wea-ry eyes no more shall weep.
I want to wear a crown of glo - ry, When I get home to that good land.
I'll drop the cross of self-de - ni - al, And en - ter in my home with God.
I'm go-ing there to meet my fa - ther, I'm go - ing there no more to roam;
I'm go-ing there to see my moth-er, She said she'd meet me when I come;
I'm go-ing there to see my classmates, Who passed be-fore me one by one;
I'm go-ing there to see my Sav-iour, Who shed for me His pre-cious blood;
I am just go-ing o - ver Jor-dan, I am just go-ing o - ver home.

75 O Word of God Incarnate

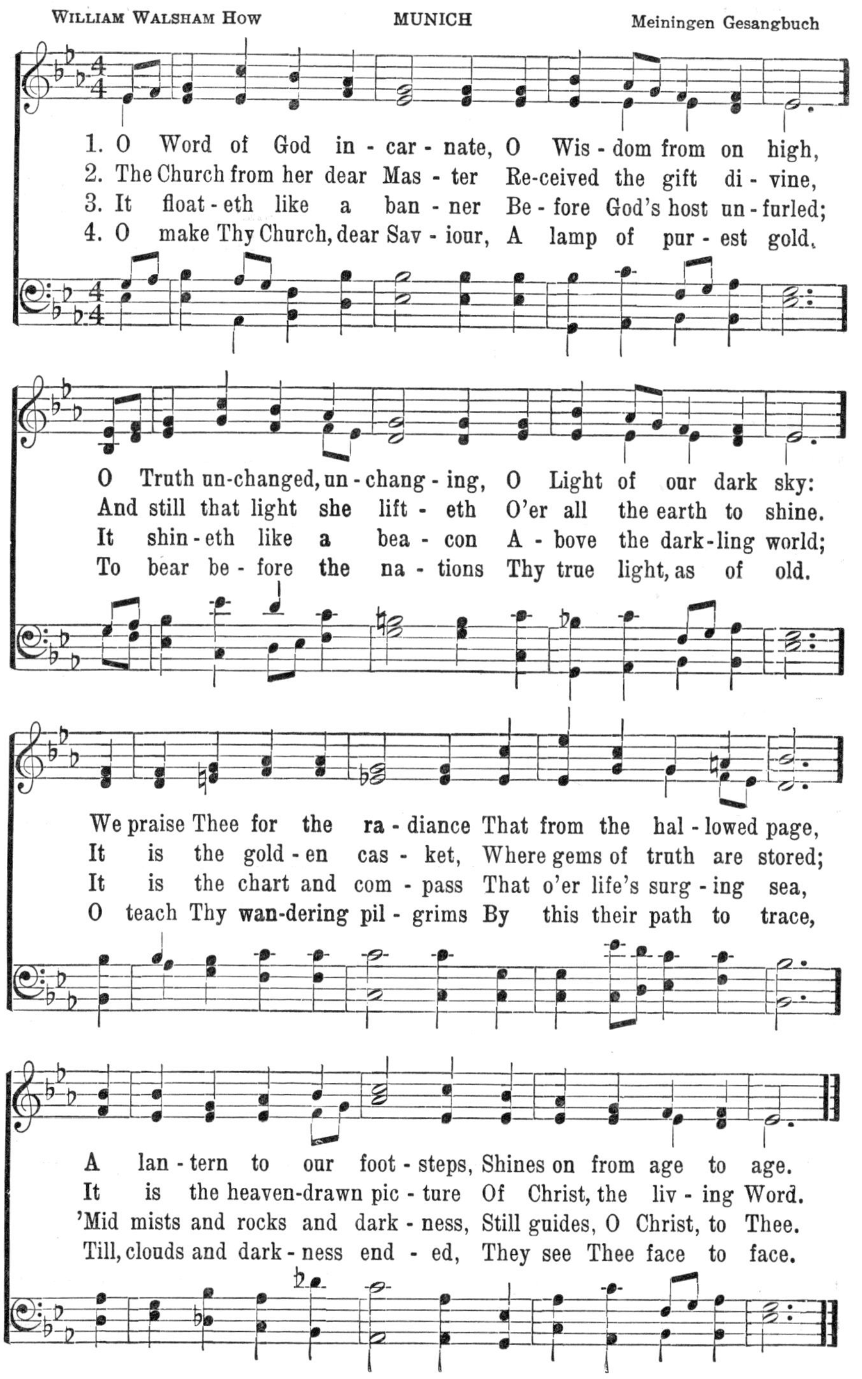
WILLIAM WALSHAM HOW
MUNICH
Meiningen Gesangbuch
1. O Word of God in - car - nate, O Wis - dom from on high,
2. The Church from her dear Mas - ter Re-ceived the gift di - vine,
3. It float - eth like a ban - ner Be - fore God's host un - furled;
4. O make Thy Church, dear Sav - iour, A lamp of pur - est gold,
O Truth un-changed, un - chang - ing, O Light of our dark sky:
And still that light she lift - eth O'er all the earth to shine.
It shin - eth like a bea - con A - bove the dark-ling world;
To bear be - fore the na - tions Thy true light, as of old.
We praise Thee for the ra - diance That from the hal - lowed page,
It is the gold - en cas - ket, Where gems of truth are stored;
It is the chart and com - pass That o'er life's surg - ing sea,
O teach Thy wan-dering pil - grims By this their path to trace,
A lan - tern to our foot - steps, Shines on from age to age.
It is the heaven-drawn pic - ture Of Christ, the liv - ing Word.
'Mid mists and rocks and dark - ness, Still guides, O Christ, to Thee.
Till, clouds and dark - ness end - ed, They see Thee face to face.

76 The Regions Beyond

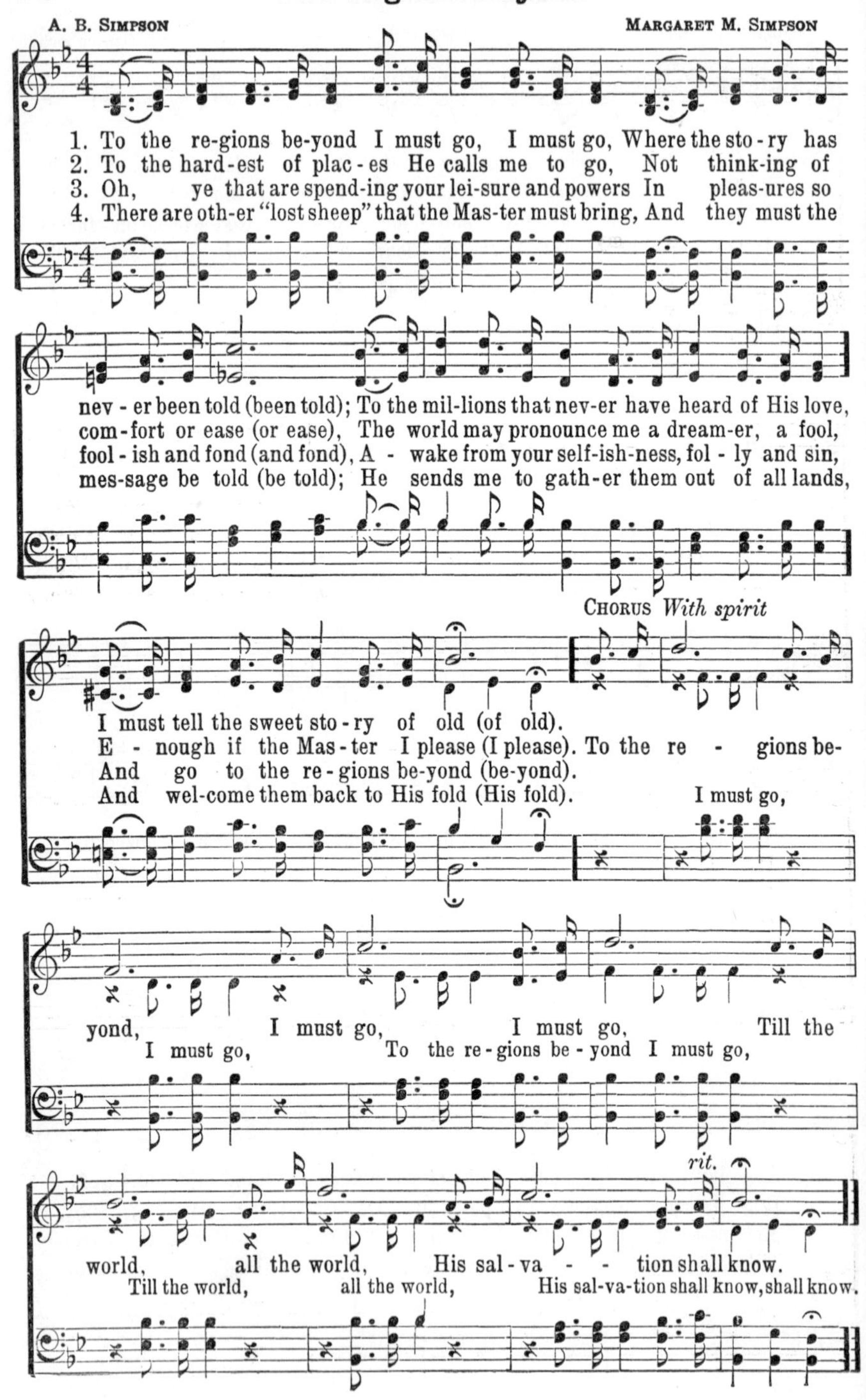

A. B. SIMPSON
MARGARET M. SIMPSON
1. To the re-gions be-yond I must go, I must go, Where the sto-ry has
2. To the hard-est of plac-es He calls me to go, Not think-ing of
3. Oh, ye that are spend-ing your lei-sure and powers In pleas-ures so
4. There are oth-er "lost sheep" that the Mas-ter must bring, And they must the
nev-er been told (been told); To the mil-lions that nev-er have heard of His love,
com-fort or ease (or ease), The world may pronounce me a dream-er, a fool,
fool-ish and fond (and fond), A - wake from your self-ish-ness, fol - ly and sin,
mes-sage be told (be told); He sends me to gath-er them out of all lands,
I must tell the sweet sto-ry of old (of old).
E - nough if the Mas-ter I please (I please).
And go to the re-gions be-yond (be-yond).
And wel-come them back to His fold (His fold).
CHORUS With spirit
To the re - gions be-yond,
I must go, I must go,
I must go, I must go, Till the world, all the world, His sal-va - - tion shall know.
To the re-gions be-yond I must go,
Till the world, all the world, His sal-va-tion shall know, shall know.
rit.

77

Others

C. D. Meigs — Elizabeth McE. Shields

1. Lord, help me live from day to day In such a self-for-getful way That even when I kneel to pray My prayer shall be for—Others.
2. Help me in all the work I do To ever be sincere and true, And know that all I'd do for you Must needs be done for—Others.
3. Let "Self" be crucified and slain And buried deep: and all in vain May efforts be to rise again, Unless to live for—Others.
4. And when my work on earth is done, And my new work in heaven's begun, May I forget the crown I've won, While thinking still of—Others.
Chorus
Others, Lord, yes, others, Let this my motto be, Help me to live for others, That I may live like Thee.
rit.

78 I Am Praying for You

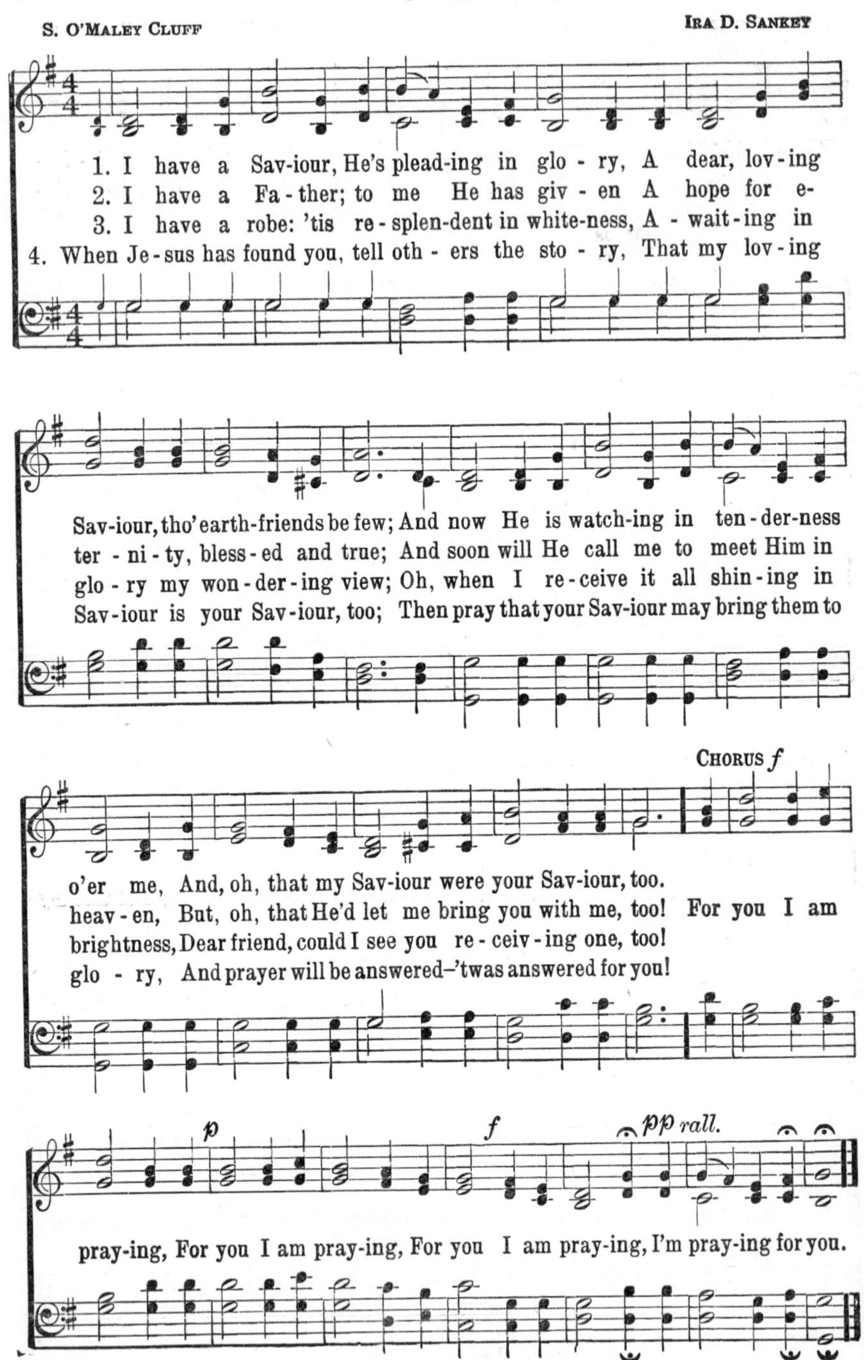
S. O'Maley Cluff
Ira D. Sankey
1. I have a Sav-iour, He's plead-ing in glo - ry, A dear, lov-ing
2. I have a Fa - ther; to me He has giv - en A hope for e-
3. I have a robe: 'tis re - splen-dent in white-ness, A - wait-ing in
4. When Je - sus has found you, tell oth - ers the sto - ry, That my lov-ing
Sav-iour, tho' earth-friends be few; And now He is watch-ing in ten - der-ness
ter - ni - ty, bless - ed and true; And soon will He call me to meet Him in
glo - ry my won - der - ing view; Oh, when I re - ceive it all shin - ing in
Sav-iour is your Sav-iour, too; Then pray that your Sav-iour may bring them to
o'er me, And, oh, that my Sav-iour were your Sav-iour, too.
heav - en, But, oh, that He'd let me bring you with me, too!
brightness, Dear friend, could I see you re - ceiv - ing one, too!
glo - ry, And prayer will be answered–'twas answered for you!
Chorus f
For you I am
pray-ing, For you I am pray-ing, For you I am pray-ing, I'm pray-ing for you.
p
f
pp rall.

79 The Haven of Rest

H. L. Gilmour
George D. Moore
1. My soul in sad ex - ile was out on life's sea, So bur-dened with
2. I yield - ed my - self to His ten - der em - brace, And, faith tak-ing
3. The song of my soul, since the Lord made me whole, Has been the old
4. Oh, come to the Sav - iour, He pa - tient - ly waits, To save by His
sin and dis - trest, Till I heard a sweet voice say-ing, "Make Me your choice,"
hold of the word, My fet - ters fell off, and I an-chored my soul:
sto - ry so blest, Of Je-sus, who'll save who-so - ev - er will have
pow - er di - vine; Come, an-chor your soul in the ha - ven of rest,
D. S.—The tem-pest may sweep o'er the wild storm - y deep,
Fine
Chorus
And I en - tered the ha - ven of rest.
The ha - ven of rest is my Lord.
A home in the ha - ven of rest.
And say, "My Be - lov - ed is mine."
I've an-chored my
In Je - sus I'm safe ev - er - more.
D. S.
soul in the ha - ven of rest, I'll sail the wild seas no more;

Rescue the Perishing

FANNY J. CROSBY WILLIAM H. DOANE

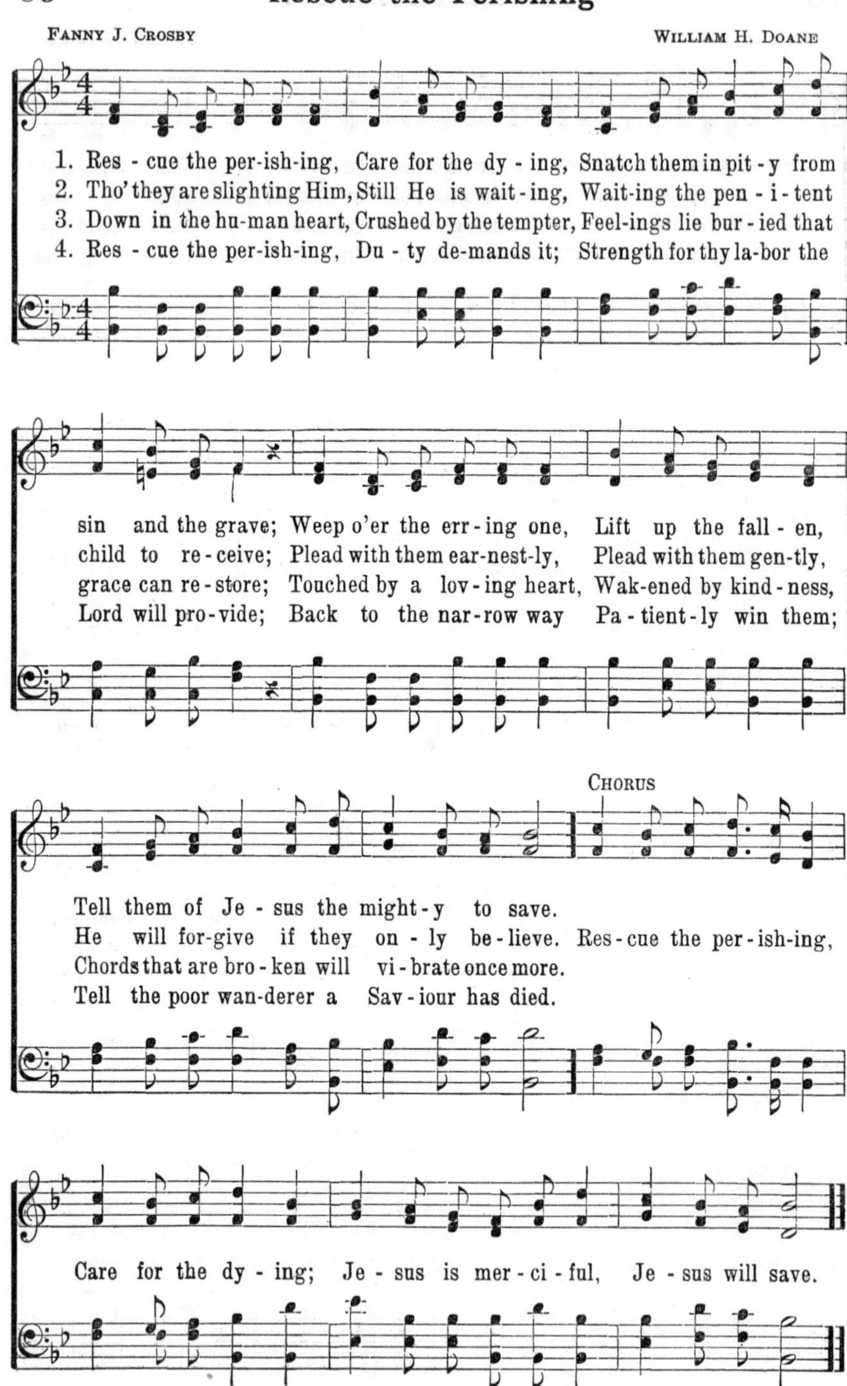
1. Res - cue the per-ish-ing, Care for the dy - ing, Snatch them in pit - y from
2. Tho' they are slighting Him, Still He is wait - ing, Wait-ing the pen - i - tent
3. Down in the hu-man heart, Crushed by the tempter, Feel-ings lie bur - ied that
4. Res - cue the per-ish-ing, Du - ty de-mands it; Strength for thy la-bor the
sin and the grave; Weep o'er the err - ing one, Lift up the fall - en,
child to re - ceive; Plead with them ear-nest-ly, Plead with them gen-tly,
grace can re - store; Touched by a lov - ing heart, Wak-ened by kind - ness,
Lord will pro - vide; Back to the nar - row way Pa - tient - ly win them;
Tell them of Je - sus the might - y to save.
He will for-give if they on - ly be - lieve.
Chords that are bro - ken will vi - brate once more.
Tell the poor wan-derer a Sav - iour has died.
CHORUS
Res - cue the per - ish-ing,
Care for the dy - ing; Je - sus is mer - ci - ful, Je - sus will save.

81

The Unclouded Day

J. K. A. Rev. J. K. Alwood

1. O they tell me of a home far be-yond the skies, O they tell me of a home far a-way; O they tell me of a home where no storm-clouds rise, O they tell me of an un-cloud-ed day.
2. O they tell me of a home where my friends have gone, O they tell me of that land far a-way, Where the tree of life in e-ter-nal bloom Sheds its fra-grance thro' the un-cloud-ed day.
3. O they tell me of a King in His beau-ty there, And they tell me that mine eyes shall be-hold Where He sits on the throne that is whit-er than snow, In the cit-y that is made of gold.
4. O they tell me that He smiles on His chil-dren there, And His smile drives their sor-rows all a-way; And they tell me that no tears ev-er come a-gain, In that love-ly land of un-cloud-ed day.
D. S.—O they tell me of a home where no storm-clouds rise, O they tell me of an un-cloud-ed day.
Fine
Chorus
O the land of cloud-less day, O the land of an un-cloud-ed day;
D. S.

82 I Surrender All

J. W. Van DeVenter
W. S. Weeden
1. All to Je - sus I sur - ren - der, All to Him I free - ly give;
2. All to Je - sus I sur - ren - der, Hum-bly at His feet I bow;
3. All to Je - sus I sur - ren - der, Make me, Sav-iour, whol - ly Thine;
4. All to Je - sus I sur - ren - der, Lord, I give my - self to Thee;
I will ev - er love and trust Him, In His pres-ence dai - ly live.
World-ly pleas-ures all for - sak - en, Take me, Je - sus, take me now.
Let me feel the Ho - ly Spir - it,—Tru - ly know that Thou art mine.
Fill me with Thy love and pow - er, Let Thy bless-ing fall on me.
Chorus
I sur-ren - der all, I sur-ren - der all;
I sur-ren-der all, I sur-ren-der all;
All to Thee, my bless - ed Sav - iour, I sur - ren - der all.

83

All On the Altar

Dedicated to young people. B. B. McK.

B. B. McK. B. B. McKinney

1. All on the al-tar, dear Je - sus, Mas-ter, I hear Thy call; . . .
2. All on the al-tar, dear Je - sus, Yield-ed am I to Thee; . .
3. All on the al-tar, dear Je - sus, On-ly Thy will is mine; . .
4. All on the al-tar, dear Je - sus, All at Thy feet I lay; . . .
Somewhere I know Thou canst use me, I must sur-ren-der my all. . . .
Take me and mold me and make me As Thou wouldst have me be. . . .
Let my lips tell the sweet sto - ry, Tell of Thy love di - vine. . .
Will-ing to toil and to suf - fer, "Thro'-out life's lit - tle day." . .
Chorus.
My all for Thee, my all for Thee, Who gave Thine all, dear Lord, for me;
My all for Thee, for Thee, Who gave Thine all for me;
Thy will di-vine, Henceforth is mine, To live for Thee, dear Saviour, for Thee.
Thy will di - vine is mine,
rit.

Rest For the Weary

WILLIAM HUNTER — J. W. DADMUN

1. In the Christian's home in glo - ry There re-mains a land of rest;
2. He is fit - ting up my man - sion, Which e - ter - nal - ly shall stand,
3. Pain and sick-ness ne'er shall en - ter, Grief nor woe my lot shall share;
4. Death it-self shall then be van-quished, And his sting shall be with-drawn;
There my Sav-iour's gone be - fore me, To ful - fill my soul's re - quest.
For my stay shall not be tran - sient, In that ho - ly, hap - py land.
But, in that ce - les - tial cen - ter, I a crown of life shall wear.
Shout for glad-ness, O ye ran - somed! Hail with joy the ris - ing morn.
CHORUS
There is rest for the wea - ry, There is rest for the wea - ry,
On the oth - er side of Jor - dan, In the sweet fields of E - den,
There is rest for the wea - ry, There is rest for you.
Where the tree of life is bloom - ing, There is rest for you.

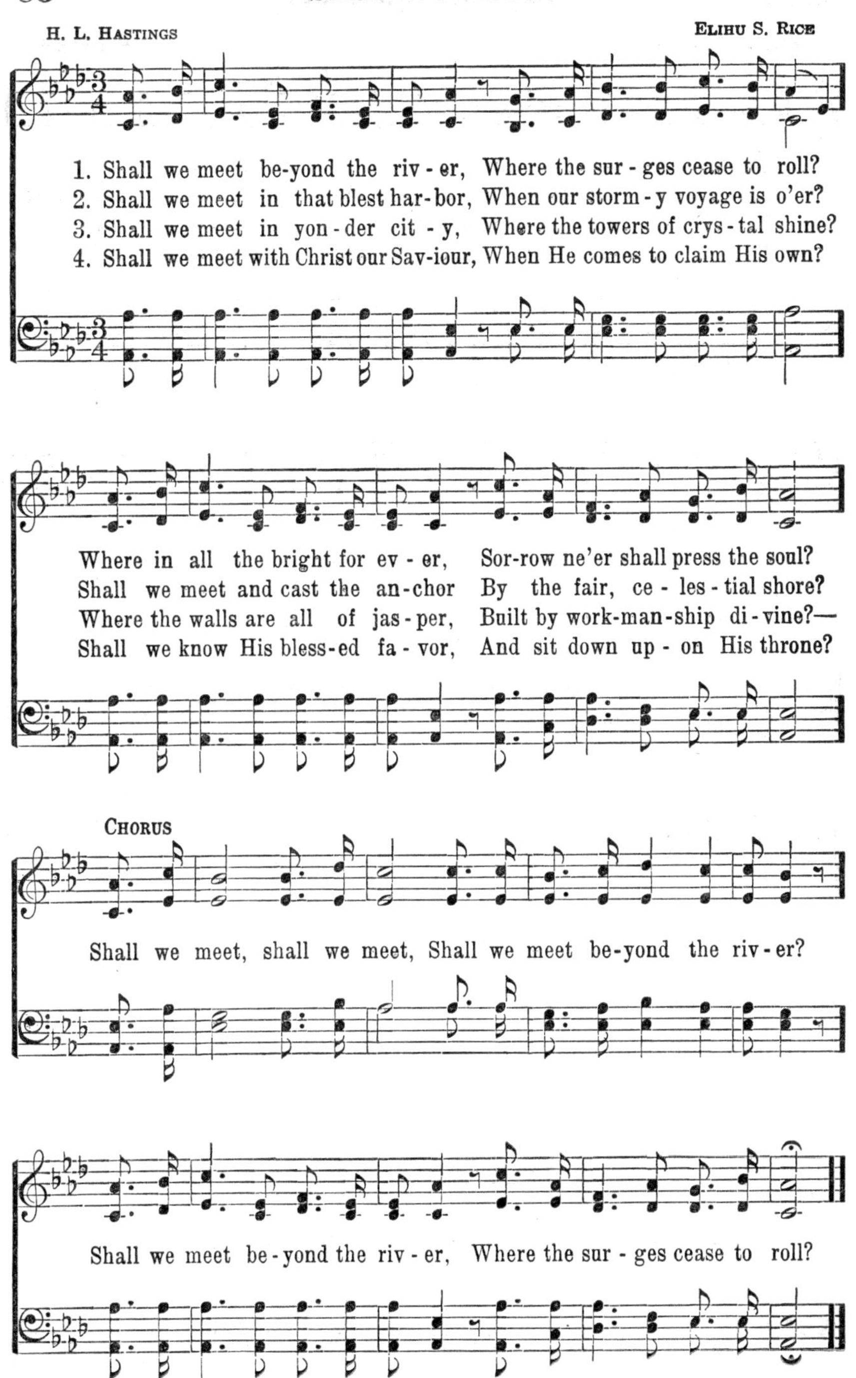
85
Shall We Meet?
H. L. Hastings
Elihu S. Rice
1. Shall we meet be-yond the riv - er, Where the sur - ges cease to roll?
2. Shall we meet in that blest har-bor, When our storm - y voyage is o'er?
3. Shall we meet in yon-der cit - y, Where the towers of crys - tal shine?
4. Shall we meet with Christ our Sav-iour, When He comes to claim His own?
Where in all the bright for ev - er, Sor-row ne'er shall press the soul?
Shall we meet and cast the an-chor By the fair, ce - les - tial shore?
Where the walls are all of jas - per, Built by work-man-ship di - vine?—
Shall we know His bless-ed fa - vor, And sit down up - on His throne?
Chorus
Shall we meet, shall we meet, Shall we meet be-yond the riv - er?
Shall we meet be - yond the riv - er, Where the sur - ges cease to roll?

86 Take Me as I Am

Eliza H. Hamilton
Ira D. Sankey
Moderato
1. Je - sus, my Lord, to Thee I cry; Un-less Thou help me I must die:
2. Help-less I am, and full of guilt; But yet for me Thy blood was spilt,
3. No prep - ar - a - tion can I make, My best re-solves I on - ly break,
4. Be - hold me, Sav-iour, at Thy feet, Deal with me as Thou see - est meet;
Oh, bring Thy free sal - va - tion nigh, And take me as I am.
And Thou canst make me what Thou wilt, And take me as I am.
Yet save me for Thine own name's sake, And take me as I am.
Thy work be - gin, Thy work com-plete, And take me as I am.
Chorus
And take me as I am, And take me as I am,
My on - ly plea—Christ died for me! Oh, take me as I am.

87 Day Is Dying in the West

MARY A. LATHBURY — WILLIAM F. SHERWIN

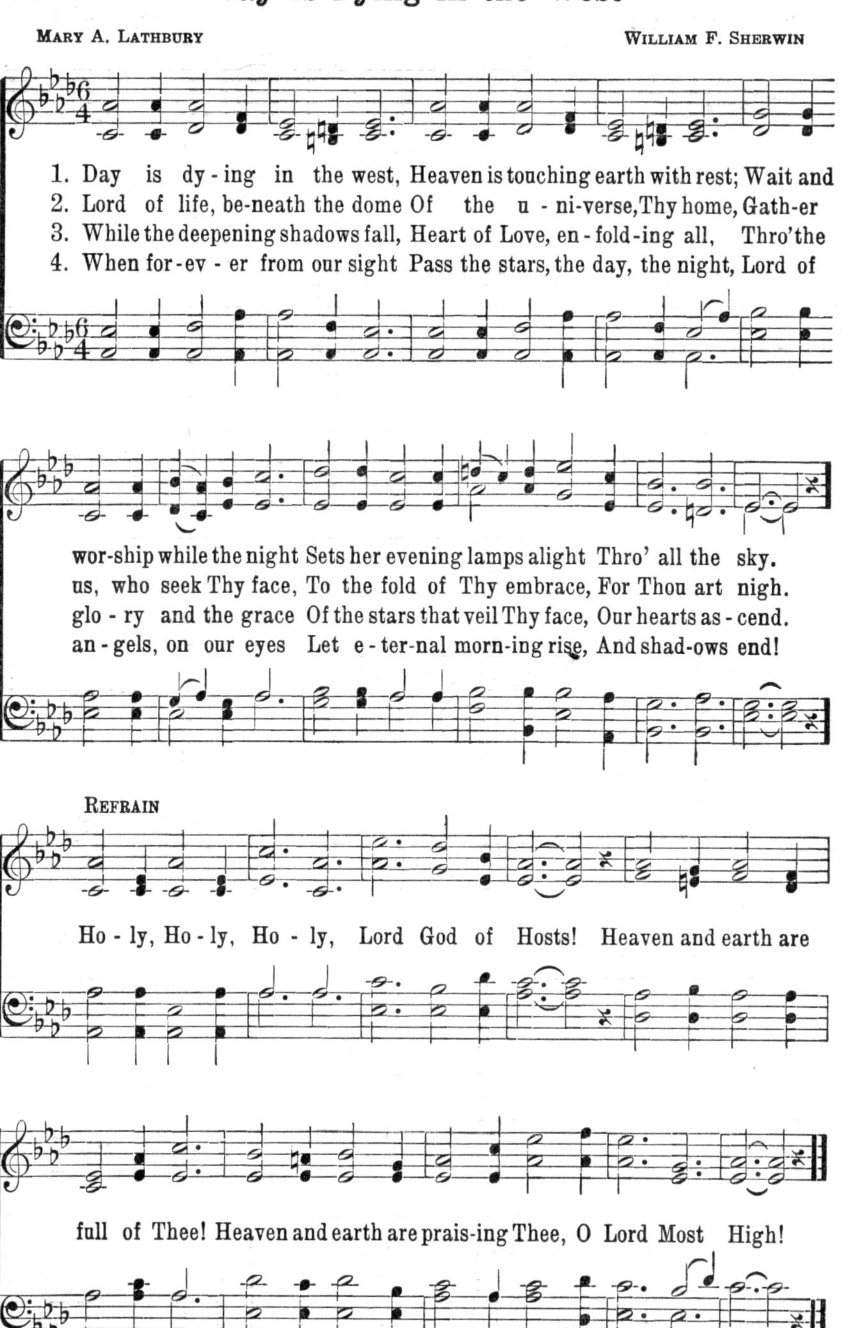
1. Day is dy-ing in the west, Heaven is touching earth with rest; Wait and wor-ship while the night Sets her evening lamps alight Thro' all the sky.
2. Lord of life, be-neath the dome Of the u-ni-verse, Thy home, Gath-er us, who seek Thy face, To the fold of Thy embrace, For Thou art nigh.
3. While the deepening shadows fall, Heart of Love, en-fold-ing all, Thro' the glo-ry and the grace Of the stars that veil Thy face, Our hearts as-cend.
4. When for-ev-er from our sight Pass the stars, the day, the night, Lord of an-gels, on our eyes Let e-ter-nal morn-ing rise, And shad-ows end!
REFRAIN
Ho-ly, Ho-ly, Ho-ly, Lord God of Hosts! Heaven and earth are full of Thee! Heaven and earth are prais-ing Thee, O Lord Most High!

88 Beyond the Sunset

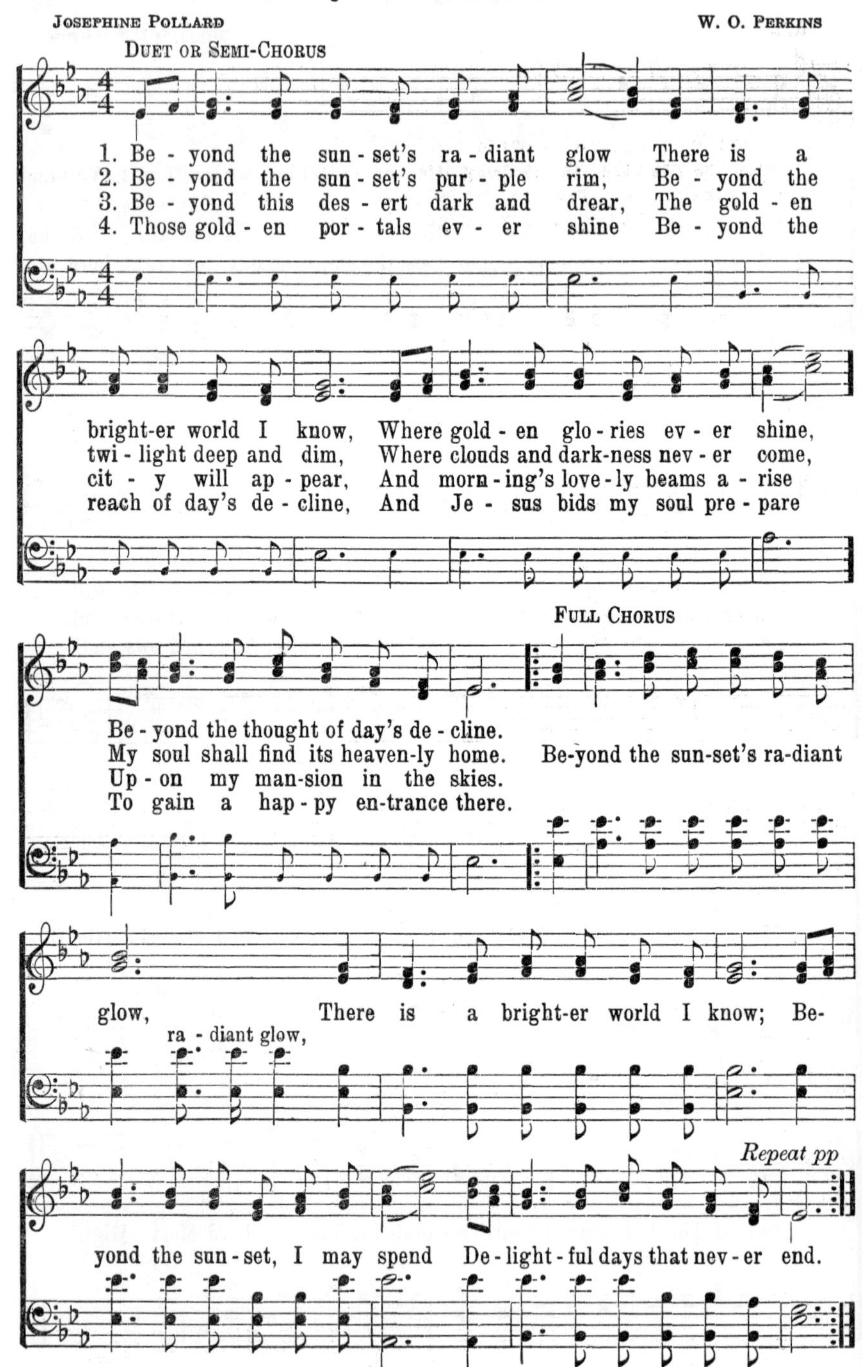
JOSEPHINE POLLARD
W. O. PERKINS
DUET OR SEMI-CHORUS
1. Be - yond the sun - set's ra - diant glow There is a bright-er world I know, Where gold - en glo - ries ev - er shine, Be - yond the thought of day's de - cline.
2. Be - yond the sun - set's pur - ple rim, Be - yond the twi - light deep and dim, Where clouds and dark-ness nev - er come, My soul shall find its heaven-ly home.
3. Be - yond this des - ert dark and drear, The gold - en cit - y will ap - pear, And morn - ing's love - ly beams a - rise Up - on my man-sion in the skies.
4. Those gold - en por - tals ev - er shine Be - yond the reach of day's de - cline, And Je - sus bids my soul pre - pare To gain a hap - py en-trance there.
FULL CHORUS
Be-yond the sun-set's ra-diant glow, There is a bright-er world I know; Be-yond the sun - set, I may spend De - light - ful days that nev - er end.
ra - diant glow,
Repeat pp

89 Where Is My Boy To-Night?

R. L. Rev. R. LOWRY

1. Where is my wan-dering boy to-night—The boy of my ten-derest care,
2. Once he was pure as morn-ing dew, As he knelt at his moth-er's knee;
3. O could I see you now, my boy, As fair as in old - en time,
4. Go for my wan-dering boy to-night; Go search for him where you will;
The boy that was once my joy and light, The child of my love and prayer?
No face was so bright, no heart more true, And none was so sweet as he.
When prat-tle and smile made home a joy, And life was a mer - ry chime!
But bring him to me with all his blight, And tell him I love him still.
CHORUS Not too fast.
O where is my boy to - night? O where is my boy to - night?
My heart o'er-flows, for I love him he knows; O where is my boy to - night?

Precious Promise

NATHANIEL NILES

P. P. BLISS

1. Pre - cious prom-ise God hath giv - en To the wea - ry pass - er - by,
2. When temp-ta - tions al - most win thee, And thy trust - ed watch-ers fly,
3. When thy se - cret hopes have per-ished In the grave of years gone by,
4. When the shades of life are fall - ing, And the hour has come to die,
On the way from earth to heav - en, "I will guide thee with Mine eye."
Let this prom - ise ring with - in thee, "I will guide thee with Mine eye."
Let this prom - ise still be cher - ished, "I will guide thee with Mine eye."
Hear the trust - y Pi - lot call - ing, "I will guide thee with Mine eye."
CHORUS
I will guide thee, I will guide thee, I will guide thee with Mine eye;
On the way from earth to heav - en, I will guide thee with Mine eye.

91 Arise, O Youth of God

WILLIAM P. MERRILL
B. B. MCKINNEY
1. A - rise, O youth of God! Have done with less - er things;
2. A - rise, O youth of God! His king - dom tar - ries long;
3. A - rise, O youth of God! The Church for you doth wait;
4. Lift high the cross of Christ! Tread where His feet have trod;
Give heart and soul and mind and strength To serve the King of kings.
Bring in the day of joy and peace, And end the night of wrong.
Her strength shall make your spir-it strong; Her serv - ice make you great.
Be loy - al to the King of kings; March on, O youth of God!
CHORUS
A - rise, . . . A - rise, ... The Mas - ter calls for thee;
A - rise, ...
A - rise, A - rise,
A - rise, A - rise, O youth of God, March on to vic - to - ry!

92

Redeemed

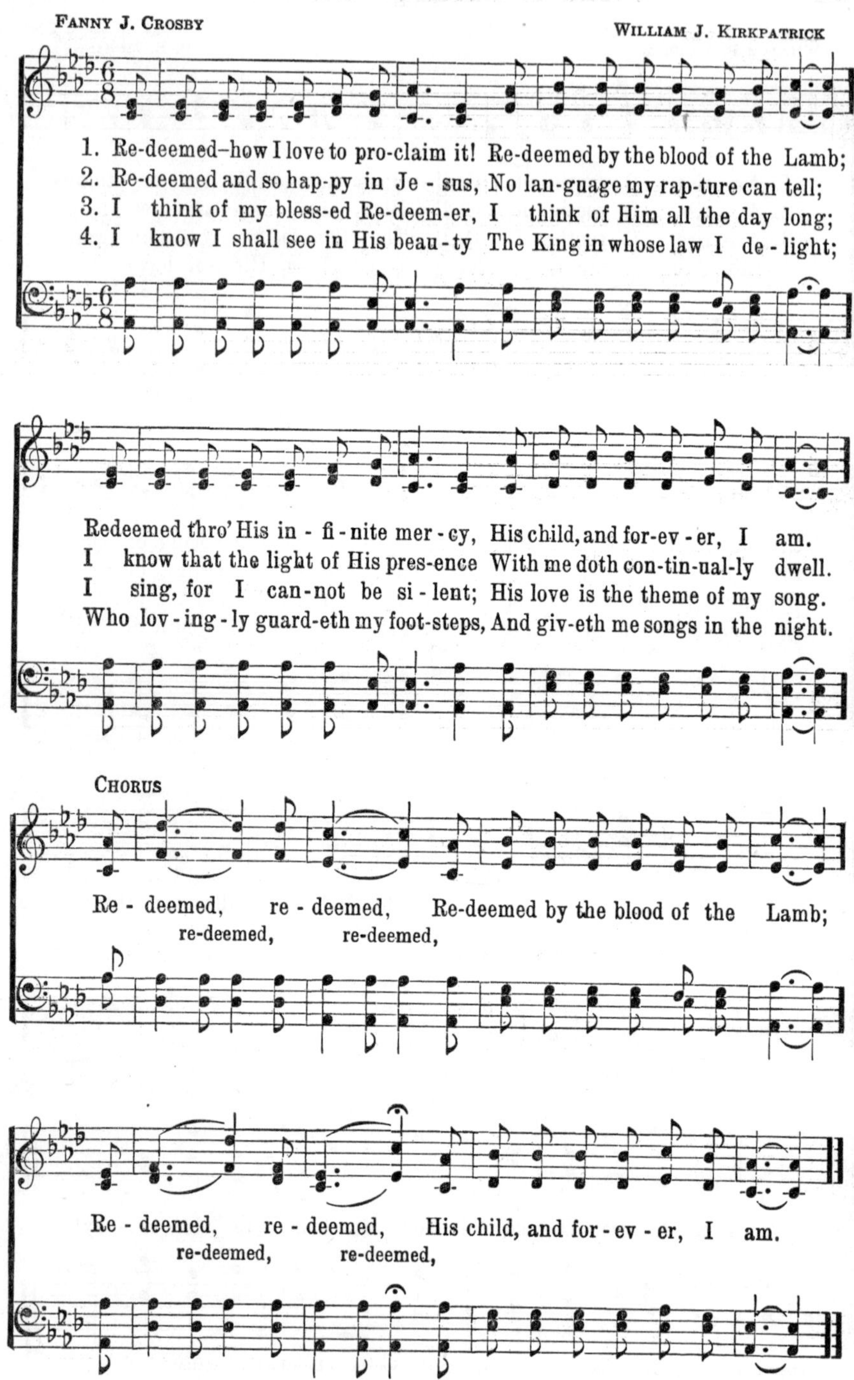

FANNY J. CROSBY
WILLIAM J. KIRKPATRICK
1. Re-deemed–how I love to pro-claim it! Re-deemed by the blood of the Lamb;
2. Re-deemed and so hap-py in Je - sus, No lan-guage my rap-ture can tell;
3. I think of my bless-ed Re-deem-er, I think of Him all the day long;
4. I know I shall see in His beau-ty The King in whose law I de - light;
Redeemed thro' His in - fi - nite mer - cy, His child, and for-ev - er, I am.
I know that the light of His pres-ence With me doth con-tin-ual-ly dwell.
I sing, for I can-not be si - lent; His love is the theme of my song.
Who lov - ing - ly guard-eth my foot-steps, And giv-eth me songs in the night.
CHORUS
Re - deemed, re - deemed, Re-deemed by the blood of the Lamb;
re-deemed, re-deemed,
Re - deemed, re - deemed, His child, and for - ev - er, I am.
re-deemed, re-deemed,

93 Jesus Is Passing This Way

Annie L. James — W. H. Doane

Gentl
1. Is there a heart that is wait-ing, Long-ing for par-don to-day?
2. Is there a heart that has wan-dered? Come with thy bur-den to-day;
3. Is there a heart that is bro-ken? Wea-ry and sigh-ing for rest?
4. Come to thy on-ly Re-deem-er, Come to His in-fi-nite love;
rit.
Hear the glad mes-sage pro-claim-ing, Je-sus is pass-ing this way.
Mer-cy is ten-der-ly plead-ing, Je-sus is pass-ing this way.
Come to the arms of thy Sav-iour, Pil-low thy head on His breast.
Come to the gate that is lead-ing Home-ward to man-sions a-bove.
Refrain
Je-sus is pass-ing this way, . . . This way, ... to-day; . . . .
Je-sus is pass-ing, is pass-ing this way, Is pass-ing this way, Is pass-ing to-day;
rit.
Je-sus is pass-ing this way, . . . Is pass-ing this way to-day.
way to-day,

94 I Know I Love Thee Better, Lord

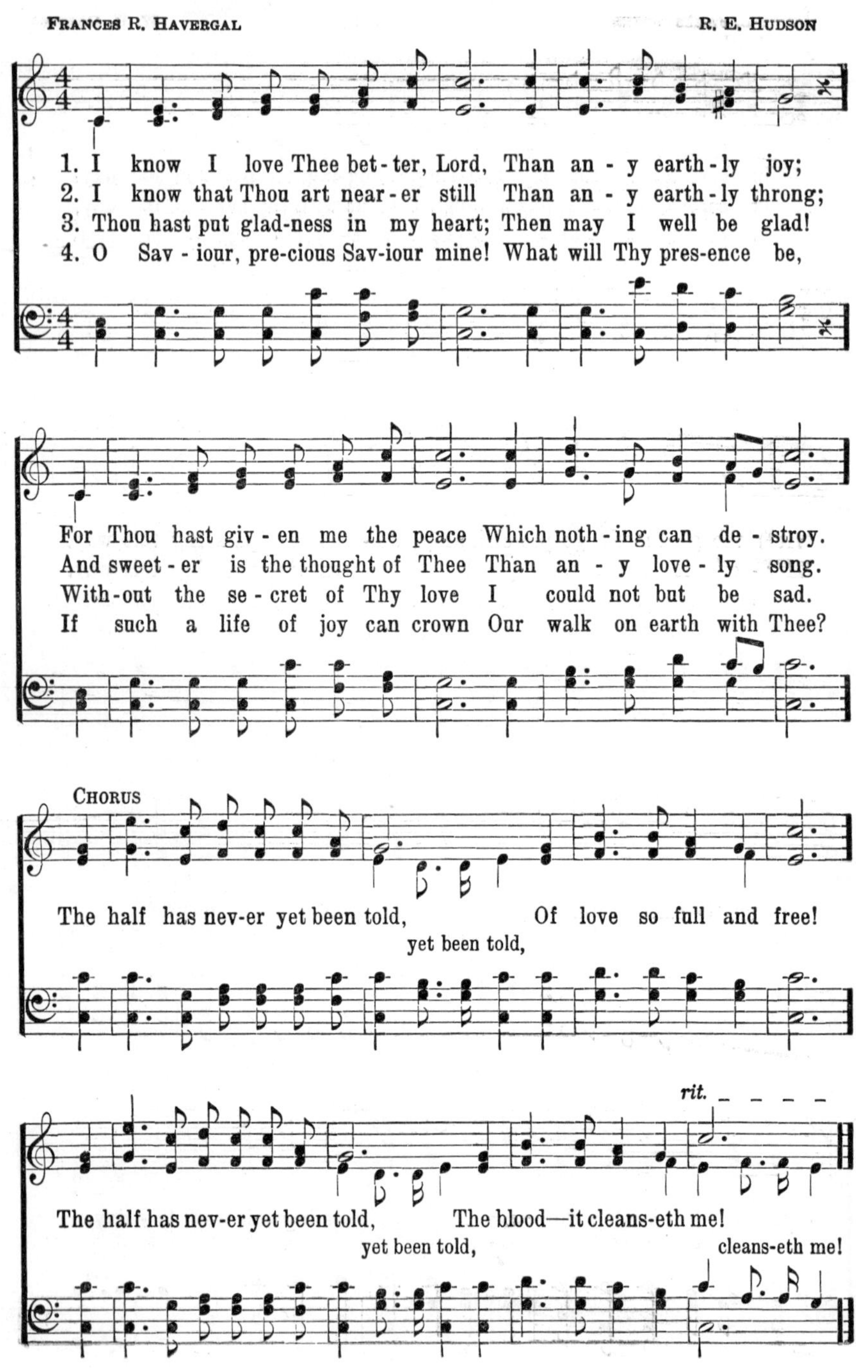
FRANCES R. HAVERGAL
R. E. HUDSON
1. I know I love Thee bet-ter, Lord, Than an-y earth-ly joy;
2. I know that Thou art near-er still Than an-y earth-ly throng;
3. Thou hast put glad-ness in my heart; Then may I well be glad!
4. O Sav-iour, pre-cious Sav-iour mine! What will Thy pres-ence be,
For Thou hast giv-en me the peace Which noth-ing can de-stroy.
And sweet-er is the thought of Thee Than an-y love-ly song.
With-out the se-cret of Thy love I could not but be sad.
If such a life of joy can crown Our walk on earth with Thee?
CHORUS
The half has nev-er yet been told, Of love so full and free!
yet been told,
rit.
The half has nev-er yet been told, The blood—it cleans-eth me!
yet been told, cleans-eth me!

95 My Mother's Prayer

J. W. Van DeVenter — W. S. Weeden

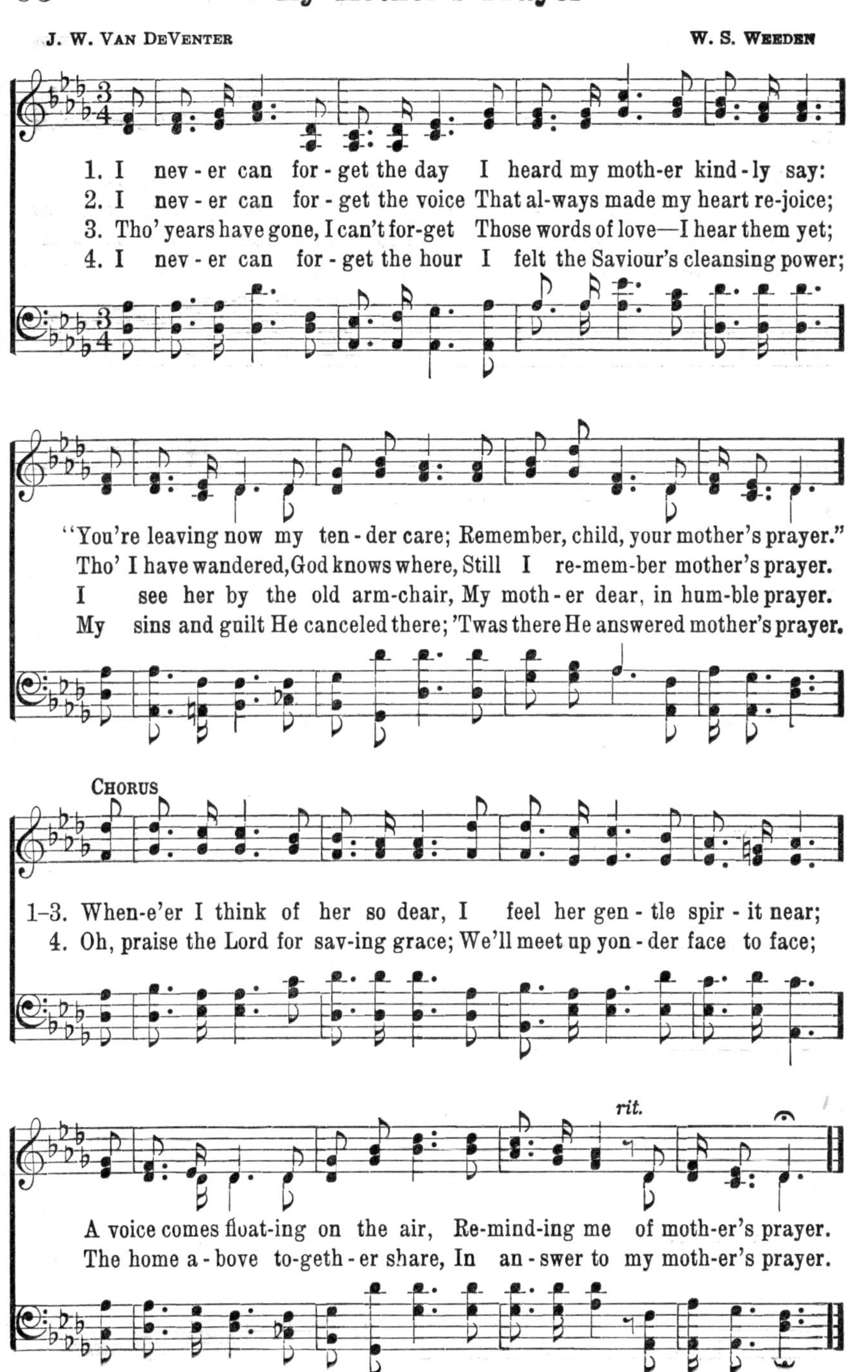
1. I nev-er can for-get the day I heard my moth-er kind-ly say:
2. I nev-er can for-get the voice That al-ways made my heart re-joice;
3. Tho' years have gone, I can't for-get Those words of love—I hear them yet;
4. I nev-er can for-get the hour I felt the Saviour's cleansing power;
"You're leaving now my ten-der care; Remember, child, your mother's prayer."
Tho' I have wandered, God knows where, Still I re-mem-ber mother's prayer.
I see her by the old arm-chair, My moth-er dear, in hum-ble prayer.
My sins and guilt He canceled there; 'Twas there He answered mother's prayer.
Chorus
1–3. When-e'er I think of her so dear, I feel her gen-tle spir-it near;
4. Oh, praise the Lord for sav-ing grace; We'll meet up yon-der face to face;
A voice comes float-ing on the air, Re-mind-ing me of moth-er's prayer.
The home a-bove to-geth-er share, In an-swer to my moth-er's prayer.
rit.

96 The Solid Rock

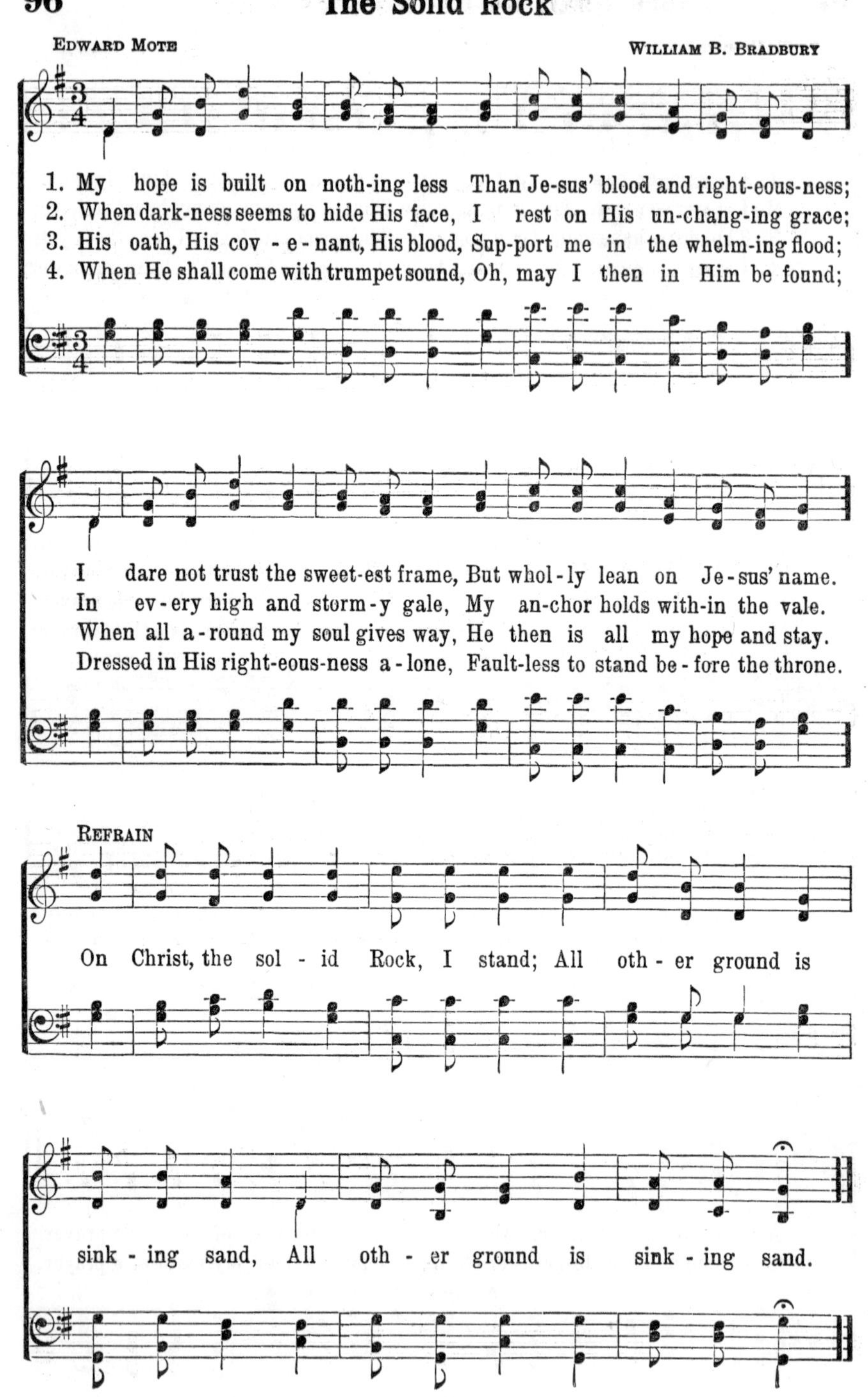
EDWARD MOTE
WILLIAM B. BRADBURY
1. My hope is built on noth-ing less Than Je-sus' blood and right-eous-ness;
2. When dark-ness seems to hide His face, I rest on His un-chang-ing grace;
3. His oath, His cov - e - nant, His blood, Sup-port me in the whelm-ing flood;
4. When He shall come with trumpet sound, Oh, may I then in Him be found;
I dare not trust the sweet-est frame, But whol-ly lean on Je-sus' name.
In ev-ery high and storm-y gale, My an-chor holds with-in the vale.
When all a-round my soul gives way, He then is all my hope and stay.
Dressed in His right-eous-ness a-lone, Fault-less to stand be-fore the throne.
REFRAIN
On Christ, the sol - id Rock, I stand; All oth - er ground is
sink - ing sand, All oth - er ground is sink - ing sand.

97 There Shall Be Showers of Blessing

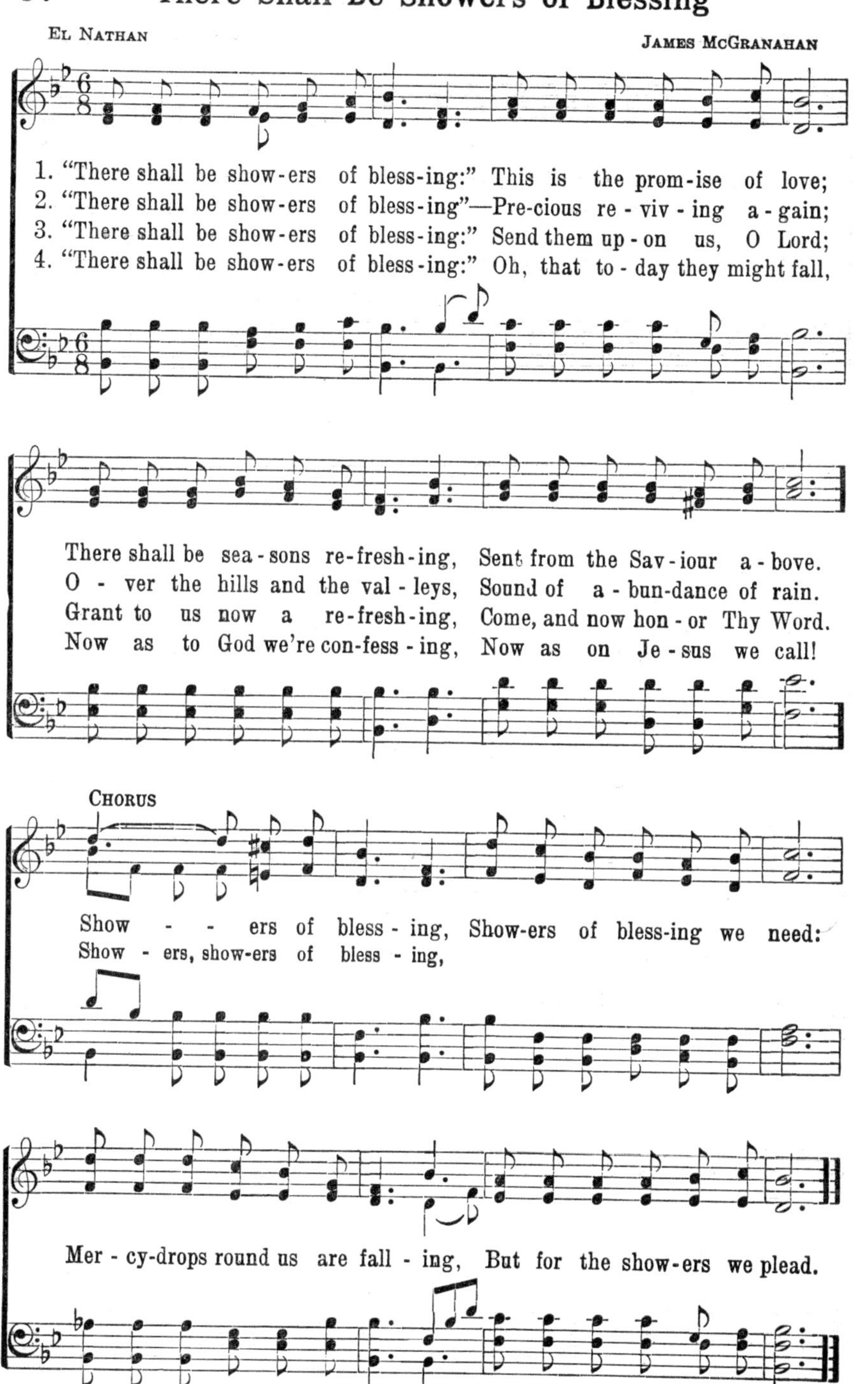

El Nathan
James McGranahan
1. "There shall be show-ers of bless-ing:" This is the prom-ise of love;
2. "There shall be show-ers of bless-ing"—Pre-cious re-viv-ing a-gain;
3. "There shall be show-ers of bless-ing:" Send them up-on us, O Lord;
4. "There shall be show-ers of bless-ing:" Oh, that to-day they might fall,
There shall be sea-sons re-fresh-ing, Sent from the Sav-iour a-bove.
O-ver the hills and the val-leys, Sound of a-bun-dance of rain.
Grant to us now a re-fresh-ing, Come, and now hon-or Thy Word.
Now as to God we're con-fess-ing, Now as on Je-sus we call!
Chorus
Show - - ers of bless-ing, Showers of bless-ing we need:
Show-ers, show-ers of bless-ing,
Mer-cy-drops round us are fall-ing, But for the show-ers we plead.

98 There Is a Green Hill Far Away

Cecil F. Alexander — Geo. C. Stebbins

1. There is a green hill far a-way, With-out a cit-y wall,
2. We may not know, we can-not tell, What pains He had to bear;
3. He died that we might be for-given, He died to make us good,
4. There was no oth-er good e-nough To pay the price of sin,
Where the dear Lord was cru-ci-fied, Who died to save us all.
But we be-lieve it was for us He hung and suf-fered there.
That we might go at last to heaven, Saved by His pre-cious blood.
He on-ly could un-lock the gate Of heaven and let us in.
Chorus
Oh, dear-ly, dear-ly has He loved, And we must love Him, too,
And trust in His re-deem-ing blood, And try His works to do.

99 Wherever He Leads I'll Go

B. B. McK. B. B. McKinney

1. "Take up thy cross and fol - low Me," I heard my Mas - ter say;
2. He drew me clos - er to His side, I sought His will to know,
3. It may be through the shad-ows dim, Or o'er the storm - y sea,
4. My heart, my life, my all I bring To Christ who loves me so;
"I gave My life to ran - som thee, Sur - ren-der your all to - day."
And in that will I now a - bide, Wher-ev - er He leads I'll go.
I take my cross and fol - low Him, Wher-ev - er He lead - eth me.
He is my Mas - ter, Lord, and King, Wher-ev - er He leads I'll go.
Chorus
Wher - ev - er He leads I'll go, . . . Wher-ev - er He leads I'll go, . . .
I'll fol-low my Christ who loves me so, Wher-ev - er He leads I'll go.

100 Softly and Tenderly

W. L. T.
WILL L. THOMPSON
Very slow pp
m
1. Soft - ly and ten-der-ly Je - sus is call-ing, Call - ing for you and for me;
2. Why should we tarry when Jesus is plead-ing, Pleading for you and for me?
3. Time is now fleeting, the moments are passing, Passing from you and from me;
4. Oh! for the won-der-ful love He has promised, Promised for you and for me;
See, on the portals He's waiting and watching, Watching for you and for me.
Why should we linger and heed not His mercies, Mer - cies for you and for me?
Shadows are gathering, death-beds are coming, Com - ing for you and for me.
Tho' we have sinned, He has mercy and pardon, Par - don for you and for me.
CHORUS m
cresc.
Come home, . . come home, . . . Ye who are wea-ry, come home; . .
Come home, come home,
pp
ppp
rit.
pp
Ear-nest-ly, ten-der-ly, Je - sus is call-ing, Call-ing, O sin-ner, come home!

101 What Will You Do with Jesus?

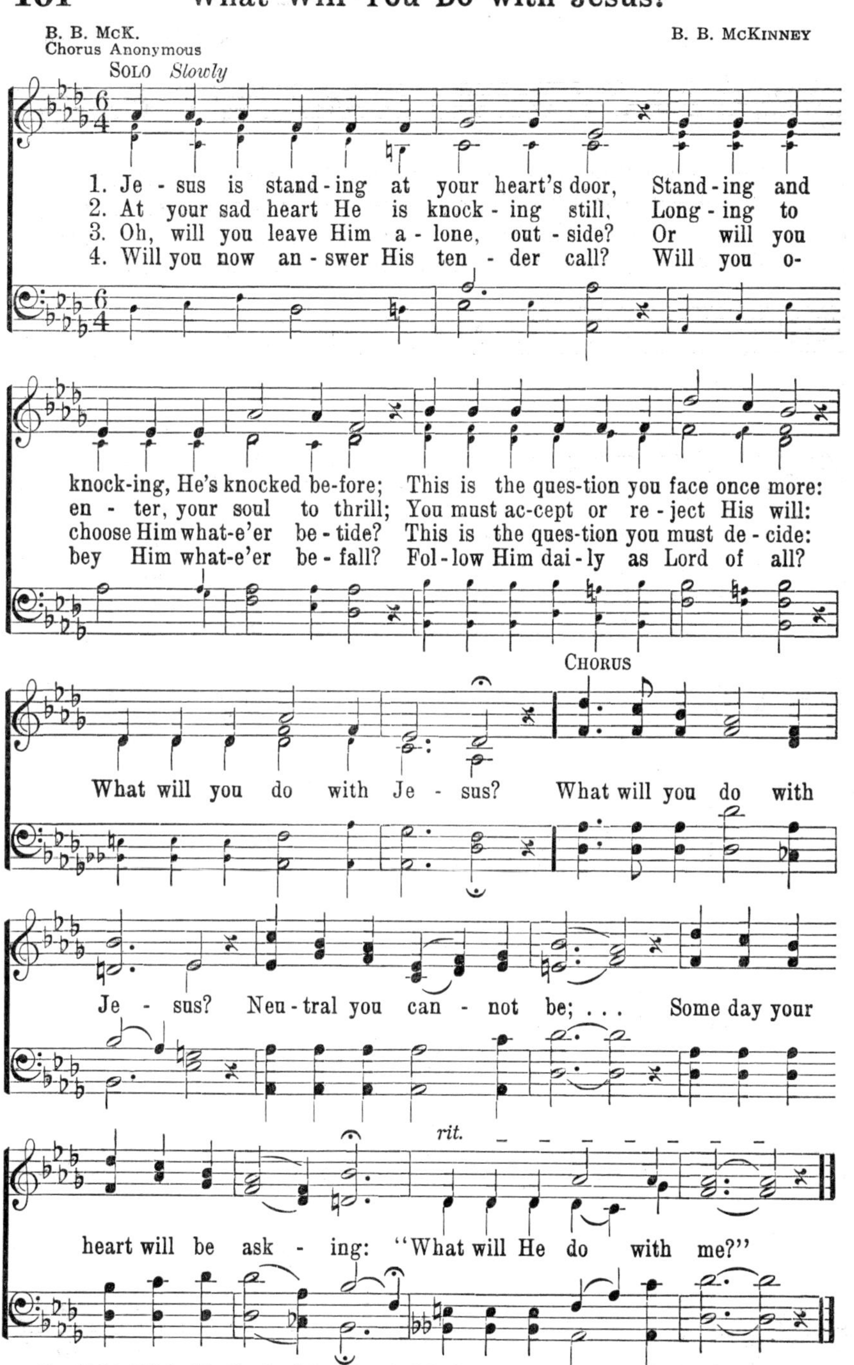
B. B. McK.
Chorus Anonymous
B. B. McKinney
Solo Slowly
1. Je - sus is stand - ing at your heart's door, Stand - ing and knock - ing, He's knocked be - fore; This is the ques - tion you face once more:
2. At your sad heart He is knock - ing still, Long - ing to en - ter, your soul to thrill; You must ac - cept or re - ject His will:
3. Oh, will you leave Him a - lone, out - side? Or will you choose Him what - e'er be - tide? This is the ques - tion you must de - cide:
4. Will you now an - swer His ten - der call? Will you o - bey Him what - e'er be - fall? Fol - low Him dai - ly as Lord of all?
What will you do with Je - sus?
Chorus
What will you do with Je - sus? Neu - tral you can - not be; . . . Some day your heart will be ask - ing: "What will He do with me?"
rit.

102 The Name of Jesus

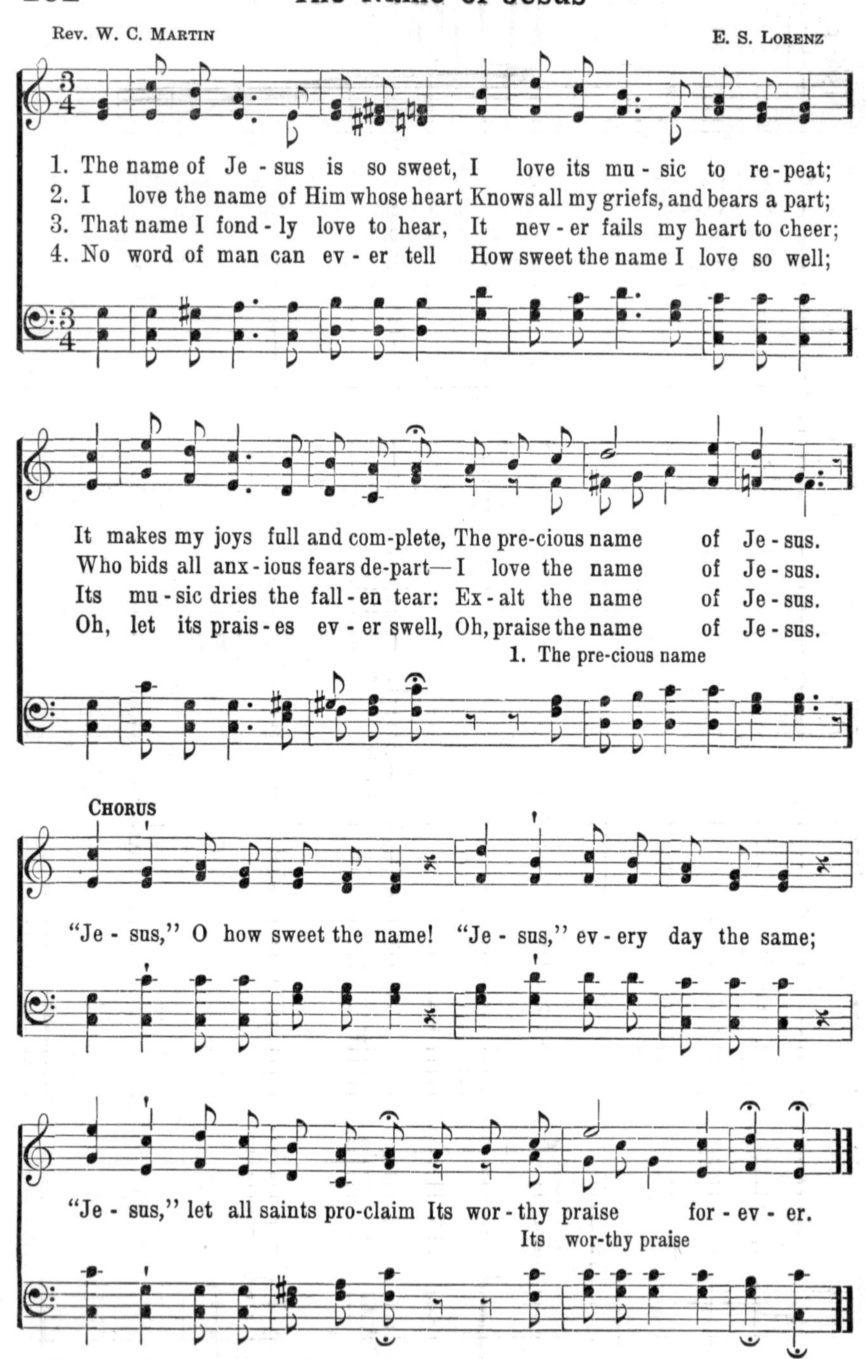
Rev. W. C. Martin
E. S. Lorenz
1. The name of Je - sus is so sweet, I love its mu - sic to re - peat;
2. I love the name of Him whose heart Knows all my griefs, and bears a part;
3. That name I fond - ly love to hear, It nev - er fails my heart to cheer;
4. No word of man can ev - er tell How sweet the name I love so well;
It makes my joys full and com - plete, The pre - cious name of Je - sus.
Who bids all anx - ious fears de - part— I love the name of Je - sus.
Its mu - sic dries the fall - en tear: Ex - alt the name of Je - sus.
Oh, let its prais - es ev - er swell, Oh, praise the name of Je - sus.
1. The pre - cious name
Chorus
"Je - sus," O how sweet the name! "Je - sus," ev - ery day the same;
"Je - sus," let all saints pro - claim Its wor - thy praise for - ev - er.
Its wor - thy praise

103 Thy Will Be Done!

CHARLOTTE ELLIOTT
Chorus by B. B. McK.

B. B. McKINNEY

1. My God and Fa - ther, while I stray Far from my home, on life's rough way, Oh, teach me from my heart to say, "Thy will be done!"
2. What tho' in lone - ly grief I sigh For friends be - loved, no lon - ger nigh, Sub-mis-sive still would I re - ply, "Thy will be done!"
3. Re - new my will from day to day; Blend it with Thine; and take a - way All now that makes it hard to say, "Thy will be done!"
4. Then when on earth I breathe no more The prayer oft mixed with tears be - fore, I'll sing up - on a bright-er shore, "Thy will be done!"
CHORUS
Thy will be done in me, This is my ear - nest plea;
Thy ho - ly will be done in me, This is my plea, my ear - nest plea;
My life, my all, I yield to Thee, Thy will be done in me.

104 Lead Me, Saviour

F. M. D. — Frank M. Davis

With expression
1. Sav-iour, lead me, lest I stray, Gen - tly lead me all the way;
2. Thou the ref-uge of my soul, When life's stormy billows roll,
3. Sav-iour, lead me, then at last, When the storm of life is past,
1. Sav - iour, lead me, lest I stray, Gen - tly lead me all the way;
I am safe when by Thy side, I would in Thy love a-bide.
I am safe when Thou art nigh, All my hopes on Thee re-ly.
To the land of end-less day, Where all tears are wiped away.
I am safe when by Thy side, I would in Thy love a-bide.
Chorus
Lead me, lead me, Sav - iour, lead me, lest I stray; . . . . Gen - tly
lest I stray;
down the stream of time, Lead me, Sav-iour, all the way.
stream of time, all the way.
rit. e dim.

105 I Am Resolved

PALMER HARTSOUGH J. H. FILLMORE

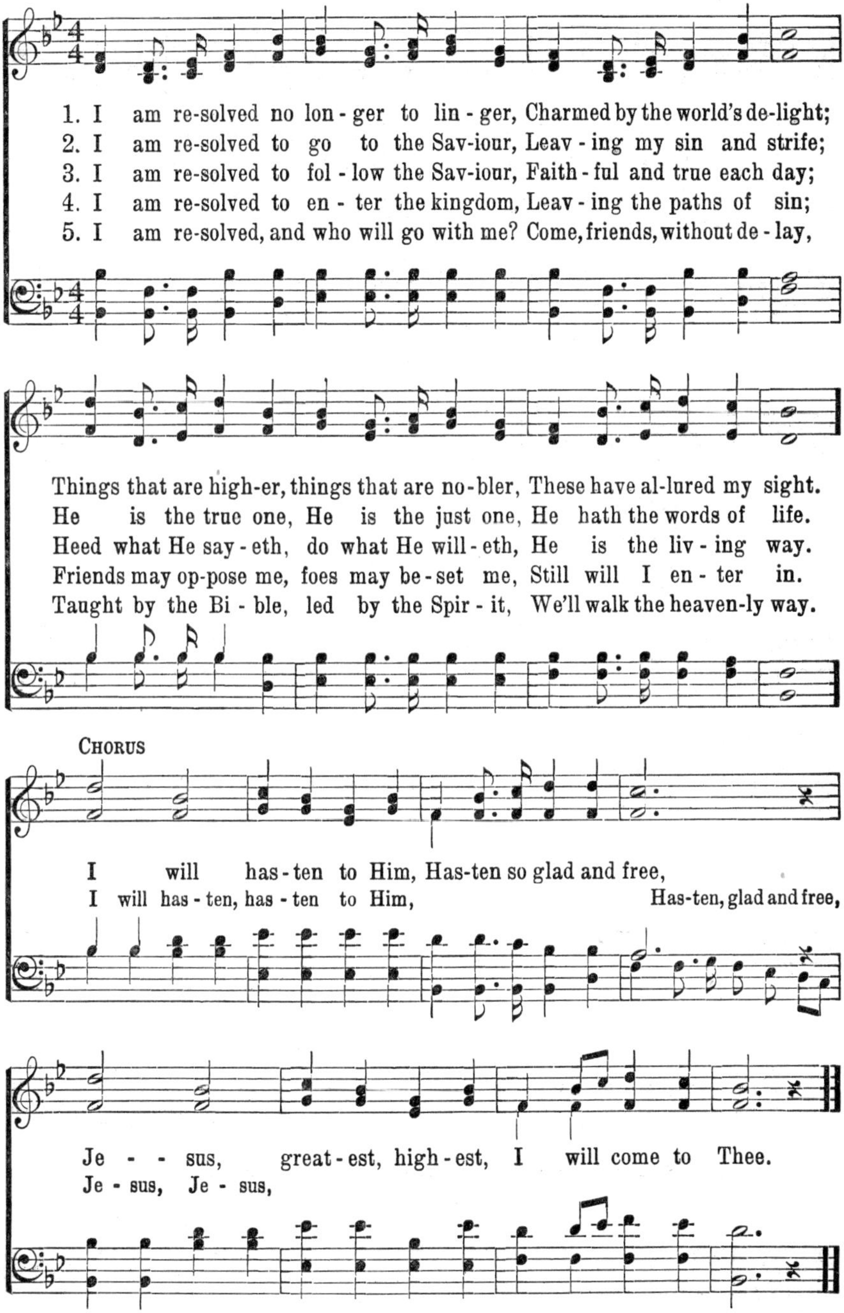

1. I am re-solved no lon-ger to lin-ger, Charmed by the world's de-light;
2. I am re-solved to go to the Sav-iour, Leav-ing my sin and strife;
3. I am re-solved to fol-low the Sav-iour, Faith-ful and true each day;
4. I am re-solved to en-ter the kingdom, Leav-ing the paths of sin;
5. I am re-solved, and who will go with me? Come, friends, without de-lay,

Things that are high-er, things that are no-bler, These have al-lured my sight.
He is the true one, He is the just one, He hath the words of life.
Heed what He say-eth, do what He will-eth, He is the liv-ing way.
Friends may op-pose me, foes may be-set me, Still will I en-ter in.
Taught by the Bi-ble, led by the Spir-it, We'll walk the heaven-ly way.

CHORUS

I will has-ten to Him, Has-ten so glad and free,
I will has-ten, has-ten to Him, Has-ten, glad and free,

Je - - sus, great-est, high-est, I will come to Thee.
Je-sus, Je-sus,

106 Face to Face

Mrs. Frank A. Breck — Grant Colfax Tullar

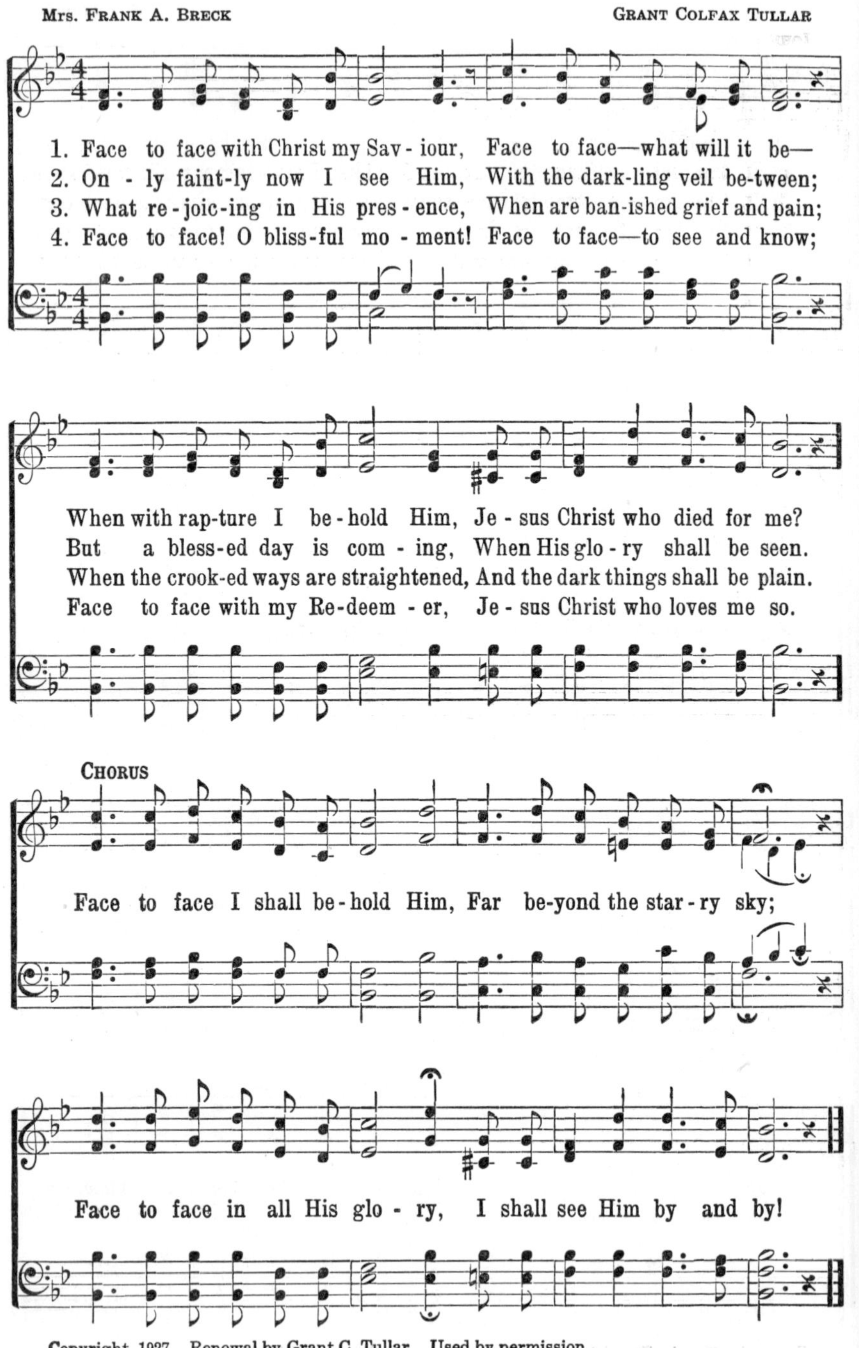
1. Face to face with Christ my Sav - iour, Face to face—what will it be—
2. On - ly faint-ly now I see Him, With the dark-ling veil be-tween;
3. What re - joic-ing in His pres - ence, When are ban-ished grief and pain;
4. Face to face! O bliss-ful mo - ment! Face to face—to see and know;
When with rap-ture I be - hold Him, Je - sus Christ who died for me?
But a bless-ed day is com - ing, When His glo - ry shall be seen.
When the crook-ed ways are straightened, And the dark things shall be plain.
Face to face with my Re-deem - er, Je - sus Christ who loves me so.
Chorus
Face to face I shall be - hold Him, Far be-yond the star - ry sky;
Face to face in all His glo - ry, I shall see Him by and by!

107 The Upper Room

JOHN C. SLEMP
B. B. McKINNEY
1. In the qui - et hours of morn - ing, When Thy pres-ence fills this place,
2. In the qui - e - tude of rev-erence, As the world moves on its way,
3. In the gen - tle hush of mu - sic We for - get our toils and tears;
4. In the hour of blest com-mun - ion Thou dost bid our cares to cease;
In the up - per room we gath - er, Spir - it God, to seek Thy face.
Here we tar - ry for a mo - ment, Seek Thy guid-ance for the day.
In the sa - cred hour of wor - ship Find re - lease from all our fears.
As we con - tem-plate Thy good-ness, Thou dost give e - ter - nal peace.
CHORUS
Here we come with ev - ery bur - den, Here we come with all our care;
rit.
In the up - per room with Je - sus, Of - fer here our morn - ing prayer.

108 Since I Have Been Redeemed

EDWIN O. EXCELL
EDWIN O. EXCELL
1. I have a song I love to sing, Since I have been re - deemed,
2. I have a Christ that sat - is - fies, Since I have been re - deemed;
3. I have a wit - ness bright and clear, Since I have been re - deemed,
4. I have a home pre-pared for me, Since I have been re - deemed,
Of my Re - deem - er, Sav - iour, King, Since I have been re-deemed.
To do His will my high - est prize, Since I have been re-deemed.
Dis - pel - ling ev - ery doubt and fear, Since I have been re-deemed.
Where I shall dwell e - ter - nal - ly, Since I have been re-deemed.
CHORUS
Since I . . . . . . have been re-deemed, Since I have been re-
Since I have been re-deemed, Since I have been re-deemed,
deemed, I will glo - ry in His name; Since I . . . . . . have been re-
Since I have been re-deemed, Since
deemed, I will glo - ry in my Sav - iour's name.
I have been re - deemed,

109 A Blessing in Prayer

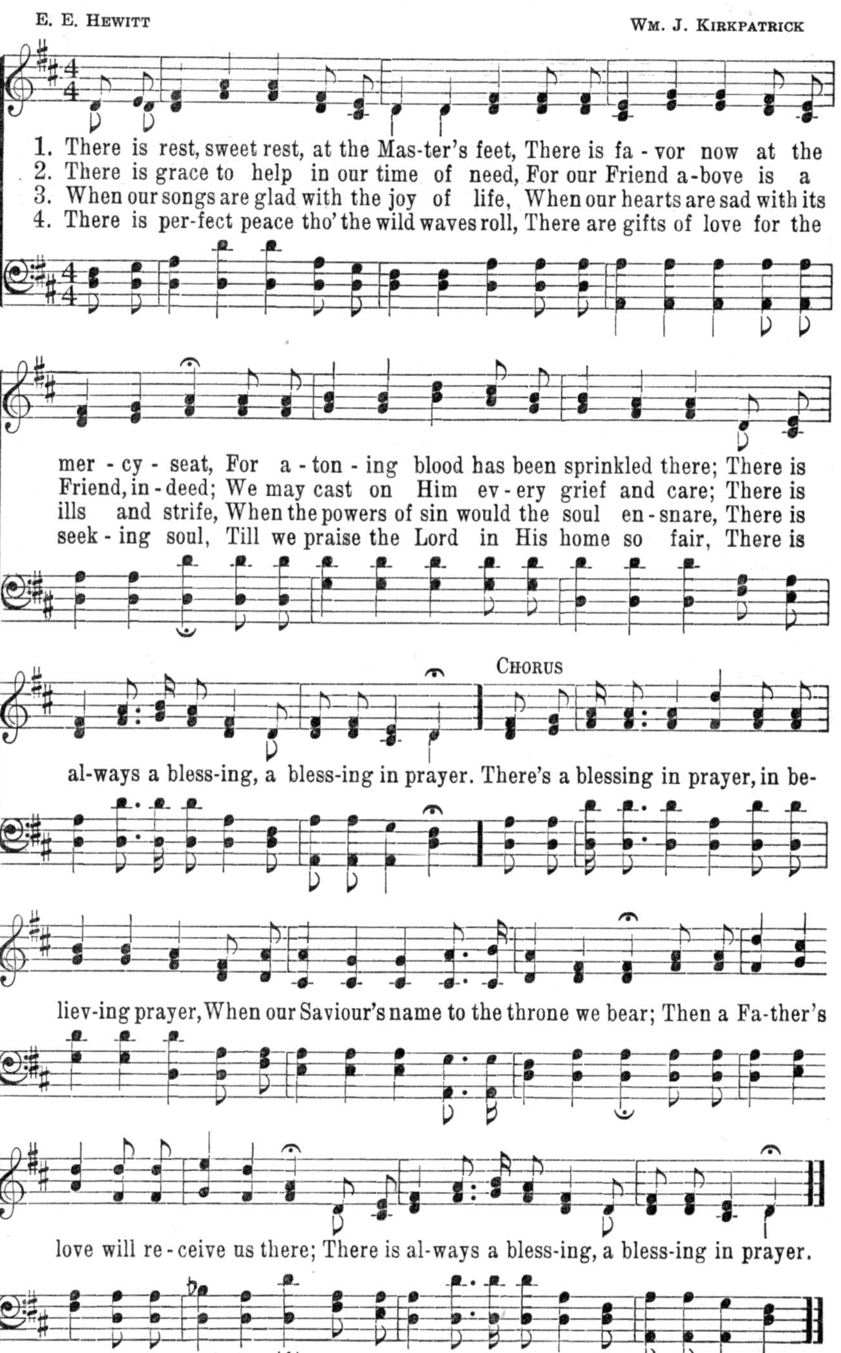
E. E. Hewitt
Wm. J. Kirkpatrick
1. There is rest, sweet rest, at the Mas-ter's feet, There is fa - vor now at the mer - cy - seat, For a - ton - ing blood has been sprinkled there; There is
2. There is grace to help in our time of need, For our Friend a-bove is a Friend, in - deed; We may cast on Him ev - ery grief and care; There is
3. When our songs are glad with the joy of life, When our hearts are sad with its ills and strife, When the powers of sin would the soul en - snare, There is
4. There is per-fect peace tho' the wild waves roll, There are gifts of love for the seek - ing soul, Till we praise the Lord in His home so fair, There is
al-ways a bless-ing, a bless-ing in prayer.
Chorus
There's a blessing in prayer, in be-liev-ing prayer, When our Saviour's name to the throne we bear; Then a Fa-ther's love will re - ceive us there; There is al-ways a bless-ing, a bless-ing in prayer.

110 Tell It to Jesus

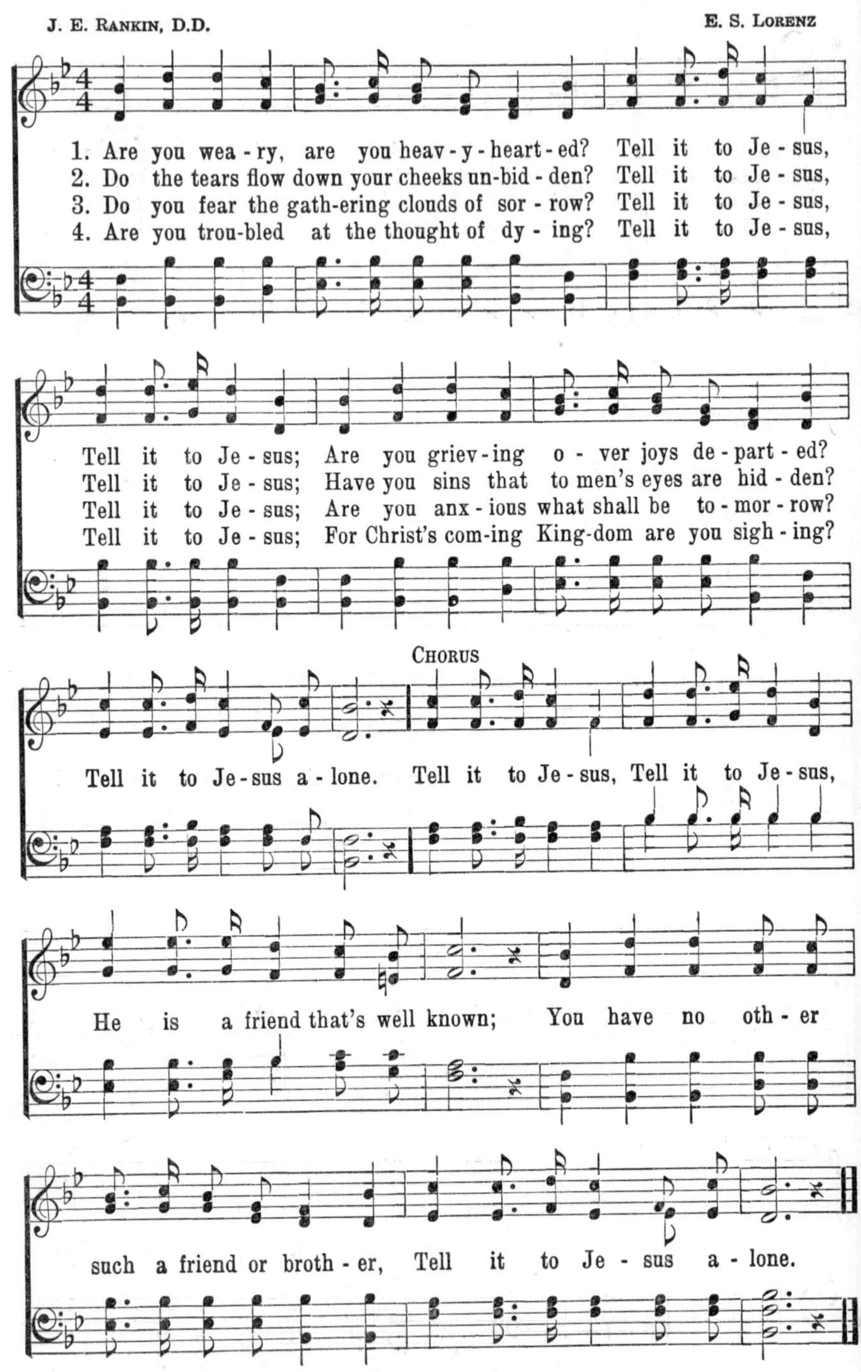
J. E. Rankin, D.D.
E. S. Lorenz
1. Are you wea - ry, are you heav - y - heart - ed? Tell it to Je - sus,
2. Do the tears flow down your cheeks un-bid - den? Tell it to Je - sus,
3. Do you fear the gath-ering clouds of sor - row? Tell it to Je - sus,
4. Are you trou-bled at the thought of dy - ing? Tell it to Je - sus,
Tell it to Je - sus; Are you griev - ing o - ver joys de - part - ed?
Tell it to Je - sus; Have you sins that to men's eyes are hid - den?
Tell it to Je - sus; Are you anx - ious what shall be to - mor - row?
Tell it to Je - sus; For Christ's com-ing King-dom are you sigh - ing?
Tell it to Je - sus a - lone.
Chorus
Tell it to Je - sus, Tell it to Je - sus,
He is a friend that's well known;
You have no oth - er
such a friend or broth - er,
Tell it to Je - sus a - lone.

111 Are You Washed in the Blood?

E. A. H. — ELISHA A. HOFFMAN

1. Have you been to Je-sus for the cleans-ing power? Are you washed in the
2. Are you walk-ing dai-ly by the Sav-iour's side? Are you washed in the
3. When the Bridegroom cometh will your robes be white? Are you washed in the
4. Lay a-side the gar-ments that are stained with sin, And be washed in the
blood of the Lamb? Are you ful-ly trust-ing in His grace this hour? Are you
blood of the Lamb? Do you rest each moment in the Cru-ci-fied? Are you
blood of the Lamb? Will your soul be read-y for the mansions bright, And be
blood of the Lamb; There's a fountain flowing for the soul un-clean, O be
CHORUS
washed in the blood of the Lamb? Are you washed in the blood,
Are you washed in the blood,
In the soul-cleans-ing blood of the Lamb? Are your gar-ments
of the Lamb?
spot-less? Are they white as snow? Are you washed in the blood of the Lamb?

112 At the Cross

Isaac Watts — R. E. Hudson

1. A - las, and did my Sav - iour bleed? And did my Sov-ereign die?
2. Was it for crimes that I have done, He groaned up-on the tree?
3. Well might the sun in dark - ness hide, And shut his glo - ries in,
4. But drops of grief can ne'er re - pay The debt of love I owe:
Would He de - vote that sa - cred head For such a worm as I?
A - maz - ing pit - y! grace un-known! And love be - yond de - gree!
When Christ, the might-y Mak - er, died For man the crea-ture's sin.
Here, Lord, I give my - self a - way, 'Tis all that I can do!
Chorus
At the cross, at the cross where I first saw the light, And the
bur - den of my heart rolled a - way (rolled a-way), It was there by faith
I re-ceived my sight, And now I am hap - py all the day!

113 Christ Receiveth Sinful Men

Arr. from NEUMASTER — JAMES MCGRANAHAN

1. Sin - ners Je - sus will re - ceive; Sound this word of grace to all
2. Come, and He will give you rest; Trust Him, for His word is plain;
3. Now my heart con-demns me not, Pure be - fore the law I stand;
4. Christ re - ceiv - eth sin - ful men, E - ven me with all my sin;
Who the heaven - ly path - way leave, All who lin - ger, all who fall.
He will take the sin - ful - est; Christ re - ceiv - eth sin - ful men.
He who cleansed me from all spot, Sat - is - fied its last de - mand.
Purged from ev - ery spot and stain, Heaven with Him I en - ter in.
REFRAIN
Sing it o'er . . . . . and o'er a - gain; . . . . Christ re-
Sing it o'er a - gain, Sing it o'er a - gain; Christ re-
ceiv - - - eth sin-ful men; . . . Make the mes - - - sage
ceiv - eth sin-ful men, Christ re-ceiv-eth sin - ful men; Make the mes-sage plain,
clear and plain: . . . . Christ re - ceiv - eth sin - ful men.
Make the mes-sage plain: Christ re - ceiv - eth sin - ful men.

114 Beulah Land

Edgar Page Stites — Jno. R. Sweney

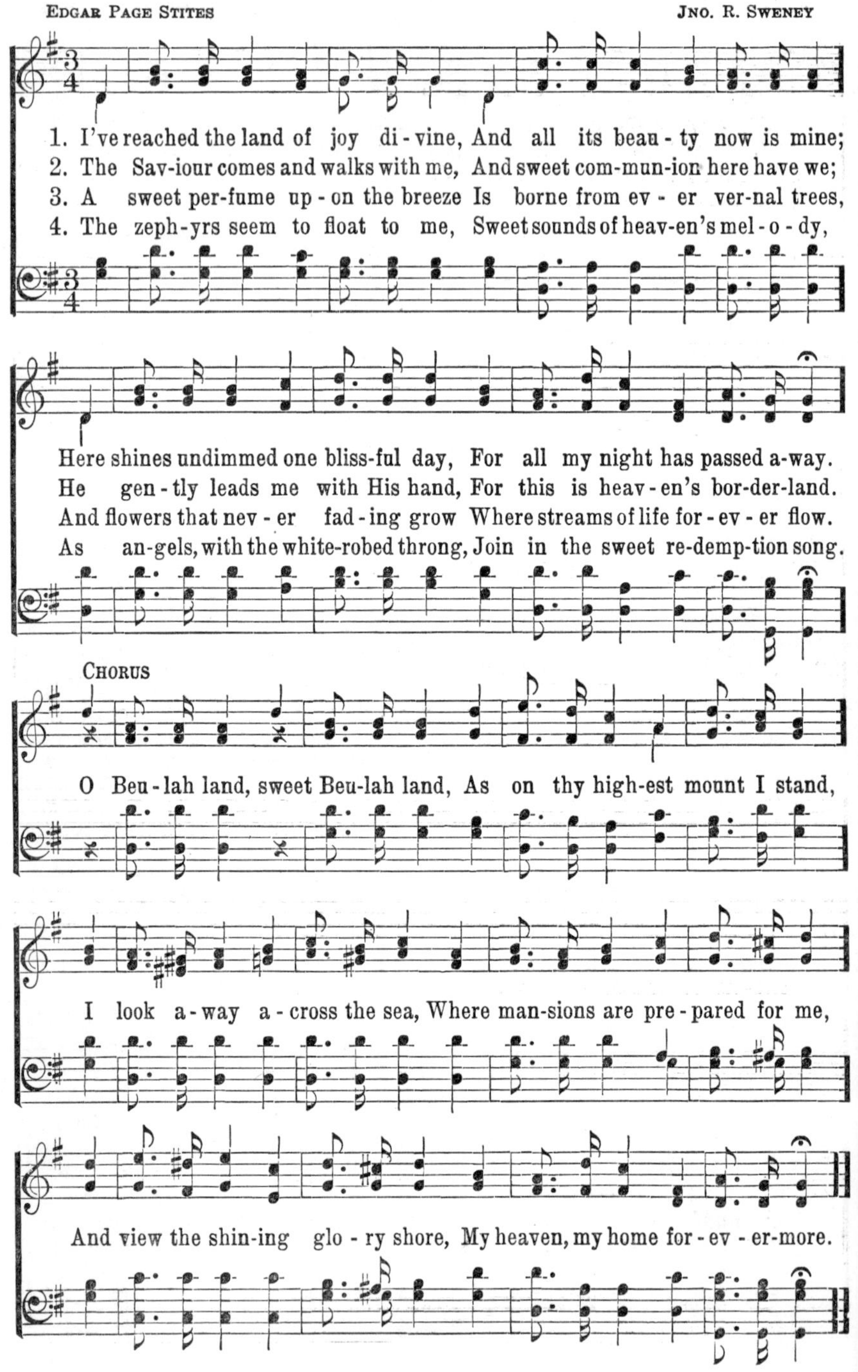

1. I've reached the land of joy di-vine, And all its beau-ty now is mine;
2. The Sav-iour comes and walks with me, And sweet com-mun-ion here have we;
3. A sweet per-fume up-on the breeze Is borne from ev-er ver-nal trees,
4. The zeph-yrs seem to float to me, Sweet sounds of heav-en's mel-o-dy,
Here shines undimmed one bliss-ful day, For all my night has passed a-way.
He gen-tly leads me with His hand, For this is heav-en's bor-der-land.
And flowers that nev-er fad-ing grow Where streams of life for-ev-er flow.
As an-gels, with the white-robed throng, Join in the sweet re-demp-tion song.
Chorus
O Beu-lah land, sweet Beu-lah land, As on thy high-est mount I stand,
I look a-way a-cross the sea, Where man-sions are pre-pared for me,
And view the shin-ing glo-ry shore, My heaven, my home for-ev-er-more.

115 Standing On the Promises

R. K. C. — R. Kelso Carter

1. Stand-ing on the prom-is-es of Christ my King, Thro' e-ter-nal a-ges let His prais-es ring; Glo-ry in the high-est, I will shout and sing, Stand-ing on the prom-is-es of God.
2. Stand-ing on the prom-is-es that can-not fail, When the howling storms of doubt and fear as-sail, By the liv-ing word of God I shall pre-vail,
3. Stand-ing on the prom-is-es of Christ the Lord, Bound to Him e-ter-nal-ly by love's strong cord, O-ver-com-ing dai-ly with the Spir-it's sword,
4. Stand-ing on the prom-is-es I can-not fall, Lis-tening ev-ery mo-ment to the Spir-it's call, Rest-ing in my Sav-iour, as my all in all,
CHORUS.
Stand - ing, stand - ing,
Standing on the promises, standing on the promises,
Stand-ing on the prom-is-es of God my Sav-iour; Stand - ing,
Standing on the prom-is-es,
stand - - ing, I'm stand-ing on the prom-is-es of God.
stand-ing on the prom-is-es,

116 Wonderful Peace of My Saviour

Rev. Alfred Barratt
I. E. Reynolds
Solo or Duet
1. Like ra - di - ant sun-shine that comes aft - er rain, Like beau - ti - ful rest aft - er sor-row and pain, Like hope that is kin-dled re-turn-ing a - gain,
2. So soft and re-fresh - ing, as sweet as the dew, A prom - ise that can-not be bro-ken to you; A light that will shine all the long journey through,
3. It bright-ens earth's dark-ness and ban - ish - es care, And helps you to car - ry the bur-dens you bear; A ref - uge in trou-ble, your sor-rows to share,
4. A guard-ian in dan - ger where e - vil is rife, A might - y de-fend-er in con-flict and strife, A beau - ti - ful guide to that heav-en-ly life,
Is the won - der - ful peace of my Sav - iour.
Chorus
Won-der-ful peace, beau - ti - ful peace, Won-der-ful peace of my Sav - iour; There's nothing on earth can such gladness im - part As this won-der-ful peace of my Sav - iour.

117 Send the Light

C. H. G. — Chas. H. Gabriel

1. There's a call comes ring-ing o'er the rest-less wave, "Send the light! . . . Send the light!" There are souls to res-cue, there are souls to save,
2. We have heard the Mac-e-do-nian call to-day, "Send the light! . . . Send the light!" And a gold-en of-fering at the cross we lay,
3. Let us pray that grace may ev-ery-where a-bound; Send the light! . . . Send the light! And a Christ-like spir-it ev-ery-where be found,
4. Let us not grow wea-ry in the work of love, Send the light! . . . Send the light! Let us gath-er jew-els for a crown a-bove,
Send the light!
Send the light! . . . Send the light! . . .
Send the light! Send the light!
Refrain
Send the light! . . . the bless-ed gos-pel light; Let it shine . . . . from shore to shore! . . . . shine . . . for-ev-er-more. . . . . .
Send the light! the bless-ed gos-pel light; Let it shine from shore to shore! Let it shine for-ev-er-more.
1
2

118 Follow On

W. O. CUSHING — ROBERT LOWRY

1. Down in the val-ley with my Sav-iour I would go, Where the flowers are bloom-ing and the sweet wa-ters flow; Ev-ery-where He leads me I would fol-low, fol-low on, Walk-ing in His foot-steps till the crown be won.
2. Down in the val-ley with my Sav-iour I would go, Where the storms are sweep-ing and the dark wa-ters flow; With His hand to lead me I will nev-er, nev-er fear, Dan-ger can-not fright me if my Lord is near.
3. Down in the val-ley, or up-on the moun-tain steep, Close be-side my Sav-iour would my soul ev-er keep; He will lead me safe-ly in the path that He has trod, Up to where they gath-er on the hills of God.
REFRAIN
Fol-low! fol-low! I would follow Je-sus! Anywhere, everywhere, I would follow on!
Fol-low! fol-low! I would follow Jesus! Everywhere He leads me I would follow on!

119 Heavenly Sunlight

Rev. H. J. Zelley G. H. Cook

1. Walk-ing in sun-light, all of my jour-ney; O-ver the moun-tains,
2. Shad-ows a-round me, shad-ows a-bove me, Nev-er con-ceal my
3. In the bright sun-light, ev-er re-joic-ing, Press-ing my way to
thro' the deep vale; Je-sus has said "I'll nev-er for-sake thee,"
Sav-iour and Guide; He is the light, in Him is no dark-ness;
man-sions a-bove; Sing-ing His prais-es glad-ly I'm walk-ing,
Prom-ise di-vine that nev-er can fail.
Ev-er I'm walk-ing close to His side.
Walk-ing in sun-light, sun-light of love.
Chorus
Heav-en-ly sun-light,
heav-en-ly sun-light, Flood-ing my soul with glo-ry di-vine: Hal-le-
lu-jah, I am re-joic-ing, Sing-ing His prais-es, Je-sus is mine.

120 Blessed Assurance

FANNY J. CROSBY — MRS. J. F. KNAPP

1. Bless-ed as-sur-ance, Je-sus is mine! Oh, what a fore-taste of glo-ry di-vine! Heir of sal-va-tion, pur-chase of God, Born of His Spir-it, washed in His blood.
2. Per-fect sub-mis-sion, per-fect de-light, Vi-sions of rap-ture now burst on my sight; An-gels de-scend-ing, bring from a-bove Ech-oes of mer-cy, whis-pers of love.
3. Per-fect sub-mis-sion, all is at rest, I in my Sav-iour am hap-py and blest; Watch-ing and wait-ing, look-ing a-bove, Filled with His good-ness, lost in His love.
CHORUS
This is my sto-ry, this is my song, Prais-ing my Sav-iour all the day long; This is my sto-ry, this is my song, Prais-ing my Sav-iour all the day long.

Have You Prayed It Through?

Rev. W. C. Poole | B. D. Ackley

1. Have you prayed all night, Till the break of day, And the morn-ing light
Drove the dark a - way? Did you lin - ger there, Till the morn - ing dew,
In pre-vail-ing prayer—Did you pray it through?

2. Did you pray it through Till the an-swer came? There's a prom-ise true
For your faith to claim; At the place of prayer Je - sus waits for you,
Did you meet Him there, Did you pray it through?

3. As the Mas-ter prayed In the gar - den lone, Let your prayer be made
To the Fa-ther's throne; If you seek His will He will an - swer you;
Are you trust-ing still, Have you prayed it through?

CHORUS

Did you pray till the an-swer came, till it came,
Did you plead in the Sav - iour's name? in His name?
Have you prayed all night till the morn-ing light, Did you pray till the an - swer came?

122 His Way with Thee

C. S. N.
Cyrus S. Nusbaum
1. Would you live for Je - sus, and be al-ways pure and good? Would you walk with
2. Would you have Him make you free, and fol-low at His call? Would you know the
3. Would you in His king-dom find a place of con-stant rest? Would you prove Him
Him with-in the nar-row road? Would you have Him bear your bur-den, car - ry
peace that comes by giv-ing all? Would you have Him save you, so that you can
true in prov - i - den - tial test? Would you in His serv - ice la - bor al-ways
Chorus
all your load? Let Him have His way with thee.
nev - er fall? Let Him have His way with thee. His power can make you what you
at your best? Let Him have His way with thee.
ought to be; His blood can cleanse your heart and make you free; His love can
rit.
fill your soul, and you will see 'Twas best for Him to have His way with thee.

Lead Me Gently Home, Father

W. L. T. — Will L. Thompson

Solo, Duet or Unison

1. Lead me gen-tly home, Fa-ther, Lead me gen-tly home, When life's toils are end - ed, and part-ing days have come; Sin no more shall tempt me, Ne'er from Thee I'll roam, If Thou'lt on - ly lead me, Fa - ther, Lead me gen-tly home.
2. Lead me gen-tly home, Fa-ther, Lead me gen-tly home, In life's dark-est hours, Fa-ther, when life's trou-bles come, Keep my feet from wan-dering, Lest from Thee I roam, Lest I fall up - on the way - side,
3. Lead me gen-tly home, Fa-ther, Lead me gen-tly home, In temp-ta-tion's hour, Fa-ther, when sore tri - als come; Be Thou near to keep me, Take me as Thine own, For I can - not live with - out Thee,

Chorus

Lead me gen-tly home, Fa - ther, (Lead me gen-tly home, Fa-ther,) Lead me gen - tly (home, Fa - ther,) lead me gen-tly, Lest I fall up-on the way-side, Lead me gen-tly (gen-tly) home.

124 Ring the Bells of Heaven

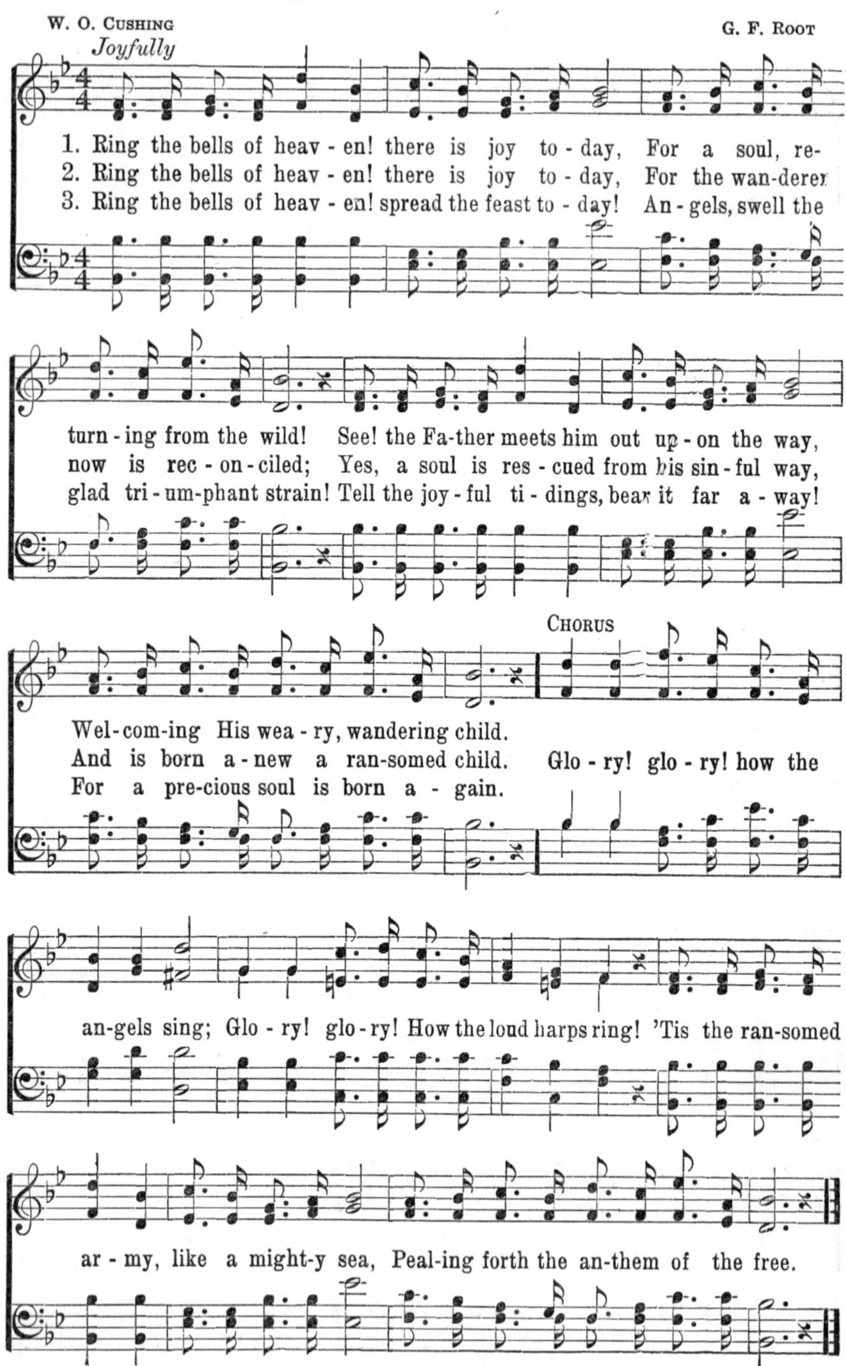
W. O. Cushing
G. F. Root
Joyfully
1. Ring the bells of heav - en! there is joy to - day, For a soul, re-
2. Ring the bells of heav - en! there is joy to - day, For the wan-derer
3. Ring the bells of heav - en! spread the feast to - day! An - gels, swell the
turn - ing from the wild! See! the Fa-ther meets him out up - on the way,
now is rec - on - ciled; Yes, a soul is res - cued from his sin - ful way,
glad tri - um-phant strain! Tell the joy - ful ti - dings, bear it far a - way!
Wel-com-ing His wea - ry, wandering child.
And is born a - new a ran-somed child.
For a pre-cious soul is born a - gain.
Chorus
Glo - ry! glo - ry! how the
an-gels sing; Glo - ry! glo - ry! How the loud harps ring! 'Tis the ran-somed
ar - my, like a might-y sea, Peal-ing forth the an-them of the free.

125 The Kingdom Is Coming

Mrs. M. B. C. Slade — R. M. McIntosh

1. From all the dark plac-es Of earth's hea-then rac-es, O see how the
2. The sun-light is glanc-ing O'er ar-mies ad-vanc-ing, To con-quer the
3. With shout-ing and sing-ing, And ju-bi-lant ring-ing, Their arms of re-
thick shad-ows fly! The voice of sal-va-tion A-wakes ev-ery na-tion,
king-doms of sin; Our Lord shall possess them, His presence shall bless them,
bel-lion cast down; At last ev-ery na-tion The Lord of sal-va-tion
Come o-ver and help us, they cry.
His beau-ty shall en-ter them in.
Their King and Re-deem-er shall crown!
Chorus
The king-dom is com-ing, O
tell ye the sto-ry, God's ban-ner ex-alt-ed shall be! The earth shall be
full of His knowledge and glo-ry, As wa-ters that cov-er the sea.

126 "Whosoever Will"

P. P. B. P. P. BLISS

1. "Who-so-ev-er hear-eth," shout, shout the sound! Spread the bless-ed ti-dings
2. Who-so-ev-er com-eth need not de-lay, Now the door is o-pen,
3. "Who-so-ev-er will!" the prom-ise is se-cure; "Who-so-ev-er will," for-
all the world a-round; Tell the joy-ful news wher-ev-er man is found,
en-ter while you may; Je-sus is the true, the on-ly Liv-ing Way:
ev-er must en-dure; "Who-so-ev-er will!" 'tis life for-ev-er-more;
"Who-so-ev-er will may come."
CHORUS
"Who-so-ev-er will, who-so-ev-er will!"
Send the proc-la-ma-tion o-ver vale and hill; 'Tis a lov-ing
Fa-ther calls the wan-derer home: "Who-so-ev-er will may come."

127 Christ Arose

ROBERT LOWRY
ROBERT LOWRY
1. Low in the grave He lay— Je-sus my Sav-iour! Wait-ing the com-ing day—
2. Vain-ly they watch His bed— Je-sus my Sav-iour! Vain-ly they seal the dead—
3. Death cannot keep his prey—Je-sus my Sav-iour! He tore the bars a-way—
Je-sus my Lord!
REFRAIN Faster
Up from the grave He a-rose (He a-rose), With a might-y tri-umph o'er His foes; (He a-rose!) He a-rose a Vic-tor from the dark do-main, And He lives for-ev-er with His saints to reign. He a-rose! He a-rose! Hal-le-lu-jah! Christ a-rose!
He a-rose! He a-rose!
rit.

128

Gathering Home

Miss Mariana B. Slade

R. M. McIntosh

1. Up to the boun-ti-ful Giv-er of life, Gath-er-ing home! gathering home!
2. Up to the cit-y where fall-eth no night, Gath-er-ing home! gathering home!
3. Up to the beau-ti-ful man-sions a-bove, Gath-er-ing home! gathering home!
Up to the dwelling where cometh no strife, The dear ones are gathering home.
Up where the Saviour's own face is the light, The dear ones are gathering home.
Safe in the arms of His in - fi-nite love, The dear ones are gathering home.
Chorus
Gath-er-ing home! . . . . Gath-er-ing home! . . . . Nev-er to
Gath-er-ing home! Gath-er-ing home! Nev-er to
sor-row more, nev-er to roam, Gath-er-ing home! . . . . .
sor-row more, nev-er to roam, Gath-er-ing home!
Gath-er-ing home! . . . . God's chil-dren are gath-er-ing home!
Gath-er-ing home! God's chil-dren are gath-er-ing home!

129 Hiding In Thee

Rev. William O. Cushing
Ira D. Sankey
1. O safe to the Rock that is high - er than I,
2. In the calm of the noon - tide, in sor - row's lone hour,
3. How oft in the con - flict, when pressed by the foe,
My soul in its con - flicts and sor - rows would fly; So
In times when temp - ta - tion casts o'er me its power; In the
I have fled to my Ref - uge and breathed out my woe; How
sin - ful, so wea - ry, Thine, Thine would I be; Thou
tem - pests of life, on its wide, heav - ing sea, Thou
oft - en, when tri - als like sea - bil - lows roll, Have I
blest "Rock of A - ges," I'm hid - ing in Thee.
blest "Rock of A - ges," I'm hid - ing in Thee.
hid - den in Thee, O Thou Rock of my soul.
Refrain
Hid - ing in Thee,
Hid - ing in Thee, Thou blest "Rock of A - ges," I'm hid - ing in Thee.

130
Make Me a Blessing
Ira B. Wilson
To the Moody Memorial Church Choir
George S. Schuler
Slowly
1. Out in the highways and byways of life, Man-y are weary and sad; . . . .
are wea-ry and sad;
2. Tell the sweet story of Christ and His love, Tell of His power to forgive; . . . .
His power to for-give;
3. Give as 'twas giv-en to you in your need, Love as the Master loved you; . . .
the Mas-ter loved you;
rit.
Car - ry the sunshine where darkness is rife, Making the sor-row-ing glad. . .
Oth - ers will trust Him if on - ly you prove True, every moment you live. . . .
Be to the help-less a help-er in - deed, Un - to your mis-sion be true. . .
Chorus
Men or Unison
Women
Make me a bless - ing, Make me a bless - ing, Out of my
rit.
Unison
life . . . . may Je - sus shine; . . Make me a bless - ing,
Out of my life
Men
Women
Parts
ad lib.
O Sav - iour, I pray, . . . Make me a bless-ing to some-one to-day.
I pray Thee, my Sav-iour,
Tenors

131 How Long Must We Wait?

Rev. S. M. Glasgow — Rev. C. T. Caldwell

Duet *Slowly*

1. Long have we sought e-ter - nal life, Years have we waited in sin and strife;
In dark-ness groped, sad mis-ery's mate, How long? how long must we wait?

2. You know the love of God man-i-fold, A - ges have bro't you their grace untold;
Peace and a hope, no fear of fate, How long? how long must we wait?

3. The a-ged faint and long for the Friend, Dark shadows gathering bring the end;
Fades now the light, 'tis grow - ing late, How long? how long must we wait?

Chorus

"How long? how long must we wait?" "How long? how long must we wait?" The la-b'rers still are few; Our Lord has need of you, How long? how long must we wait?

Rev. Motte Martin, of Africa, recites the moving incident of a seeker after a teacher for his distant village who, when thrice refused, there being none to send, cried out in his broken-heartedness, in response to the answer, "You must wait;" "HOW LONG MUST WE WAIT?" Oh, Teacher, ask the white man in your land, "HOW LONG MUST WE WAIT?"

132 Looking Unto Jesus

H. D. L.
Harry Dixon Loes
1. Look-ing un-to Je-sus, in faith I came, Seek-ing sins for-given through His ho-ly name; Rest-ing in His love, leav-ing all to Him, Find-ing joy in serv-ice no cloud can dim.
2. Look-ing un-to Je-sus, I fear no night; Bright-ly beams His smile with a cheer-ing light: But one hope I cher-ish—to be found true, Add-ing to His glo-ry all I can do.
3. Look-ing un-to Je-sus, be this my aim: Trained to be a work-er with-out a shame: If He finds me faith-ful, no price too dear, 'Twill for me be glo-ry, "Well done" to hear.
Chorus
Look-ing un-to Je-sus, the Way of Life, Find-ing grace in tri-al and peace in strife: He, my Friend un-fail-ing, wondrous love hath shown—Looking un-to Je-sus, to Him a-lone.

133 The Rock That Is Higher Than I

E. JOHNSON WILLIAM G. FISCHER

1. O sometimes the shadows are deep, And rough seems the path to the goal,
2. O sometimes how long seems the day, And sometimes how wea-ry my feet;
3. O near to the Rock let me keep, If bless-ings or sor-rows pre-vail;
And sorrows, sometimes how they sweep Like tempests down o - ver the soul!
But toil - ing in life's dust-y way, The Rock's blessed shadow, how sweet!
Or climb-ing the mountain way steep, Or walk-ing the shad-ow - y vale.
REFRAIN
O then to the Rock let me fly, To the
let me fly,
Rock that is high - er than I; O then to the
is high - er than I;
Rock let me fly, To the Rock that is high - er than I!
let me fly,

134 When the Morning Comes

Words Adapted

Southern Melody
Arr. by B. B. McKinney

Slowly
1. Tri-als dark on ev-ery hand, And we can-not un-der-stand All the ways that God would lead us to that bless-ed promised land; But He'll guide us with His eye, And we'll fol-low till we die; We will un-der-stand it bet-ter by and by.
2. Oft our cherished plans have failed, Disappointments have prevailed, And we've wandered in the darkness, heav-y-heart-ed and a-lone; But we're trusting in the Lord, And, ac-cord-ing to His word, We will un-der-stand it bet-ter by and by.
3. Temp-ta-tions, hid-den snares, Of-ten take us un-a-wares, And our hearts are made to bleed for some tho't-less word or deed, And we won-der why the test When we try to do our best, But we'll un-der-stand it bet-ter by and by.
Chorus
By and by, when the morning comes, When the saints of God are gathered home, We will tell the sto-ry How we've overcome; We will un-der-stand it bet-ter by and by.

135 In the Shadow of His Wings

John B. Atchinson | Edwin O. Excell

1. In the shad-ow of His wings There is rest, sweet rest; There is rest from care and
2. In the shad-ow of His wings There is peace, sweet peace, Peace that passeth under-
3. In the shad-ow of His wings There is joy, glad joy, There is joy to tell the
la - bor, There is rest for friend and neigh-bor; In the shad-ow of His wings
standing, Peace, sweet peace that knows no end-ing; In the shad-ow of His wings
sto - ry, Joy ex - ceed - ing, full of glo - ry; In the shad-ow of His wings
There is rest, sweet rest, In the shad-ow of His wings There is rest (sweet rest).
There is peace, sweet peace, In the shad-ow of His wings There is peace (sweet peace).
There is joy, glad joy, In the shad-ow of His wings There is joy (glad joy).
Chorus
There is rest, There is peace, There is joy, In the shadow of His wings:
sweet rest, sweet peace, glad joy,
There is rest, There is peace, There is joy, In the shadow of His wings.
sweet rest, sweet peace, glad joy,

136 Come, Ye Thankful People

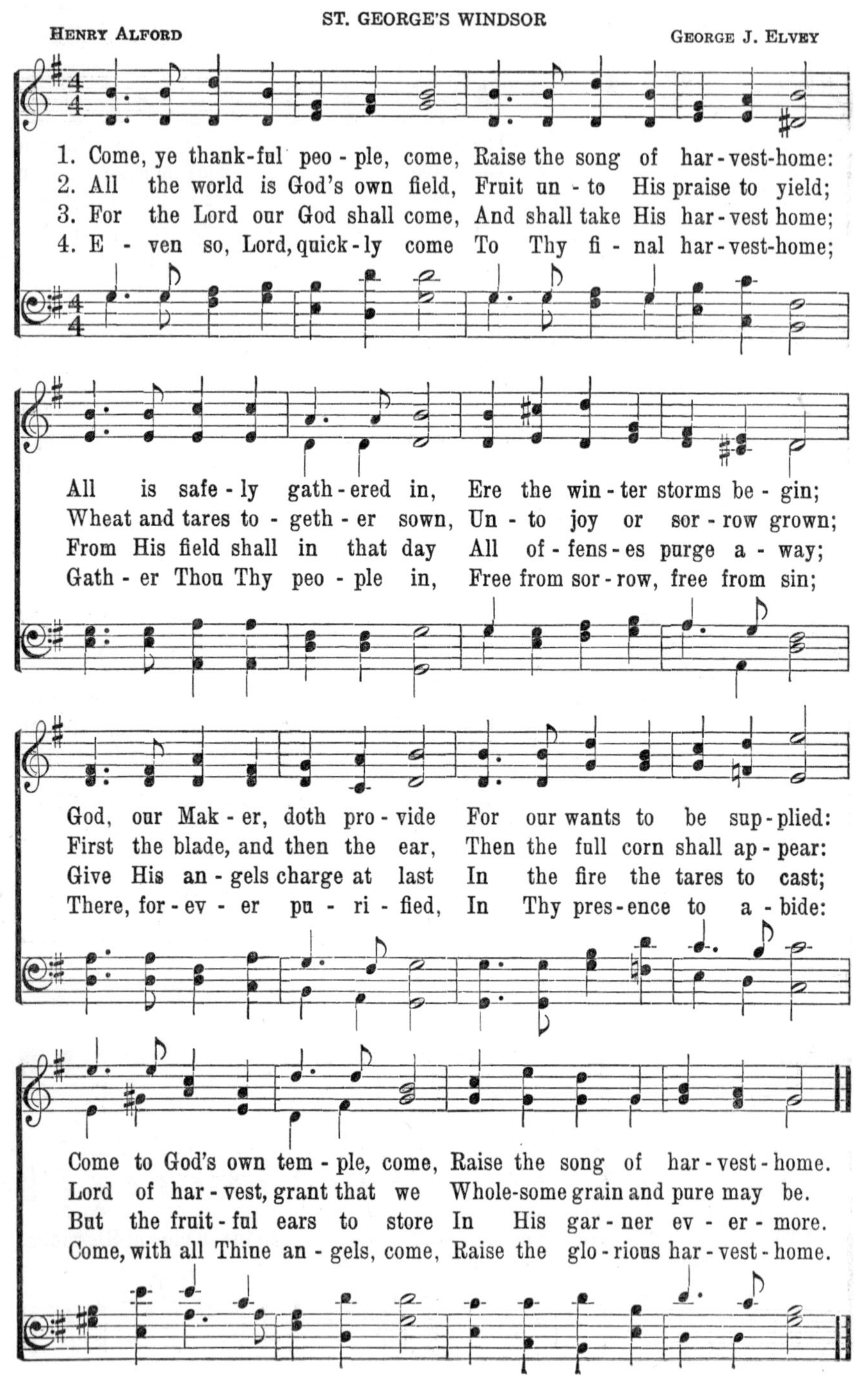
ST. GEORGE'S WINDSOR
HENRY ALFORD
GEORGE J. ELVEY
1. Come, ye thank-ful peo - ple, come, Raise the song of har - vest-home:
2. All the world is God's own field, Fruit un - to His praise to yield;
3. For the Lord our God shall come, And shall take His har - vest home;
4. E - ven so, Lord, quick - ly come To Thy fi - nal har - vest-home;
All is safe - ly gath - ered in, Ere the win - ter storms be - gin;
Wheat and tares to - geth - er sown, Un - to joy or sor - row grown;
From His field shall in that day All of - fens - es purge a - way;
Gath - er Thou Thy peo - ple in, Free from sor - row, free from sin;
God, our Mak - er, doth pro - vide For our wants to be sup - plied:
First the blade, and then the ear, Then the full corn shall ap - pear:
Give His an - gels charge at last In the fire the tares to cast;
There, for - ev - er pu - ri - fied, In Thy pres - ence to a - bide:
Come to God's own tem - ple, come, Raise the song of har - vest - home.
Lord of har - vest, grant that we Whole-some grain and pure may be.
But the fruit - ful ears to store In His gar - ner ev - er - more.
Come, with all Thine an - gels, come, Raise the glo - rious har - vest - home.

137 Joy to the World!

ANTIOCH
Isaac Watts
George F. Handel
1. Joy to the world! the Lord is come; Let earth re-
2. Joy to the earth! the Saviour reigns; Let men their
3. No more let sins and sor - rows grow, Nor thorns in-
4. He rules the world with truth and grace, And makes the
ceive her King; Let ev - ery heart pre - pare Him room,
songs em - ploy; While fields and floods, rocks, hills and plains
fest the ground; He comes to make His bless - ings flow
na - tions prove The glo - ries of His right - eous - ness,
And heaven and na - ture sing, And heaven and na - ture
Re - peat the sound - ing joy, Re - peat the sound - ing
Far as the curse is found, Far as the curse is
And won - ders of His love, And won - ders of His
1. And heaven and na - ture sing,........... And
sing, And heaven, and heaven and na - ture sing.
joy, Re - peat, re - peat the sound - ing joy.
found, Far as, far as the curse is found.
love, And won-ders, and won - ders of His love.
heaven and na - ture sing,

138 Thou Didst Leave Thy Throne

MARGARET

EMILY E. S. ELLIOTT — TIMOTHY R. MATTHEWS

1. Thou didst leave Thy throne And Thy king - ly crown, When Thou
2. Heav-en's arch - es rang When the an - gels sang, Pro-
3. The fox - es found rest, And the birds their nest In the
4. Thou cam - est, O Lord, With the liv - ing word That should
5. When the heav - ens shall ring, And the an - gels sing, At Thy
cam - est to earth for me; But in Beth - le - hem's home
claim - ing Thy roy - al de - gree; But of low - ly birth
shade of the for - est tree; But Thy couch was the sod,
set Thy peo - ple free; But with mock - ing scorn,
com - ing to vic - to - ry, Let Thy voice call me home,
Was there found no room For Thy ho - ly na - tiv - i - ty.
Didst Thou come to earth, And in great hu - mil - i - ty.
O Thou Son of God, In the des - erts of Gal - i - lee.
And with crown of thorn, They bore Thee to Cal - va - ry.
Say - ing, "Yet there is room, There is room at My side for thee."
REFRAIN
1-4. O come to my heart, Lord Je - sus, There is room in my heart for Thee.
5. My heart shall rejoice, Lord Je - sus, When Thou comest and call-est for me.

139 We Three Kings of Orient Are

KINGS OF ORIENT
JOHN H. HOPKINS
JOHN H. HOPKINS
1. We three kings of O - ri - ent are, Bear - ing gifts we trav-erse a - far
2. Born a King on Beth-le-hem's plain, Gold I bring to crown Him a-gain,
3. Frank-in-cense to of - fer have I, In - cense owns a De - i - ty nigh;
4. Myrrh is mine; its bit - ter per-fume Breathes a life of gath-er-ing gloom;
5. Glo - rious now be - hold Him a - rise, King and God and Sac - ri - fice;
Field and foun - tain, moor and moun-tain, Fol - low - ing yon - der star.
King for - ev - er, ceas - ing nev - er O - ver us all to reign.
Prayer and prais - ing, all men rais - ing, Wor-ship Him, God on high.
Sor-rowing, sigh - ing, bleed-ing, dy - ing, Sealed in the stone-cold tomb.
Al - le - lu - ia, Al - le - lu - ia! Peals through the earth and skies.
REFRAIN a tempo
O star of won - der, star of night, Star with loy - al beau - ty bright,
West-ward lead - ing, still pro - ceed-ing, Guide us to thy per - fect light.

140 The First Noel the Angel Did Say

THE FIRST NOEL

Traditional | Traditional

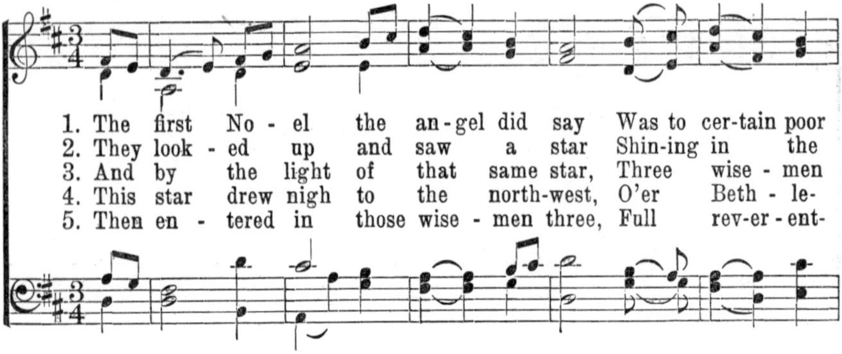

1. The first No - el the an - gel did say Was to cer - tain poor
2. They look - ed up and saw a star Shin - ing in the
3. And by the light of that same star, Three wise - men
4. This star drew nigh to the north-west, O'er Beth - le-
5. Then en - tered in those wise - men three, Full rev - er - ent-

shepherds in fields as they lay; In fields where they lay keep - ing their
east, be - yond them far, And to the earth it gave great
came from coun - try far; To seek for a king was their in-
hem it took its rest, And there it did both stop and
ly up - on the knee, And of - fered there, in His pres-

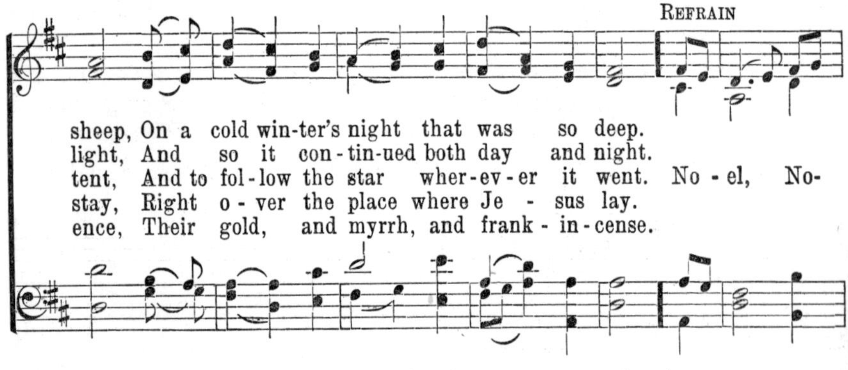

sheep, On a cold win - ter's night that was so deep.
light, And so it con - tin - ued both day and night.
tent, And to fol - low the star wher - ev - er it went.
stay, Right o - ver the place where Je - sus lay.
ence, Their gold, and myrrh, and frank - in - cense.

REFRAIN

No - el, No - el, No - el, No - el, Born is the King of Is - ra - el.

141 It Came Upon the Midnight Clear

CAROL
Edmund H. Sears
Richard S. Willis
1. It came up - on the mid-night clear, That glo-rious song of old,
2. Still thro' the clo - ven skies they come, With peace-ful wings un - furled,
3. And ye, be - neath life's crush-ing load, Whose forms are bend-ing low,
4. For lo, the days are has-tening on, By proph-et bards fore - told,
From an - gels bend-ing near the earth To touch their harps of gold:
And still their heaven-ly mu - sic floats O'er all the wea - ry world:
Who toil a - long the climb - ing way With pain - ful steps and slow,
When with the ev - er - cir - cling years Comes round the age of gold;
"Peace on the earth, good-will to men, From heaven's all-gra-cious King:"
A - bove its sad and low - ly plains They bend on hov-ering wing,
Look now! for glad and gold - en hours Come swift - ly on the wing:
When peace shall o - ver all the earth Its an - cient splen-dors fling,
The world in sol - emn still - ness lay To hear the an - gels sing.
And ev - er o'er its Ba - bel sounds The bless - ed an - gels sing.
O rest be - side the wea - ry road, And hear the an - gels sing.
And the whole world give back the song Which now the an - gels sing.

142 Hark, the Herald Angels Sing

MENDELSSOHN
Charles Wesley
Felix Mendelssohn
1. Hark! the her - ald an - gels sing, "Glo - ry to the new-born King;
2. Christ, by high - est heaven a - dored; Christ, the ev - er - last - ing Lord:
3. Hail the heaven-born Prince of Peace! Hail the Sun of right-eous-ness!
4. Come, De - sire of na - tions, come! Fix in us Thy hum - ble home:
Peace on earth, and mer - cy mild; God and sin - ners rec - on - ciled."
Late in time be - hold Him come, Off - spring of a vir-gin's womb.
Light and life to all He brings, Risen with heal - ing in His wings:
Rise, the wom - an's conquering seed, Bruise in us the ser-pent's head;
Joy - ful, all ye na - tions, rise, Join the tri - umph of the skies;
Veiled in flesh the God - head see, Hail th' in-car - nate De - i - ty!
Mild He lays His glo - ry by, Born that man no more may die;
Ad - am's like-ness now ef - face, Stamp Thine im-age in its place:
With th' an-gel - ic hosts pro - claim, "Christ is born in Beth - le - hem."
Pleased as man with men t' ap - pear, Je - sus our Im-man - uel here.
Born to raise the sons of earth; Born to give them sec - ond birth.
Sec - ond Ad - am from a - bove, Re - in - state us in Thy love.

Hark! the Herald Angels Sing

Hark! the her-ald an-gels sing, "Glo-ry to the new-born King."

143 O Come, All Ye Faithful

Tr. by FREDERICK OAKELEY | ADESTE FIDELES | WADE'S Cantus Diversi

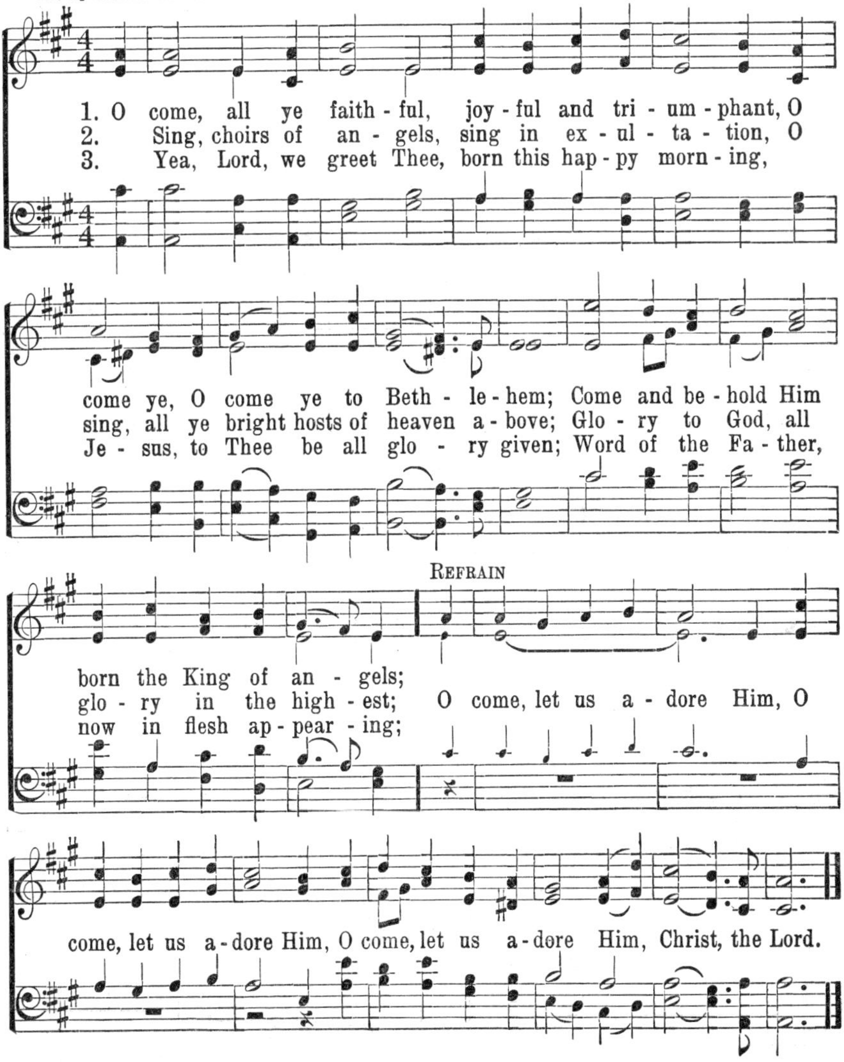

1. O come, all ye faith-ful, joy-ful and tri-um-phant, O come ye, O come ye to Beth-le-hem; Come and be-hold Him born the King of an-gels;
2. Sing, choirs of an-gels, sing in ex-ul-ta-tion, O sing, all ye bright hosts of heaven a-bove; Glo-ry to God, all glo-ry in the high-est;
3. Yea, Lord, we greet Thee, born this hap-py morn-ing, Je-sus, to Thee be all glo-ry given; Word of the Fa-ther, now in flesh ap-pear-ing;

REFRAIN

O come, let us a-dore Him, O come, let us a-dore Him, O come, let us a-dore Him, Christ, the Lord.

144 O Little Town of Bethlehem

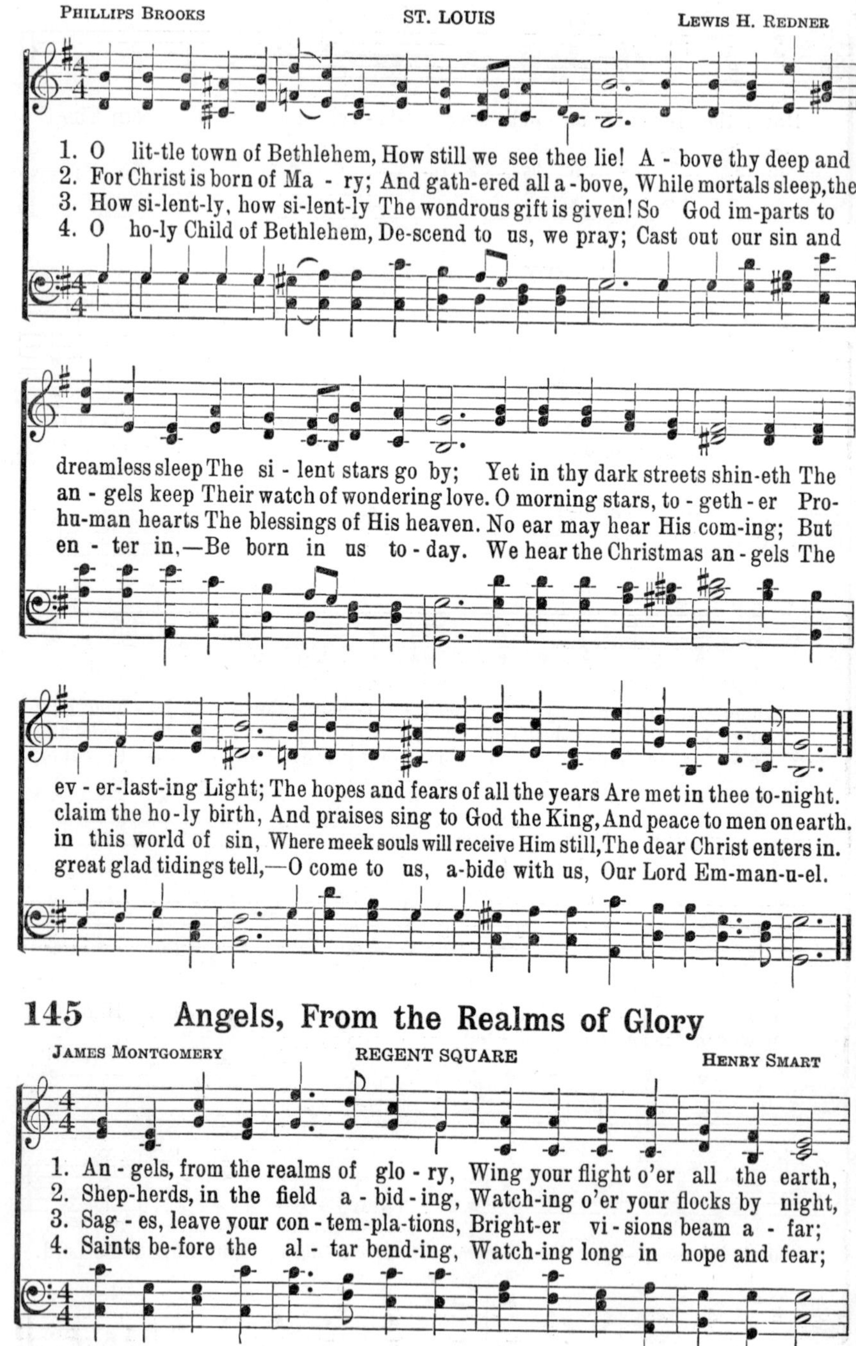
PHILLIPS BROOKS
ST. LOUIS
LEWIS H. REDNER
1. O lit-tle town of Bethlehem, How still we see thee lie! A - bove thy deep and dreamless sleep The si - lent stars go by; Yet in thy dark streets shin-eth The ev - er-last-ing Light; The hopes and fears of all the years Are met in thee to-night.
2. For Christ is born of Ma - ry; And gath-ered all a - bove, While mortals sleep, the an - gels keep Their watch of wondering love. O morning stars, to - geth - er Pro-claim the ho-ly birth, And praises sing to God the King, And peace to men on earth.
3. How si-lent-ly, how si-lent-ly The wondrous gift is given! So God im-parts to hu-man hearts The blessings of His heaven. No ear may hear His com-ing; But in this world of sin, Where meek souls will receive Him still, The dear Christ enters in.
4. O ho-ly Child of Bethlehem, De-scend to us, we pray; Cast out our sin and en - ter in,—Be born in us to - day. We hear the Christmas an - gels The great glad tidings tell,—O come to us, a-bide with us, Our Lord Em-man-u-el.
145 Angels, From the Realms of Glory
JAMES MONTGOMERY
REGENT SQUARE
HENRY SMART
1. An - gels, from the realms of glo - ry, Wing your flight o'er all the earth,
2. Shep-herds, in the field a - bid - ing, Watch-ing o'er your flocks by night,
3. Sag - es, leave your con - tem-pla-tions, Bright-er vi - sions beam a - far;
4. Saints be-fore the al - tar bend-ing, Watch-ing long in hope and fear;

Angels, From the Realms of Glory
Ye, who sang cre - a - tion's sto - ry, Now pro-claim Mes - si - ah's birth:
God with man is now re - sid - ing, Yon-der shines the In - fant-Light;
Seek the great De - sire of na - tions, Ye have seen His na - tal star;
Sud - den - ly the Lord, de - scend-ing, In His tem - ple shall ap - pear;
Come and wor-ship, come and wor-ship, Wor - ship Christ, the new-born King.
146
Silent Night, Holy Night
JOSEPH MOHR
STILLE NACHT
FRANZ GRÜBER
1. Si - lent night, ho - ly night, All is calm, all is bright
2. Si - lent night, ho - ly night, Dark-ness flies, all is light;
3. Si - lent night, ho - ly night, Guid - ing Star, lend thy light;
4. Si - lent night, ho - ly night, Wondrous Star, lend thy light;
Round yon Vir - gin Moth-er and Child, Ho - ly In-fant so ten-der and mild,
Shep-herds hear the an - gels sing, "Al - le - lu - ia! hail the King!
See the east - ern wise men bring Gifts and hom - age to our King!
With the an - gels let us sing Al - le - lu - ia to our King!
Sleep in heav - en - ly peace, Sleep in heav - en - ly peace.
Christ the Sav - iour is born, Christ the Sav - iour is born."
Christ the Sav - iour is born, Christ the Sav - iour is born.
Christ the Sav - iour is born, Christ the Sav - iour is born.

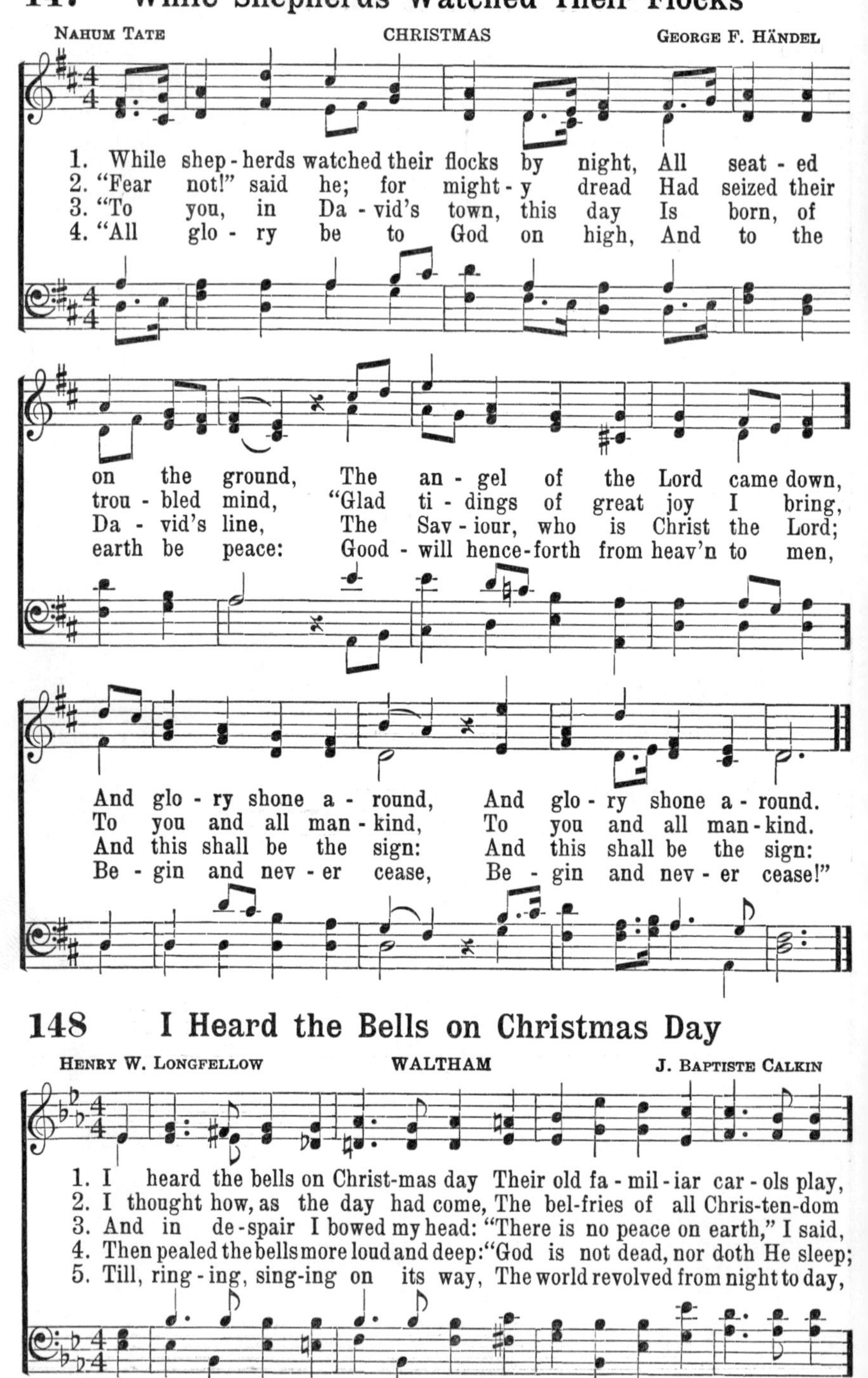
147 While Shepherds Watched Their Flocks
Nahum Tate
CHRISTMAS
George F. Händel
1. While shep-herds watched their flocks by night, All seat-ed on the ground, The an-gel of the Lord came down, And glo-ry shone a-round, And glo-ry shone a-round.
2. "Fear not!" said he; for might-y dread Had seized their trou-bled mind, "Glad ti-dings of great joy I bring, To you and all man-kind, To you and all man-kind.
3. "To you, in Da-vid's town, this day Is born, of Da-vid's line, The Sav-iour, who is Christ the Lord; And this shall be the sign: And this shall be the sign:
4. "All glo-ry be to God on high, And to the earth be peace: Good-will hence-forth from heav'n to men, Be-gin and nev-er cease, Be-gin and nev-er cease!"
148 I Heard the Bells on Christmas Day
Henry W. Longfellow
WALTHAM
J. Baptiste Calkin
1. I heard the bells on Christ-mas day Their old fa-mil-iar car-ols play,
2. I thought how, as the day had come, The bel-fries of all Chris-ten-dom
3. And in de-spair I bowed my head: "There is no peace on earth," I said,
4. Then pealed the bells more loud and deep: "God is not dead, nor doth He sleep;
5. Till, ring-ing, sing-ing on its way, The world revolved from night to day,

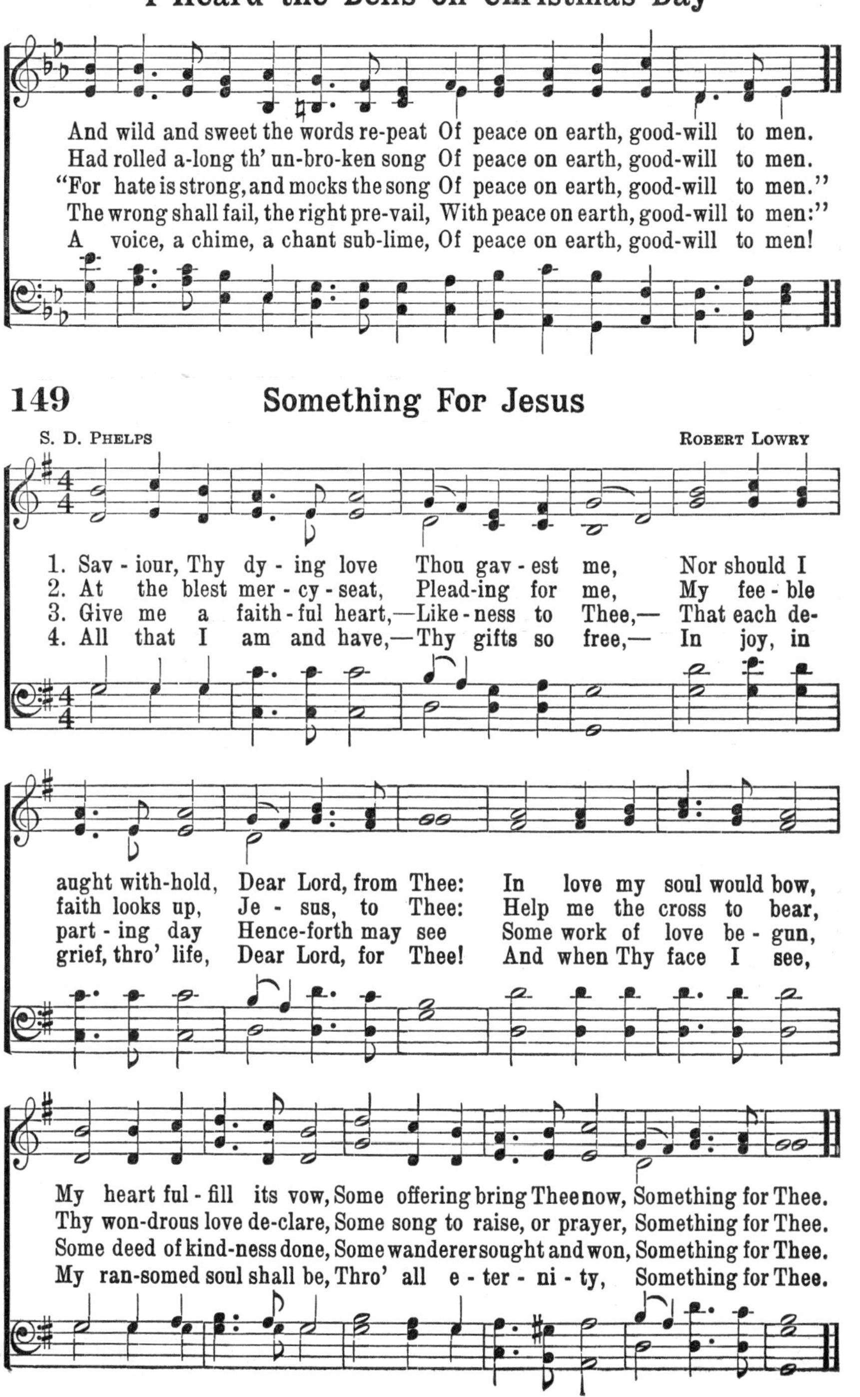
I Heard the Bells on Christmas Day
And wild and sweet the words re-peat Of peace on earth, good-will to men.
Had rolled a-long th' un-bro-ken song Of peace on earth, good-will to men.
"For hate is strong, and mocks the song Of peace on earth, good-will to men."
The wrong shall fail, the right pre-vail, With peace on earth, good-will to men:"
A voice, a chime, a chant sub-lime, Of peace on earth, good-will to men!
149
Something For Jesus
S. D. Phelps
Robert Lowry
1. Sav - iour, Thy dy - ing love Thou gav - est me, Nor should I
2. At the blest mer - cy - seat, Plead-ing for me, My fee - ble
3. Give me a faith - ful heart,—Like - ness to Thee,— That each de-
4. All that I am and have,—Thy gifts so free,— In joy, in
aught with-hold, Dear Lord, from Thee: In love my soul would bow,
faith looks up, Je - sus, to Thee: Help me the cross to bear,
part - ing day Hence-forth may see Some work of love be - gun,
grief, thro' life, Dear Lord, for Thee! And when Thy face I see,
My heart ful - fill its vow, Some offering bring Thee now, Something for Thee.
Thy won-drous love de-clare, Some song to raise, or prayer, Something for Thee.
Some deed of kind-ness done, Some wanderer sought and won, Something for Thee.
My ran-somed soul shall be, Thro' all e - ter - ni - ty, Something for Thee.

150 Jesus Shall Reign

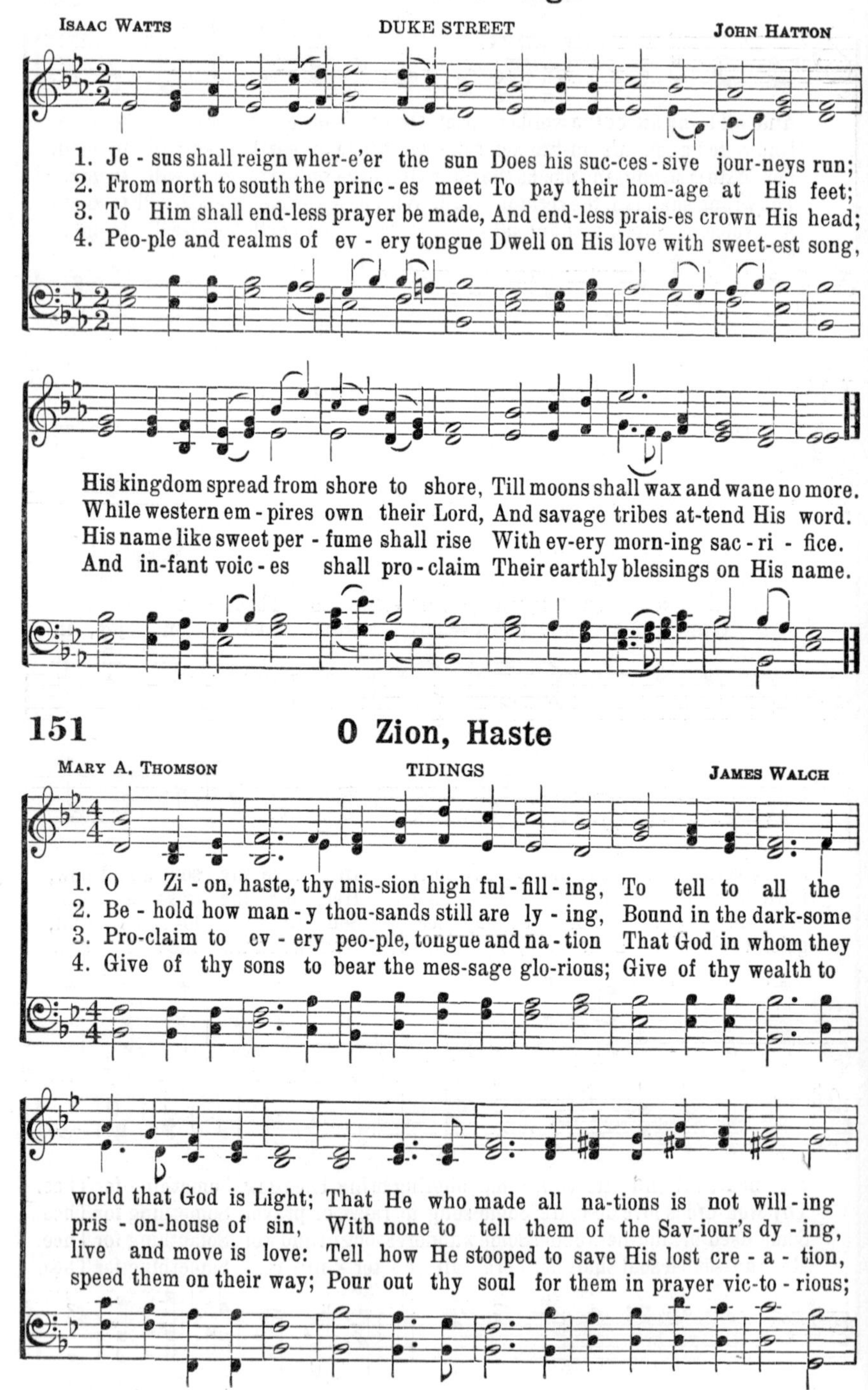
ISAAC WATTS
DUKE STREET
JOHN HATTON
1. Je - sus shall reign wher-e'er the sun Does his suc-ces - sive jour-neys run;
2. From north to south the princ - es meet To pay their hom-age at His feet;
3. To Him shall end-less prayer be made, And end-less prais-es crown His head;
4. Peo-ple and realms of ev - ery tongue Dwell on His love with sweet-est song,
His kingdom spread from shore to shore, Till moons shall wax and wane no more.
While western em - pires own their Lord, And savage tribes at-tend His word.
His name like sweet per - fume shall rise With ev-ery morn-ing sac - ri - fice.
And in-fant voic - es shall pro - claim Their earthly blessings on His name.
151
O Zion, Haste
MARY A. THOMSON
TIDINGS
JAMES WALCH
1. O Zi - on, haste, thy mis-sion high ful - fill - ing, To tell to all the
2. Be - hold how man - y thou-sands still are ly - ing, Bound in the dark-some
3. Pro-claim to ev - ery peo-ple, tongue and na - tion That God in whom they
4. Give of thy sons to bear the mes-sage glo-rious; Give of thy wealth to
world that God is Light; That He who made all na-tions is not will - ing
pris - on-house of sin, With none to tell them of the Sav-iour's dy - ing,
live and move is love: Tell how He stooped to save His lost cre - a - tion,
speed them on their way; Pour out thy soul for them in prayer vic-to - rious;

O Zion, Haste

REFRAIN
One soul should per-ish, lost in shades of night.
Or of the life He died for them to win. Pub-lish glad ti-dings,
And died on earth that man might live a-bove.
And all thou spend-est Je-sus will re-pay.
Ti-dings of peace; Ti-dings of Je - sus, Re-demp-tion and re-lease.
152 Fling Out the Banner! Let It Float
GEORGE W. DOANE
DOANE
J. BAPTISTE CALKIN
1. Fling out the ban-ner! let it float Sky-ward and sea-ward, high and wide;
2. Fling out the ban-ner! an-gels bend In anx-ious si-lence o'er the sign,
3. Fling out the ban-ner! hea-then lands Shall see from far the glo-rious sight,
4. Fling out the ban-ner! sin-sick souls, That sink and per-ish in the strife,
5. Fling out the ban-ner! wide and high, Sea-ward and sky-ward, let it shine:
The sun that lights its shin-ing folds, The cross on which the Sav-iour died.
And vain-ly seek to com-pre-hend The won-der of the love di-vine.
And na-tions crowd-ing to be born, Bap-tize their spir-its in its light.
Shall touch in faith its ra-diant hem, And spring im-mor-tal in-to life.
Nor skill, nor might, nor mer-it ours; We con-quer on-ly in that sign.

153 Must Jesus Bear the Cross Alone?

THOMAS SHEPHERD | MAITLAND | GEORGE N. ALLEN

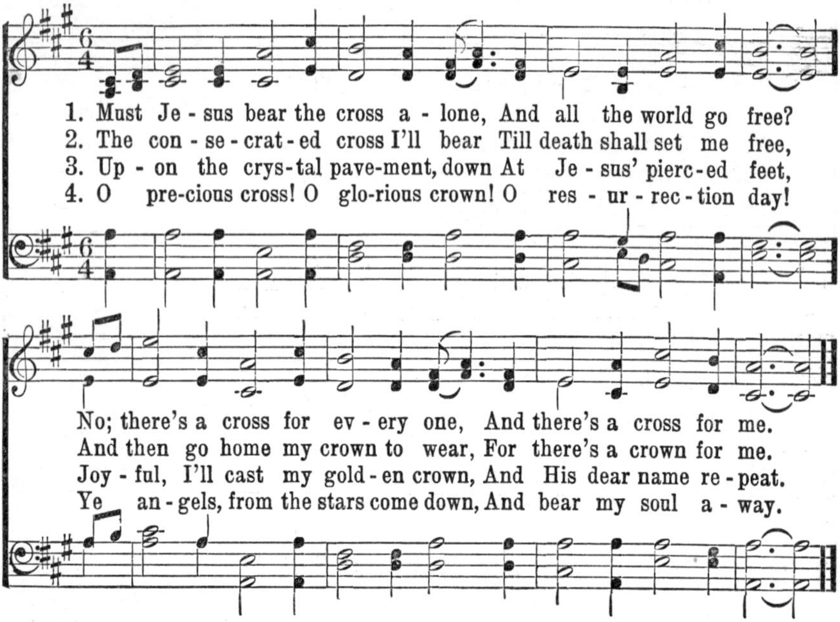

1. Must Je - sus bear the cross a - lone, And all the world go free?
2. The con - se - crat - ed cross I'll bear Till death shall set me free,
3. Up - on the crys - tal pave - ment, down At Je - sus' pierc - ed feet,
4. O pre - cious cross! O glo - rious crown! O res - ur - rec - tion day!

No; there's a cross for ev - ery one, And there's a cross for me.
And then go home my crown to wear, For there's a crown for me.
Joy - ful, I'll cast my gold - en crown, And His dear name re - peat.
Ye an - gels, from the stars come down, And bear my soul a - way.

154 My Jesus, I Love Thee

Anonymous | GORDON | A. J. GORDON

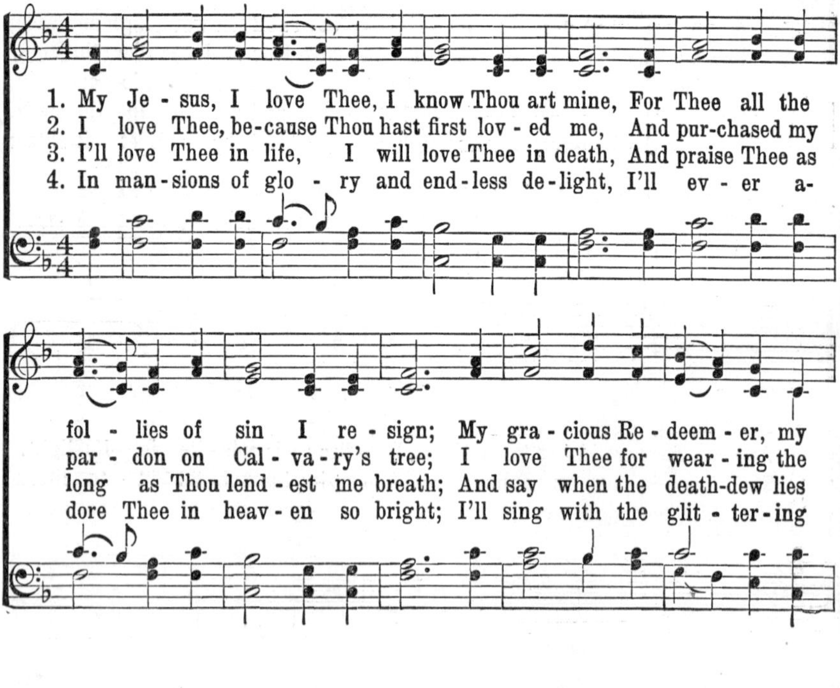

1. My Je - sus, I love Thee, I know Thou art mine, For Thee all the
2. I love Thee, be - cause Thou hast first lov - ed me, And pur - chased my
3. I'll love Thee in life, I will love Thee in death, And praise Thee as
4. In man - sions of glo - ry and end - less de - light, I'll ev - er a-

fol - lies of sin I re - sign; My gra - cious Re - deem - er, my
par - don on Cal - va - ry's tree; I love Thee for wear - ing the
long as Thou lend - est me breath; And say when the death - dew lies
dore Thee in heav - en so bright; I'll sing with the glit - ter - ing

My Jesus, I Love Thee

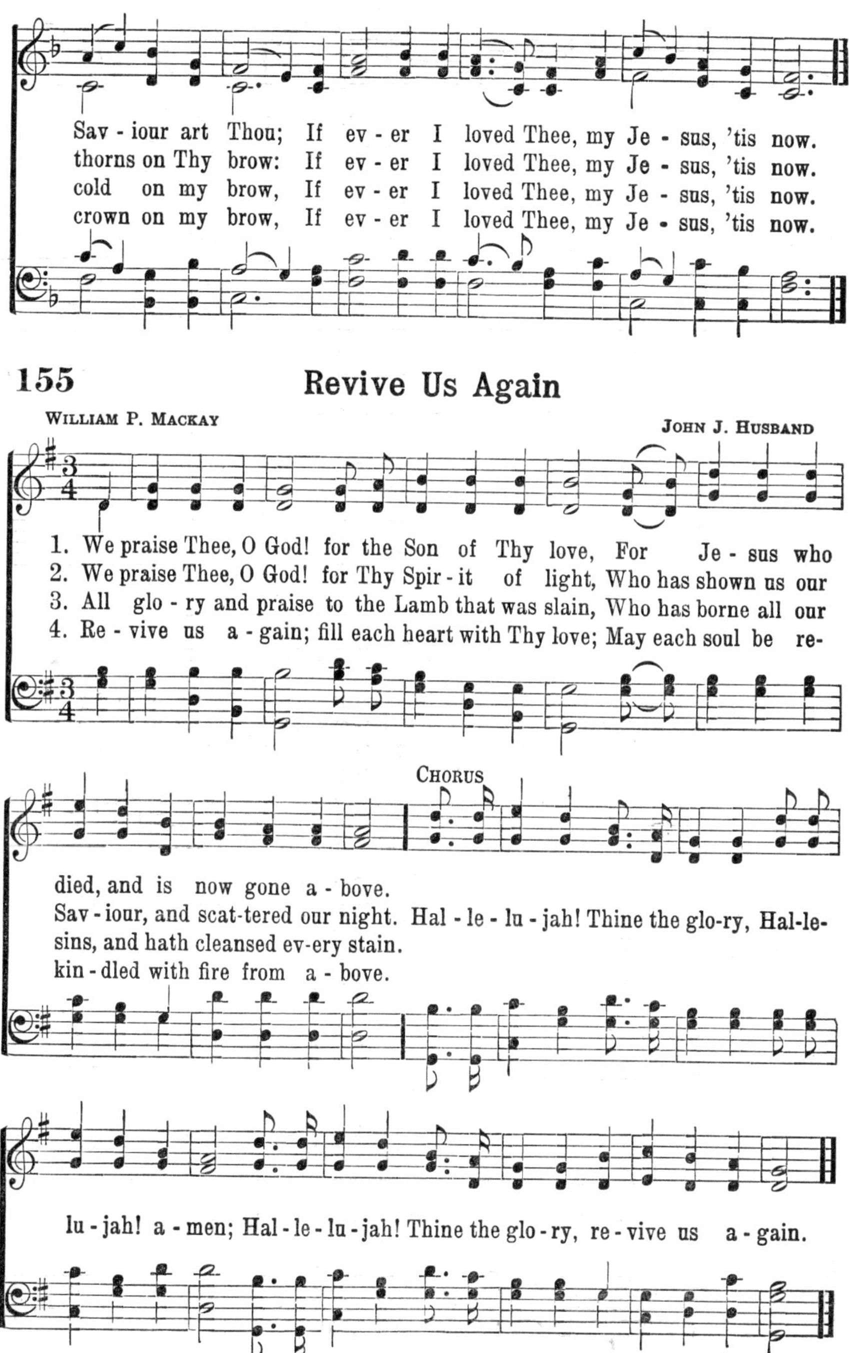

Sav - iour art Thou; If ev - er I loved Thee, my Je - sus, 'tis now.
thorns on Thy brow: If ev - er I loved Thee, my Je - sus, 'tis now.
cold on my brow, If ev - er I loved Thee, my Je - sus, 'tis now.
crown on my brow, If ev - er I loved Thee, my Je - sus, 'tis now.
155
Revive Us Again
William P. Mackay
John J. Husband
1. We praise Thee, O God! for the Son of Thy love, For Je - sus who died, and is now gone a - bove.
2. We praise Thee, O God! for Thy Spir - it of light, Who has shown us our Sav - iour, and scat-tered our night.
3. All glo - ry and praise to the Lamb that was slain, Who has borne all our sins, and hath cleansed ev-ery stain.
4. Re - vive us a - gain; fill each heart with Thy love; May each soul be re- kin - dled with fire from a - bove.
Chorus
Hal - le - lu - jah! Thine the glo-ry, Hal-le- lu - jah! a - men; Hal - le - lu - jah! Thine the glo - ry, re - vive us a - gain.

156 'Tis the Blessed Hour of Prayer

FANNY J. CROSBY WILLIAM H. DOANE

1. 'Tis the bless-ed hour of prayer, when our hearts low-ly bend,
2. 'Tis the bless-ed hour of prayer, when the Sav-iour draws near,
3. 'Tis the bless-ed hour of prayer, when the tempt-ed and tried
4. At the bless-ed hour of prayer, trust-ing Him we be-lieve
And we gath-er to Je-sus, our Sav-iour and Friend; If we
With a ten-der com-pas-sion His chil-dren to hear; When He
To the Sav-iour who loves them their sor-row con-fide; With a
That the bless-ings we're need-ing we'll sure-ly re-ceive; In the
come to Him in faith, His pro-tec-tion to share, What a balm for the
tells us we may cast at His feet ev-ery care, What a balm for the
sym-pa-thiz-ing heart He re-moves ev-ery care; What a balm for the
full-ness of this trust we shall lose ev-ery care; What a balm for the
wea-ry! O how sweet to be there!
CHORUS
Bless-ed hour of prayer, Bless-ed hour of prayer; What a balm for the wea-ry! O how sweet to be there!

157 A Charge to Keep

CHARLES WESLEY — BOYLSTON — LOWELL MASON

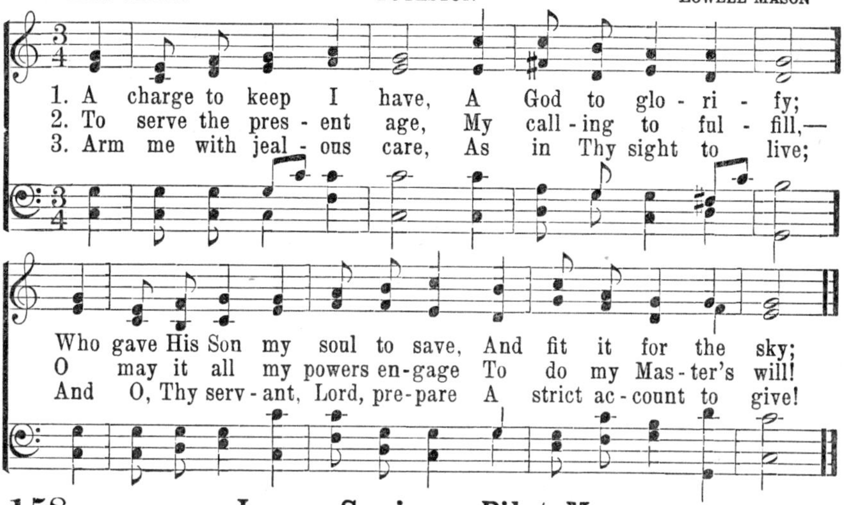

1. A charge to keep I have, A God to glo - ri - fy;
2. To serve the pres - ent age, My call - ing to ful - fill,—
3. Arm me with jeal - ous care, As in Thy sight to live;

Who gave His Son my soul to save, And fit it for the sky;
O may it all my powers en-gage To do my Mas-ter's will!
And O, Thy serv - ant, Lord, pre-pare A strict ac-count to give!

158 Jesus, Saviour, Pilot Me

EDWARD HOPPER — PILOT — J. E. GOULD

1. Je - sus, Sav - iour, pi - lot me O - ver life's tem-pes-tuous sea:
2. As a moth - er stills her child, Thou canst hush the o - cean wild;
3. When at last I near the shore, And the fear - ful break-ers roar

Un-known waves be - fore me roll, Hid - ing rocks and treacherous shoal;
Bois-terous waves o - bey Thy will When Thou sayest to them "Be still!"
'Twixt me and the peace-ful rest, Then, while lean-ing on Thy breast,

Chart and com - pass come from Thee, Je - sus, Sav - iour, pi - lot me.
Won-drous Sov-ereign of the sea, Je - sus, Sav - iour, pi - lot me.
May I hear Thee say to me, "Fear not, I will pi - lot thee."

159 Jesus Calls Us

Mrs. Cecil F. Alexander — GALILEE — William H. Jude

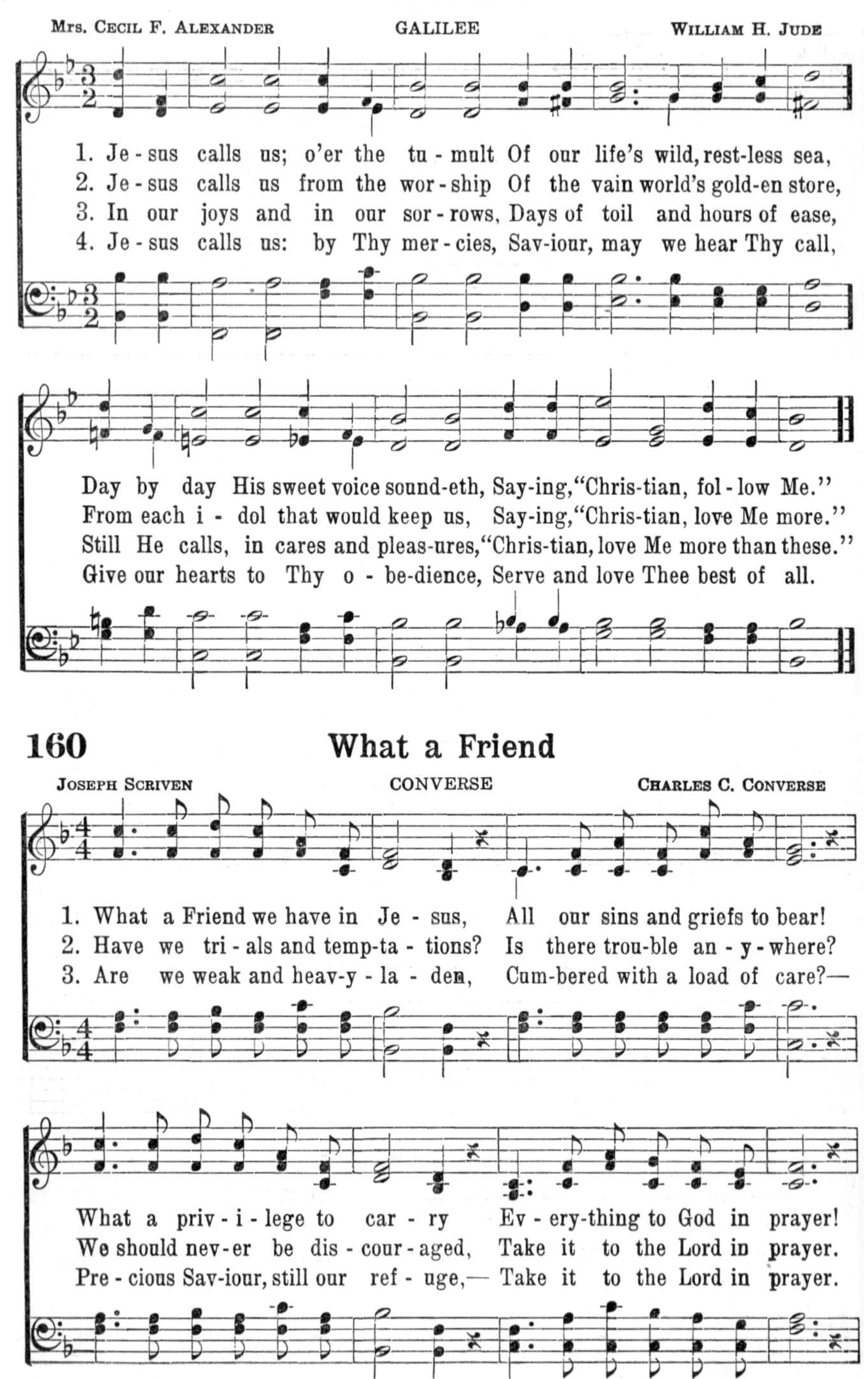

1. Je-sus calls us; o'er the tu-mult Of our life's wild, rest-less sea,
2. Je-sus calls us from the wor-ship Of the vain world's gold-en store,
3. In our joys and in our sor-rows, Days of toil and hours of ease,
4. Je-sus calls us: by Thy mer-cies, Sav-iour, may we hear Thy call,
Day by day His sweet voice sound-eth, Say-ing, "Chris-tian, fol-low Me."
From each i-dol that would keep us, Say-ing, "Chris-tian, love Me more."
Still He calls, in cares and pleas-ures, "Chris-tian, love Me more than these."
Give our hearts to Thy o-be-dience, Serve and love Thee best of all.

160 What a Friend

Joseph Scriven — CONVERSE — Charles C. Converse

1. What a Friend we have in Je-sus, All our sins and griefs to bear!
2. Have we tri-als and temp-ta-tions? Is there trou-ble an-y-where?
3. Are we weak and heav-y-la-den, Cum-bered with a load of care?—
What a priv-i-lege to car-ry Ev-ery-thing to God in prayer!
We should nev-er be dis-cour-aged, Take it to the Lord in prayer.
Pre-cious Sav-iour, still our ref-uge,— Take it to the Lord in prayer.

What a Friend

O what peace we of - ten for - feit, O what need-less pain we bear,
Can we find a friend so faith - ful Who will all our sor - rows share?
Do thy friends de-spise, for - sake thee? Take it to the Lord in prayer;

All be-cause we do not car - ry Ev - ery-thing to God in prayer!
Je - sus knows our ev - ery weak-ness, Take it to the Lord in prayer.
In His arms He'll take and shield thee, Thou wilt find a sol - ace there.

161 Amazing Grace

JOHN NEWTON | McINTOSH | Arr. by E. O. EXCELL

1. A - maz - ing grace! how sweet the sound, That saved a wretch like me!
2. 'Twas grace that taught my heart to fear, And grace my fears re - lieved;
3. Thro' man - y dan - gers, toils and snares, I have al - read - y come;
4. When we've been there ten thou-sand years, Bright shin-ing as the sun,

I once was lost, but now am found, Was blind, but now I see.
How pre - cious did that grace ap - pear The hour I first be-lieved!
'Tis grace hath bro't me safe thus far, And grace will lead me home.
We've no less days to sing God's praise Than when we first be - gun.

162 Just As I Am
Charlotte Elliott
WOODWORTH
William B. Bradbury
1. Just as I am, with-out one plea, But that Thy blood was shed for me,
2. Just as I am, and wait-ing not To rid my soul of one dark blot,
3. Just as I am, though tossed a-bout With many a con-flict, many a doubt,
4. Just as I am—poor,wretched,blind; Sight, rich-es, heal-ing of the mind,
5. Just as I am—Thou wilt re-ceive, Wilt welcome, pardon, cleanse, relieve,
And that Thou bidd'st me come to Thee, O Lamb of God, I come! I come!
To Thee whose blood can cleanse each spot, O Lamb of God, I come! I come!
Fightings and fears with-in, with-out, O Lamb of God, I come! I come!
Yea, all I need in Thee to find, O Lamb of God, I come! I come!
Be-cause Thy prom-ise I be-lieve, O Lamb of God, I come! I come!
163 I Heard the Voice of Jesus Say
Horatius Bonar
Old English Air
Arr. by B. B. McKinney
1. I heard the voice of Je-sus say, "Come un-to Me and rest;
2. I heard the voice of Je-sus say, "Be-hold, I free-ly give
3. I heard the voice of Je-sus say, "I am this dark world's Light;
Lay down, thou wear-y one, lay down Thy head up-on My breast."
The liv-ing wa-ter; thirst-y one, Stoop down and drink, and live."
Look un-to Me, thy morn shall rise, And all thy day be bright."

I Heard the Voice of Jesus Say

DUET
I came to Je - sus as I was, Wea - ry and worn and sad,
I came to Je - sus and I drank Of that life - giv - ing stream;
I looked to Je - sus and I found In Him my Star, my Sun;
PARTS
I found in Him a rest - ing-place, And He has made me glad.
My thirst was quenched, my soul re - vived, And now I live in Him.
And in that light of life I'll walk, Till traveling days are done.

164 Where He Leads Me

E. W. BLANDY — J. S. NORRIS

1. I can hear my Sav - iour call-ing, I can hear my Sav - iour call-ing,
2. I'll go with Him through the garden, I'll go with Him through the garden,
3. I'll go with Him through the judgment, I'll go with Him through the judgment,
4. He will give me grace and glo - ry, He will give me grace and glo - ry,

REF.—*Where He leads me I will fol - low, Where He leads me I will fol - low,*

I can hear my Sav-iour call-ing, "Take thy cross and fol-low, fol - low Me."
I'll go with Him through the gar-den, I'll go with Him, with Him all the way.
I'll go with Him through the judgment, I'll go with Him, with Him all the way.
He will give me grace and glo - ry, And go with me, with me all the way.

Where He leads me I will fol - low, I'll go with Him, with Him all the way.

165 Asleep in Jesus! Blessed Sleep

MARGARET MACKAY | REST | WILLIAM B. BRADBURY

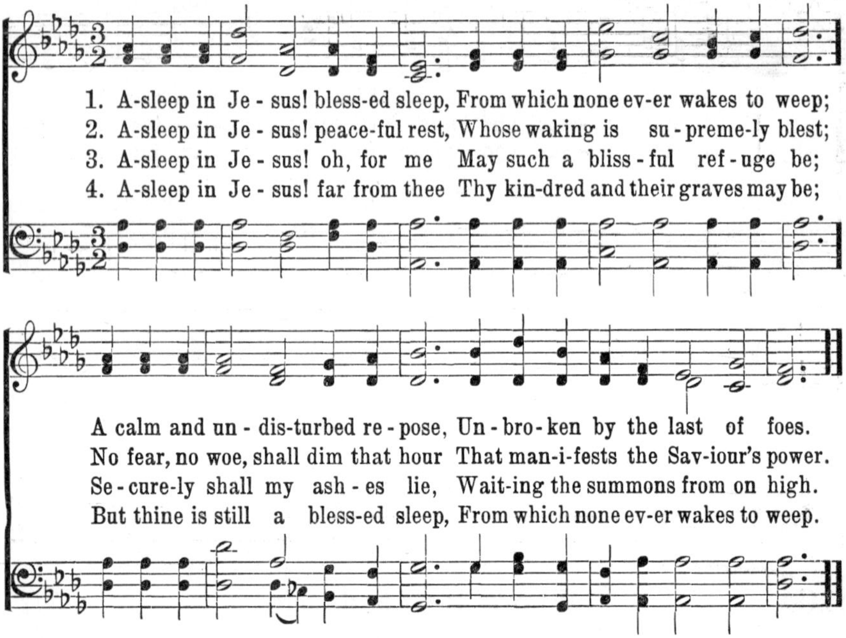

1. A-sleep in Je - sus! bless-ed sleep, From which none ev-er wakes to weep;
2. A-sleep in Je - sus! peace-ful rest, Whose waking is su - preme-ly blest;
3. A-sleep in Je - sus! oh, for me May such a bliss - ful ref - uge be;
4. A-sleep in Je - sus! far from thee Thy kin-dred and their graves may be;

A calm and un - dis-turbed re - pose, Un - bro - ken by the last of foes.
No fear, no woe, shall dim that hour That man-i-fests the Sav-iour's power.
Se - cure-ly shall my ash - es lie, Wait-ing the summons from on high.
But thine is still a bless-ed sleep, From which none ev-er wakes to weep.

166 Beautiful Valley of Eden

WALTER O. CUSHING | KELLEY | WILLIAM F. SHERWIN

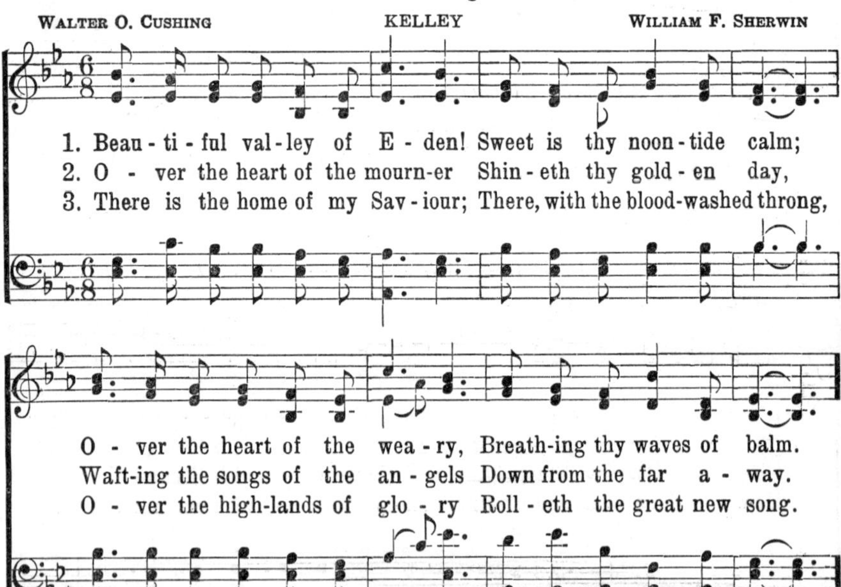
1. Beau - ti - ful val - ley of E - den! Sweet is thy noon - tide calm;
2. O - ver the heart of the mourn-er Shin - eth thy gold - en day,
3. There is the home of my Sav - iour; There, with the blood-washed throng,
O - ver the heart of the wea - ry, Breath-ing thy waves of balm.
Waft-ing the songs of the an - gels Down from the far a - way.
O - ver the high-lands of glo - ry Roll - eth the great new song.

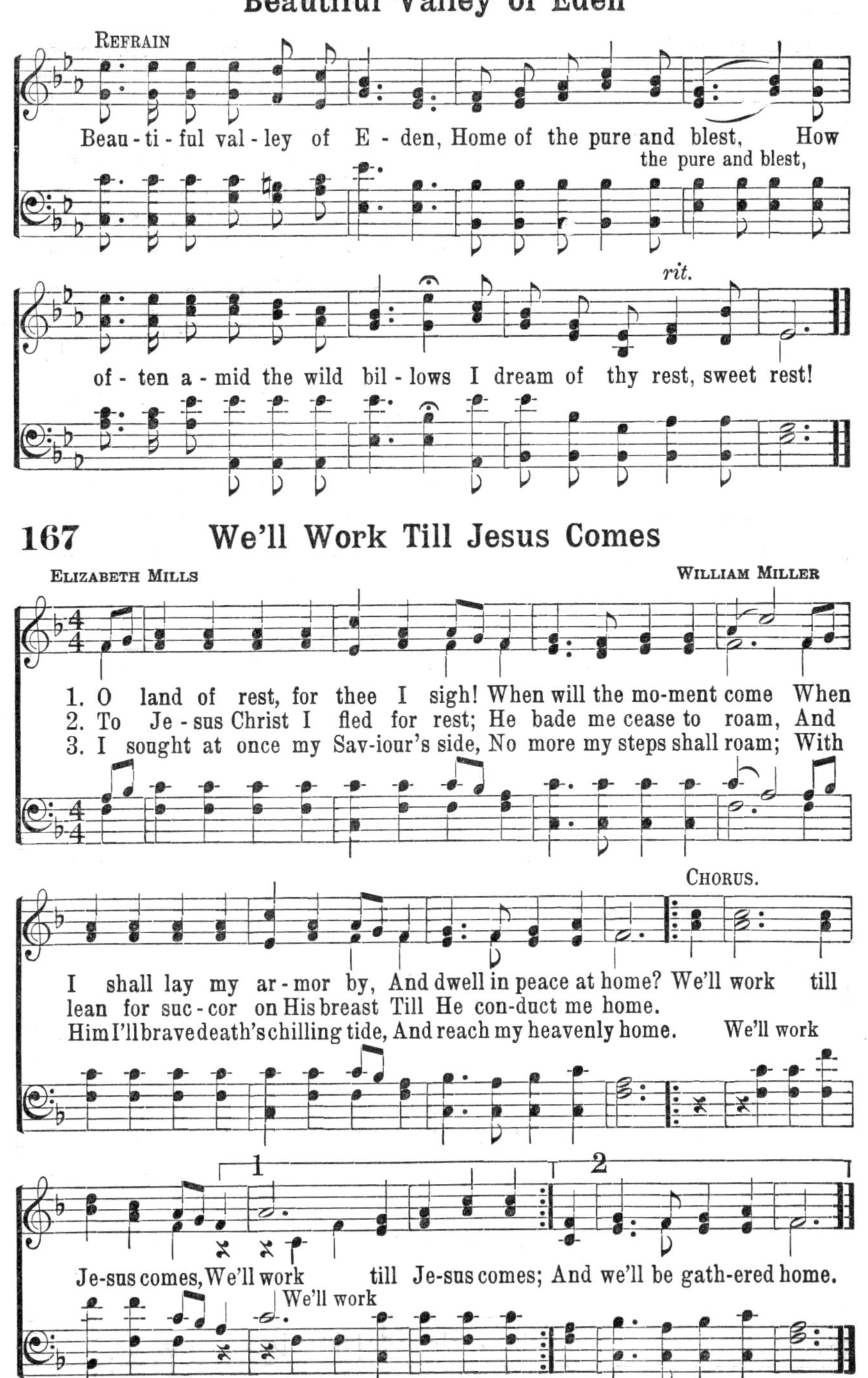
Beautiful Valley of Eden
Refrain
Beau-ti-ful val-ley of E-den, Home of the pure and blest, How
the pure and blest,
of-ten a-mid the wild bil-lows I dream of thy rest, sweet rest!
rit.
167
We'll Work Till Jesus Comes
Elizabeth Mills
William Miller
1. O land of rest, for thee I sigh! When will the mo-ment come When
2. To Je-sus Christ I fled for rest; He bade me cease to roam, And
3. I sought at once my Sav-iour's side, No more my steps shall roam; With
I shall lay my ar-mor by, And dwell in peace at home? We'll work till
lean for suc-cor on His breast Till He con-duct me home.
Him I'll brave death's chilling tide, And reach my heavenly home. We'll work
Chorus.
Je-sus comes, We'll work till Je-sus comes; And we'll be gath-ered home.
We'll work

168 I'll Live For Him

R. E. Hudson — C. R. Dunbar

169 Almost Persuaded

P. P. B. — P. P. Bliss

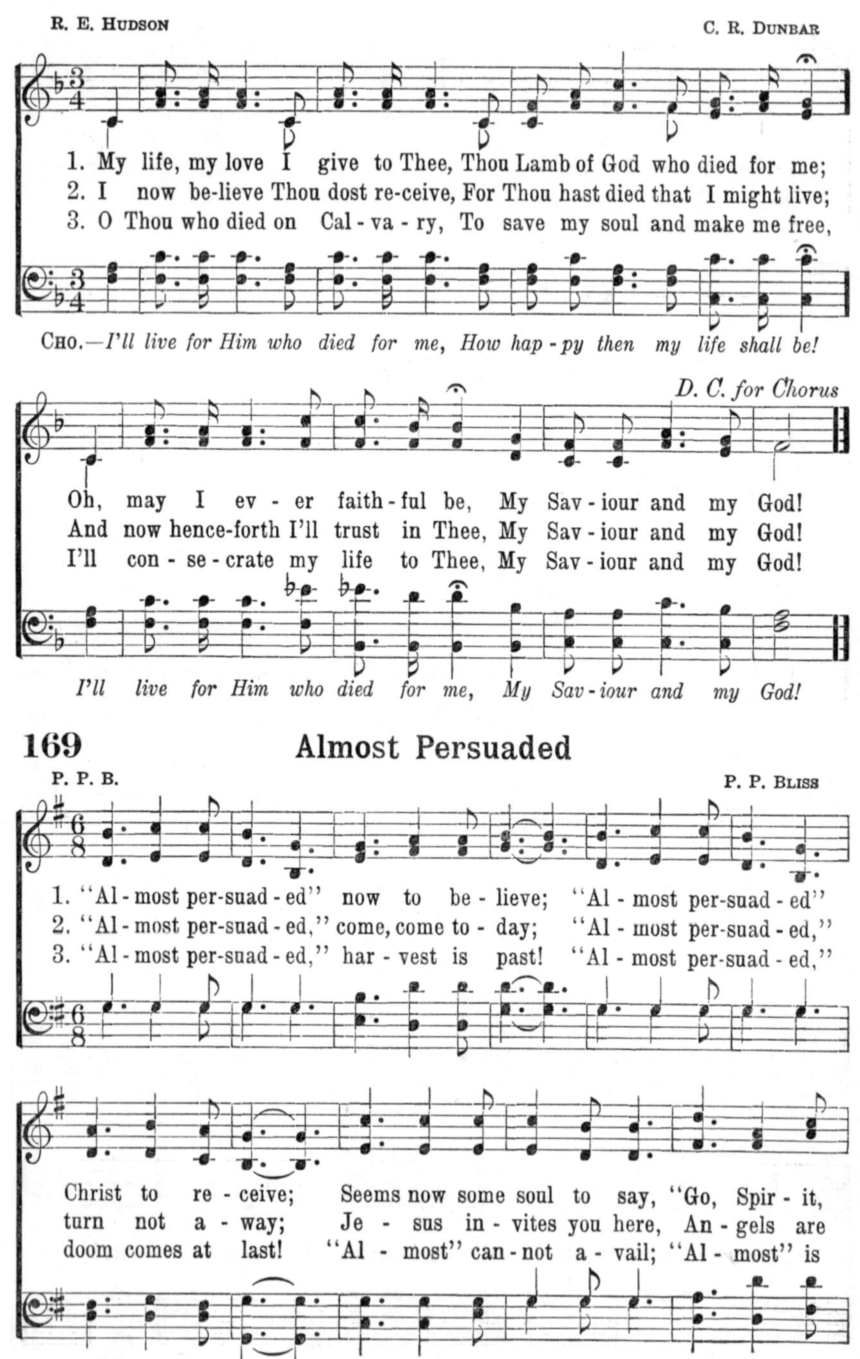
168
I'll Live For Him
R. E. Hudson
C. R. Dunbar
1. My life, my love I give to Thee, Thou Lamb of God who died for me;
2. I now be-lieve Thou dost re-ceive, For Thou hast died that I might live;
3. O Thou who died on Cal-va-ry, To save my soul and make me free,
Cho.—I'll live for Him who died for me, How hap-py then my life shall be!
D. C. for Chorus
Oh, may I ev-er faith-ful be, My Sav-iour and my God!
And now hence-forth I'll trust in Thee, My Sav-iour and my God!
I'll con-se-crate my life to Thee, My Sav-iour and my God!
I'll live for Him who died for me, My Sav-iour and my God!
169
Almost Persuaded
P. P. B.
P. P. Bliss
1. "Al-most per-suad-ed" now to be-lieve; "Al-most per-suad-ed" Christ to re-ceive; Seems now some soul to say, "Go, Spir-it,
2. "Al-most per-suad-ed," come, come to-day; "Al-most per-suad-ed," turn not a-way; Je-sus in-vites you here, An-gels are
3. "Al-most per-suad-ed," har-vest is past! "Al-most per-suad-ed," doom comes at last! "Al-most" can-not a-vail; "Al-most" is

Almost Persuaded

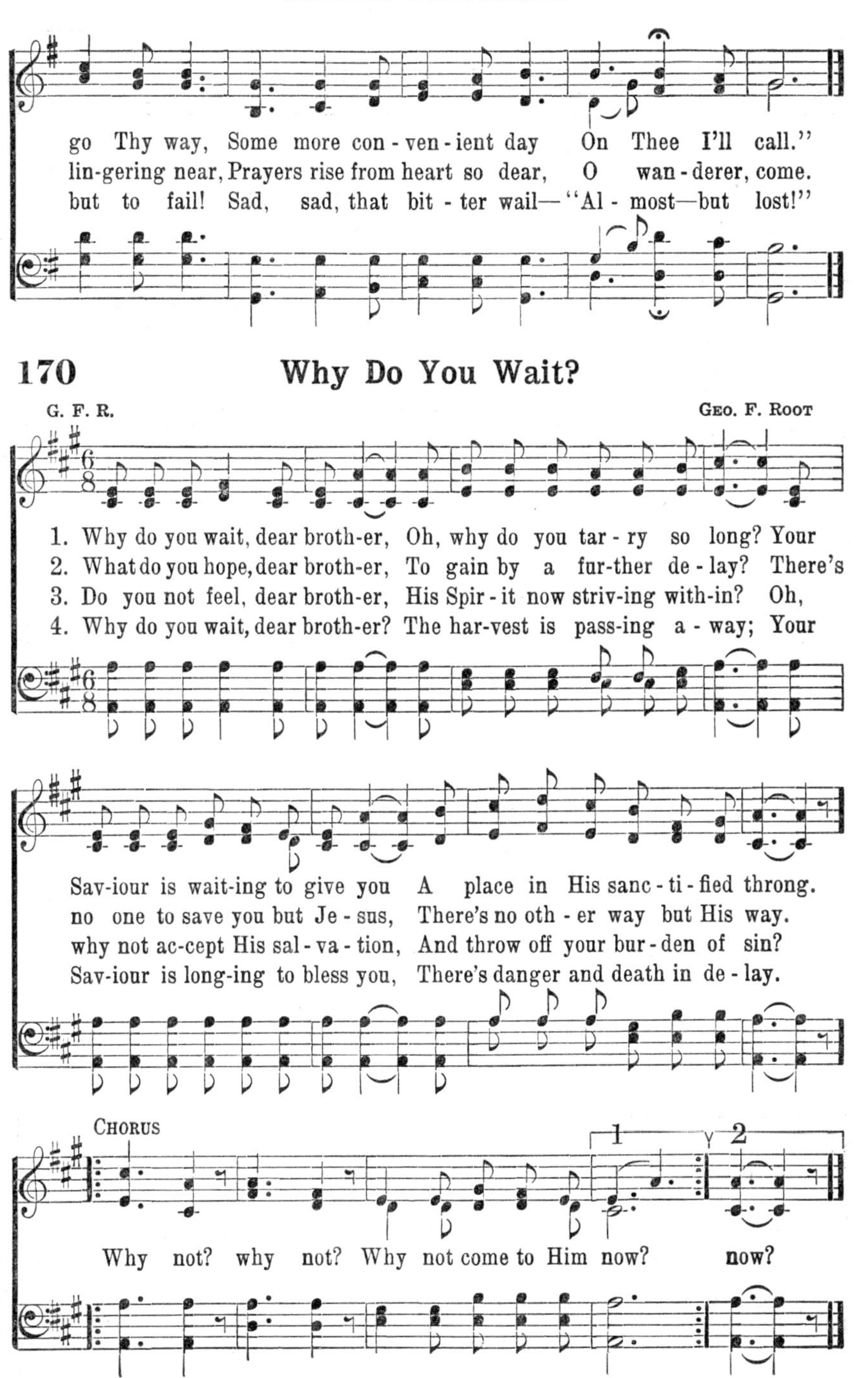
go Thy way, Some more con - ven - ient day On Thee I'll call."
lin-gering near, Prayers rise from heart so dear, O wan - derer, come.
but to fail! Sad, sad, that bit - ter wail— "Al - most—but lost!"
170 Why Do You Wait?
G. F. R.
Geo. F. Root
1. Why do you wait, dear broth-er, Oh, why do you tar - ry so long? Your
2. What do you hope, dear broth-er, To gain by a fur-ther de - lay? There's
3. Do you not feel, dear broth-er, His Spir - it now striv-ing with-in? Oh,
4. Why do you wait, dear broth-er? The har-vest is pass-ing a - way; Your
Sav-iour is wait-ing to give you A place in His sanc - ti - fied throng.
no one to save you but Je - sus, There's no oth - er way but His way.
why not ac-cept His sal - va - tion, And throw off your bur - den of sin?
Sav-iour is long-ing to bless you, There's danger and death in de - lay.
Chorus
Why not? why not? Why not come to Him now? now?

171 Rock of Ages
Augustus M. Toplady
TOPLADY
Thomas Hastings
1. Rock of A - ges, cleft for me, Let me hide my - self in Thee;
2. Could my tears for - ev - er flow, Could my zeal no lan - guor know,
3. While I draw this fleet - ing breath, When my eyes shall close in death,
Let the wa - ter and the blood, From Thy wound-ed side which flowed,
These for sin could not a - tone; Thou must save, and Thou a - lone:
When I rise to worlds un-known, And be - hold Thee on Thy throne,
Be of sin the dou - ble cure, Save from wrath and make me pure.
In my hand no price I bring, Sim - ply to Thy cross I cling.
Rock of A - ges, cleft for me, Let me hide my - self in Thee.
172 Jesus, Lover of My Soul
Charles Wesley
MARTYN
Simeon B. Marsh
Fine
1. Je - sus, Lov - er of my soul, Let me to Thy bos - om fly,
While the near - er wa - ters roll, While the tem-pest still is high!
D. C.—Safe in - to the ha - ven guide, O re-ceive my soul at last.
D. C.
Hide me, O my Sav - iour, hide, Till the storm of life is past;

173 Jesus, Lover of My Soul

CHARLES WESLEY
REFUGE
JOSEPH P. HOLBROOK
1. Je - sus, Lov - er of my soul, Let me to Thy bos - om fly,
2. Oth - er ref - uge have I none; Hangs my help - less soul on Thee;
3. Thou, O Christ, art all I want; More than all in Thee I find:
4. Plen-teous grace with Thee is found, Grace to cov - er all my sin;
While the near - er wa - ters roll, While the tem - pest still is high!
Leave, O leave me not a - lone, Still sup - port and com-fort me:
Raise the fall - en, cheer the faint, Heal the sick, and lead the blind.
Let the heal - ing streams a-bound; Make me, keep me pure with-in.
Hide me, O my Sav - iour, hide, Till the storm of life is past;
All my trust on Thee is stayed, All my help from Thee I bring;
Just and ho - ly is Thy name, I am all un - right-eous-ness;
Thou of life the foun - tain art, Free - ly let me take of Thee;
Safe in - to the ha - ven guide, O re - ceive my soul at last.
Cov - er my de - fense-less head With the shad - ow of Thy wing.
False, and full of sin I am, Thou art full of truth and grace.
Spring Thou up with - in my heart, Rise to all e - ter - ni - ty.

174 Take My Life, and Let It Be

F. R. HAVERGAL — YARBROUGH — WM. B. BRADBURY

1. Take my life, and let it be Con-se-crat-ed, Lord, to Thee;
2. Take my feet, and let them be Swift and beau-ti-ful for Thee;
3. Take my sil-ver and my gold, Not a mite would I with-hold;
4. Take my will, and make it Thine, It shall be no lon-ger mine;
CHO.—Lord, I give my life to Thee, Thine for-ev-er-more to be;
D. C.
Take my hands and let them move At the im-pulse of Thy love.
Take my voice, and let me sing, Al-ways, on-ly, for my King.
Take my mo-ments and my days, Let them flow in cease-less praise.
Take my heart, it is Thine own, It shall be Thy roy-al throne.
Lord, I give my life to Thee, Thine for-ev-er-more to be.

175 Welcome, Delightful Morn

HAYWARD — LISCHER — FRIEDRICH SCHNEIDER

1. Wel-come, de-light-ful morn, Thou day of sa-cred rest!
2. Now may the King de-scend, And fill His throne with grace;
3. De-scend, ce-les-tial Dove, With all Thy quick-ening powers;
I hail thy kind re-turn; Lord, make these mo-ments blest:
Thy scep-ter, Lord ex-tend, While saints ad-dress Thy face:
Dis-close a Sav-iour's love, And bless the sa-cred hours:

Welcome, Delightful Morn

From the low train of mor - tal toys, I soar to reach im-
Let sin - ners feel Thy quick-ening word, And learn to know and
Then shall my soul new life ob - tain, Nor Sab - baths be en-

mor - tal joys, I soar to reach im - mor - tal . . . joys.
fear the Lord, And learn to know and fear the . . . Lord.
joyed in vain, Nor Sab - baths be en - joyed in . . . vain.

(1) I soar to reach

176 Am I a Soldier of the Cross?

Isaac Watts — ARLINGTON — Thomas A. Arne

1. Am I a sol - dier of the cross, A fol-lower of the Lamb?
2. Must I be car - ried to the skies On flow - ery beds of ease,
3. Are there no foes for me to face? Must I not stem the flood?
4. Sure I must fight, if I would reign; In - crease my cour - age, Lord;

And shall I fear to own His cause, Or blush to speak His name?
While oth - ers fought to win the prize, And sailed thro' blood - y seas?
Is this vile world a friend to grace, To help me on to God?
I'll bear the toil, en - dure the pain, Sup - port - ed by Thy word.

177 Sun of My Soul

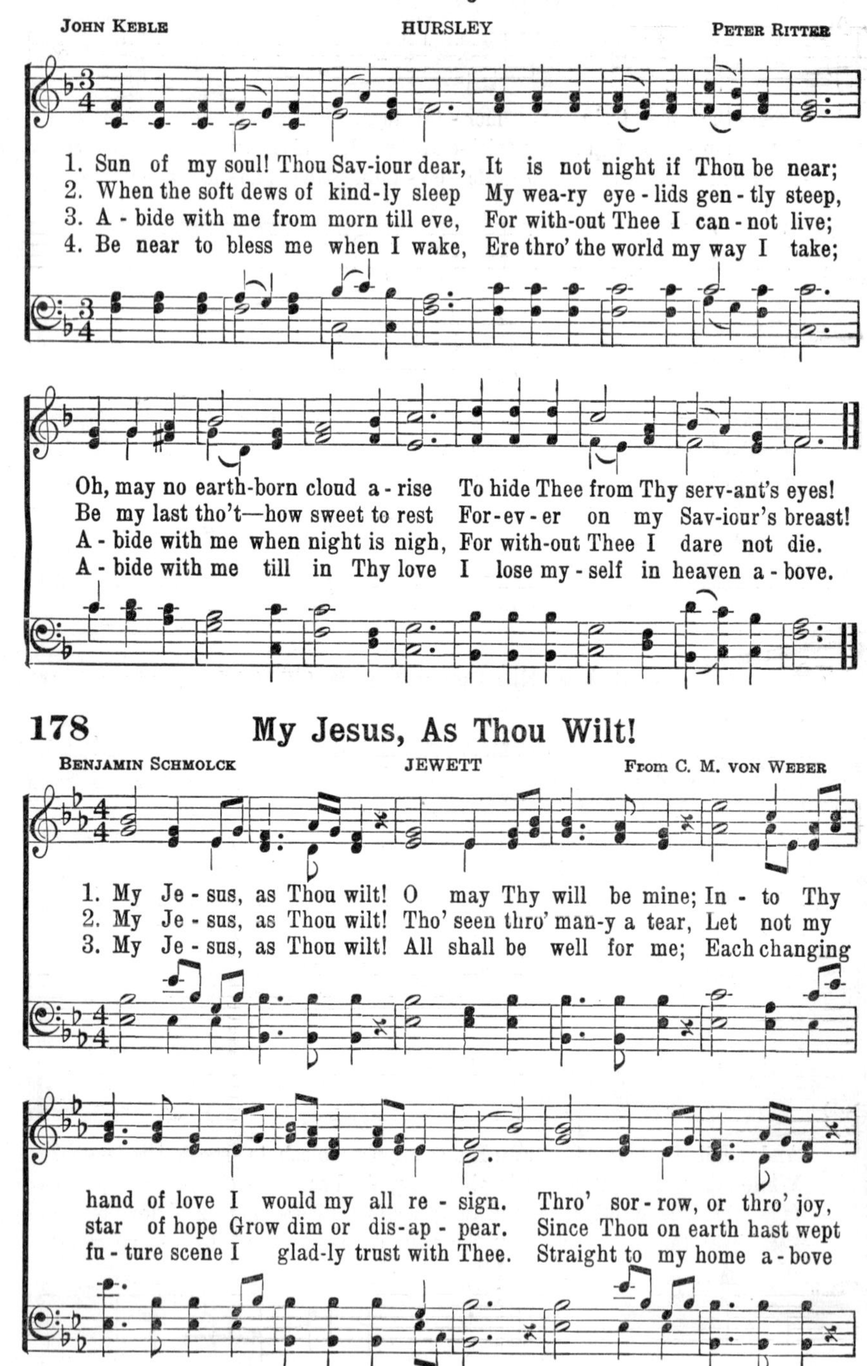
JOHN KEBLE
HURSLEY
PETER RITTER
1. Sun of my soul! Thou Sav-iour dear, It is not night if Thou be near;
2. When the soft dews of kind-ly sleep My wea-ry eye-lids gen-tly steep,
3. A-bide with me from morn till eve, For with-out Thee I can-not live;
4. Be near to bless me when I wake, Ere thro' the world my way I take;
Oh, may no earth-born cloud a-rise To hide Thee from Thy serv-ant's eyes!
Be my last tho't—how sweet to rest For-ev-er on my Sav-iour's breast!
A-bide with me when night is nigh, For with-out Thee I dare not die.
A-bide with me till in Thy love I lose my-self in heaven a-bove.
178 My Jesus, As Thou Wilt!
BENJAMIN SCHMOLCK
JEWETT
From C. M. VON WEBER
1. My Je-sus, as Thou wilt! O may Thy will be mine; In-to Thy
2. My Je-sus, as Thou wilt! Tho' seen thro' man-y a tear, Let not my
3. My Je-sus, as Thou wilt! All shall be well for me; Each changing
hand of love I would my all re-sign. Thro' sor-row, or thro' joy,
star of hope Grow dim or dis-ap-pear. Since Thou on earth hast wept
fu-ture scene I glad-ly trust with Thee. Straight to my home a-bove

My Jesus, As Thou Wilt!

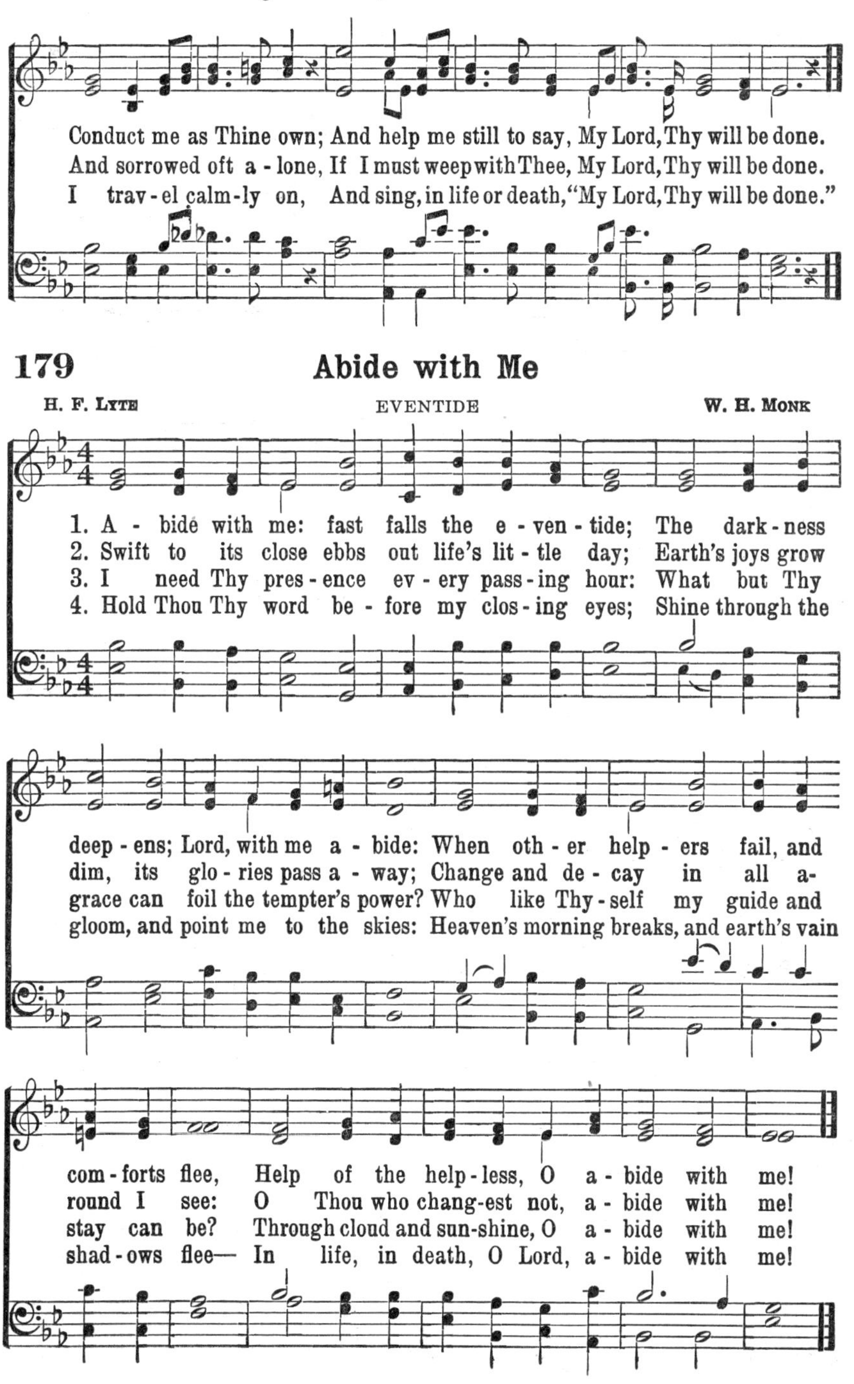
Conduct me as Thine own; And help me still to say, My Lord, Thy will be done.
And sorrowed oft a-lone, If I must weep with Thee, My Lord, Thy will be done.
I trav-el calm-ly on, And sing, in life or death, "My Lord, Thy will be done."
179
Abide with Me
H. F. Lyte
EVENTIDE
W. H. Monk
1. A-bide with me: fast falls the e-ven-tide; The dark-ness deep-ens; Lord, with me a-bide: When oth-er help-ers fail, and com-forts flee, Help of the help-less, O a-bide with me!
2. Swift to its close ebbs out life's lit-tle day; Earth's joys grow dim, its glo-ries pass a-way; Change and de-cay in all a-round I see: O Thou who chang-est not, a-bide with me!
3. I need Thy pres-ence ev-ery pass-ing hour: What but Thy grace can foil the tempter's power? Who like Thy-self my guide and stay can be? Through cloud and sun-shine, O a-bide with me!
4. Hold Thou Thy word be-fore my clos-ing eyes; Shine through the gloom, and point me to the skies: Heaven's morning breaks, and earth's vain shad-ows flee— In life, in death, O Lord, a-bide with me!

180 In the Cross of Christ

Sir John Bowring — RATHBUN — Ithamar Conkey

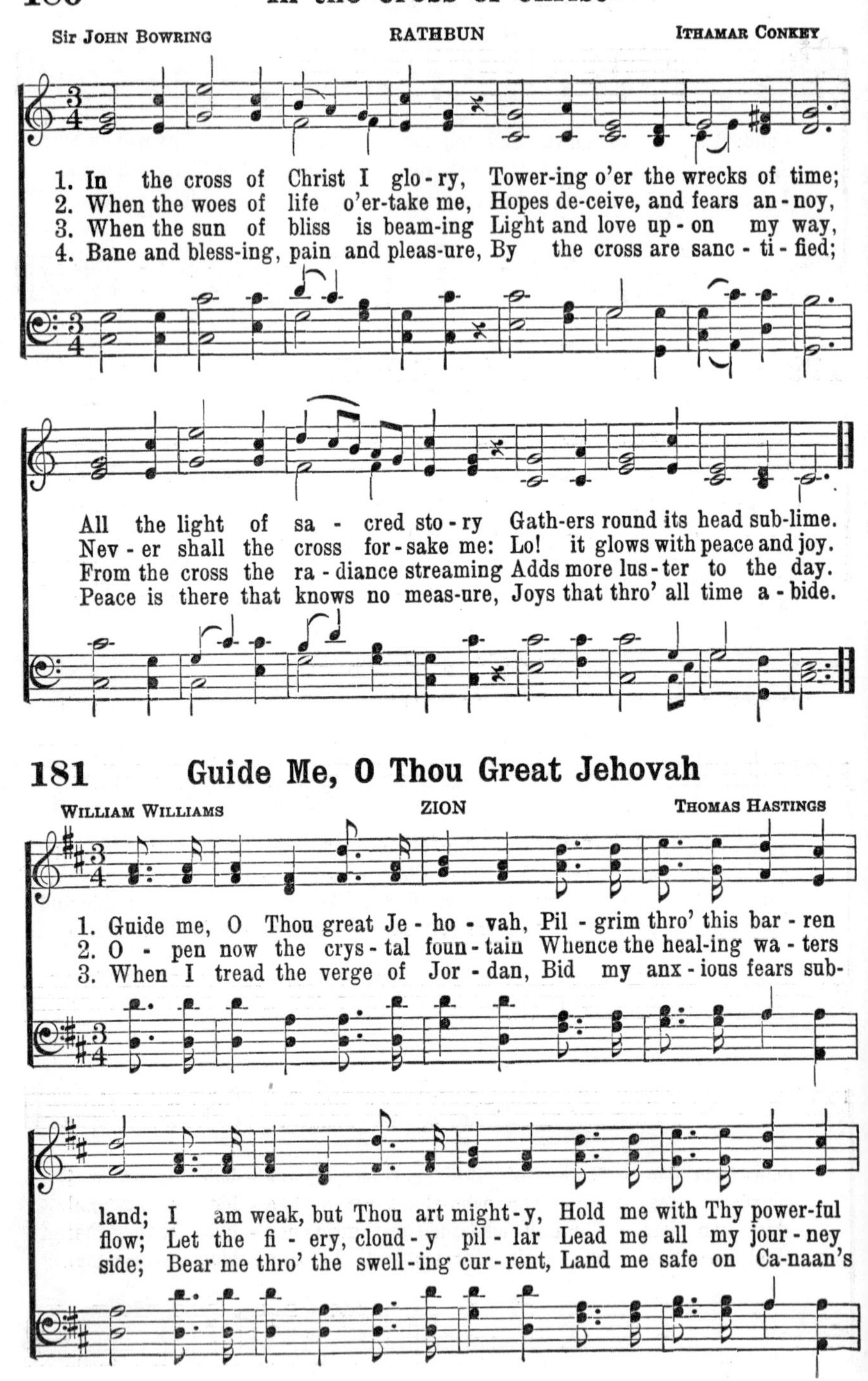

1. In the cross of Christ I glo-ry, Tower-ing o'er the wrecks of time;
2. When the woes of life o'er-take me, Hopes de-ceive, and fears an-noy,
3. When the sun of bliss is beam-ing Light and love up-on my way,
4. Bane and bless-ing, pain and pleas-ure, By the cross are sanc-ti-fied;
All the light of sa-cred sto-ry Gath-ers round its head sub-lime.
Nev-er shall the cross for-sake me: Lo! it glows with peace and joy.
From the cross the ra-diance streaming Adds more lus-ter to the day.
Peace is there that knows no meas-ure, Joys that thro' all time a-bide.
181 Guide Me, O Thou Great Jehovah
William Williams ZION Thomas Hastings
1. Guide me, O Thou great Je-ho-vah, Pil-grim thro' this bar-ren
2. O-pen now the crys-tal foun-tain Whence the heal-ing wa-ters
3. When I tread the verge of Jor-dan, Bid my anx-ious fears sub-
land; I am weak, but Thou art might-y, Hold me with Thy power-ful
flow; Let the fi-ery, cloud-y pil-lar Lead me all my jour-ney
side; Bear me thro' the swell-ing cur-rent, Land me safe on Ca-naan's

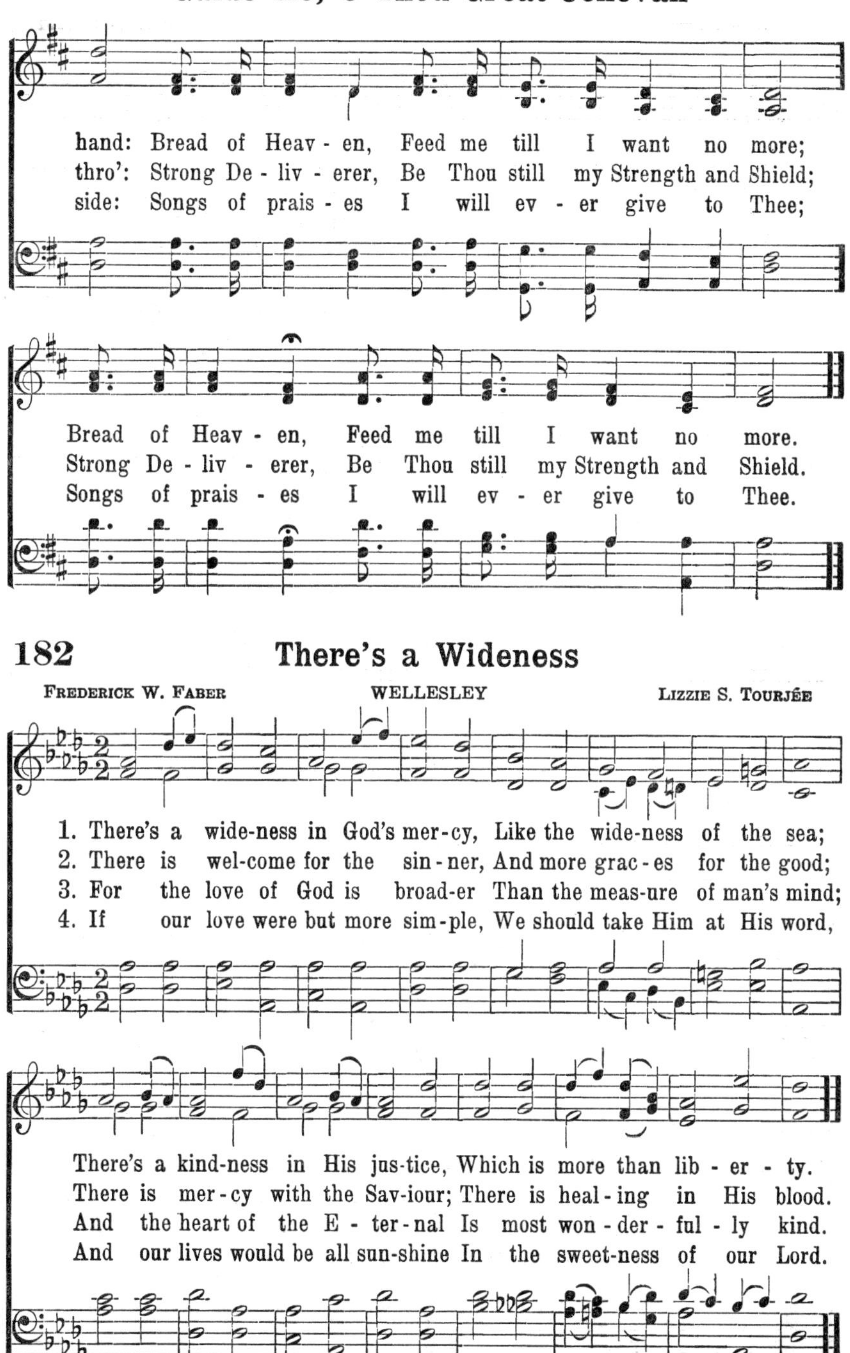
Guide Me, O Thou Great Jehovah
hand: Bread of Heav - en, Feed me till I want no more;
thro': Strong De - liv - erer, Be Thou still my Strength and Shield;
side: Songs of prais - es I will ev - er give to Thee;
Bread of Heav - en, Feed me till I want no more.
Strong De - liv - erer, Be Thou still my Strength and Shield.
Songs of prais - es I will ev - er give to Thee.
182
There's a Wideness
FREDERICK W. FABER
WELLESLEY
LIZZIE S. TOURJÉE
1. There's a wide-ness in God's mer-cy, Like the wide-ness of the sea;
2. There is wel-come for the sin - ner, And more grac - es for the good;
3. For the love of God is broad-er Than the meas-ure of man's mind;
4. If our love were but more sim-ple, We should take Him at His word,
There's a kind-ness in His jus-tice, Which is more than lib - er - ty.
There is mer - cy with the Sav-iour; There is heal - ing in His blood.
And the heart of the E - ter - nal Is most won - der - ful - ly kind.
And our lives would be all sun-shine In the sweet-ness of our Lord.

183 One Sweetly Solemn Thought

PHŒBE CARY
PHILIP PHILLIPS
1. One sweet-ly sol-emn thought Comes to me o'er and o'er; I'm near-er
2. Near-er my Fa-ther's house, Where man-y man-sions be; Near-er the
3. Near-er the bound of life, Where I lay my bur-dens down; Near-er to
4. Be near me when my feet Are slip-ping o'er the brink; For I am
CHORUS
home to-day, to-day, Than I have been be-fore:
great white throne today, Near-er the crys-tal sea:
leave the cross to-day, And near-er to the crown.
near-er home to-day, Per-haps, than now I think.
Near-er my home,
Near-er my home, Near-er my home to-day, to-day, Than I have been be-fore.
184 Take My Life, and Let It Be
FRANCES R. HAVERGAL
HENDON
C. H. A. MALAN
1. Take my life, and let it be Con-se-cra-ted, Lord, to Thee; Take my hands, and
2. Take my feet, and let them be Swift and beau-ti-ful for Thee; Take my voice, and
3. Take my sil-ver and my gold, Not a mite would I with-hold; Take my mo-ments
4. Take my will, and make it Thine, It shall be no lon-ger mine; Take my heart, it

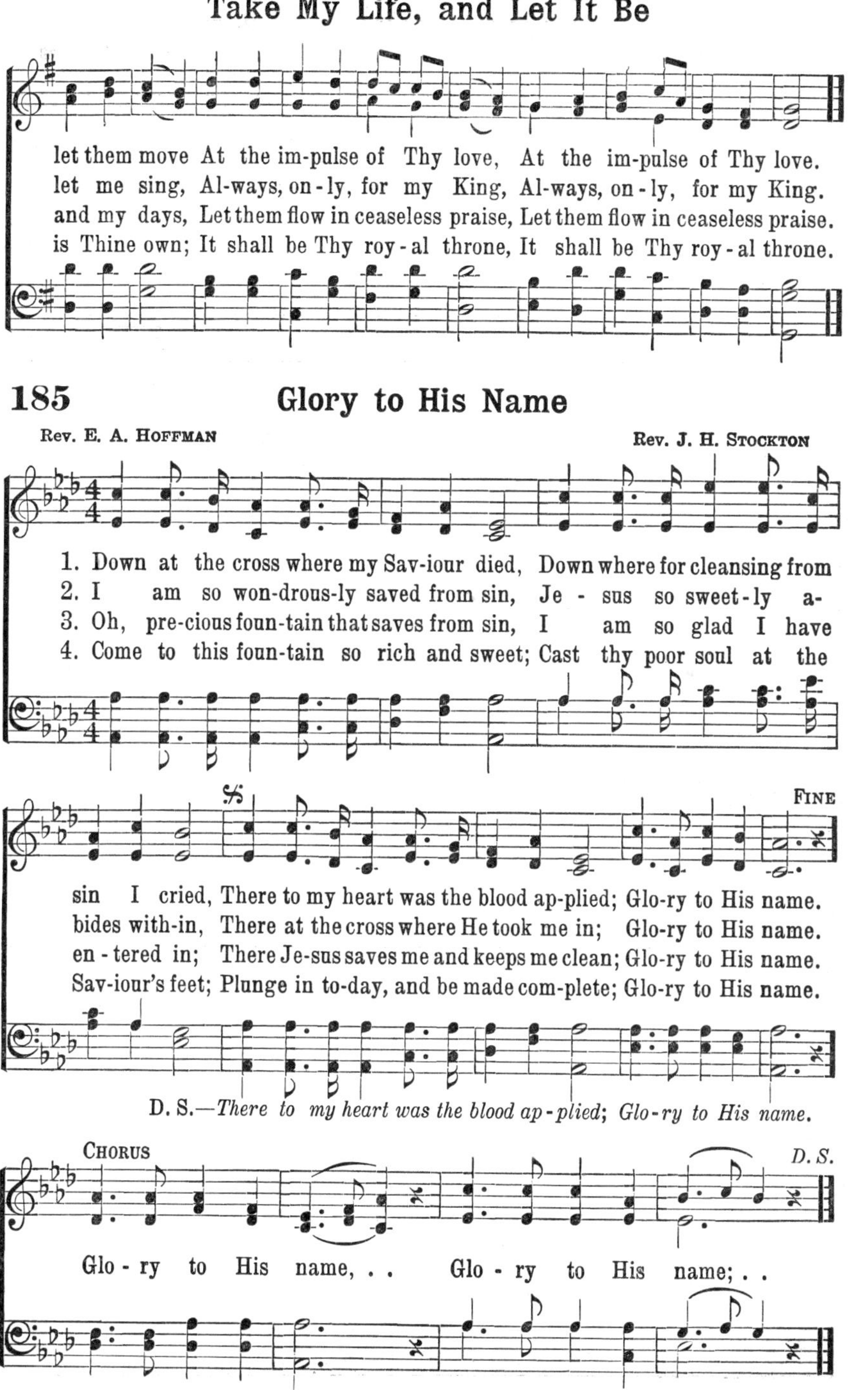
Take My Life, and Let It Be
let them move At the im-pulse of Thy love, At the im-pulse of Thy love.
let me sing, Al-ways, on-ly, for my King, Al-ways, on-ly, for my King.
and my days, Let them flow in ceaseless praise, Let them flow in ceaseless praise.
is Thine own; It shall be Thy roy-al throne, It shall be Thy roy-al throne.
185
Glory to His Name
Rev. E. A. HOFFMAN
Rev. J. H. STOCKTON
1. Down at the cross where my Sav-iour died, Down where for cleansing from sin I cried, There to my heart was the blood ap-plied; Glo-ry to His name.
2. I am so won-drous-ly saved from sin, Je - sus so sweet-ly a-bides with-in, There at the cross where He took me in; Glo-ry to His name.
3. Oh, pre-cious foun-tain that saves from sin, I am so glad I have en-tered in; There Je-sus saves me and keeps me clean; Glo-ry to His name.
4. Come to this foun-tain so rich and sweet; Cast thy poor soul at the Sav-iour's feet; Plunge in to-day, and be made com-plete; Glo-ry to His name.
FINE
D. S.—There to my heart was the blood ap-plied; Glo-ry to His name.
CHORUS
Glo-ry to His name, . . Glo-ry to His name; . .
D. S.

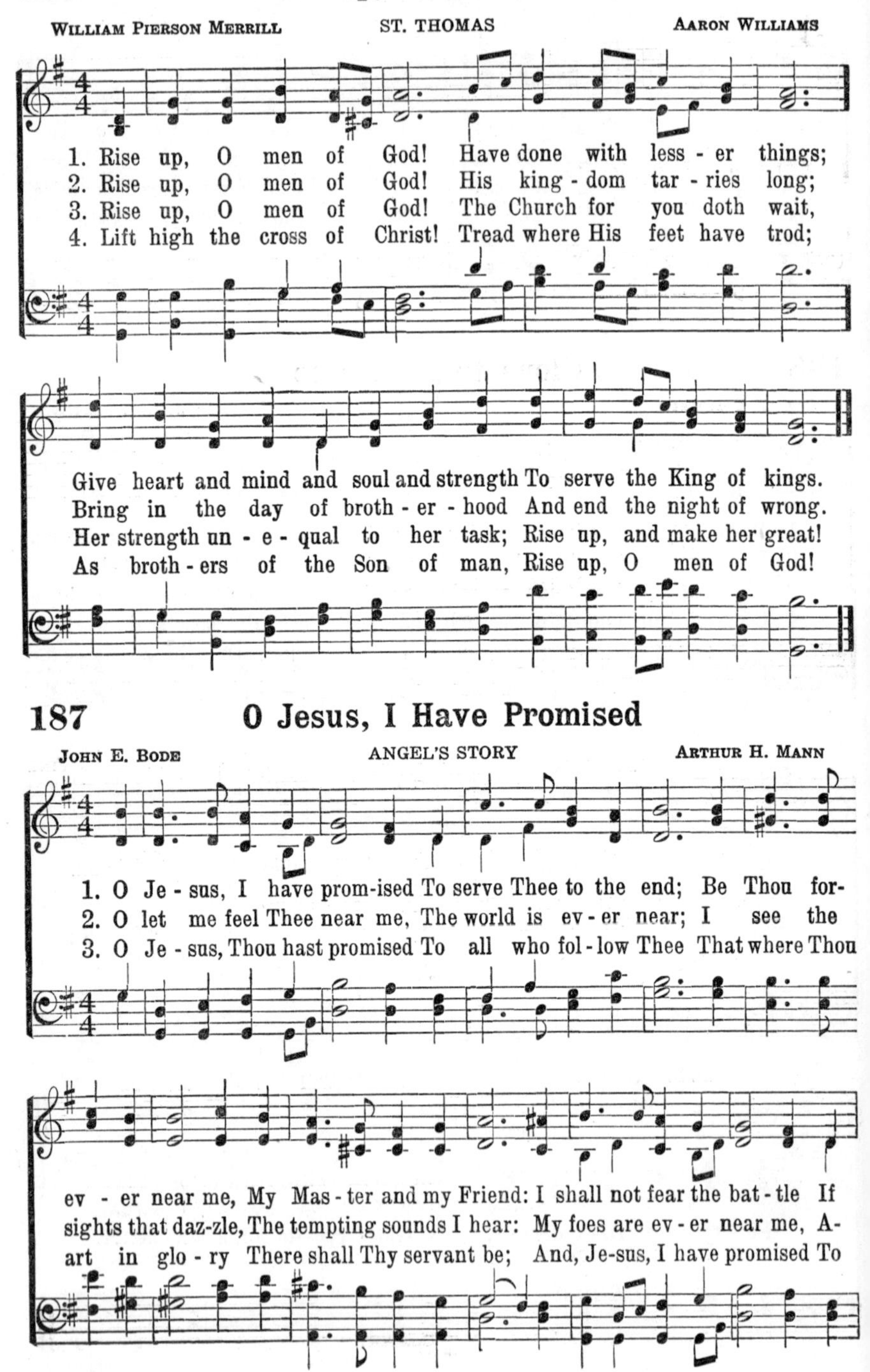
186
Rise Up, O Men of God
William Pierson Merrill
ST. THOMAS
Aaron Williams
1. Rise up, O men of God! Have done with less - er things;
2. Rise up, O men of God! His king - dom tar - ries long;
3. Rise up, O men of God! The Church for you doth wait,
4. Lift high the cross of Christ! Tread where His feet have trod;
Give heart and mind and soul and strength To serve the King of kings.
Bring in the day of broth - er - hood And end the night of wrong.
Her strength un - e - qual to her task; Rise up, and make her great!
As broth - ers of the Son of man, Rise up, O men of God!
187
O Jesus, I Have Promised
John E. Bode
ANGEL'S STORY
Arthur H. Mann
1. O Je - sus, I have prom-ised To serve Thee to the end; Be Thou for-
2. O let me feel Thee near me, The world is ev - er near; I see the
3. O Je - sus, Thou hast promised To all who fol - low Thee That where Thou
ev - er near me, My Mas - ter and my Friend: I shall not fear the bat - tle If
sights that daz-zle, The tempting sounds I hear: My foes are ev - er near me, A-
art in glo - ry There shall Thy servant be; And, Je-sus, I have promised To

O Jesus, I Have Promised
Thou art by my side, Nor wan-der from the path-way If Thou wilt be my Guide.
round me and with-in; But, Je-sus, draw Thou near-er, And shield my soul from sin.
serve Thee to the end; O give me grace to fol-low My Mas-ter and my Friend.
188 Majestic Sweetness Sits Enthroned
Samuel Stennett
ORTONVILLE
Thomas Hastings
1. Ma-jes-tic sweet-ness sits en-throned Up-on the Sav-iour's brow; His head with ra-diant glo-ries crowned, His lips with grace o'er-flow, His lips with grace o'er-flow.
2. No mor-tal can with Him com-pare, A-mong the sons of men; Fair-er is He than all the fair Who fill the heaven-ly train, Who fill the heaven-ly train.
3. He saw me plunged in deep dis-tress, And flew to my re-lief; For me He bore the shame-ful cross, And car-ried all my grief, And car-ried all my grief.
4. To Him I owe my life and breath, And all the joys I have; He makes me tri-umph o-ver death, And saves me from the grave, And saves me from the grave.

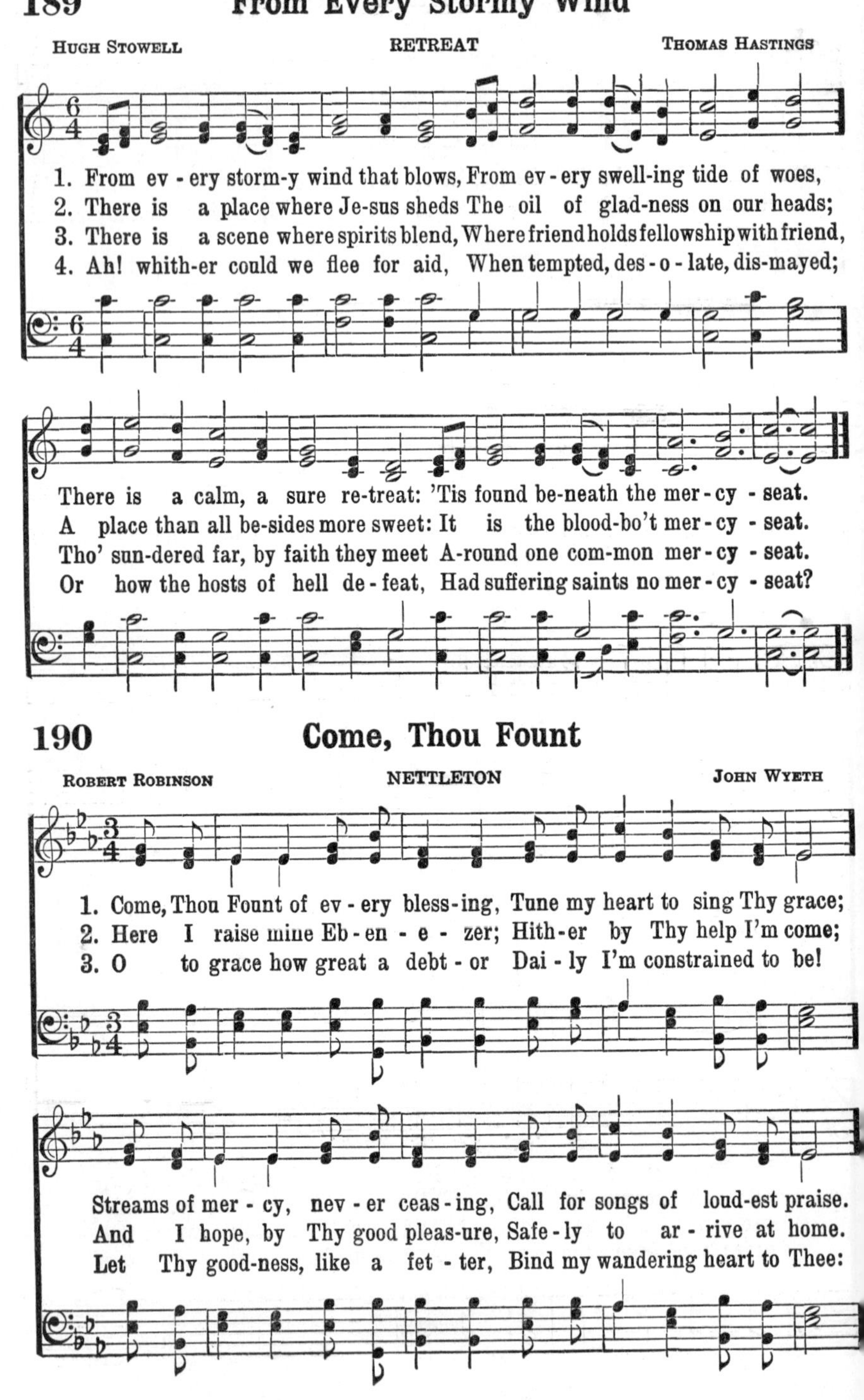
189
From Every Stormy Wind
Hugh Stowell
RETREAT
Thomas Hastings
1. From ev - ery storm-y wind that blows, From ev - ery swell-ing tide of woes,
2. There is a place where Je-sus sheds The oil of glad-ness on our heads;
3. There is a scene where spirits blend, Where friend holds fellowship with friend,
4. Ah! whith-er could we flee for aid, When tempted, des - o - late, dis-mayed;
There is a calm, a sure re-treat: 'Tis found be-neath the mer - cy - seat.
A place than all be-sides more sweet: It is the blood-bo't mer - cy - seat.
Tho' sun-dered far, by faith they meet A-round one com-mon mer - cy - seat.
Or how the hosts of hell de - feat, Had suffering saints no mer - cy - seat?
190
Come, Thou Fount
Robert Robinson
NETTLETON
John Wyeth
1. Come, Thou Fount of ev - ery bless-ing, Tune my heart to sing Thy grace;
2. Here I raise mine Eb - en - e - zer; Hith-er by Thy help I'm come;
3. O to grace how great a debt - or Dai - ly I'm constrained to be!
Streams of mer - cy, nev - er ceas - ing, Call for songs of loud-est praise.
And I hope, by Thy good pleas-ure, Safe - ly to ar - rive at home.
Let Thy good-ness, like a fet - ter, Bind my wandering heart to Thee:

Come, Thou Fount

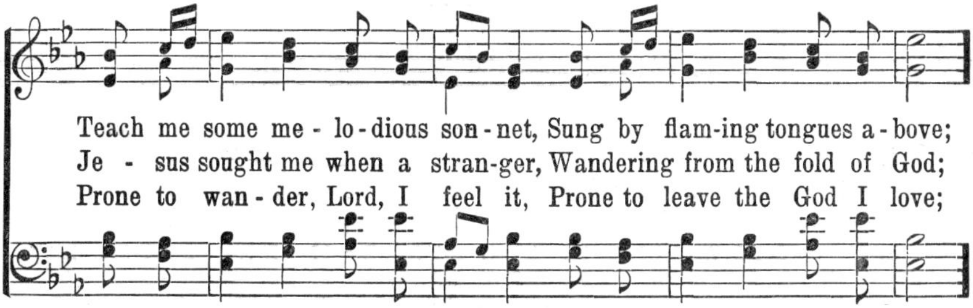

Teach me some me - lo - dious son - net, Sung by flam-ing tongues a - bove;
Je - sus sought me when a stran-ger, Wandering from the fold of God;
Prone to wan - der, Lord, I feel it, Prone to leave the God I love;

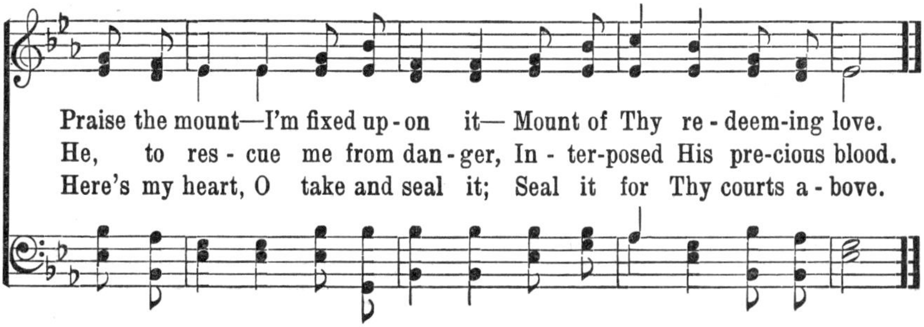

Praise the mount—I'm fixed up - on it— Mount of Thy re - deem-ing love.
He, to res - cue me from dan - ger, In - ter-posed His pre-cious blood.
Here's my heart, O take and seal it; Seal it for Thy courts a - bove.

191 When I Survey the Wondrous Cross

ISAAC WATTS HAMBURG Arr. by LOWELL MASON

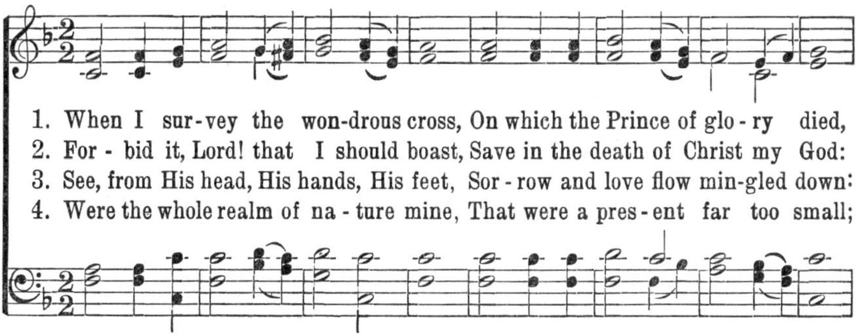

1. When I sur-vey the won-drous cross, On which the Prince of glo - ry died,
2. For - bid it, Lord! that I should boast, Save in the death of Christ my God:
3. See, from His head, His hands, His feet, Sor - row and love flow min-gled down:
4. Were the whole realm of na - ture mine, That were a pres - ent far too small;

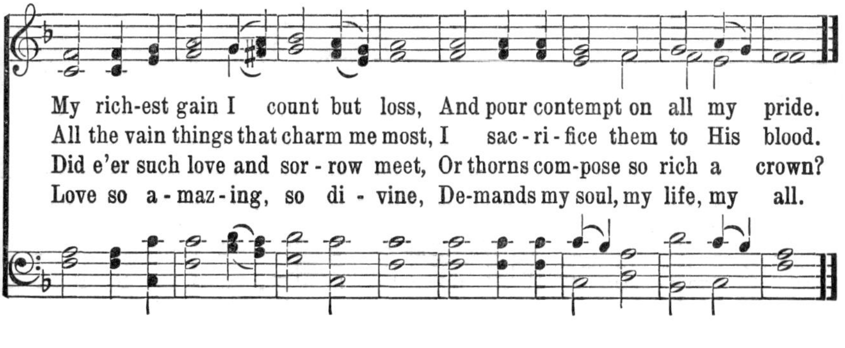

My rich-est gain I count but loss, And pour contempt on all my pride.
All the vain things that charm me most, I sac - ri - fice them to His blood.
Did e'er such love and sor - row meet, Or thorns com-pose so rich a crown?
Love so a - maz - ing, so di - vine, De-mands my soul, my life, my all.

192 Break Thou the Bread of Life

MARY ANN LATHBURY — BREAD OF LIFE — WILLIAM F. SHERWIN

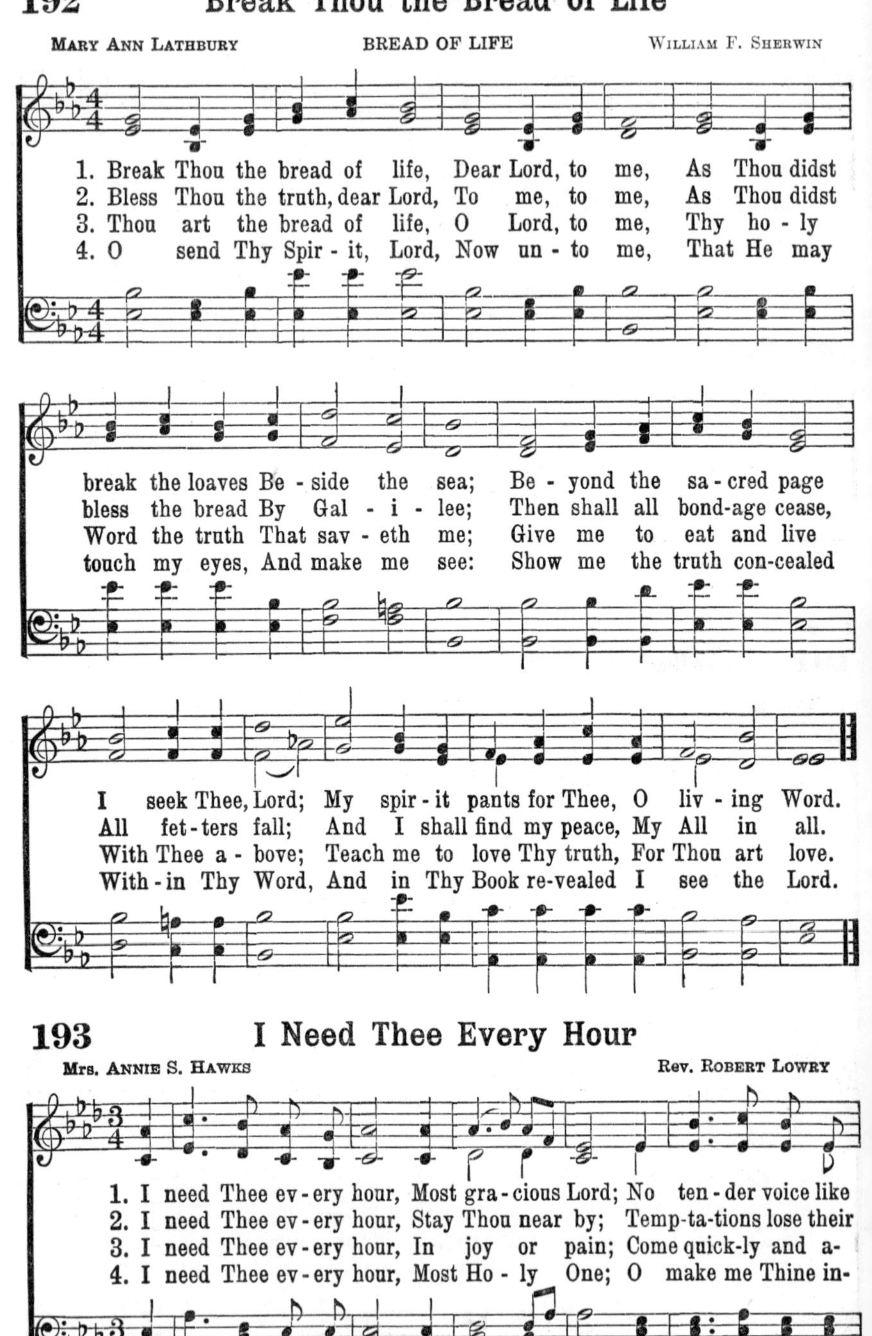
1. Break Thou the bread of life, Dear Lord, to me, As Thou didst break the loaves Be - side the sea; Be - yond the sa - cred page I seek Thee, Lord; My spir - it pants for Thee, O liv - ing Word.
2. Bless Thou the truth, dear Lord, To me, to me, As Thou didst bless the bread By Gal - i - lee; Then shall all bond-age cease, All fet - ters fall; And I shall find my peace, My All in all.
3. Thou art the bread of life, O Lord, to me, Thy ho - ly Word the truth That sav - eth me; Give me to eat and live With Thee a - bove; Teach me to love Thy truth, For Thou art love.
4. O send Thy Spir - it, Lord, Now un - to me, That He may touch my eyes, And make me see: Show me the truth con-cealed With - in Thy Word, And in Thy Book re-vealed I see the Lord.

193 I Need Thee Every Hour

MRS. ANNIE S. HAWKS — REV. ROBERT LOWRY

1. I need Thee ev - ery hour, Most gra - cious Lord; No ten - der voice like
2. I need Thee ev - ery hour, Stay Thou near by; Temp-ta-tions lose their
3. I need Thee ev - ery hour, In joy or pain; Come quick-ly and a-
4. I need Thee ev - ery hour, Most Ho - ly One; O make me Thine in-

I Need Thee Every Hour

CHORUS
Thine Can peace af - ford.
power When Thou art nigh. I need Thee, O, I need Thee; Ev - ery hour I
bide, Or life is vain.
deed, Thou bless - ed Son.
need Thee! O bless me now, my Sav - iour, I come to Thee!
194 Now the Day Is Over
SABINE BARING-GOULD
BARNBY
JOSEPH BARNBY
1. Now the day is o - ver, Night is draw - ing nigh,
2. Je - sus, give the wea - ry Calm and sweet re - pose;
3. Grant to lit - tle chil - dren Vi - sions bright of Thee;
4. Through the long night-watch-es May Thine an - gels spread
5. When the morn - ing wak - ens, Then may I a - rise
Shad - ows of the eve - ning Steal a - cross the sky.
With Thy ten - derest bless - ing May our eye - lids close.
Guard the sail - ors toss - ing On the deep blue sea.
Their white wings a - bove me, Watch-ing round my bed.
Pure, and fresh, and sin - less In Thy ho - ly eyes.
(1) eve - ning Steal a - cross the sky.

195 Blessed Saviour, Thee I Love

Rev. George Duffield — SPANISH HYMN — Arr. by Benjamin Carr

1. Bless-ed Sav-iour, Thee I love, All my oth-er joys a-bove;
2. Once a-gain be-side the cross, All my gain I count but loss;
3. Bless-ed Sav-iour, Thine am I, Thine to live, and Thine to die;

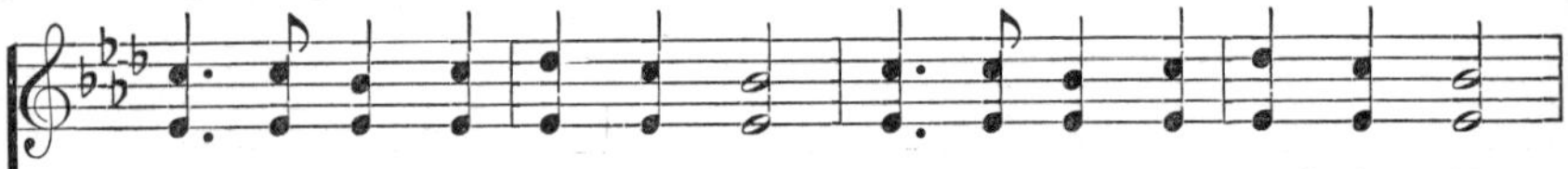

All my hopes in Thee a-bide, Thou my hope, and naught be-side;
Earth-ly pleas-ures fade a-way,—Clouds they are that hide my day;
Height or depth, or crea-ture power, Ne'er shall hide my Sav-iour more;

Ev-er let my glo-ry be, On-ly, on-ly, on-ly Thee.
Hence, vain shad-ows! let me see Je-sus, cru-ci-fied for me.
Ev-er shall my glo-ry be, On-ly, on-ly, on-ly Thee.

196 I Love Thy Kingdom, Lord

Timothy Dwight — ST. THOMAS — Aaron Williams, Coll.

1. I love Thy king-dom, Lord, The house of Thine a-bode,
2. I love Thy Church, O God! Her walls be-fore Thee stand,
3. For her my tears shall fall; For her my prayers as-cend;
4. Be-yond my high-est joy I prize her heaven-ly ways,
5. Sure as Thy truth shall last, To Zi-on shall be given

I Love Thy Kingdom, Lord

The Church our blest Re-deem-er saved With His own pre-cious blood.
Dear as the ap-ple of Thine eye, And grav-en on Thy hand.
To her my cares and toils be given, Till toils and cares shall end.
Her sweet com-mun-ion, sol-emn vows, Her hymns of love and praise.
The bright-est glo-ries earth can yield, And bright-er bliss of heaven.

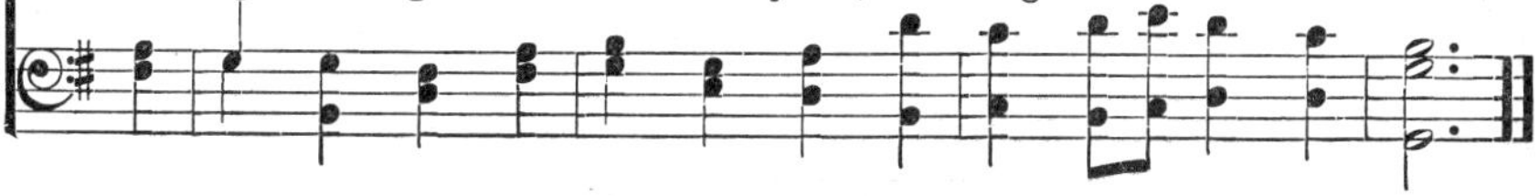

197 Only Trust Him

J. H. S. J. H. STOCKTON

1. Come, ev-ery soul by sin op-pressed, There's mer-cy with the Lord,
2. For Je-sus shed His pre-cious blood, Rich bless-ings to be-stow;
3. Yes, Je-sus is the Truth, the Way, That leads you in-to rest;
4. Come, then, and join this ho-ly band, And on to glo-ry go,

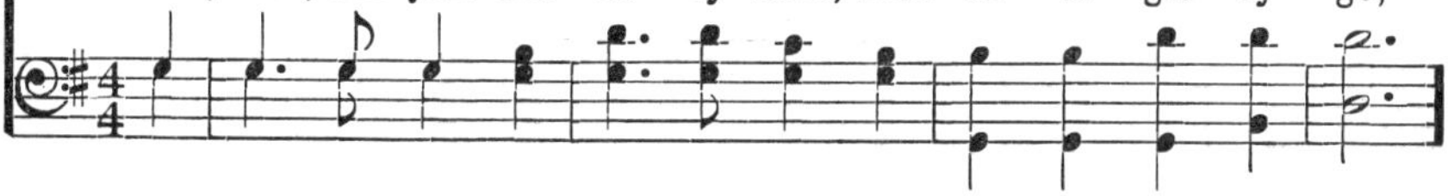

And He will sure-ly give you rest By trust-ing in His word.
Plunge now in-to the crim-son flood That wash-es white as snow.
Be-lieve in Him with-out de-lay, And you are ful-ly blest.
To dwell in that ce-les-tial land, Where joys im-mor-tal flow.

CHORUS.

1 2

{On-ly trust Him, on-ly trust Him, On-ly trust Him now;}
{He will save you, He will save you, He will (*Omit. . . .*)} save you now.

198 Brethren, We Have Met to Worship

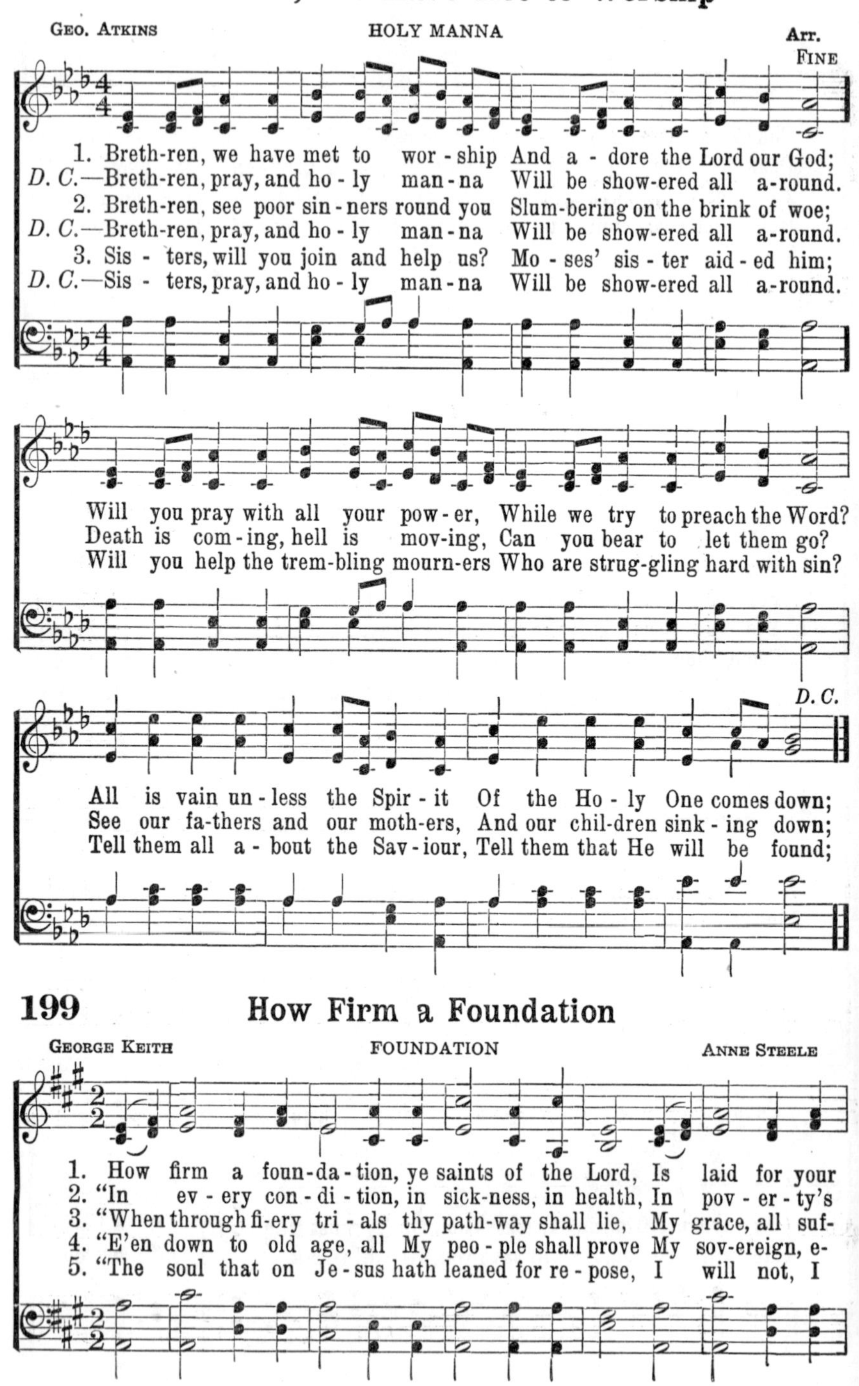
GEO. ATKINS
HOLY MANNA
ARR.
FINE
1. Breth-ren, we have met to wor - ship And a - dore the Lord our God;
D. C.—Breth-ren, pray, and ho - ly man - na Will be show-ered all a-round.
2. Breth-ren, see poor sin - ners round you Slum-bering on the brink of woe;
D. C.—Breth-ren, pray, and ho - ly man - na Will be show-ered all a-round.
3. Sis - ters, will you join and help us? Mo - ses' sis - ter aid - ed him;
D. C.—Sis - ters, pray, and ho - ly man - na Will be show-ered all a-round.
Will you pray with all your pow - er, While we try to preach the Word?
Death is com - ing, hell is mov-ing, Can you bear to let them go?
Will you help the trem-bling mourn-ers Who are strug-gling hard with sin?
D. C.
All is vain un - less the Spir - it Of the Ho - ly One comes down;
See our fa-thers and our moth-ers, And our chil-dren sink - ing down;
Tell them all a - bout the Sav - iour, Tell them that He will be found;
199 How Firm a Foundation
GEORGE KEITH
FOUNDATION
ANNE STEELE
1. How firm a foun-da - tion, ye saints of the Lord, Is laid for your
2. "In ev - ery con - di - tion, in sick-ness, in health, In pov - er - ty's
3. "When through fi-ery tri - als thy path-way shall lie, My grace, all suf-
4. "E'en down to old age, all My peo - ple shall prove My sov-ereign, e-
5. "The soul that on Je - sus hath leaned for re - pose, I will not, I

How Firm a Foundation

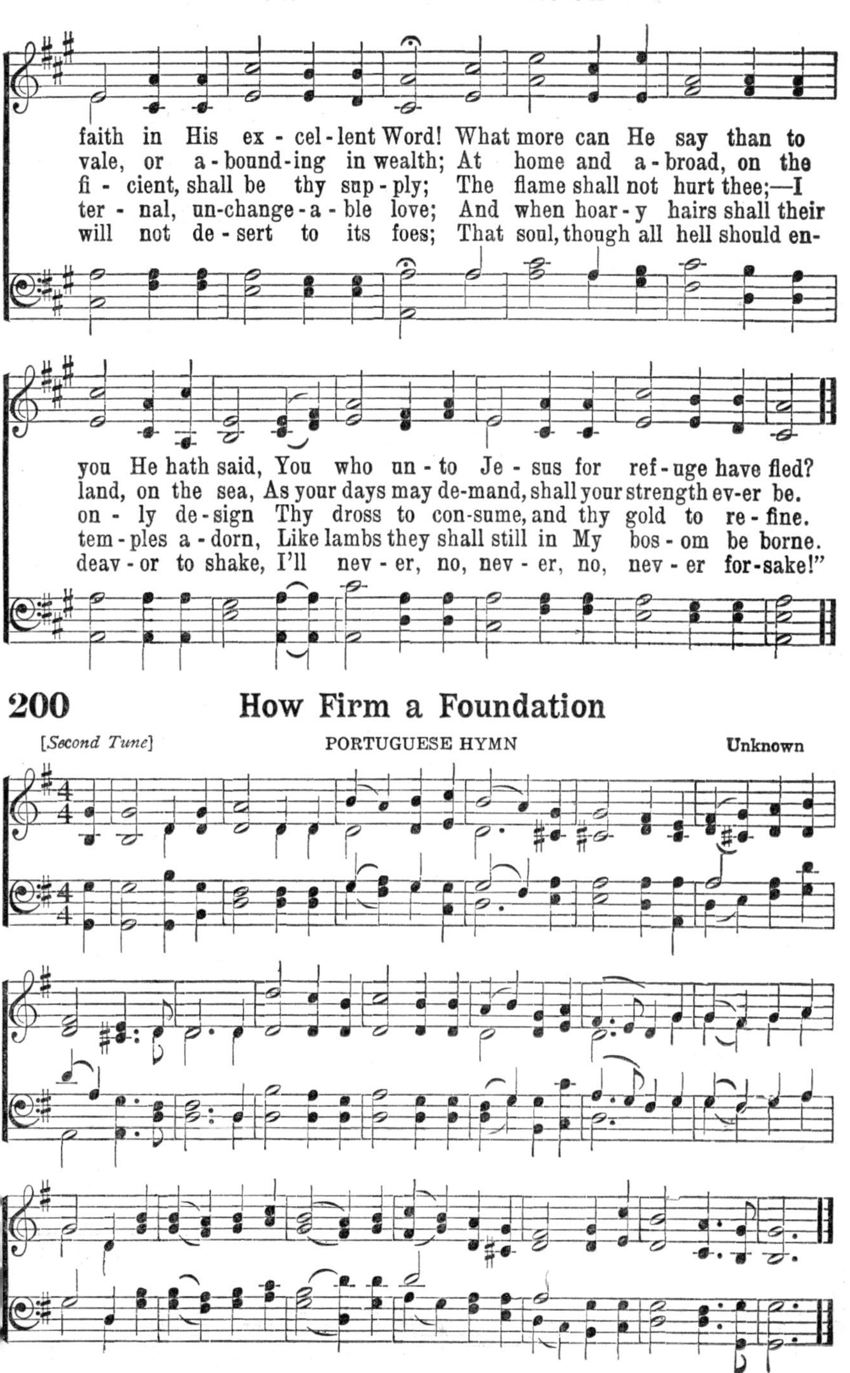
faith in His ex - cel - lent Word! What more can He say than to
vale, or a - bound - ing in wealth; At home and a - broad, on the
fi - cient, shall be thy sup - ply; The flame shall not hurt thee;—I
ter - nal, un-change - a - ble love; And when hoar - y hairs shall their
will not de - sert to its foes; That soul, though all hell should en-
you He hath said, You who un - to Je - sus for ref - uge have fled?
land, on the sea, As your days may de-mand, shall your strength ev - er be.
on - ly de - sign Thy dross to con - sume, and thy gold to re - fine.
tem - ples a - dorn, Like lambs they shall still in My bos - om be borne.
deav - or to shake, I'll nev - er, no, nev - er, no, nev - er for - sake!"
200 How Firm a Foundation
[Second Tune]
PORTUGUESE HYMN
Unknown

201 Faith of Our Fathers

FREDERICK W. FABER — ST. CATHERINE — H. F. HEMY

1. Faith of our fa-thers! liv-ing still In spite of dun-geon, fire, and sword:
O how our hearts beat high with joy When-e'er we hear that glo-rious word!
Faith of our fa-thers! ho-ly faith! We will be true to thee till death!

2. Our fa-thers, chained in pris-ons dark, Were still in heart and conscience free:
How sweet would be their children's fate, If they, like them, could die for thee!
Faith of our fa-thers! ho-ly faith! We will be true to thee till death!

3. Faith of our fa-thers! we will love Both friend and foe in all our strife:
And preach thee, too, as love knows how, By kind-ly words and vir-tuous life:
Faith of our fa-thers! ho-ly faith! We will be true to thee till death!

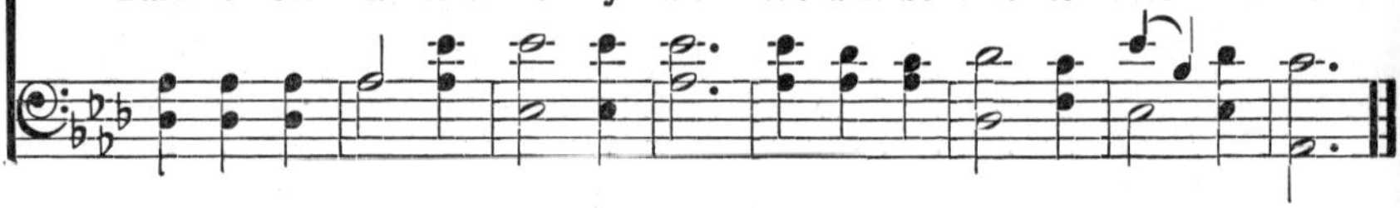

202 O Master, Let Me Walk with Thee

W. GLADDEN — MARYTON — H. P. SMITH

1. O Mas-ter, let me walk with Thee In low-ly paths of serv-ice free;
2. Help me the slow of heart to move By some clear, winning word of love;
3. Teach me Thy patience! still with Thee In clos-er, dear-er com-pa-ny,
4. In hope that sends a shin-ing ray Far down the fu-ture's broadening way,

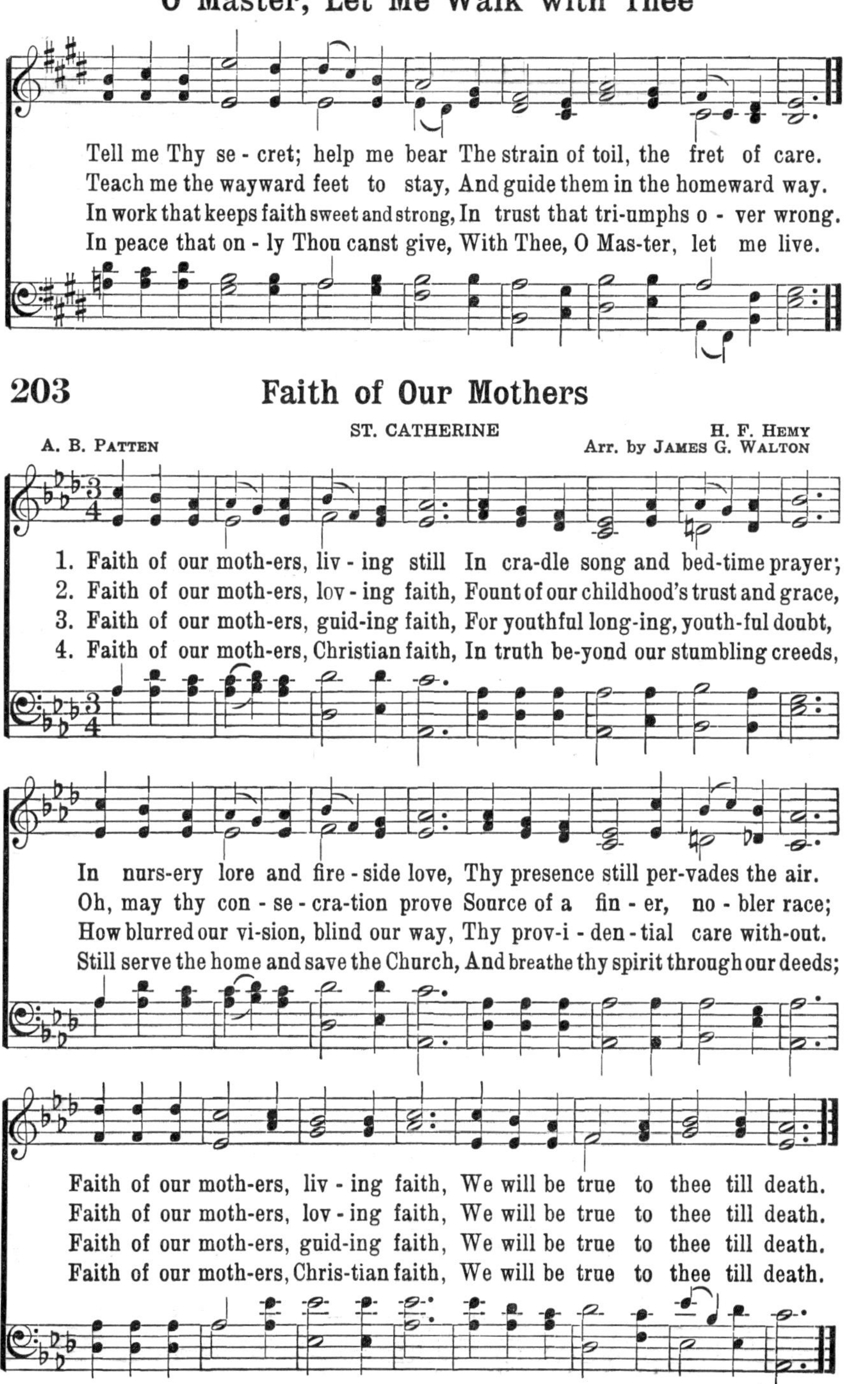
O Master, Let Me Walk with Thee
Tell me Thy se - cret; help me bear The strain of toil, the fret of care.
Teach me the wayward feet to stay, And guide them in the homeward way.
In work that keeps faith sweet and strong, In trust that tri-umphs o - ver wrong.
In peace that on - ly Thou canst give, With Thee, O Mas-ter, let me live.
203
Faith of Our Mothers
ST. CATHERINE
H. F. HEMY
A. B. PATTEN
Arr. by JAMES G. WALTON
1. Faith of our moth-ers, liv - ing still In cra-dle song and bed-time prayer;
2. Faith of our moth-ers, lov - ing faith, Fount of our childhood's trust and grace,
3. Faith of our moth-ers, guid-ing faith, For youthful long-ing, youth-ful doubt,
4. Faith of our moth-ers, Christian faith, In truth be-yond our stumbling creeds,
In nurs-ery lore and fire - side love, Thy presence still per-vades the air.
Oh, may thy con - se - cra-tion prove Source of a fin - er, no - bler race;
How blurred our vi-sion, blind our way, Thy prov-i - den - tial care with-out.
Still serve the home and save the Church, And breathe thy spirit through our deeds;
Faith of our moth-ers, liv - ing faith, We will be true to thee till death.
Faith of our moth-ers, lov - ing faith, We will be true to thee till death.
Faith of our moth-ers, guid-ing faith, We will be true to thee till death.
Faith of our moth-ers, Chris-tian faith, We will be true to thee till death.

204 Holy Ghost, with Light Divine

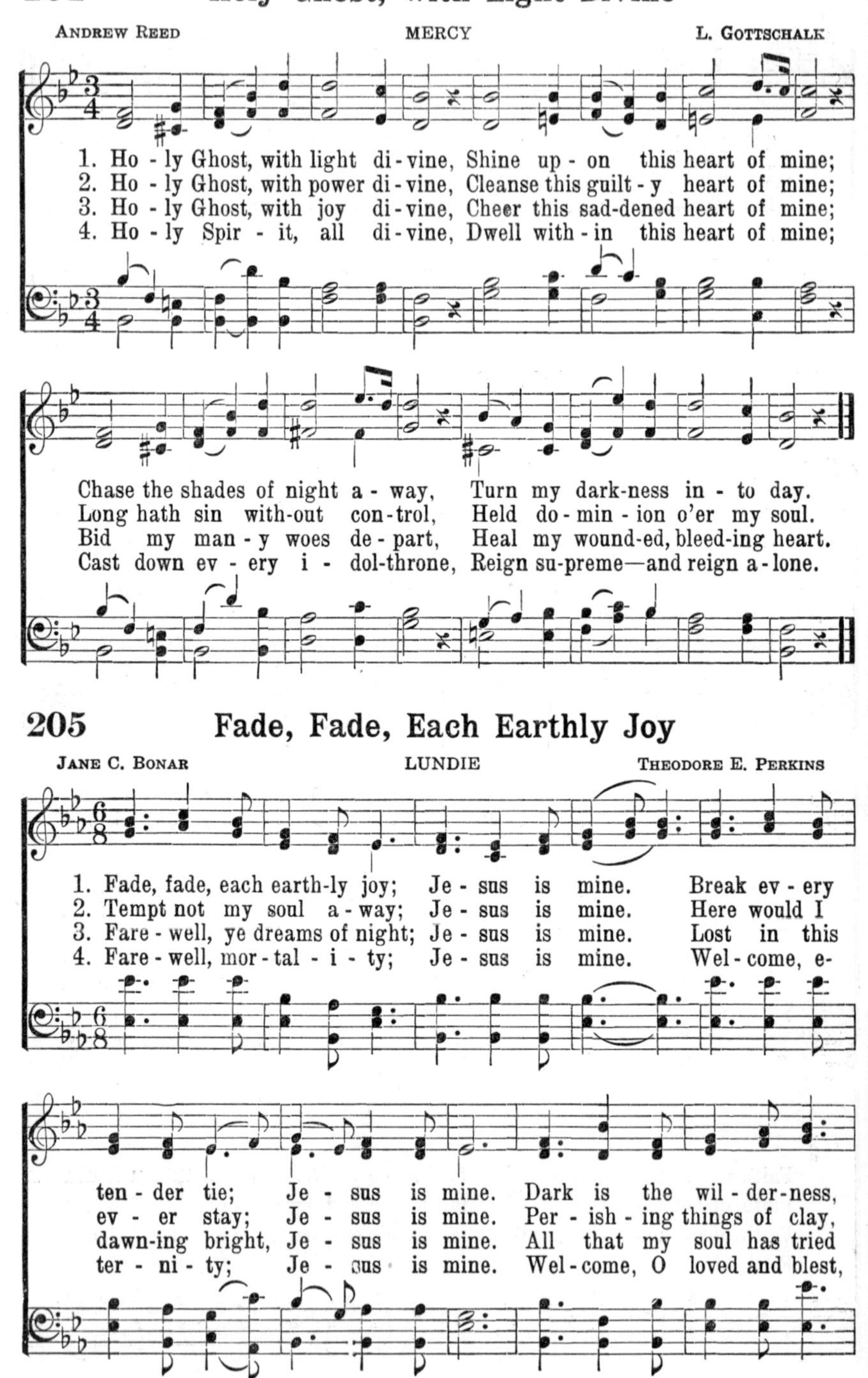
ANDREW REED
MERCY
L. GOTTSCHALK
1. Ho - ly Ghost, with light di - vine, Shine up - on this heart of mine;
2. Ho - ly Ghost, with power di - vine, Cleanse this guilt - y heart of mine;
3. Ho - ly Ghost, with joy di - vine, Cheer this sad-dened heart of mine;
4. Ho - ly Spir - it, all di - vine, Dwell with - in this heart of mine;
Chase the shades of night a - way, Turn my dark-ness in - to day.
Long hath sin with-out con-trol, Held do - min - ion o'er my soul.
Bid my man - y woes de - part, Heal my wound-ed, bleed-ing heart.
Cast down ev - ery i - dol-throne, Reign su-preme—and reign a - lone.
205 Fade, Fade, Each Earthly Joy
JANE C. BONAR
LUNDIE
THEODORE E. PERKINS
1. Fade, fade, each earth-ly joy; Je - sus is mine. Break ev - ery
2. Tempt not my soul a - way; Je - sus is mine. Here would I
3. Fare - well, ye dreams of night; Je - sus is mine. Lost in this
4. Fare - well, mor - tal - i - ty; Je - sus is mine. Wel - come, e-
ten - der tie; Je - sus is mine. Dark is the wil - der-ness,
ev - er stay; Je - sus is mine. Per - ish - ing things of clay,
dawn-ing bright, Je - sus is mine. All that my soul has tried
ter - ni - ty; Je - sus is mine. Wel - come, O loved and blest,

Fade, Fade, Each Earthly Joy
Earth has no rest-ing-place, Je - sus a - lone can bless; Je - sus is mine.
Born but for one brief day, Pass from my heart a - way; Je - sus is mine.
Left but a dis - mal void; Je - sus has sat - is - fied; Je - sus is mine.
Wel - come, sweet scenes of rest, Welcome, my Saviour's breast; Je - sus is mine.
206 Nearer, My God, to Thee
Sarah F. Adams
BETHANY
Lowell Mason
1. Near - er, my God, to Thee, Near - er to Thee! E'en though it
2. Though like the wan - der - er, The sun gone down, Dark - ness be
3. There let the way ap - pear, Steps un - to heaven: All that Thou
4. Then with my wak-ing thoughts Bright with Thy praise, Out of my
5. Or if on joy - ful wing, Cleav - ing the sky, Sun, moon, and
be a cross That rais - eth me; Still all my song shall be,
o - ver me, My rest a stone; Yet in my dreams I'd be
send - est me, In mer - cy given: An - gels to beck - on me
ston - y griefs Beth - el I'll raise; So by my woes to be
stars for - got, Up - ward I fly, Still all my song shall be,
Near - er, my God, to Thee, Near - er, my God, to Thee, Near - er to Thee!

207 Hold Thou My Hand

FANNY J. CROSBY
HUBERT P. MAIN
Moderato
1. Hold Thou my hand; so weak I am, and help-less, I dare not take one step with-out Thy aid; Hold Thou my hand; for then, O lov-ing Sav-iour, No dread of ill shall make my soul a-fraid.
2. Hold Thou my hand, and clos-er, clos-er draw me To Thy dear self—my hope, my joy, my all; Hold Thou my hand, lest hap-ly I should wan-der, And, miss-ing Thee, my trem-bling feet shall fall.
3. Hold Thou my hand; the way is dark be-fore me With-out the sun-light of Thy face di-vine; But when by faith I catch its ra-diant glo-ry, What heights of joy, what rap-turous songs are mine!
4. Hold Thou my hand, that when I reach the mar-gin Of that lone riv-er Thou didst cross for me, A heaven-ly light may flash a-long its wa-ters, And ev-ery wave like crys-tal bright shall be.
208 Oh, for a Closer Walk
WILLIAM COWPER
BALERMA
ROBT. SIMPSON
1. Oh, for a clos-er walk with God, A calm and heaven-ly frame;
2. Where is the bless-ed-ness I knew When first I saw the Lord?
3. What peace-ful hours I once en-joyed! How sweet their mem-ory still!
4. Re-turn, O Ho-ly Dove, re-turn, Sweet mes-sen-ger of rest;

Oh, for a Closer Walk

209 My Faith Looks Up to Thee

RAY PALMER — OLIVET — LOWELL MASON

A light to shine up-on the road That leads me to the Lamb!
Where is the soul-re-fresh-ing view Of Je-sus and His Word?
But they have left an ach-ing void The world can nev-er fill.
I hate the sins that made Thee mourn, And drove Thee from my breast.
1. My faith looks up to Thee, Thou Lamb of Cal-va-ry, Sav-iour di-vine! Now hear me while I pray, Take all my guilt a-way, O let me from this day Be whol-ly Thine!
2. May Thy rich grace im-part Strength to my faint-ing heart, My zeal in-spire; As Thou hast died for me, O may my love to Thee Pure, warm and change-less be, A liv-ing fire!
3. While life's dark maze I tread, And griefs a-round me spread, Be Thou my guide; Bid dark-ness turn to day, Wipe sor-row's tears a-way, Nor let me ev-er stray From Thee a-side.
4. When ends life's tran-sient dream, When death's cold, sul-len stream Shall o'er me roll; Blest Sav-iour, then, in love, Fear and dis-trust re-move; O bear me safe a-bove, A ran-somed soul!

210 I Love Him

English Hymn Book S. C. Foster

1. Gone from my heart the world and all its charm; Gone are my sins and
2. Once I was lost up - on the plains of sin; Once was a slave to
3. Once I was bound, but now I am set free; Once I was blind, but

all that would a - larm; Gone ev - er - more, and by His grace I know The
doubts and fears with-in; Once was a-fraid to trust a lov-ing God, But
now the light I see; Once I was dead, but now in Christ I live, To

D. S.—*Be-cause He first loved me, And*

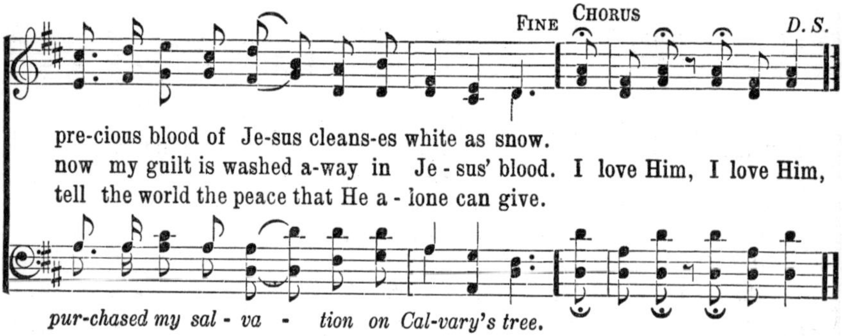

FINE CHORUS D. S.

pre-cious blood of Je-sus cleans-es white as snow.
now my guilt is washed a-way in Je - sus' blood. I love Him, I love Him,
tell the world the peace that He a - lone can give.

pur-chased my sal - va - tion on Cal-vary's tree.

211 Fairest Lord Jesus

Anonymous CRUSADER'S HYMN Arr. by R. S. Willis

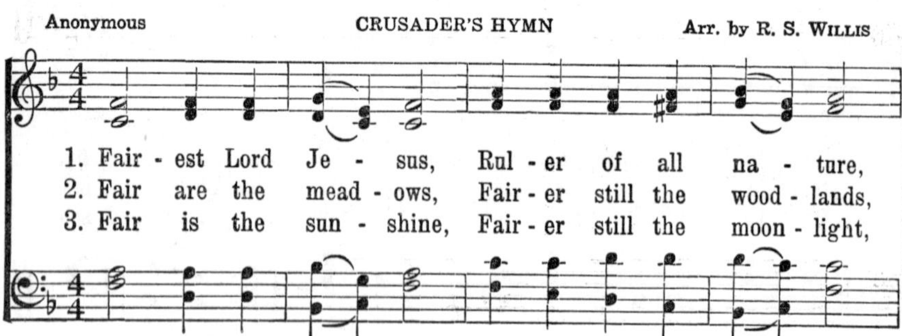
1. Fair - est Lord Je - sus, Rul - er of all na - ture,
2. Fair are the mead - ows, Fair - er still the wood - lands,
3. Fair is the sun - shine, Fair - er still the moon - light,

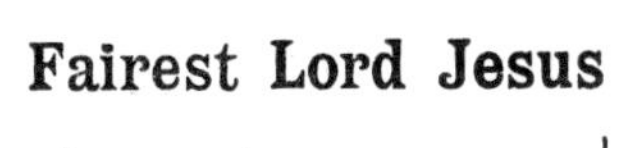

Fairest Lord Jesus

O Thou of God and man the Son, Thee will I cher - ish,
Robed in the bloom - ing garb of spring; Je - sus is fair - er,
And all the twin - kling, star - ry host; Je - sus shines bright - er,

Thee will I hon - or, Thou my soul's glo - ry, joy, and crown.
Je - sus is pur - er, Who makes the woe - ful heart to sing.
Je - sus shines pur - er, Than all the an - gels heaven can boast.

212 Come, Sinner, Come!

W. E. WITTER — H. R. PALMER

1. {While Je-sus whis-pers to you, Come, sin-ner, come!
{While we are pray-ing for you, (*Omit*. . . . .) Come, sin-ner, come!

2. {Are you too heav-y - la - den! Come, sin-ner, come!
{Je - sus will bear your bur-den, (*Omit*. . . . .) Come, sin-ner, come!

3. {Oh, hear His ten-der plead-ing, Come, sin-ner, come!
{Come and re-ceive the bless-ing, (*Omit*. . . . .) Come, sin-ner, come!

{Now is the time to own Him, Come, sin-ner, come!
{Now is the time to know Him, (*Omit*. . . . . . .) Come, sin-ner, come!

{Je - sus will not de-ceive you, Come, sin-ner, come!
{Je - sus can now re-deem you, (*Omit*. . . . . . .) Come, sin-ner, come!

{While Je-sus whis-pers to you, Come, sin-ner, come!
{While we are pray-ing for you, (*Omit*. . . . . . .) Come, sin-ner, come!

213 Saviour, More Than Life

FANNY J. CROSBY — W. H. DOANE

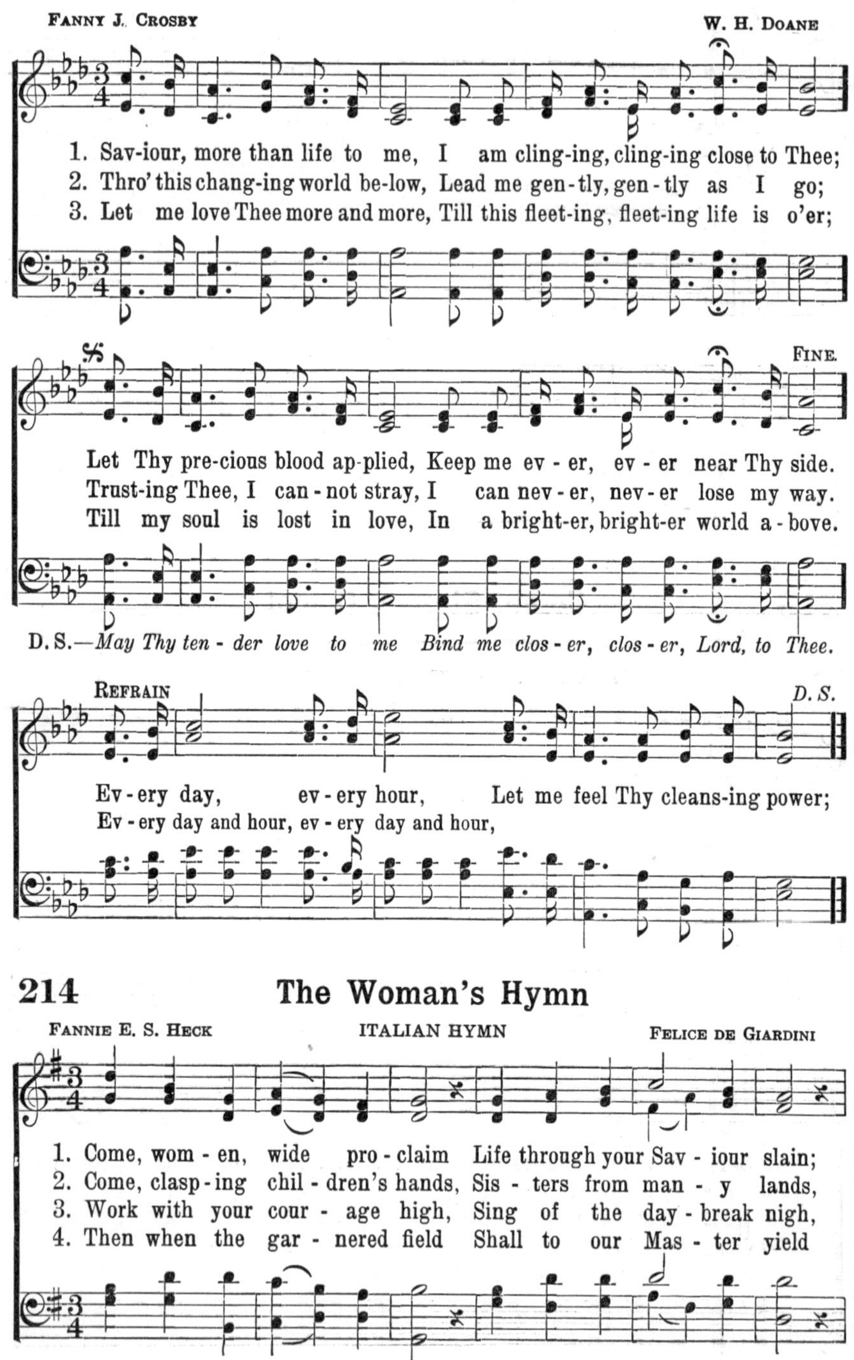
1. Sav-iour, more than life to me, I am cling-ing, cling-ing close to Thee;
2. Thro' this chang-ing world be-low, Lead me gen-tly, gen-tly as I go;
3. Let me love Thee more and more, Till this fleet-ing, fleet-ing life is o'er;
FINE.
Let Thy pre-cious blood ap-plied, Keep me ev-er, ev-er near Thy side.
Trust-ing Thee, I can-not stray, I can nev-er, nev-er lose my way.
Till my soul is lost in love, In a bright-er, bright-er world a-bove.
D. S.—May Thy ten-der love to me Bind me clos-er, clos-er, Lord, to Thee.
REFRAIN
D. S.
Ev-ery day, ev-ery hour, Let me feel Thy cleans-ing power;
Ev-ery day and hour, ev-ery day and hour,

214 The Woman's Hymn

FANNIE E. S. HECK — ITALIAN HYMN — FELICE DE GIARDINI

1. Come, wom-en, wide pro-claim Life through your Sav-iour slain;
2. Come, clasp-ing chil-dren's hands, Sis-ters from man-y lands,
3. Work with your cour-age high, Sing of the day-break nigh,
4. Then when the gar-nered field Shall to our Mas-ter yield

The Woman's Hymn

Sing ev - er - more. Christ, God's ef - ful-gence bright, Christ, who a-
Teach to a - dore, For the sin - sick and worn, The weak and
Your love out - pour. Stars shall your brow a - dorn, Your heart leap
A boun-teous store, Christ, hope of all the meek, Christ, whom all
rose in might, Christ, who crowns you with light, Praise and a - dore.
o - ver-borne, All who in dark-ness mourn, Pray, work, yet more.
with the morn, And, by His love up-borne, Hope and a - dore.
earth shall seek, Christ, your re - ward shall speak, Joy ev - er - more.
215 Jesus! and Shall It Ever Be
JOSEPH GRIGG
WOODWORTH
WM. BRADBURY
1. Je - sus! and shall it ev - er be, A mor - tal man a-shamed of Thee?
2. A-shamed of Je-sus! that dear Friend On whom my hopes of heaven de-pend!
3. A-shamed of Je - sus! yes, I may, When I've no guilt to wash a - way,
4. Till then—nor is my boast-ing vain—Till then I boast a Sav-iour slain;
A-shamed of Thee, whom an-gels praise, Whose glories shine thro' endless days?
No; when I blush, be this my shame, That I no more re-vere His name.
No tear to wipe, no good to crave, No fear to quell, no soul to save.
And oh, may this my glo - ry be, That Christ is not a-shamed of me.

216 There Is a Land of Pure Delight

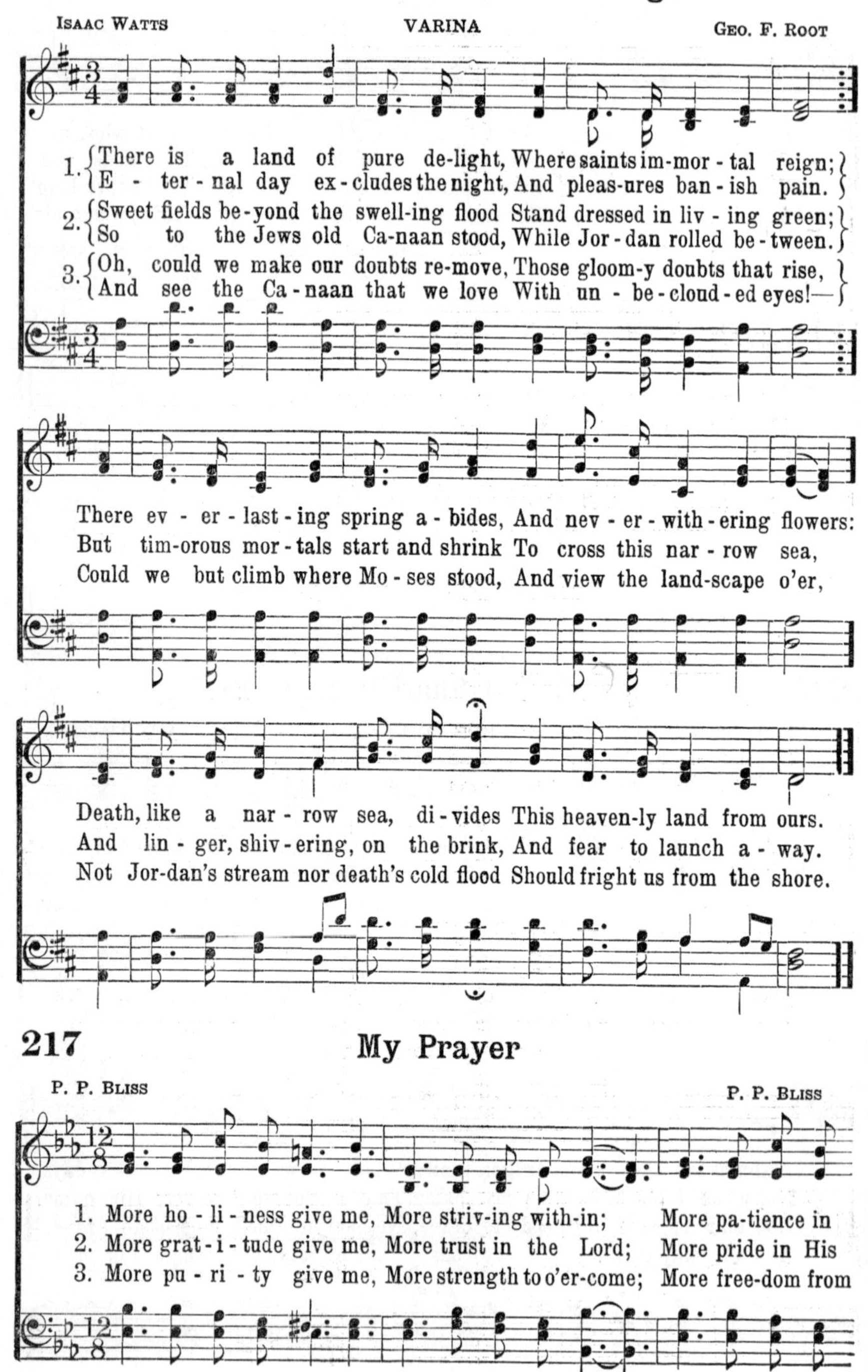
ISAAC WATTS
VARINA
GEO. F. ROOT
1. There is a land of pure de-light, Where saints im-mor-tal reign;
E - ter-nal day ex-cludes the night, And pleas-ures ban-ish pain.
2. Sweet fields be-yond the swell-ing flood Stand dressed in liv-ing green;
So to the Jews old Ca-naan stood, While Jor-dan rolled be-tween.
3. Oh, could we make our doubts re-move, Those gloom-y doubts that rise,
And see the Ca-naan that we love With un-be-cloud-ed eyes!—
There ev-er-last-ing spring a-bides, And nev-er-with-ering flowers:
But tim-orous mor-tals start and shrink To cross this nar-row sea,
Could we but climb where Mo-ses stood, And view the land-scape o'er,
Death, like a nar-row sea, di-vides This heaven-ly land from ours.
And lin-ger, shiv-ering, on the brink, And fear to launch a-way.
Not Jor-dan's stream nor death's cold flood Should fright us from the shore.
217 My Prayer
P. P. BLISS
P. P. BLISS
1. More ho-li-ness give me, More striv-ing with-in; More pa-tience in
2. More grat-i-tude give me, More trust in the Lord; More pride in His
3. More pu-ri-ty give me, More strength to o'er-come; More free-dom from

My Prayer
suf - fering, More sor - row for sin; More faith in my Sav - iour,
glo - ry, More hope in His Word; More tears for His sor - rows,
earth-stains, More long-ings for home; More fit for the king - dom,
More sense of His care; More joy in His serv - ice, More pur-pose in prayer.
More pain at His grief; More meekness in tri - al, More praise for re - lief.
More used would I be; More bless-ed and ho - ly, More, Sav-iour, like Thee.
rit.
218
More Love to Thee
Elizabeth Prentiss
W. H. Doane
1. More love to Thee, O Christ, More love to Thee! Hear Thou the
2. Once earth-ly joy I craved, Sought peace and rest; Now Thee a-
3. Then shall my lat - est breath Whis - per Thy praise; This be the
prayer I make On bend - ed knee; This is my ear - nest plea:
lone I seek, Give what is best; This all my prayer shall be;
part - ing cry My heart shall raise; This still its prayer shall be;
More love, O Christ, to Thee, More love to Thee, More love to Thee!

219 Jerusalem, the Golden

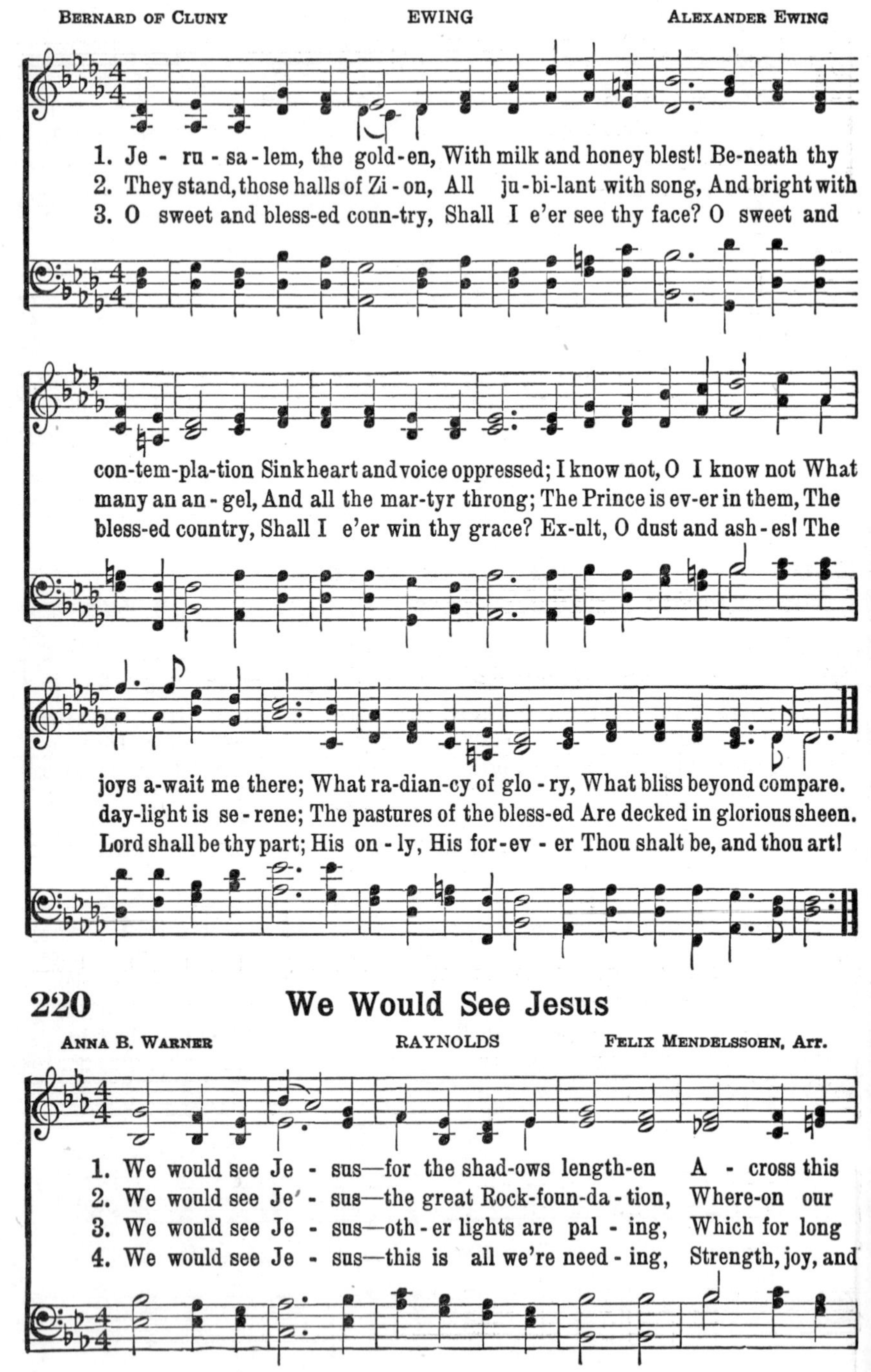
BERNARD OF CLUNY
EWING
ALEXANDER EWING
1. Je - ru - sa - lem, the gold-en, With milk and honey blest! Be-neath thy con-tem-pla-tion Sink heart and voice oppressed; I know not, O I know not What joys a-wait me there; What ra-dian-cy of glo - ry, What bliss beyond compare.
2. They stand, those halls of Zi - on, All ju-bi-lant with song, And bright with many an an - gel, And all the mar-tyr throng; The Prince is ev-er in them, The day-light is se - rene; The pastures of the bless-ed Are decked in glorious sheen.
3. O sweet and bless-ed coun-try, Shall I e'er see thy face? O sweet and bless-ed country, Shall I e'er win thy grace? Ex-ult, O dust and ash - es! The Lord shall be thy part; His on - ly, His for - ev - er Thou shalt be, and thou art!
220
We Would See Jesus
ANNA B. WARNER
RAYNOLDS
FELIX MENDELSSOHN, ARR.
1. We would see Je - sus—for the shad-ows length-en A - cross this
2. We would see Je - sus—the great Rock-foun-da - tion, Where-on our
3. We would see Je - sus—oth - er lights are pal - ing, Which for long
4. We would see Je - sus—this is all we're need - ing, Strength, joy, and

We Would See Jesus

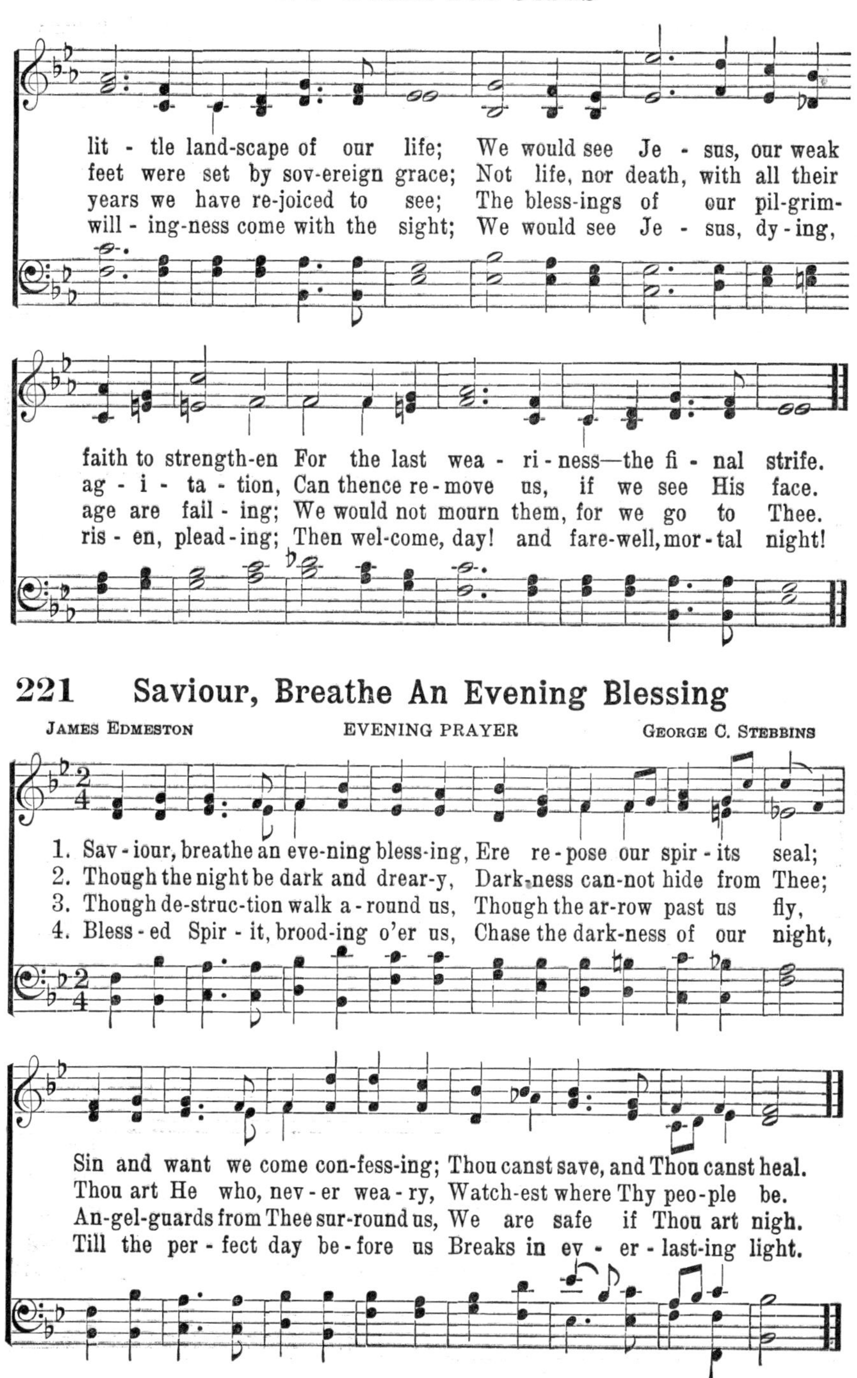
lit - tle land-scape of our life; We would see Je - sus, our weak
feet were set by sov-ereign grace; Not life, nor death, with all their
years we have re-joiced to see; The bless-ings of our pil-grim-
will - ing-ness come with the sight; We would see Je - sus, dy - ing,
faith to strength-en For the last wea - ri - ness—the fi - nal strife.
ag - i - ta - tion, Can thence re - move us, if we see His face.
age are fail - ing; We would not mourn them, for we go to Thee.
ris - en, plead - ing; Then wel-come, day! and fare-well, mor - tal night!
221 Saviour, Breathe An Evening Blessing
JAMES EDMESTON
EVENING PRAYER
GEORGE C. STEBBINS
1. Sav - iour, breathe an eve-ning bless-ing, Ere re - pose our spir - its seal;
2. Though the night be dark and drear-y, Dark-ness can-not hide from Thee;
3. Though de-struc-tion walk a - round us, Though the ar-row past us fly,
4. Bless - ed Spir - it, brood-ing o'er us, Chase the dark-ness of our night,
Sin and want we come con-fess-ing; Thou canst save, and Thou canst heal.
Thou art He who, nev - er wea - ry, Watch-est where Thy peo-ple be.
An-gel-guards from Thee sur-round us, We are safe if Thou art nigh.
Till the per - fect day be - fore us Breaks in ev - er - last-ing light.

222 I Gave My Life for Thee

FRANCES R. HAVERGAL — P. P. BLISS

1. I gave My life for thee, My pre - cious blood I shed,
2. My Fa - ther's house of light,— My glo - ry - cir - cled throne,—
3. I suf - fered much for thee, More than thy tongue can tell,
4. And I have brought to thee, Down from My home a - bove,
That thou might'st ran-somed be, And quick-ened from the dead;
I left for earth - ly night, For wan-derings sad and lone;
Of bit - terest ag - o - ny, To res - cue thee from hell;
Sal - va - tion full and free, My par - don and My love;
f
I gave, I gave My life for thee, What hast thou given for Me?
I left, I left it all for thee, Hast thou left aught for Me?
I've borne, I've borne it all for thee, What hast thou borne for Me?
I bring, I bring rich gifts to thee, What hast thou brought to Me?
223 Close to Thee
FANNY J. CROSBY
SILAS J. VAIL
1. Thou, my ev - er - last - ing por - tion, More than friend or life to me;
2. Not for ease or world - ly pleas - ure, Nor for fame my prayer shall be;
3. Lead me through the vale of shad - ows, Bear me o'er life's fit - ful sea;

Close to Thee

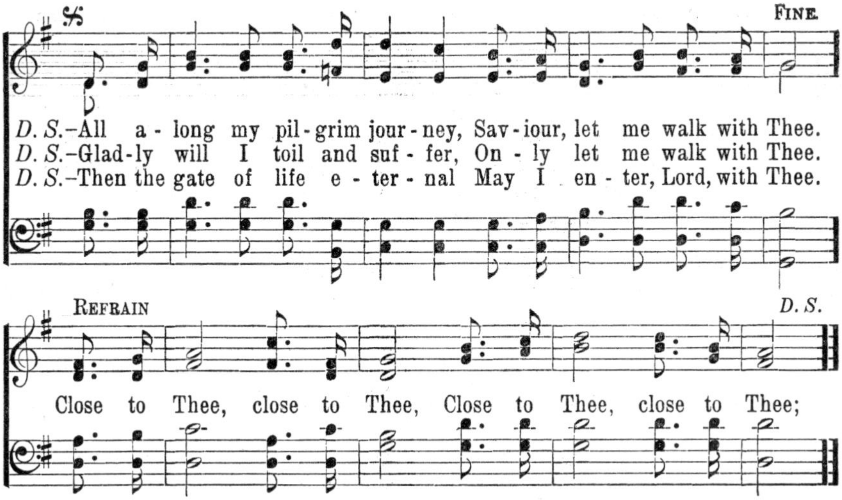

FINE.

D. S.–All a-long my pil-grim jour-ney, Sav-iour, let me walk with Thee.
D. S.–Glad-ly will I toil and suf-fer, On-ly let me walk with Thee.
D. S.–Then the gate of life e-ter-nal May I en-ter, Lord, with Thee.

REFRAIN *D. S.*

Close to Thee, close to Thee, Close to Thee, close to Thee;

224 God of Our Fathers

RUDYARD KIPLING — ST. CATHERINE — H. F. HEMY

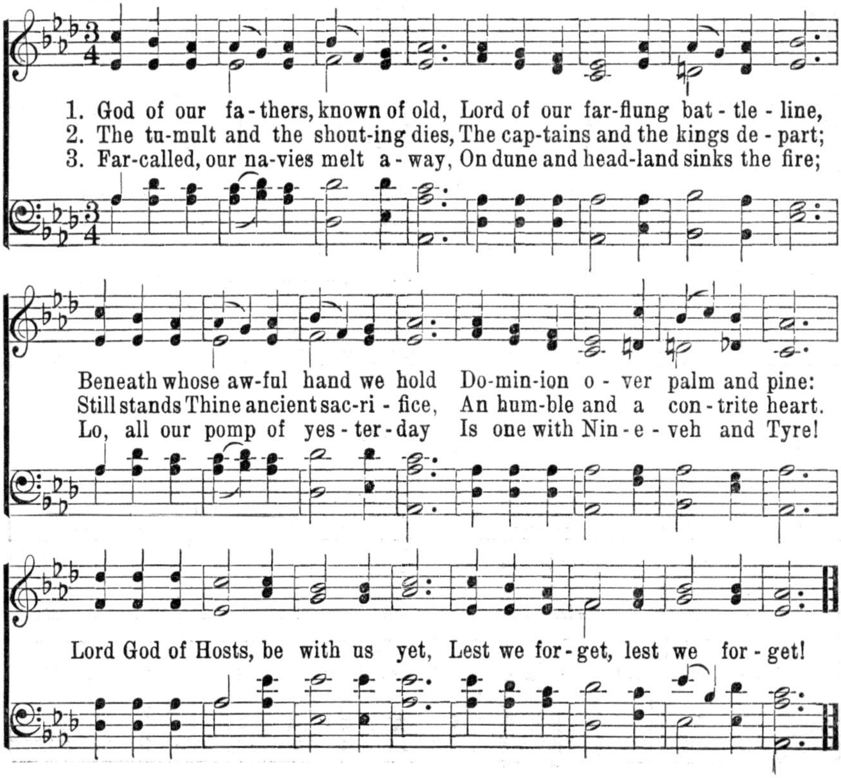

1. God of our fa-thers, known of old, Lord of our far-flung bat-tle-line,
2. The tu-mult and the shout-ing dies, The cap-tains and the kings de-part;
3. Far-called, our na-vies melt a-way, On dune and head-land sinks the fire;

Beneath whose aw-ful hand we hold Do-min-ion o-ver palm and pine:
Still stands Thine ancient sac-ri-fice, An hum-ble and a con-trite heart.
Lo, all our pomp of yes-ter-day Is one with Nin-e-veh and Tyre!

Lord God of Hosts, be with us yet, Lest we for-get, lest we for-get!

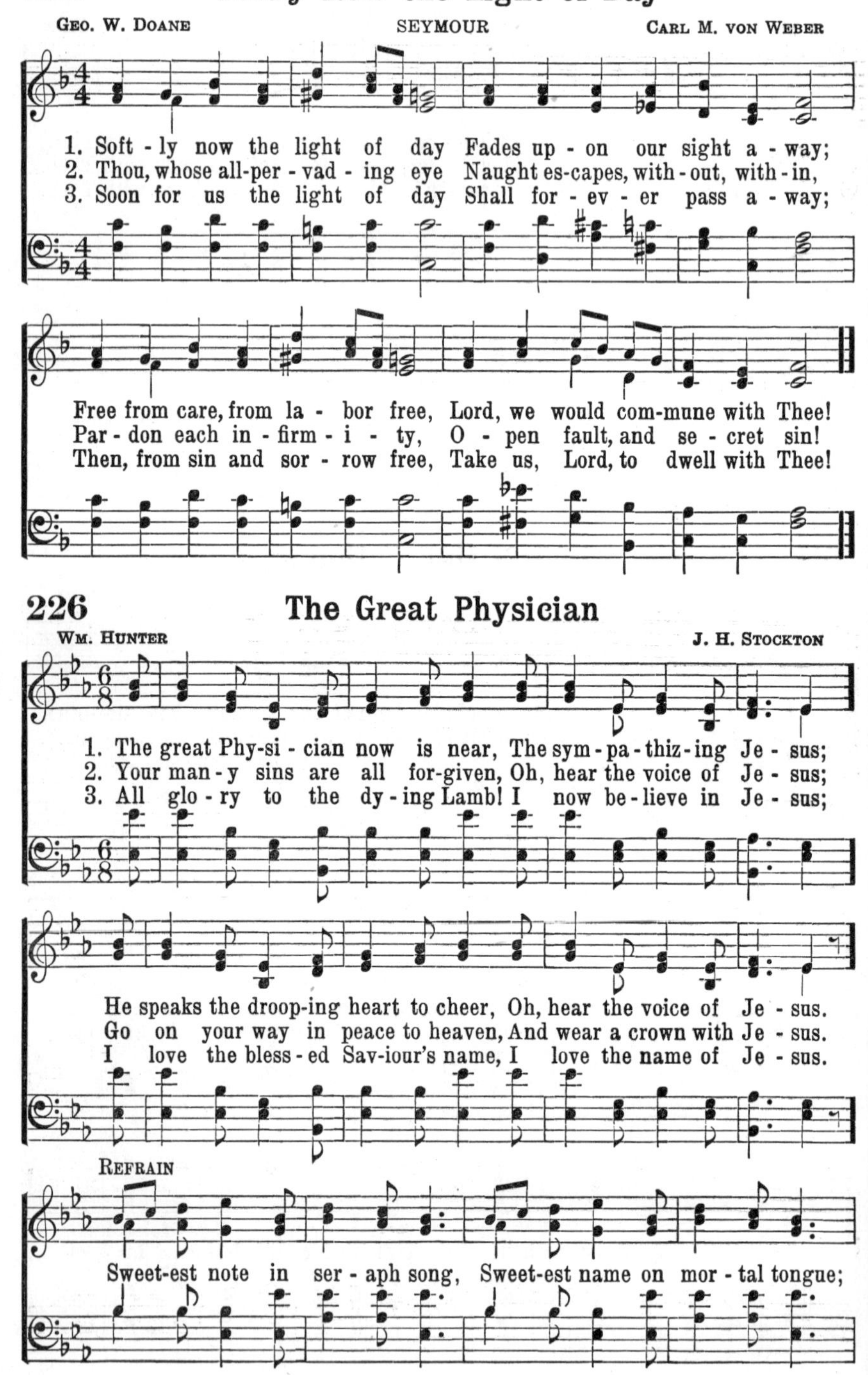

225
Softly Now the Light of Day
Geo. W. Doane
SEYMOUR
Carl M. von Weber
1. Soft - ly now the light of day Fades up - on our sight a - way;
2. Thou, whose all-per - vad - ing eye Naught es-capes, with - out, with - in,
3. Soon for us the light of day Shall for - ev - er pass a - way;
Free from care, from la - bor free, Lord, we would com-mune with Thee!
Par - don each in - firm - i - ty, O - pen fault, and se - cret sin!
Then, from sin and sor - row free, Take us, Lord, to dwell with Thee!
226
The Great Physician
Wm. Hunter
J. H. Stockton
1. The great Phy-si - cian now is near, The sym - pa - thiz - ing Je - sus;
2. Your man - y sins are all for-given, Oh, hear the voice of Je - sus;
3. All glo - ry to the dy - ing Lamb! I now be - lieve in Je - sus;
He speaks the droop-ing heart to cheer, Oh, hear the voice of Je - sus.
Go on your way in peace to heaven, And wear a crown with Je - sus.
I love the bless - ed Sav-iour's name, I love the name of Je - sus.
Refrain
Sweet-est note in ser - aph song, Sweet-est name on mor - tal tongue;

The Great Physician

Sweet-est car-ol ev-er sung, Je-sus, bless-ed Je-sus.
227 Hark, Ten Thousand Harps
THOMAS KELLY
HARWELL
LOWELL MASON
1. Hark, ten thou-sand harps and voic-es Sound the note of praise a-bove!
2. Je-sus, hail! whose glo-ry bright-ens All a-bove, and gives it worth;
3. Sav-iour, has-ten Thine ap-pear-ing; Bring, O bring the glo-rious day,
Je-sus reigns, and heaven re-joic-es, Je-sus reigns, the God of love;
Lord of life, Thy smile en-light-ens, Cheers and charms Thy saints on earth;
When, the aw-ful sum-mons hear-ing, Heaven and earth shall pass a-way;
See, He sits on yon-der throne; Je-sus rules the world a-lone.
When we think of love like Thine, Lord, we own it love di-vine.
Then with gold-en harps we'll sing, "Glo-ry, glo-ry to our King!"
Hal-le-lu-jah! hal-le-lu-jah! Hal-le-lu-jah! A-men!

228 Footsteps of Jesus

Mary B. C. Slade
A. B. Everett
1. Sweet-ly, Lord, have we heard Thee call-ing, Come, fol-low Me! And we see where Thy foot-prints falling Lead us to Thee.
2. Though they lead o'er the cold, dark mountains, Seek-ing His sheep; Or a-long by Si-lo-am's fountains, Help-ing the weak:
3. If they lead thro' the tem-ple ho-ly, Preaching the Word; Or in homes of the poor and low-ly, Serv-ing the Lord:
4. Then at last, when on high He sees us, Our jour-ney done, We will rest where the steps of Je-sus End at His throne.
Chorus.
Foot-prints of Je-sus, that make the pathway glow; We will follow the steps of Je-sus wher-e'er they go.
229
I Will Arise and Go to Jesus
J. Hart
Arranged
1. Come, ye sin-ners, poor and need-y, Weak and wound-ed, sick and sore;
2. Come, ye thirst-y, come, and wel-come, God's free boun-ty glo-ri-fy;
3. Come, ye wea-ry, heav-y-la-den, Lost and ru-ined by the fall;
4. Let not conscience make you lin-ger, Nor of fit-ness fond-ly dream;
Cho.—I will a-rise and go to Je-sus, He will em-brace me in His arms,

I Will Arise and Go to Jesus

D.C. for Chorus
Je - sus read - y stands to save you, Full of pit - y, love and power.
True be - lief and true re - pent-ance, Ev - ery grace that brings you nigh.
If you tar - ry till you're bet - ter, You will nev - er come at all.
All the fit - ness He re - quir-eth Is to feel your need of Him.
In the arms of my dear Sav - iour, Oh, there are ten thou-sand charms.
230
Pass Me Not
Fanny J. Crosby
W. H. Doane
1. Pass me not, O gen-tle Sav - iour, Hear my humble cry; While on oth - ers
2. Let me at a throne of mer - cy Find a sweet re - lief; Kneeling there in
3. Trust-ing on - ly in Thy mer - it, Would I seek Thy face; Heal my wounded,
4. Thou the Spring of all my com-fort, More than life to me, Whom have I on
Chorus
Thou art call-ing, Do not pass me by.
deep con-tri - tion, Help my un - be - lief. Sav-iour, Sav-iour, Hear my humble
bro - ken spir - it, Save me by Thy grace.
earth beside Thee? Whom in heaven but Thee?
cry; While on oth - ers Thou art call - ing, Do not pass me by.

231 O Love That Wilt Not Let Me Go

GEORGE MATHESON — MARGARET — A. L. PEACE

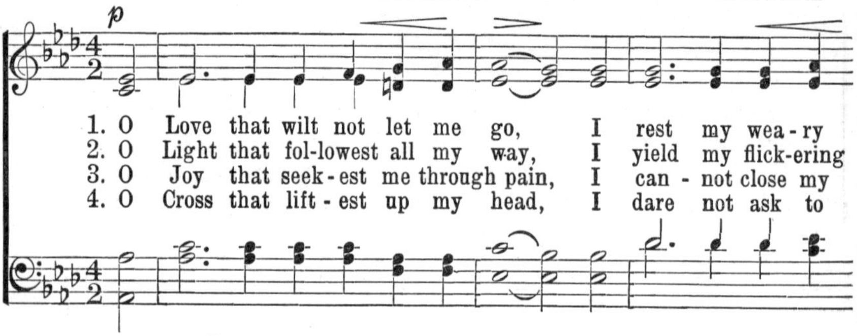

p

1. O Love that wilt not let me go, I rest my wea-ry
2. O Light that fol-lowest all my way, I yield my flick-ering
3. O Joy that seek-est me through pain, I can-not close my
4. O Cross that lift-est up my head, I dare not ask to

soul in Thee; I give Thee back the life I owe, That
torch to Thee; My heart re-stores its bor-rowed ray, That
heart to Thee; I trace the rain-bow through the rain, And
hide from Thee; I lay in dust life's glo-ry dead, And

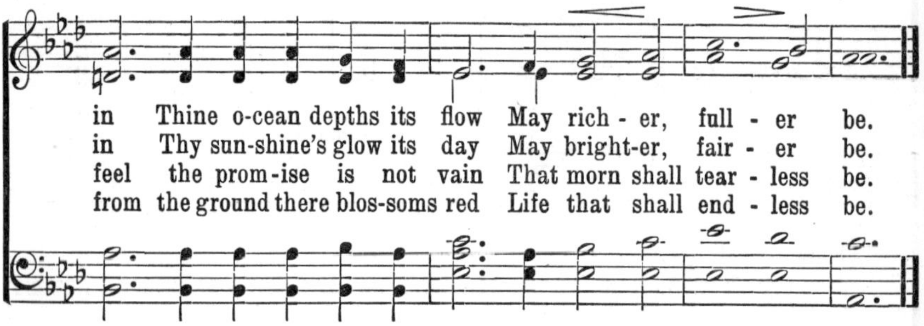

in Thine o-cean depths its flow May rich-er, full-er be.
in Thy sun-shine's glow its day May bright-er, fair-er be.
feel the prom-ise is not vain That morn shall tear-less be.
from the ground there blos-soms red Life that shall end-less be.

232 Bread of Heaven, On Thee We Feed

JOSIAH CONDER — HOLLEY — G. HEWS

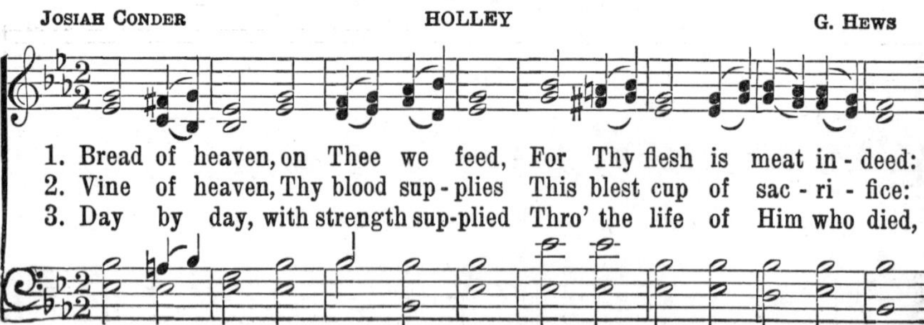

1. Bread of heaven, on Thee we feed, For Thy flesh is meat in-deed:
2. Vine of heaven, Thy blood sup-plies This blest cup of sac-ri-fice:
3. Day by day, with strength sup-plied Thro' the life of Him who died,

Bread of Heaven, On Thee We Feed

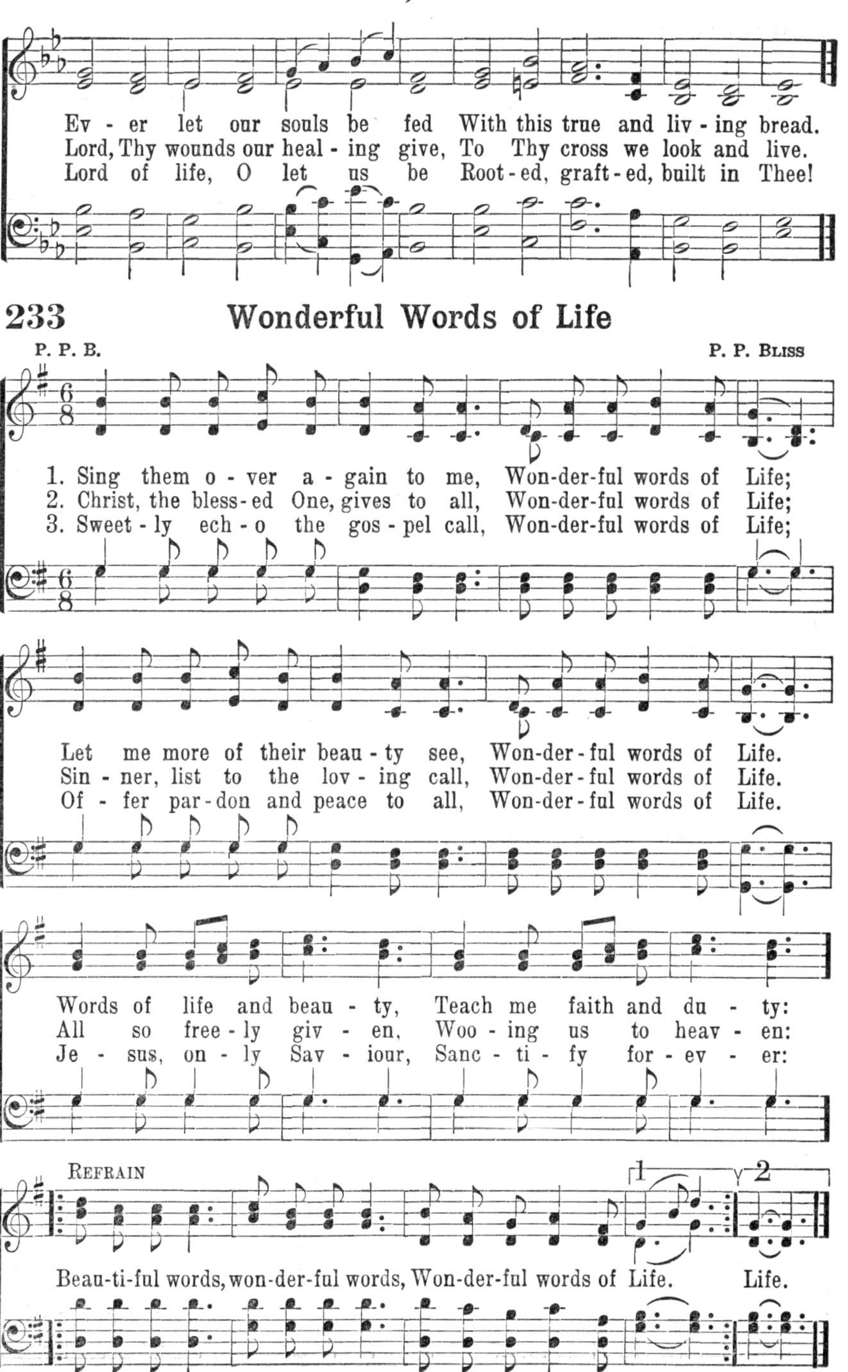
Ev - er let our souls be fed With this true and liv - ing bread.
Lord, Thy wounds our heal - ing give, To Thy cross we look and live.
Lord of life, O let us be Root - ed, graft - ed, built in Thee!
233 Wonderful Words of Life
P. P. B.
P. P. Bliss
1. Sing them o - ver a - gain to me, Won-der-ful words of Life;
2. Christ, the bless - ed One, gives to all, Won-der-ful words of Life;
3. Sweet - ly ech - o the gos - pel call, Won-der-ful words of Life;
Let me more of their beau - ty see, Won-der - ful words of Life.
Sin - ner, list to the lov - ing call, Won-der - ful words of Life.
Of - fer par - don and peace to all, Won-der - ful words of Life.
Words of life and beau - ty, Teach me faith and du - ty:
All so free - ly giv - en, Woo - ing us to heav - en:
Je - sus, on - ly Sav - iour, Sanc - ti - fy for - ev - er:
Refrain
Beau-ti-ful words, won-der-ful words, Won-der-ful words of Life. Life.

234 Beneath the Cross of Jesus

ELIZABETH C. CLEPHANE
ST. CHRISTOPHER
FREDERICK C. MAKER
1. Be-neath the cross of Je-sus I fain would take my stand,
2. Up-on that cross of Je-sus Mine eye at times can see
3. I take, O cross, thy shad-ow For my a-bid-ing place;
The shad-ow of a might-y Rock With-in a wea-ry land;
The ver-y dy-ing form of One Who suf-fered there for me;
I ask no oth-er sun-shine than The sun-shine of His face;
A home with-in the wil-der-ness, A rest up-on the way,
And from my smit-ten heart with tears, Two won-ders I con-fess,—
Con-tent to let the world go by, To know no gain nor loss,
From the burn-ing of the noon-tide heat, And the bur-den of the day.
The won-ders of His glo-rious love And my own worth-less-ness.
My sin-ful self my on-ly shame, My glo-ry all the cross!
235 Ye Christian Heralds!
B. H. DRAPER
MISSIONARY CHANT
H. C. ZEUNER
1. Ye Chris-tian her-alds! go pro-claim Sal-va-tion thro' Im-man-uel's name;
2. He'll shield you with a wall of fire, With flaming zeal your hearts in-spire,
3. And when our la-bors all are o'er, Then shall we meet to part no more—

Ye Christian Heralds!

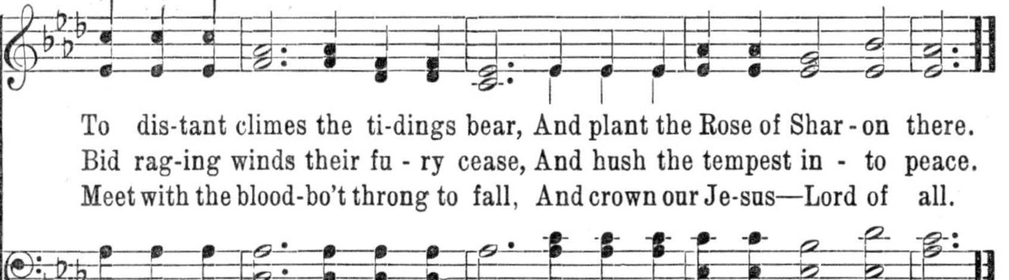
To dis-tant climes the ti-dings bear, And plant the Rose of Shar-on there.
Bid rag-ing winds their fu-ry cease, And hush the tempest in-to peace.
Meet with the blood-bo't throng to fall, And crown our Je-sus—Lord of all.

236 Lead On, O King Eternal

ERNEST W. SHURTLEFF LANCASHIRE HENRY SMART

1. Lead on, O King E-ter-nal, The day of march has come; Henceforth in fields of
2. Lead on, O King E-ter-nal, Till sin's fierce war shall cease, And ho-li-ness shall
3. Lead on, O King E-ter-nal, We fol-low, not with fears; For gladness breaks like

con-quest Thy tents shall be our home. Thro' days of prep-a-ra-tion Thy
whis-per The sweet A-men of peace; For not with swords loud clashing, Nor
morn-ing Where'er Thy face ap-pears; Thy cross is lift-ed o'er us; We

grace has made us strong, And now, O King E-ter-nal, We lift our bat-tle song.
roll of stir-ring drums; With deeds of love and mercy, The heavenly kingdom comes.
jour-ney in its light: The crown awaits the conquest; Lead on, O God of might.

237 Holy Bible, Book Divine

JOHN BURTON
ALETTA
WM. B. BRADBURY
1. Ho - ly Bi - ble, Book di - vine, Pre - cious treas-ure, thou art mine;
2. Mine to chide me when I rove; Mine to show a Sav-iour's love;
3. Mine to com - fort in dis - tress, Suf-fering in this wil - der - ness;
4. Mine to tell of joys to come, And the reb - el sin - ner's doom;
Mine to tell me whence I came; Mine to teach me what I am;
Mine thou art to guide and guard; Mine to pun - ish or re - ward;
Mine to show, by liv - ing faith, Man can tri - umph o - ver death;
O thou ho - ly Book di - vine, Pre - cious treas - ure, thou art mine.
238
Lead, Kindly Light
JOHN H. NEWMAN
LUX BENIGNA
JOHN B. DYKES
1. Lead, kind-ly Light, a-mid th' en-cir-cling gloom, Lead Thou me on!
2. I was not ev - er thus, nor prayed that Thou Shouldst lead me on;
3. So long Thy power hath blest me, sure it still Will lead me on
The night is dark, and I am far from home; Lead Thou me on!
I loved to choose and see my path; but now Lead Thou me on!
O'er moor and fen, o'er crag and tor-rent, till The night is gone,

Lead, Kindly Light

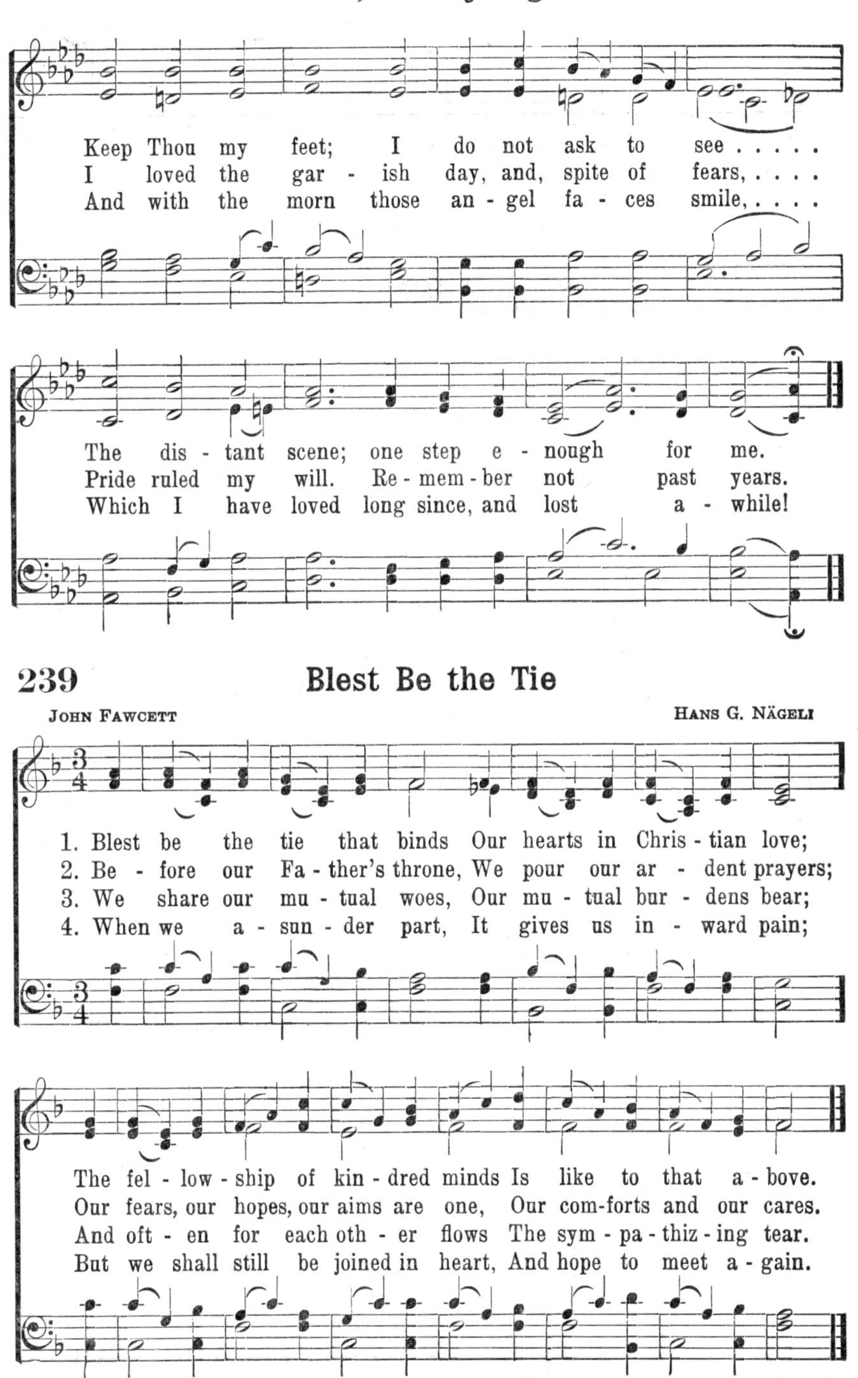

Keep Thou my feet; I do not ask to see . . . . .
I loved the gar - ish day, and, spite of fears, ...
And with the morn those an - gel fa - ces smile, ...
The dis - tant scene; one step e - nough for me.
Pride ruled my will. Re - mem - ber not past years.
Which I have loved long since, and lost a - while!

239 Blest Be the Tie

John Fawcett — Hans G. Nägeli

1. Blest be the tie that binds Our hearts in Chris - tian love;
2. Be - fore our Fa - ther's throne, We pour our ar - dent prayers;
3. We share our mu - tual woes, Our mu - tual bur - dens bear;
4. When we a - sun - der part, It gives us in - ward pain;
The fel - low - ship of kin - dred minds Is like to that a - bove.
Our fears, our hopes, our aims are one, Our com-forts and our cares.
And oft - en for each oth - er flows The sym - pa - thiz - ing tear.
But we shall still be joined in heart, And hope to meet a - gain.

240 God of Our Fathers, Whose Almighty Hand

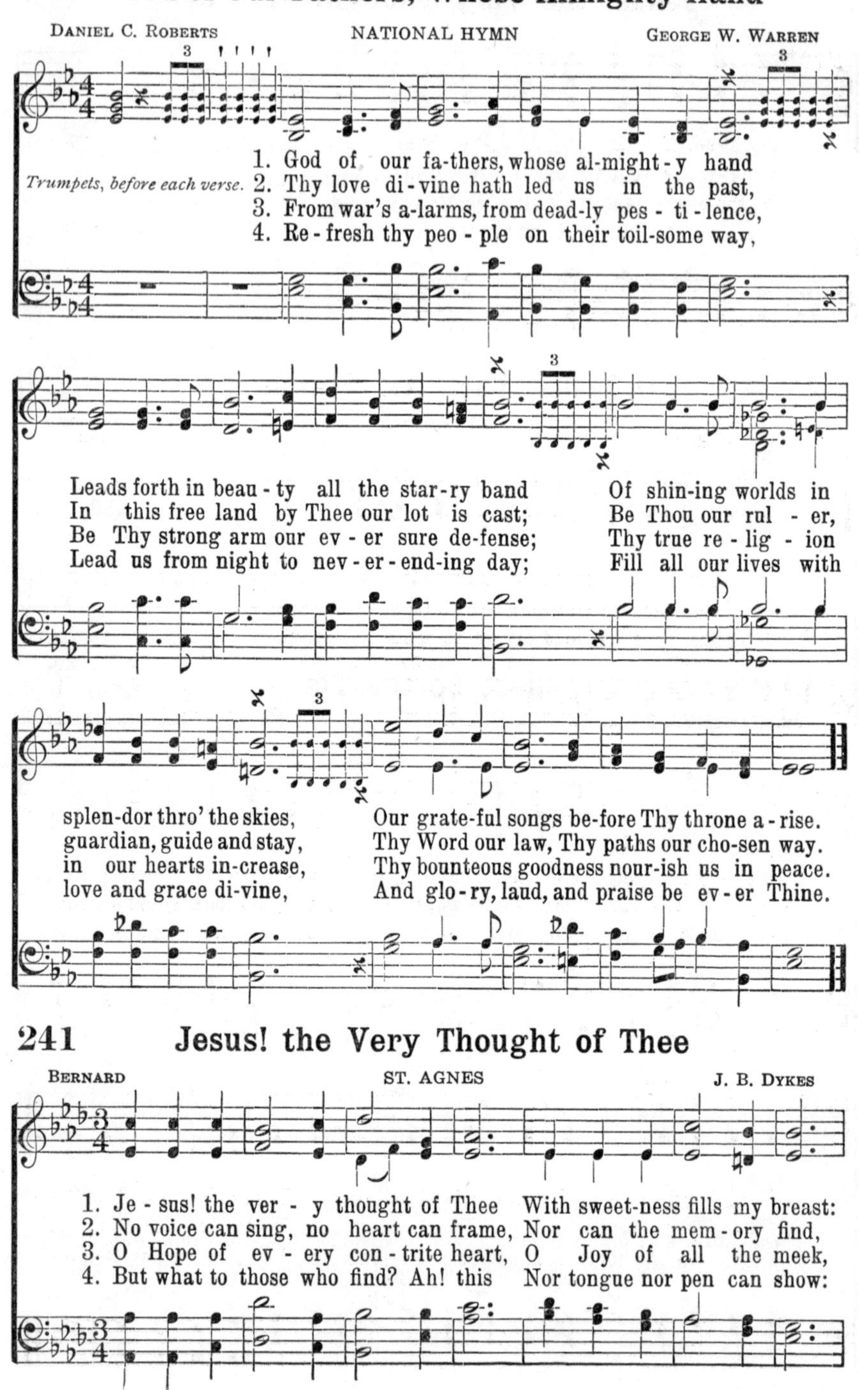

Daniel C. Roberts
NATIONAL HYMN
George W. Warren
Trumpets, before each verse.
1. God of our fa-thers, whose al-might-y hand
2. Thy love di-vine hath led us in the past,
3. From war's a-larms, from dead-ly pes-ti-lence,
4. Re-fresh thy peo-ple on their toil-some way,
Leads forth in beau-ty all the star-ry band
In this free land by Thee our lot is cast;
Be Thy strong arm our ev-er sure de-fense;
Lead us from night to nev-er-end-ing day;
Of shin-ing worlds in
Be Thou our rul-er,
Thy true re-lig-ion
Fill all our lives with
splen-dor thro' the skies,
guardian, guide and stay,
in our hearts in-crease,
love and grace di-vine,
Our grate-ful songs be-fore Thy throne a-rise.
Thy Word our law, Thy paths our cho-sen way.
Thy bounteous goodness nour-ish us in peace.
And glo-ry, laud, and praise be ev-er Thine.

241 Jesus! the Very Thought of Thee

Bernard
ST. AGNES
J. B. Dykes
1. Je-sus! the ver-y thought of Thee With sweet-ness fills my breast:
2. No voice can sing, no heart can frame, Nor can the mem-ory find,
3. O Hope of ev-ery con-trite heart, O Joy of all the meek,
4. But what to those who find? Ah! this Nor tongue nor pen can show:

Jesus! the Very Thought of Thee

But sweet-er far Thy face to see, And in Thy pres-ence rest.
A sweet-er sound than Je-sus' name, The Sav-iour of man-kind.
To those who ask, how kind Thou art! How good to those who seek!
The love of Je-sus, what it is None but His loved ones know.

242 O Jesus, Thou Art Standing

ST. HILDA

WILLIAM W. HOW

JUSTIN H. KNECHT
EDWARD HUSBAND

1. O Je-sus, Thou art standing Outside the fast-closed door, In low-ly pa-tience wait-ing To pass the thresh-old o'er: Shame on us, Chris-tian broth-ers, His name and sign who bear, O shame, thrice shame upon us, To keep Him standing there!

2. O Je-sus, Thou art knocking; And lo! that hand is scarred, And thorns Thy brow en-cir-cle, And tears Thy face have marred: O love that pass-eth knowledge, So pa-tient-ly to wait! O sin that hath no e-qual, So fast to bar the gate!

3. O Je-sus, Thou art pleading In ac-cents meek and low, "I died for you, My chil-dren, And will ye treat Me so?" O Lord, with shame and sor-row We o-pen now the door; Dear Saviour, en-ter, en-ter, And leave us nev-er-more!

243 Work, for the Night Is Coming

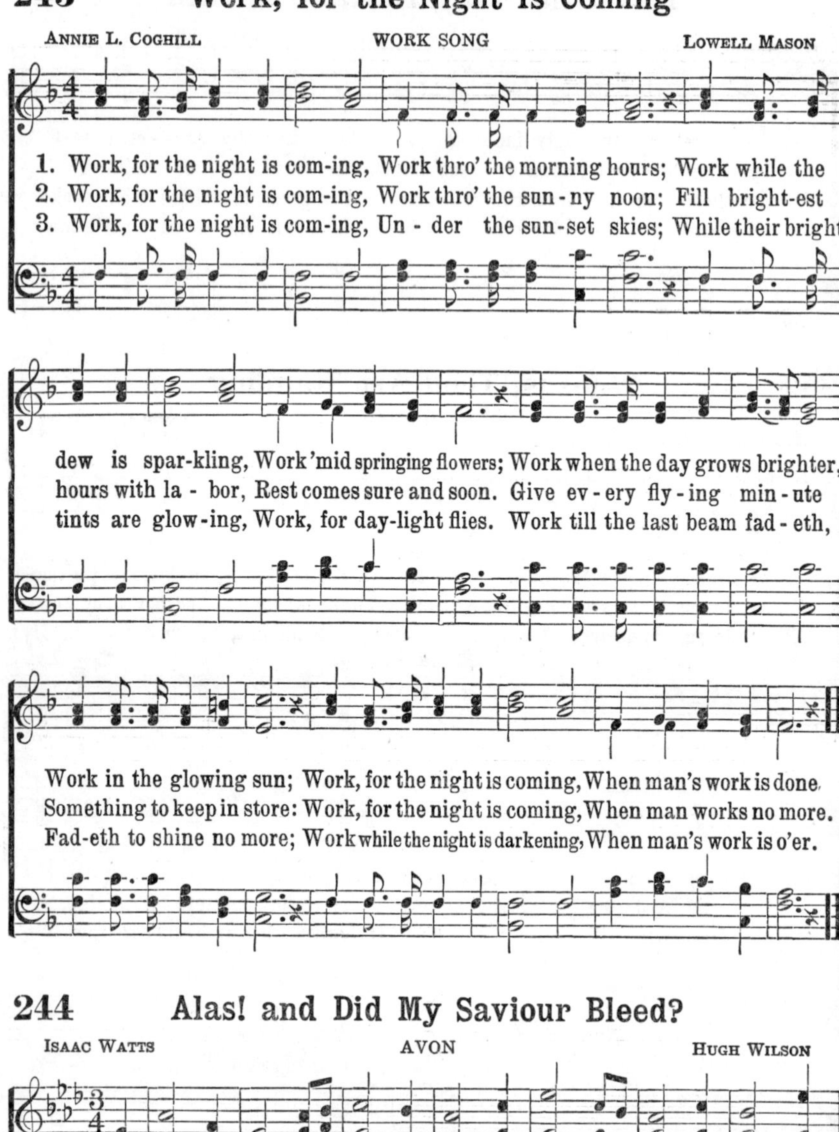

ANNIE L. COGHILL
WORK SONG
LOWELL MASON
1. Work, for the night is com-ing, Work thro' the morning hours; Work while the
2. Work, for the night is com-ing, Work thro' the sun - ny noon; Fill bright-est
3. Work, for the night is com-ing, Un - der the sun-set skies; While their bright
dew is spar-kling, Work 'mid springing flowers; Work when the day grows brighter,
hours with la - bor, Rest comes sure and soon. Give ev - ery fly - ing min - ute
tints are glow - ing, Work, for day-light flies. Work till the last beam fad - eth,
Work in the glowing sun; Work, for the night is coming, When man's work is done.
Something to keep in store: Work, for the night is coming, When man works no more.
Fad-eth to shine no more; Work while the night is darkening, When man's work is o'er.

244 Alas! and Did My Saviour Bleed?

ISAAC WATTS — AVON — HUGH WILSON

1. A - las! and did my Sav-iour bleed? And did my Sov-ereign die? Would
2. Was it for crimes that I had done He groaned up-on the tree? A-
3. Well might the sun in dark-ness hide, And shut his glo-ries in, When
4. But drops of grief can ne'er re - pay The debt of love I owe; Here,

Alas! and Did My Saviour Bleed?

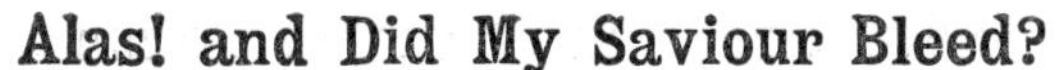

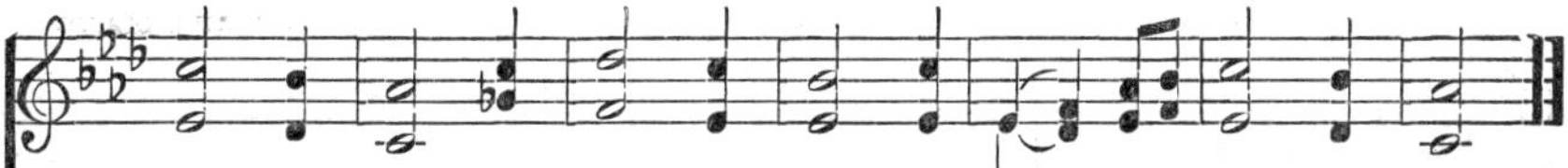

He de - vote that sa - cred head For such a worm as I?
maz - ing pit - y! grace un-known! And love be - yond de - gree!
Christ, the might - y Mak - er, died For man, the crea-ture's sin.
Lord, I give my - self a - way, 'Tis all that I can do.

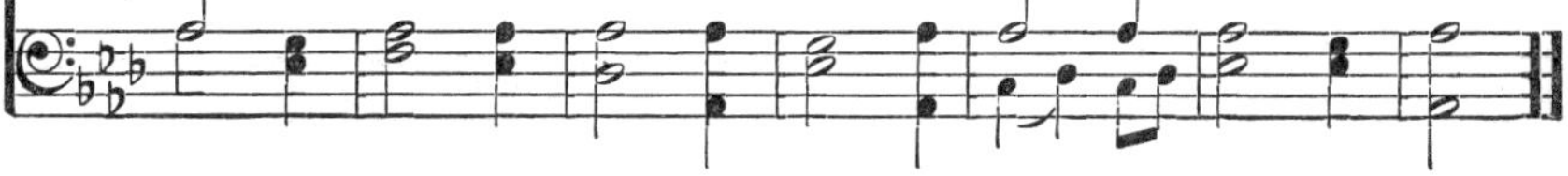

245 Holy Spirit, Faithful Guide

MARCUS M. WELLS — FAITHFUL GUIDE — MARCUS M. WELLS

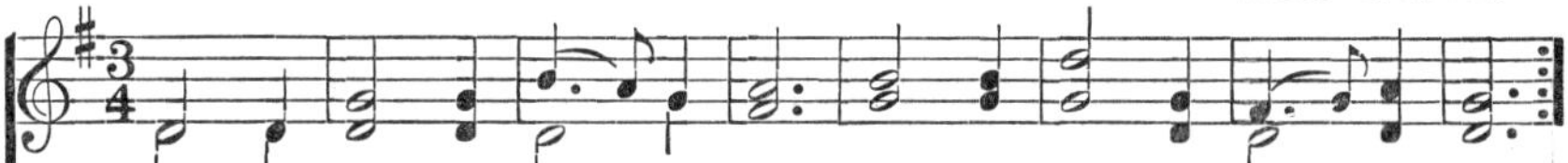

1. {Ho - ly Spir - it, faith - ful Guide, Ev - er near the Chris-tian's side;
{Gen - tly lead us by the hand, Pil - grims in a des - ert land;}
2. {Ev - er pres - ent, tru - est Friend, Ev - er near Thine aid to lend,
{Leave us not to doubt and fear, Grop-ing on in dark-ness drear;}
3. {When our days of toil shall cease, Wait-ing still for sweet re-lease,
{Look - ing up to heaven in prayer, Joy - ful that our names are there:}

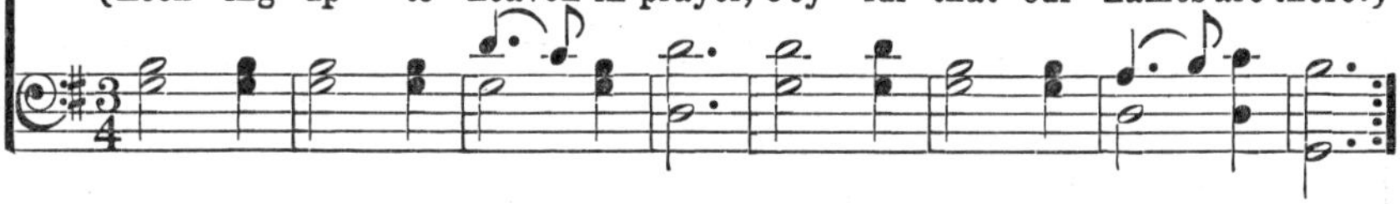

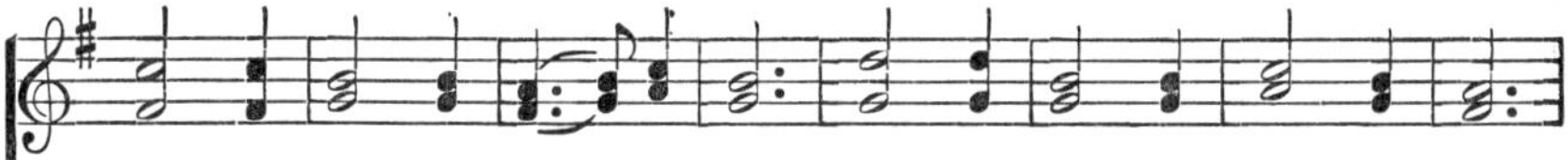

Wea - ry souls for - e'er re - joice, While they hear that sweet - est voice,
When the storms are rag - ing sore, Hearts grow faint, and hopes give o'er,
Fear - ing not the dis - mal flood, Plead - ing naught but Je - sus' blood,

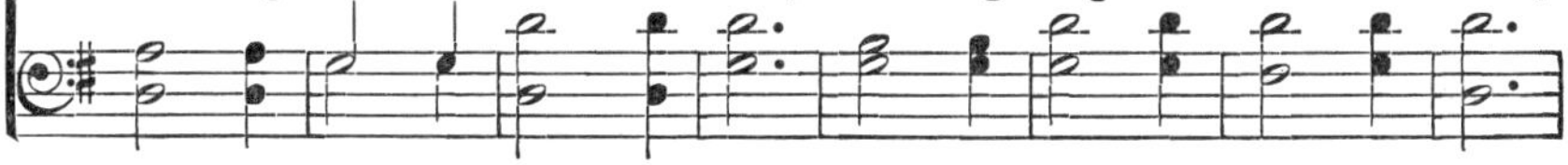

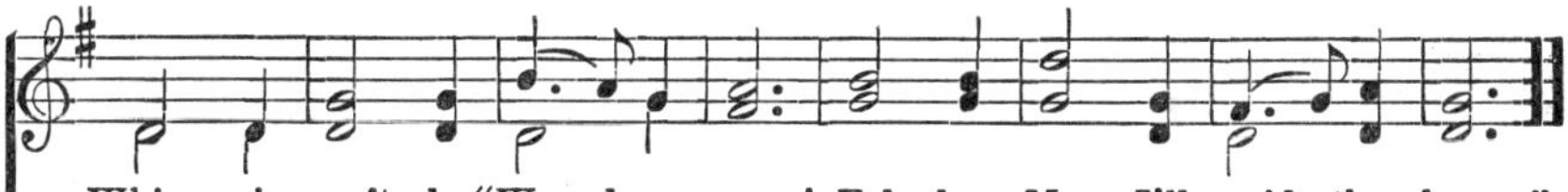

Whis-pering soft - ly, "Wan-derer, come! Fol - low Me, I'll guide thee home."
Whis - per soft - ly, "Wan-derer, come! Fol - low Me, I'll guide thee home."
Whis - per soft - ly, "Wan-derer, come! Fol - low Me, I'll guide thee home."

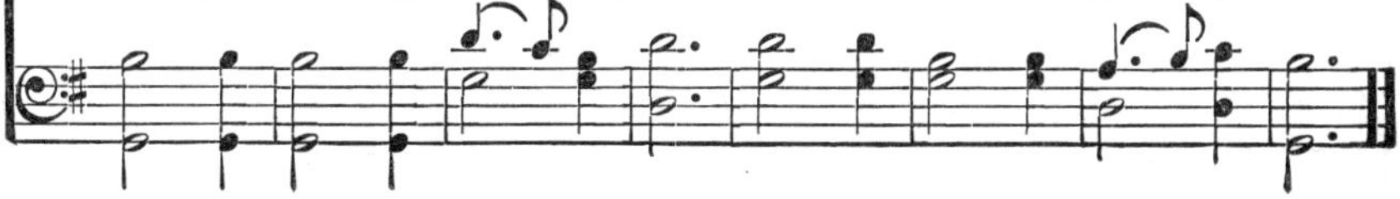

246 For the Beauty of the Earth

Folliott S. Pierpont
DIX
Conrad Kocher
1. For the beau - ty of the earth, For the glo - ry of the skies,
2. For the won - der of each hour Of the day and of the night,
3. For the joy of hu - man love, Broth-er, sis - ter, par - ent, child,
4. For Thy Church that ev - er - more Lift - eth ho - ly hands a - bove,
For the love which from our birth O - ver and a - round us lies;
Hill and vale, and tree and flower, Sun and moon, and stars of light;
Friends on earth, and friends a - bove, For all gen-tle thoughts and mild;
Of - fering up on ev - ery shore Her pure sac - ri - fice of love;
Christ our God, to Thee we raise This our hymn of grate - ful praise.
Christ our God, to Thee we raise This our hymn of grate - ful praise.
Christ our God, to Thee we raise This our hymn of grate - ful praise.
Christ our God, to Thee we raise This our hymn of grate - ful praise.
247 My Soul, Be On Thy Guard
George Heath
LABAN
Lowell Mason
1. My soul, be on Thy guard; Ten thou-sand foes a - rise; The
2. O watch, and fight, and pray; The bat - tle ne'er give o'er; Re-
3. Ne'er think the vic - t'ry won, Nor lay thine ar - mor down; The
4. Fight on, my soul, till death Shall bring thee to thy God; He'll

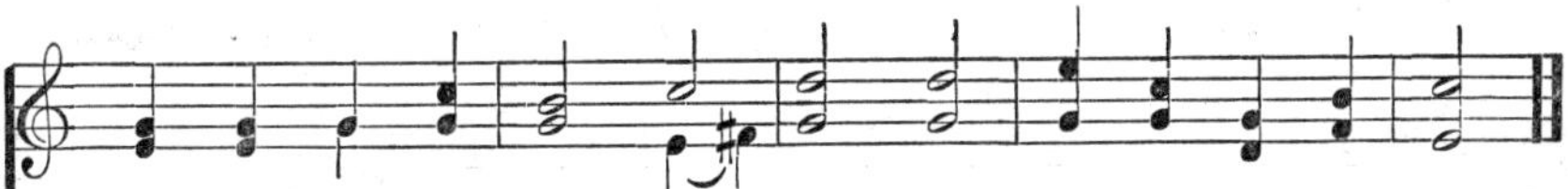

hosts of sin are press - ing hard To draw thee from the skies.
new it bold - ly ev - ery day, And help di - vine im - plore.
work of faith will not be done, Till thou ob - tain the crown.
take thee, at thy part - ing breath, To His di - vine a - bode.

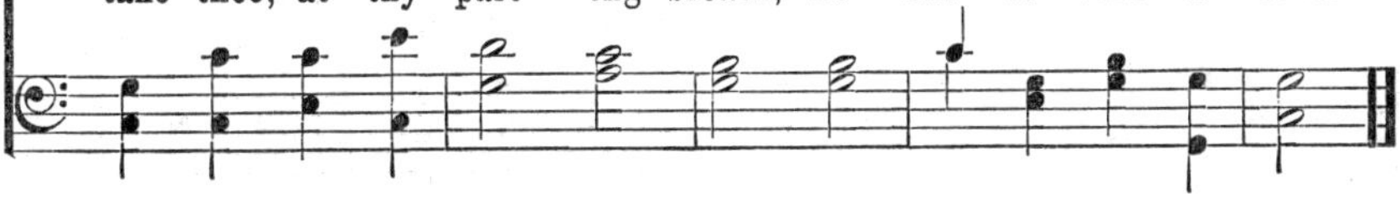

248 Hail to the Brightness

THOMAS HASTINGS — WESLEY — LOWELL MASON

1. Hail to the bright-ness of Zi - on's glad morn-ing! Joy to the lands that in dark - ness have lain! Hushed be the ac - cents of sor-row and mourn-ing, Zi - on in tri-umph be - gins her mild reign.

2. Hail to the bright-ness of Zi - on's glad morn-ing, Long by the proph - ets of Is - rael fore - told! Hail to the mil - lions from bond-age re - turn - ing! Gen - tiles and Jews the blest vi - sion be - hold.

3. Lo, in the des - ert rich flow - ers are spring-ing, Streams ev - er co - pious are glid - ing a - long; Loud from the moun-tain - tops ech - oes are ring - ing, Wastes rise in ver-dure and min - gle in song.

4. See, from all lands, from the isles of the o - cean, Praise to Je - ho - vah as - cend - ing on high; Fallen are the en - gines of war and com - mo - tion, Shouts of sal - va - tion are rend-ing the sky.

249 On Jordan's Stormy Banks

SAMUEL STENNETT
Arr. by R. M. McINTOSH
1. On Jor-dan's storm-y banks I stand, And cast a wish-ful eye
2. All o'er those wide-ex-tend-ed plains Shines one e-ter-nal day;
3. No chill-ing winds, nor poisonous breath, Can reach that health-ful shore;
4. When shall I reach that hap-py place, And be for-ev-er blest?
FINE
To Ca-naan's fair and hap-py land, Where my pos-ses-sions lie.
There God the Son for-ev-er reigns, And scat-ters night a-way.
Sick-ness and sor-row, pain and death, Are felt and feared no more.
When shall I see my Fa-ther's face, And in His bos-om rest?
D. S.—O who will come and go with me? I am bound for the prom-ised land.
REFRAIN
D. S.
I am bound for the promised land, ... I am bound for the promised land;
promised land,
250 On Jordan's Stormy Banks
[Second Tune]
T. C. O'KANE
(The words of the four stanzas same as First Tune.)

On Jordan's Stormy Banks

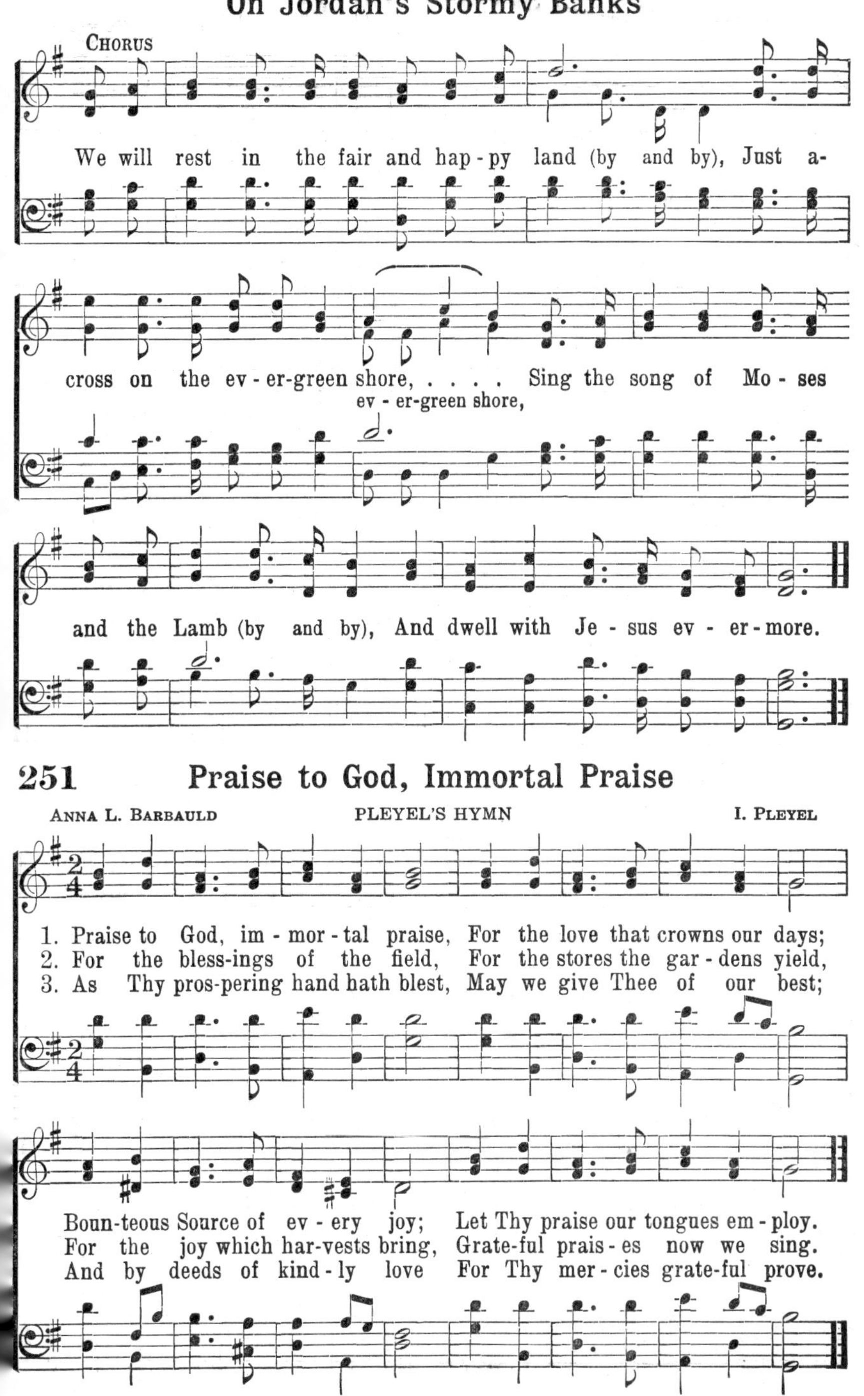
CHORUS
We will rest in the fair and hap - py land (by and by), Just a-
cross on the ev - er-green shore, ... Sing the song of Mo - ses
ev - er-green shore,
and the Lamb (by and by), And dwell with Je - sus ev - er - more.
251 Praise to God, Immortal Praise
ANNA L. BARBAULD
PLEYEL'S HYMN
I. PLEYEL
1. Praise to God, im - mor - tal praise, For the love that crowns our days;
2. For the bless-ings of the field, For the stores the gar - dens yield,
3. As Thy pros-pering hand hath blest, May we give Thee of our best;
Boun-teous Source of ev - ery joy; Let Thy praise our tongues em - ploy.
For the joy which har-vests bring, Grate-ful prais - es now we sing.
And by deeds of kind - ly love For Thy mer - cies grate-ful prove.

252 Saviour, Again

JOHN ELLERTON ELLERS E. J. HOPKINS

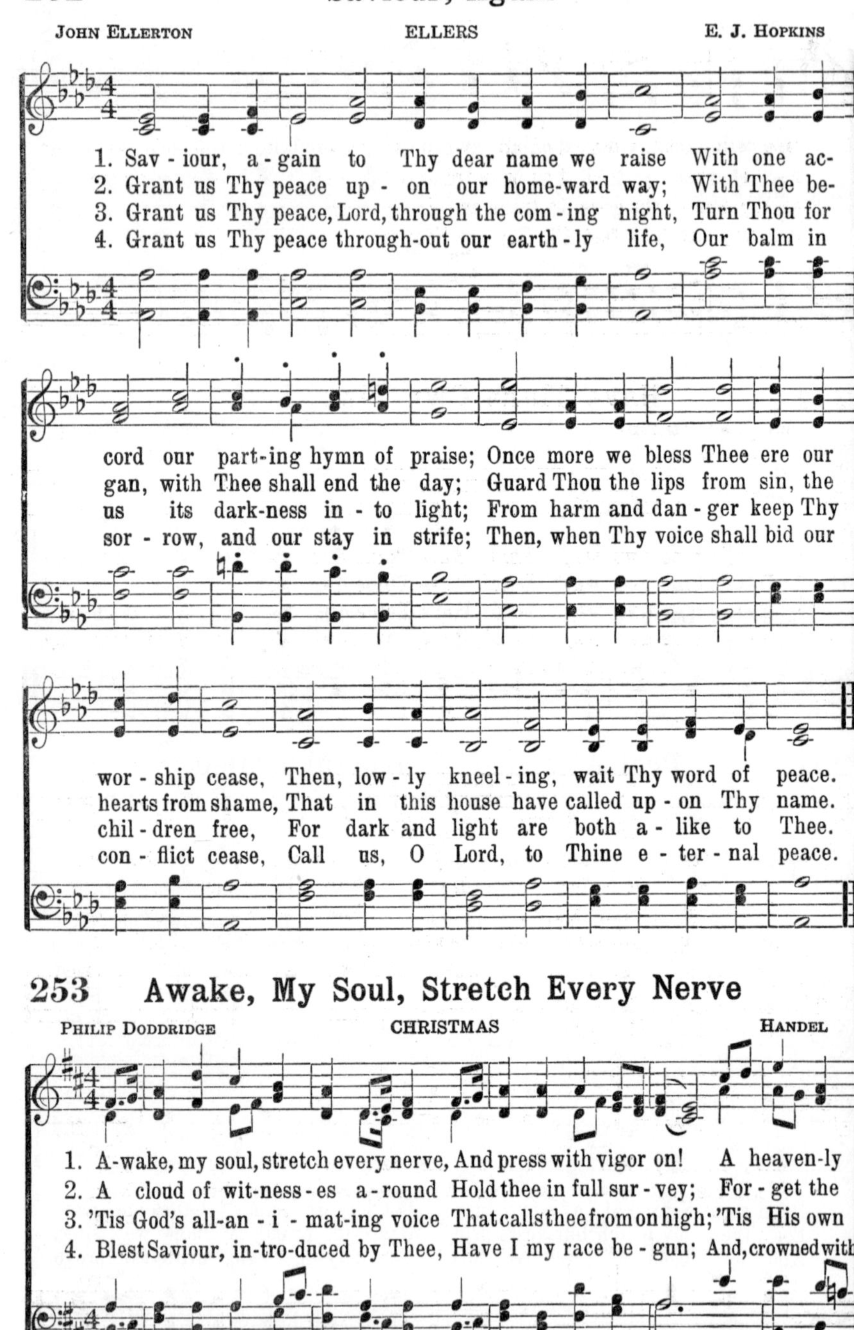
1. Sav - iour, a - gain to Thy dear name we raise With one ac-
2. Grant us Thy peace up - on our home-ward way; With Thee be-
3. Grant us Thy peace, Lord, through the com - ing night, Turn Thou for
4. Grant us Thy peace through-out our earth - ly life, Our balm in
cord our part-ing hymn of praise; Once more we bless Thee ere our
gan, with Thee shall end the day; Guard Thou the lips from sin, the
us its dark-ness in - to light; From harm and dan - ger keep Thy
sor - row, and our stay in strife; Then, when Thy voice shall bid our
wor - ship cease, Then, low - ly kneel - ing, wait Thy word of peace.
hearts from shame, That in this house have called up - on Thy name.
chil - dren free, For dark and light are both a - like to Thee.
con - flict cease, Call us, O Lord, to Thine e - ter - nal peace.
253 Awake, My Soul, Stretch Every Nerve
PHILIP DODDRIDGE CHRISTMAS HANDEL
1. A-wake, my soul, stretch every nerve, And press with vigor on! A heaven-ly
2. A cloud of wit-ness - es a - round Hold thee in full sur - vey; For - get the
3. 'Tis God's all-an - i - mat-ing voice That calls thee from on high; 'Tis His own
4. Blest Saviour, in-tro-duced by Thee, Have I my race be - gun; And, crowned with

Awake, My Soul, Stretch Every Nerve

race de-mands thy zeal, And an im-mor-tal crown, And an im-mor-tal crown.
steps al-read-y trod, And on-ward urge thy way, And on-ward urge thy way.
hand pre-sents the prize To thine as-pir-ing eye, To thine as-pir-ing eye.
vic-tory, at Thy feet I'll lay my hon-ors down, I'll lay my hon-ors down.
254 Have Thine Own Way, Lord!
Adelaide A. Pollard
Geo. C. Stebbins
Slowly
1. Have Thine own way, Lord! Have Thine own way! Thou art the Pot-ter, I am the clay. Mould me and make me Aft-er Thy will, While I am wait-ing, Yield-ed and still.
2. Have Thine own way, Lord! Have Thine own way! Search me and try me, Mas-ter, to-day! Whit-er than snow, Lord, Wash me just now, As in Thy pres-ence Hum-bly I bow.
3. Have Thine own way, Lord! Have Thine own way! Wound-ed and wea-ry, Help me, I pray! Pow-er— all pow-er— Sure-ly is Thine! Touch me and heal me, Sav-iour di-vine!
4. Have Thine own way, Lord! Have Thine own way! Hold o'er my be-ing Ab-so-lute sway! Fill with Thy Spir-it Till all shall see Christ on-ly, al-ways, Liv-ing in me!

255 **All Hail the Power**

E. PERRONET | DIADEM | JAMES ELLOR

1. All hail the power of Je - sus' name! Let an-gels pros-trate fall,
2. Ye cho - sen seed of Is - rael's race, Ye ran-somed from the fall,
3. Let ev - ery kin - dred, ev - ery tribe, On this ter - res-trial ball,
4. O that with yon - der sa - cred throng We at His feet may fall,
Let an - gels pros-trate fall; Bring forth the roy - al di - a - dem,
Ye ran-somed from the fall, Hail Him who saves you by His grace,
On this ter - res - trial ball, To Him all maj - es - ty as - cribe,
We at His feet may fall! We'll join the ev - er - last - ing song,
And crown.................................. Him, Crown Him,
And crown Him, crown Him, crown Him, crown Him, And crown Him Lord of
And crown.................................. Him, Crown Him,
And crown Him, crown Him, crown Him, Crown.........................
crown Him, crown Him;
all, crown Him; And crown Him Lord of all!
crown............ Him;
.... Him; And crown Him Lord of all!

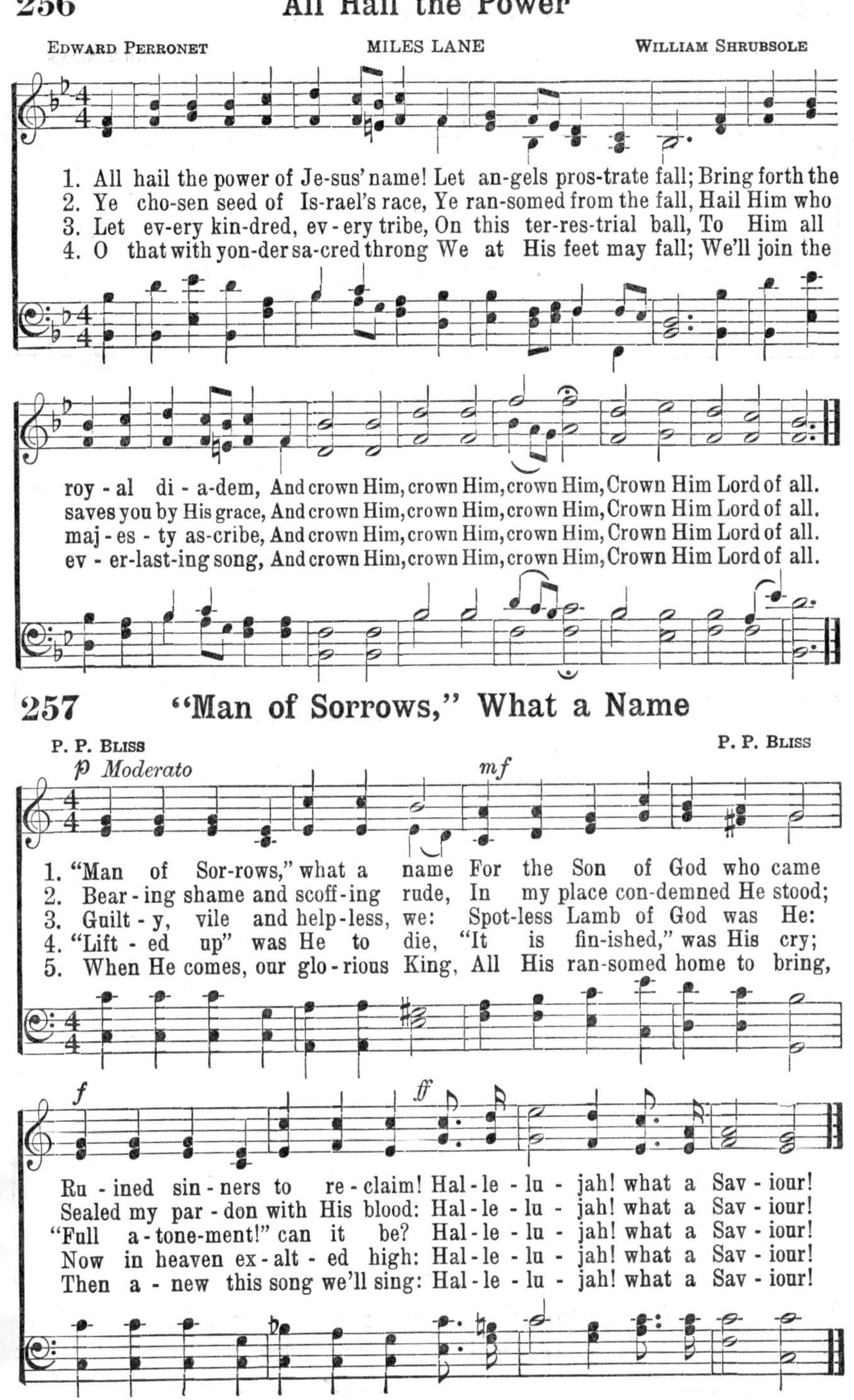
256 All Hail the Power
Edward Perronet
MILES LANE
William Shrubsole
1. All hail the power of Je-sus' name! Let an-gels pros-trate fall; Bring forth the
2. Ye cho-sen seed of Is-rael's race, Ye ran-somed from the fall, Hail Him who
3. Let ev-ery kin-dred, ev-ery tribe, On this ter-res-trial ball, To Him all
4. O that with yon-der sa-cred throng We at His feet may fall; We'll join the
roy - al di - a-dem, And crown Him, crown Him, crown Him, Crown Him Lord of all.
saves you by His grace, And crown Him, crown Him, crown Him, Crown Him Lord of all.
maj - es - ty as-cribe, And crown Him, crown Him, crown Him, Crown Him Lord of all.
ev - er-last-ing song, And crown Him, crown Him, crown Him, Crown Him Lord of all.
257 "Man of Sorrows," What a Name
P. P. Bliss
P. P. Bliss
p Moderato
mf
1. "Man of Sor-rows," what a name For the Son of God who came
2. Bear - ing shame and scoff-ing rude, In my place con-demned He stood;
3. Guilt - y, vile and help-less, we: Spot-less Lamb of God was He:
4. "Lift - ed up" was He to die, "It is fin-ished," was His cry;
5. When He comes, our glo - rious King, All His ran-somed home to bring,
f
ff
Ru - ined sin - ners to re - claim! Hal - le - lu - jah! what a Sav - iour!
Sealed my par - don with His blood: Hal - le - lu - jah! what a Sav - iour!
"Full a - tone-ment!" can it be? Hal - le - lu - jah! what a Sav - iour!
Now in heaven ex - alt - ed high: Hal - le - lu - jah! what a Sav - iour!
Then a - new this song we'll sing: Hal - le - lu - jah! what a Sav - iour!

258 Jesus Paid It All

Mrs. H. M. Hall — John T. Grape

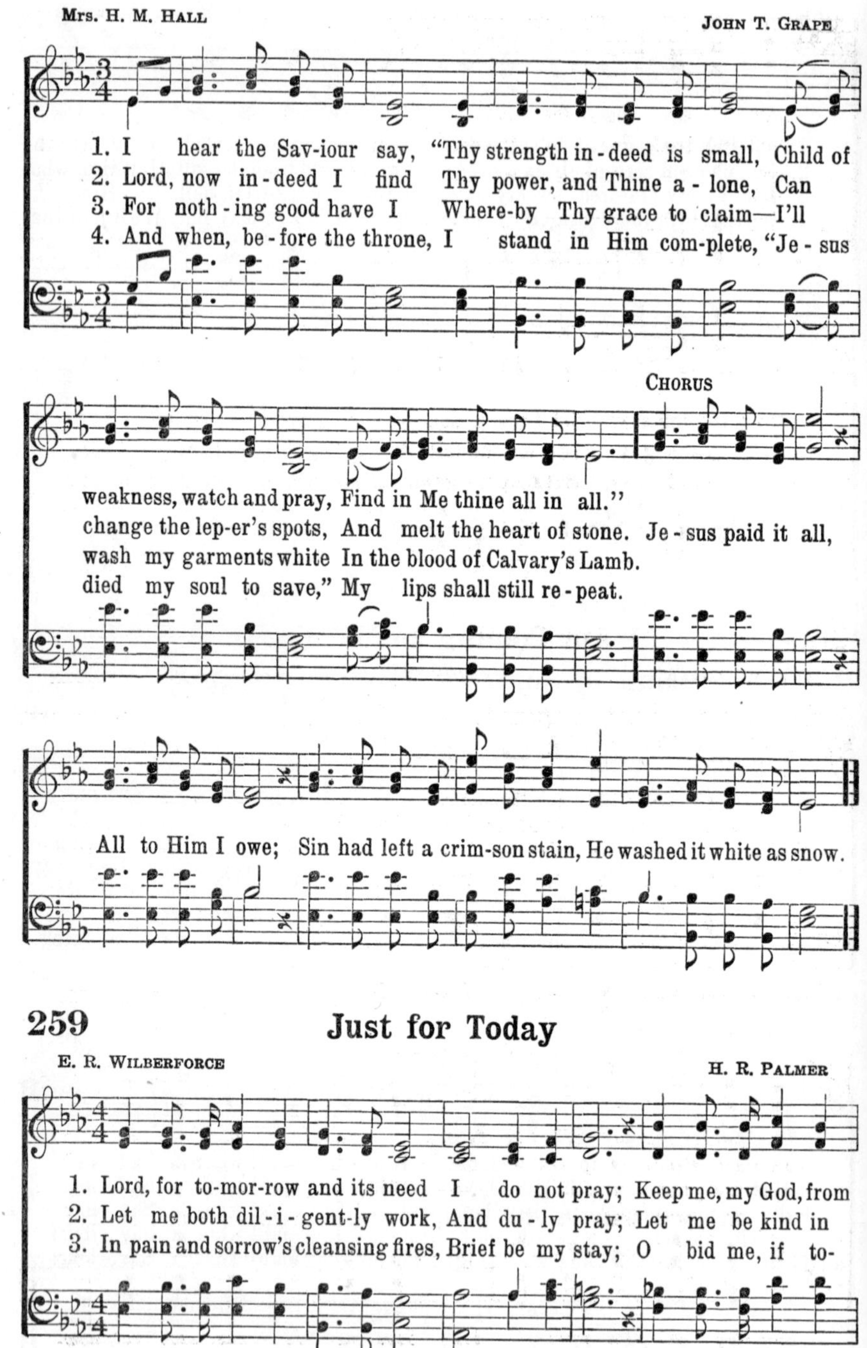
1. I hear the Sav-iour say, "Thy strength in-deed is small, Child of weakness, watch and pray, Find in Me thine all in all."
2. Lord, now in-deed I find Thy power, and Thine a-lone, Can change the lep-er's spots, And melt the heart of stone.
3. For noth-ing good have I Where-by Thy grace to claim—I'll wash my garments white In the blood of Calvary's Lamb.
4. And when, be-fore the throne, I stand in Him com-plete, "Je-sus died my soul to save," My lips shall still re-peat.
Chorus
Je-sus paid it all, All to Him I owe; Sin had left a crim-son stain, He washed it white as snow.

259 Just for Today

E. R. Wilberforce — H. R. Palmer

1. Lord, for to-mor-row and its need I do not pray; Keep me, my God, from
2. Let me both dil-i-gent-ly work, And du-ly pray; Let me be kind in
3. In pain and sorrow's cleansing fires, Brief be my stay; O bid me, if to-

Just for To-day

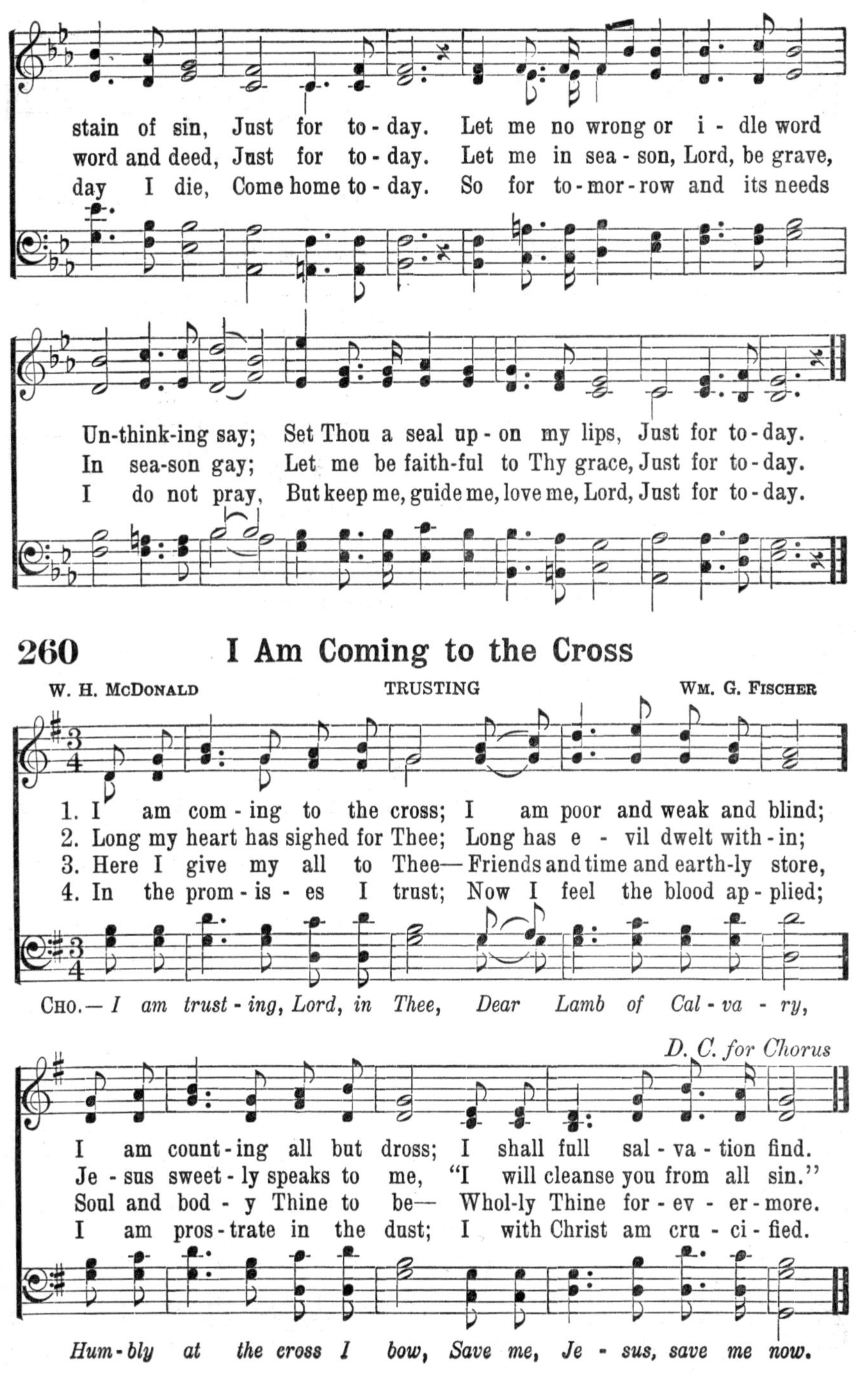

stain of sin, Just for to-day. Let me no wrong or i-dle word
word and deed, Just for to-day. Let me in sea-son, Lord, be grave,
day I die, Come home to-day. So for to-mor-row and its needs
Un-think-ing say; Set Thou a seal up-on my lips, Just for to-day.
In sea-son gay; Let me be faith-ful to Thy grace, Just for to-day.
I do not pray, But keep me, guide me, love me, Lord, Just for to-day.
260
I Am Coming to the Cross
W. H. McDONALD
TRUSTING
WM. G. FISCHER
1. I am com-ing to the cross; I am poor and weak and blind;
2. Long my heart has sighed for Thee; Long has e-vil dwelt with-in;
3. Here I give my all to Thee— Friends and time and earth-ly store,
4. In the prom-is-es I trust; Now I feel the blood ap-plied;
CHO.— I am trust-ing, Lord, in Thee, Dear Lamb of Cal-va-ry,
D. C. for Chorus
I am count-ing all but dross; I shall full sal-va-tion find.
Je-sus sweet-ly speaks to me, "I will cleanse you from all sin."
Soul and bod-y Thine to be— Whol-ly Thine for-ev-er-more.
I am pros-trate in the dust; I with Christ am cru-ci-fied.
Hum-bly at the cross I bow, Save me, Je-sus, save me now.

261 I'm Going Home

Rev. Wm. Hunter
Wm. Miller
1. My heaven-ly home is bright and fair, Nor pain nor death can en - ter there;
2. My Fa-ther's house is built on high, Far, far a - bove the star-ry sky;
3. Let oth - ers seek a home be - low, Which flames devour, or waves o'er-flow;
Cho.—I'm go - ing home, I'm go - ing home, I'm go - ing home to die no more,
D.C. for Chorus
Its glittering towers the sun out-shine, That heavenly man-sion shall be mine.
When from this earth-ly pris - on free, That heavenly man-sion mine shall be.
Be mine a hap - pier lot to own A heaven-ly man-sion near the throne.
To die no more, to die no more; I'm go - ing home to die no more.
262 Let the Lower Lights Be Burning
P. P. Bliss
P. P. Bliss
1. Bright-ly beams our Fa-ther's mer - cy From His light-house ev - er - more,
2. Dark the night of sin has set - tled, Loud the an - gry bil-lows roar;
3. Trim your fee - ble lamp, my broth - er: Some poor sail - or tem-pest tossed,
Fine.
But to us He gives the keep-ing Of the lights a - long the shore.
Ea - ger eyes are watch-ing, long-ing, For the lights a - long the shore.
Try - ing now to make the har - bor, In the dark-ness may be lost.
D. S.–Some poor faint-ing, strug-gling sea - man You may res - cue, you may save.

Let the Lower Lights Be Burning

Chorus
D.S.
Let the low - er lights be burn-ing! Send a gleam a - cross the wave!
263
Sweet Hour of Prayer
W. W. Walford
Wm. B. Bradbury
1. Sweet hour of prayer! sweet hour of prayer! That calls me from a world of care,
2. Sweet hour of prayer! sweet hour of prayer! Thy wings shall my pe - ti - tion bear
3. Sweet hour of prayer! sweet hour of prayer! May I thy con - so - la - tion share,
And bids me at my Fa-ther's throne Make all my wants and wish-es known;
To Him whose truth and faith-ful - ness En-gage the wait-ing soul to bless;
Till, from Mount Pisgah's loft - y height, I view my home, and take my flight:
In sea - sons of dis - tress and grief, My soul has of - ten found re - lief,
And since He bids me seek His face, Be-lieve His Word and trust His grace,
This robe of flesh I'll drop, and rise To seize the ev - er - last - ing prize;
And oft es-caped the tempt-er's snare By thy re-turn, sweet hour of prayer.
I'll cast on Him my ev - ery care, And wait for thee, sweet hour of prayer.
And shout, while passing through the air, Farewell, farewell, sweet hour of prayer.

264 Prayer Is the Soul's Sincere Desire

JAS. MONTGOMERY — NEWCASTLE — A. B. EVERETT

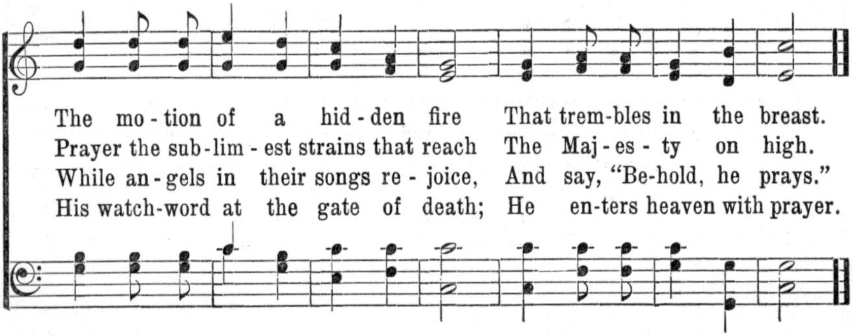

1. Prayer is the soul's sin - cere de - sire, Un - ut-tered or ex - pressed;
The mo - tion of a hid - den fire That trem-bles in the breast.

2. Prayer is the sim - plest form of speech That in-fant lips can try;
Prayer the sub-lim - est strains that reach The Maj - es - ty on high.

3. Prayer is the con - trite sin-ner's voice Re - turn-ing from his ways,
While an - gels in their songs re - joice, And say, "Be-hold, he prays."

4. Prayer is the Chris-tian's vi - tal breath, The Chris-tian's na-tive air,
His watch-word at the gate of death; He en-ters heaven with prayer.

265 I Am Coming, Lord

L. H. — L. HARTSOUGH

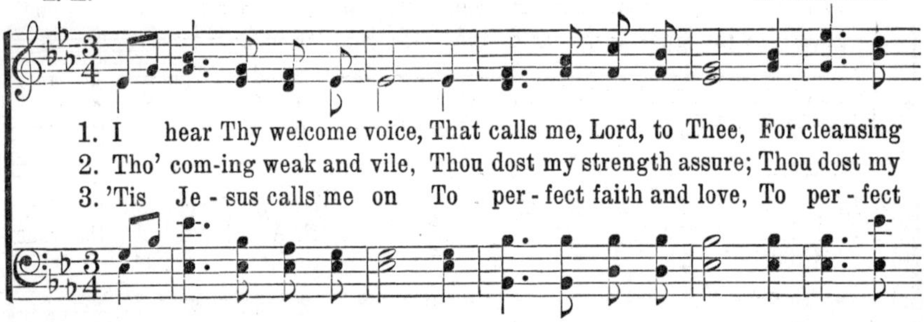

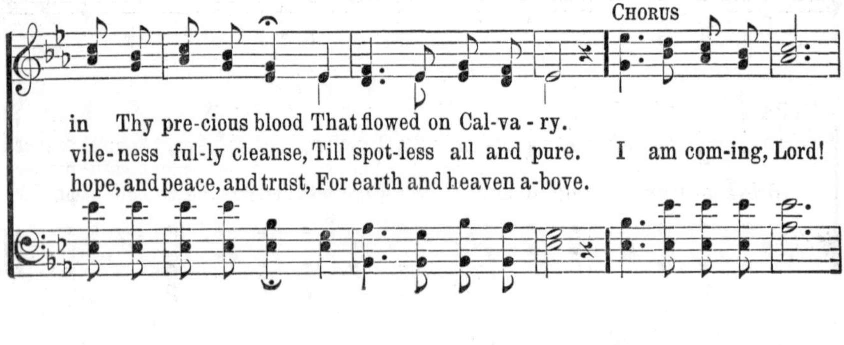

1. I hear Thy welcome voice, That calls me, Lord, to Thee, For cleansing in Thy pre-cious blood That flowed on Cal-va - ry.

2. Tho' com-ing weak and vile, Thou dost my strength assure; Thou dost my vile-ness ful-ly cleanse, Till spot-less all and pure.

3. 'Tis Je - sus calls me on To per - fect faith and love, To per - fect hope, and peace, and trust, For earth and heaven a-bove.

CHORUS

I am com-ing, Lord!

I Am Coming, Lord
Coming now to Thee! Wash me, cleanse me in the blood That flowed on Cal-va-ry!
266
Bring Them In
Alexcenah Thomas
W. A. Ogden
1. Hark! 'tis the Shepherd's voice I hear, Out in the des-ert dark and drear,
2. Who'll go and help this Shepherd kind, Help Him the wandering ones to find?
3. Out in the des-ert hear their cry, Out on the mountains wild and high;
Call-ing the sheep who've gone a-stray, Far from the Shepherd's fold a-way.
Who'll bring the lost ones to the fold, Where they'll be sheltered from the cold?
Hark! 'tis the Mas-ter speaks to thee, "Go find My sheep wher-e'er they be."
Chorus
Bring them in, bring them in, Bring them in from the fields of sin;
Bring them in, bring them in, Bring the wandering ones to Je-sus.

267 Christ for the World We Sing

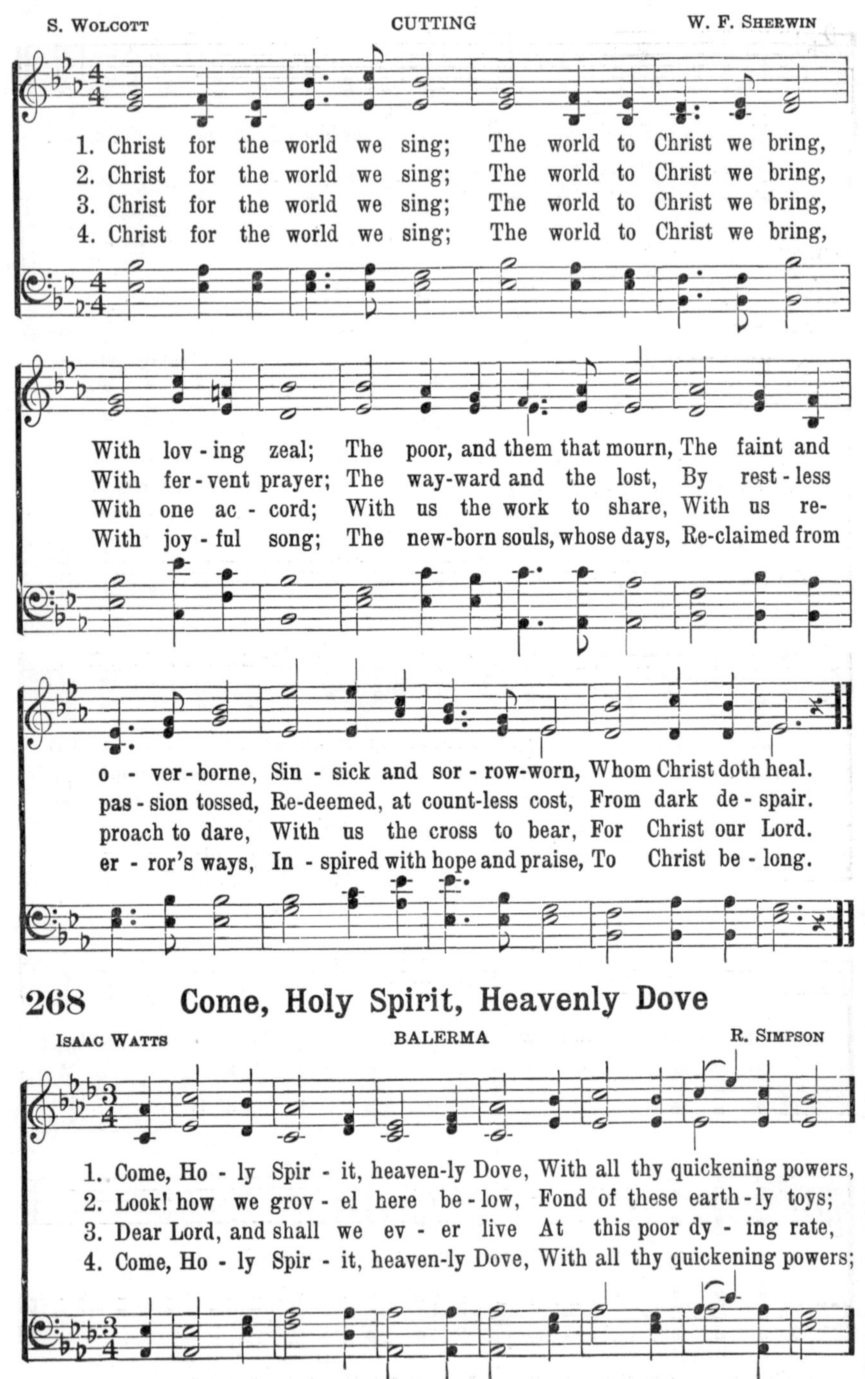
S. Wolcott
CUTTING
W. F. Sherwin
1. Christ for the world we sing; The world to Christ we bring, With lov-ing zeal; The poor, and them that mourn, The faint and o-ver-borne, Sin-sick and sor-row-worn, Whom Christ doth heal.
2. Christ for the world we sing; The world to Christ we bring, With fer-vent prayer; The way-ward and the lost, By rest-less pas-sion tossed, Re-deemed, at count-less cost, From dark de-spair.
3. Christ for the world we sing; The world to Christ we bring, With one ac-cord; With us the work to share, With us re-proach to dare, With us the cross to bear, For Christ our Lord.
4. Christ for the world we sing; The world to Christ we bring, With joy-ful song; The new-born souls, whose days, Re-claimed from er-ror's ways, In-spired with hope and praise, To Christ be-long.
268 Come, Holy Spirit, Heavenly Dove
Isaac Watts
BALERMA
R. Simpson
1. Come, Ho-ly Spir-it, heaven-ly Dove, With all thy quickening powers,
2. Look! how we grov-el here be-low, Fond of these earth-ly toys;
3. Dear Lord, and shall we ev-er live At this poor dy-ing rate,
4. Come, Ho-ly Spir-it, heaven-ly Dove, With all thy quickening powers;

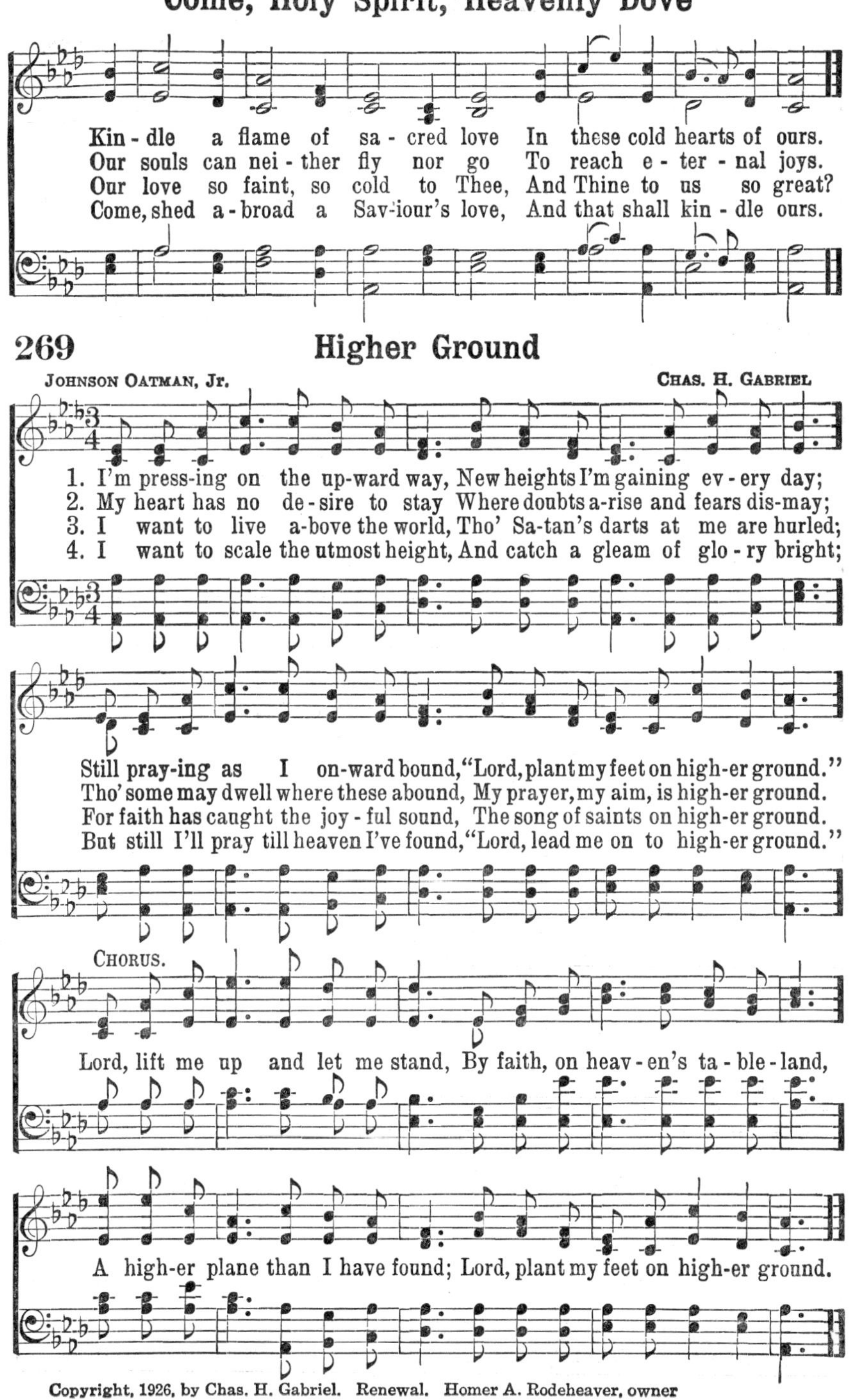
Come, Holy Spirit, Heavenly Dove
Kin - dle a flame of sa - cred love In these cold hearts of ours.
Our souls can nei - ther fly nor go To reach e - ter - nal joys.
Our love so faint, so cold to Thee, And Thine to us so great?
Come, shed a - broad a Sav-iour's love, And that shall kin - dle ours.
269
Higher Ground
JOHNSON OATMAN, Jr.
CHAS. H. GABRIEL
1. I'm press-ing on the up-ward way, New heights I'm gaining ev - ery day;
2. My heart has no de - sire to stay Where doubts a-rise and fears dis-may;
3. I want to live a-bove the world, Tho' Sa-tan's darts at me are hurled;
4. I want to scale the utmost height, And catch a gleam of glo - ry bright;
Still pray-ing as I on-ward bound, "Lord, plant my feet on high-er ground."
Tho' some may dwell where these abound, My prayer, my aim, is high-er ground.
For faith has caught the joy - ful sound, The song of saints on high-er ground.
But still I'll pray till heaven I've found, "Lord, lead me on to high-er ground."
CHORUS.
Lord, lift me up and let me stand, By faith, on heav - en's ta - ble - land,
A high-er plane than I have found; Lord, plant my feet on high-er ground.

270 Fight the Good Fight

JOHN S. B. MONSELL — PENTECOST — WILLIAM BOYD

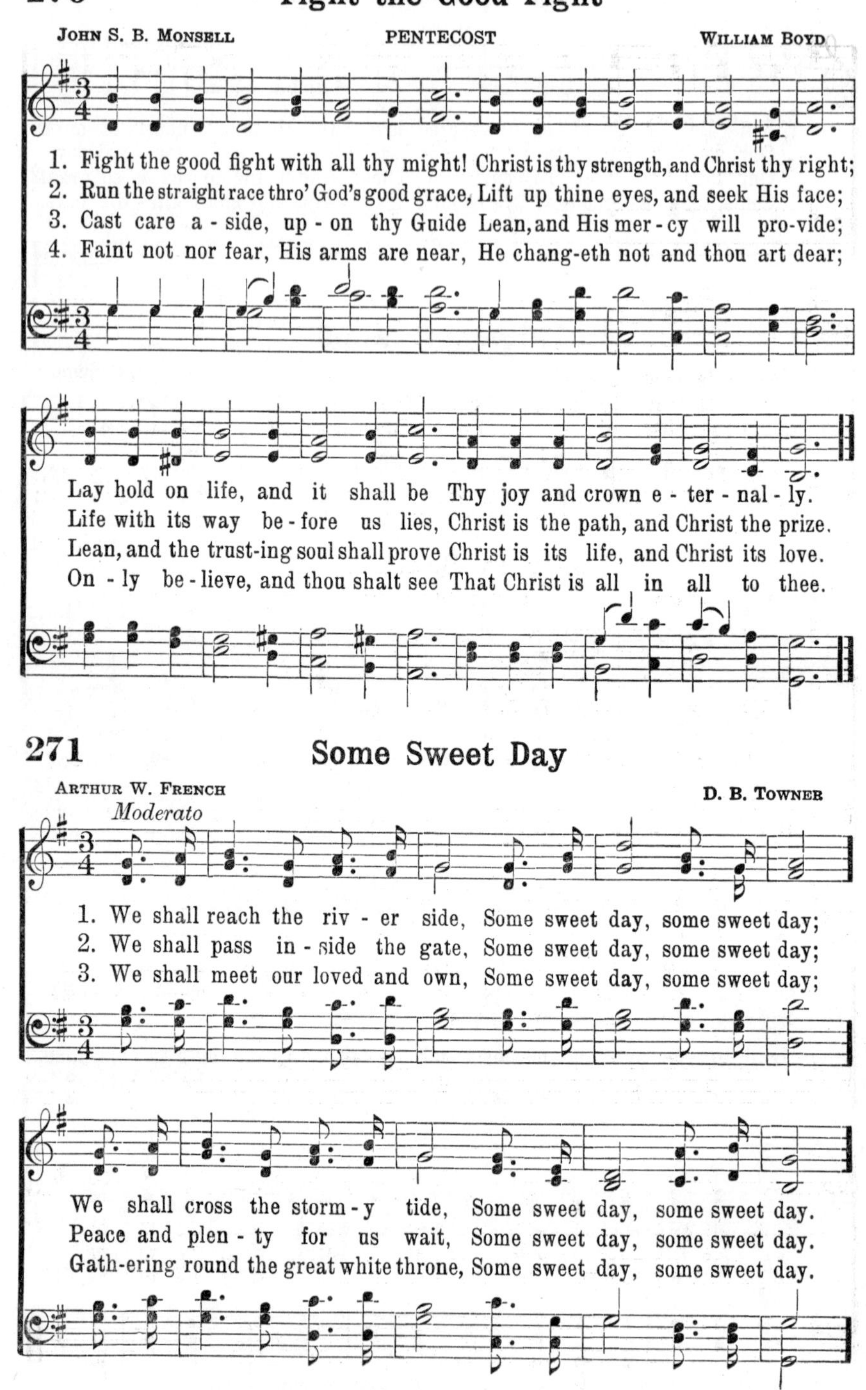
1. Fight the good fight with all thy might! Christ is thy strength, and Christ thy right;
2. Run the straight race thro' God's good grace, Lift up thine eyes, and seek His face;
3. Cast care a - side, up - on thy Guide Lean, and His mer - cy will pro-vide;
4. Faint not nor fear, His arms are near, He chang-eth not and thou art dear;
Lay hold on life, and it shall be Thy joy and crown e - ter - nal - ly.
Life with its way be - fore us lies, Christ is the path, and Christ the prize.
Lean, and the trust-ing soul shall prove Christ is its life, and Christ its love.
On - ly be - lieve, and thou shalt see That Christ is all in all to thee.
271 Some Sweet Day
ARTHUR W. FRENCH
D. B. TOWNER
Moderato
1. We shall reach the riv - er side, Some sweet day, some sweet day;
2. We shall pass in - side the gate, Some sweet day, some sweet day;
3. We shall meet our loved and own, Some sweet day, some sweet day;
We shall cross the storm - y tide, Some sweet day, some sweet day.
Peace and plen - ty for us wait, Some sweet day, some sweet day.
Gath-ering round the great white throne, Some sweet day, some sweet day.

Some Sweet Day

We shall press the sands of gold, While be-fore our eyes un-fold
We shall hear the won-drous strain, Glo-ry to the Lamb that's slain,
By the tree of life so fair, Joy and rap-ture ev-'ry-where,
Heav-en's splen-dor yet un-told, Some sweet day, some sweet day.
Christ was dead, but lives a-gain, Some sweet day, some sweet day.
O, the bliss of o-ver there! Some sweet day, some sweet day.
272
Purer In Heart, O God
Mrs. A. L. Davison
PURER IN HEART
J. H. Fillmore
1. Pur-er in heart, O God, Help me to be; May I de-
2. Pur-er in heart, O God, Help me to be; Teach me to
3. Pur-er in heart, O God, Help me to be; That I Thy
vote my life Whol-ly to Thee. Watch Thou my way-ward feet,
do Thy will Most lov-ing-ly. Be Thou my Friend and Guide,
ho-ly face One day may see. Keep me from se-cret sin,
Guide me with coun-sel sweet; Pur-er in heart, Help me to be.
Let me with Thee a-bide; Pur-er in heart, Help me to be.
Reign Thou my soul with-in; Pur-er in heart, Help me to be.

273 Near to the Heart of God
C. B. McA.
C. B. McAfee
1. There is a place of qui - et rest, Near to the heart of God,
2. There is a place of com - fort sweet, Near to the heart of God,
3. There is a place of full re - lease, Near to the heart of God,
A place where sin can - not mo - lest, Near to the heart of God.
A place where we our Sav - iour meet, Near to the heart of God.
A place where all is joy and peace, Near to the heart of God.
Refrain
O Je - sus, blest Re - deem - er, Sent from the heart of God,
Hold us, who wait be - fore Thee, Near to the heart of God.
Copyright, 1931, by the Lorenz Publishing Co. Renewal. Used by permission
274 Father, I Stretch My Hands to Thee
Charles Wesley
St. Agnes
Rev. J. B. Dykes
1. Fa - ther, I stretch my hands to Thee; No oth - er help I know;
2. What did Thine on - ly Son en - dure Be - fore I drew my breath!
3. Au - thor of faith, to Thee I lift My wea - ry, long - ing eyes;

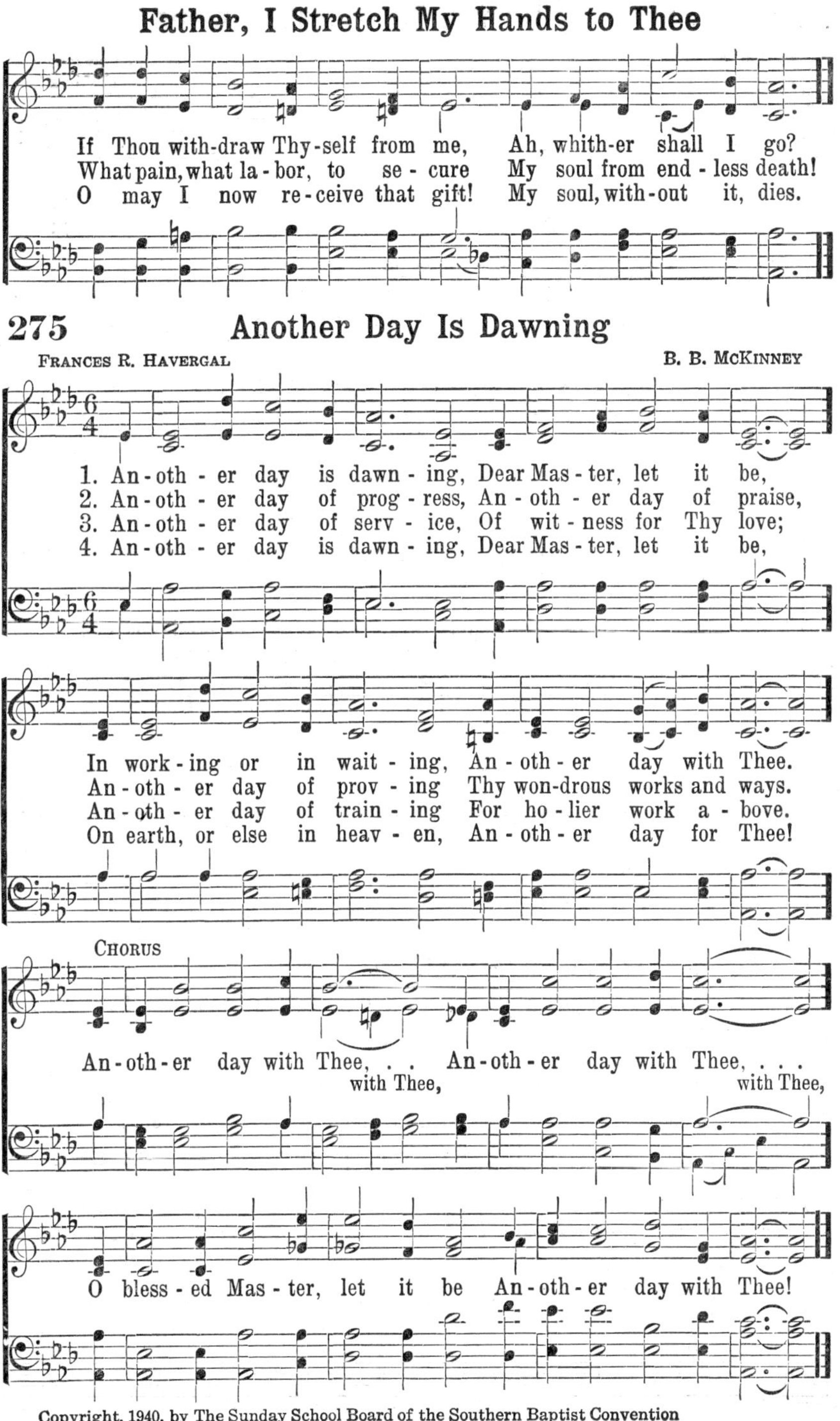
Father, I Stretch My Hands to Thee
If Thou with-draw Thy-self from me, Ah, whith-er shall I go?
What pain, what la-bor, to se-cure My soul from end-less death!
O may I now re-ceive that gift! My soul, with-out it, dies.
275
Another Day Is Dawning
FRANCES R. HAVERGAL
B. B. MCKINNEY
1. An-oth-er day is dawn-ing, Dear Mas-ter, let it be,
2. An-oth-er day of prog-ress, An-oth-er day of praise,
3. An-oth-er day of serv-ice, Of wit-ness for Thy love;
4. An-oth-er day is dawn-ing, Dear Mas-ter, let it be,
In work-ing or in wait-ing, An-oth-er day with Thee.
An-oth-er day of prov-ing Thy won-drous works and ways.
An-oth-er day of train-ing For ho-lier work a-bove.
On earth, or else in heav-en, An-oth-er day for Thee!
CHORUS
An-oth-er day with Thee, . . An-oth-er day with Thee, . . .
with Thee,
with Thee,
O bless-ed Mas-ter, let it be An-oth-er day with Thee!

276 Leaning On the Everlasting Arms

Rev. E. A. Hoffman — A. J. Showalter

1. What a fel-low-ship, what a joy di-vine, Lean-ing on the ev-er-last-ing arms;
2. Oh, how sweet to walk in this pilgrim way, Lean-ing on the ev-er-last-ing arms;
3. What have I to dread, what have I to fear, Lean-ing on the ev-er-last-ing arms;
What a bless-ed-ness, what a peace is mine, Leaning on the ev-er-last-ing arms.
Oh, how bright the path grows from day to day, Leaning on the ev-er-last-ing arms.
I have bless-ed peace with my Lord so near, Leaning on the ev-er-last-ing arms.
Refrain
Lean - ing, lean - ing, Safe and se-cure from all a-larms;
Lean-ing on Je - sus, lean-ing on Je - sus,
Lean - ing, lean - ing, Lean-ing on the ev-er-last-ing arms.
Lean-ing on Je - sus, lean - ing on Je - sus,
277 O, for a Faith That Will Not Shrink
Wm. H. Bathurst
St. Agnes
John B. Dykes
1. O, for a faith that will not shrink, Tho' pressed by ev - ery foe,
2. That will not mur - mur nor com - plain Be-neath the chas-tening rod,
3. A faith that shines more bright and clear When tem-pests rage with-out;
4. Lord, give us such a faith as this, And then, what-e'er may come,

O, for a Faith That Will Not Shrink

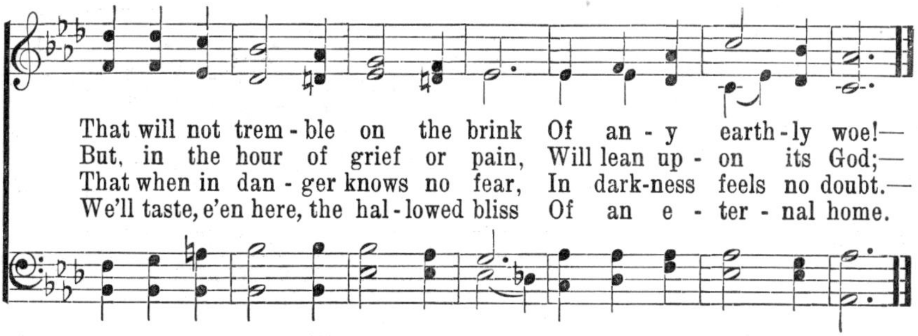

That will not trem - ble on the brink Of an - y earth - ly woe!—
But, in the hour of grief or pain, Will lean up - on its God;—
That when in dan - ger knows no fear, In dark-ness feels no doubt.—
We'll taste, e'en here, the hal - lowed bliss Of an e - ter - nal home.

278 Blessed Quietness

Mrs. M. P. Ferguson, alt. — Arr. from Marshall

1. Joys are flow - ing like a riv - er, Since the Com - fort - er has come;
2. Like the rain that falls from heav-en, Like the sun - light from the sky,
3. What a won - der - ful sal - va - tion Where we al - ways see His face!

He a - bides with us for - ev - er, Makes the trust-ing heart His home.
So the Ho - ly Spir - it giv - en, Falls up - on us from on high.
What a peace - ful hab - i - ta - tion! What a qui - et rest - ing place!

CHORUS

Bless-ed qui - et-ness, ho - ly qui - et-ness, Blest as - sur - ance in my soul!
On the storm-y sea Je - sus speaks to me, And the bil-lows cease to roll.

279 Blessed Be the Name

CHARLES WESLEY — R. E. HUDSON

1. O for a thou-sand tongues to sing, Bless-ed be the name of the Lord!
2. Je - sus, the name that charms our fears, Bless-ed be the name of the Lord!
3. He breaks the power of can-celed sin, Bless-ed be the name of the Lord!
The glo - ries of my God and King, Bless-ed be the name of the Lord!
'Tis mu - sic in the sin-ner's ears, Bless-ed be the name of the Lord!
His blood can make the foul-est clean, Bless-ed be the name of the Lord!
CHORUS
Bless-ed be the name, Bless-ed be the name, Bless-ed be the name of the Lord!
Bless-ed be the name, Bless-ed be the name, Bless-ed be the name of the Lord.

280 This Is the Day the Lord Hath Made

ISAAC WATTS — ARLINGTON — Dr. T. A. ARNE

1. This is the day the Lord hath made; He calls the hours His own;
2. To - day He rose and left the dead, And Sa-tan's em - pire fell;
3. Ho - san - na to th' a-noint-ed King, To Da-vid's ho - ly Son:
4. Blest be the Lord, who comes to men With mes-sag-es of grace;

This Is the Day the Lord Hath Made
Let heaven re-joice, let earth be glad, And praise sur-round the throne.
To-day the saints His tri-umph spread, And all His won-ders tell.
Help us, O Lord! de-scend and bring Sal-va-tion from Thy throne.
Who comes, in God His Fa-ther's name, To save our sin-ful race.
281 When We All Get to Heaven
E. E. Hewitt
Mrs. J. G. Wilson
1. Sing the won-drous love of Je-sus, Sing His mer-cy and His grace;
2. While we walk the pil-grim path-way, Clouds will o-ver-spread the sky;
3. On-ward to the prize be-fore us! Soon His beau-ty we'll be-hold;
In the man-sions bright and bless-ed, He'll pre-pare for us a place.
But when trav-eling days are o-ver, Not a shad-ow, not a sigh.
Soon the pearl-y gates will o-pen, We shall tread the streets of gold.
1. for us a place.
Chorus
When we all get to heav-en, What a day of rejoicing that will be!
When we all What a day of rejoicing that will be!
When we all see Je-sus, We'll sing and shout the vic-to-ry. . . . .
When we all and shout the vic-to-ry.

282 Down to the Sacred Wave

SAMUEL F. SMITH
STATE STREET
JONATHAN C. WOODMAN
1. Down to the sa-cred wave The Lord of life was led; And He who came our souls to save, In Jor-dan bowed His head.
2. With will-ing hearts we tread The path the Sav-iour trod; We love th' ex-am-ple of our Head, The glo-rious Lamb of God.
3. On Thee, on Thee a-lone Our hope and faith re-ly, O Thou, who didst for sin a-tone, Who didst for sin-ners die.
4. We trust Thy sac-ri-fice; To Thy dear cross we flee; O may we die to sin, and rise To life and bliss in Thee.
283 There Is a Name I Love to Hear
F. WHITFIELD
HOW I LOVE JESUS
1. There is a name I love to hear, I love to sing its worth; It sounds like mu-sic in mine ear, The sweetest name on earth.
2. It tells me of a Saviour's love, Who died to set me free; It tells me of His precious blood, The sin-ner's per-fect plea.
3. It tells me what my Fa-ther hath In store for ev-'ry day, And though I tread a darksome path, Yields sunshine all the way.
4. It tells of One whose loving heart Can feel my deepest woe, Who in each sor-row bears a part, That none can bear be-low.
CHORUS
Oh, how I love Je-sus,

There Is a Name I Love to Hear

Oh, how I love Je - sus, Oh, how I love Je - sus, Because He first loved me.

284 'Tis so Sweet to Trust in Jesus
Louisa M. R. Stead
Wm. J. Kirkpatrick
1. 'Tis so sweet to trust in Je - sus, Just to take Him at His word;
2. O how sweet to trust in Je - sus, Just to trust His cleansing blood;
3. Yes, 'tis sweet to trust in Je - sus, Just from sin and self to cease;
4. I'm so glad I learned to trust Thee, Pre-cious Je - sus, Sav-iour, Friend;
Just to rest up - on His prom-ise, Just to know "Thus saith the Lord."
Just in sim - ple faith to plunge me 'Neath the heal-ing, cleans-ing flood!
Just from Je - sus sim - ply tak - ing Life and rest, and joy and peace.
And I know that Thou art with me, Wilt be with me to the end.
Chorus
Je - sus, Je - sus, how I trust Him, How I've proved Him o'er and o'er!
p
Je - sus, Je - sus, pre - cious Je - sus! O for grace to trust Him more!

285 Rejoice, Ye Pure in Heart

EDWARD H. PLUMPTRE — MARION — ARTHUR H. MESSITER

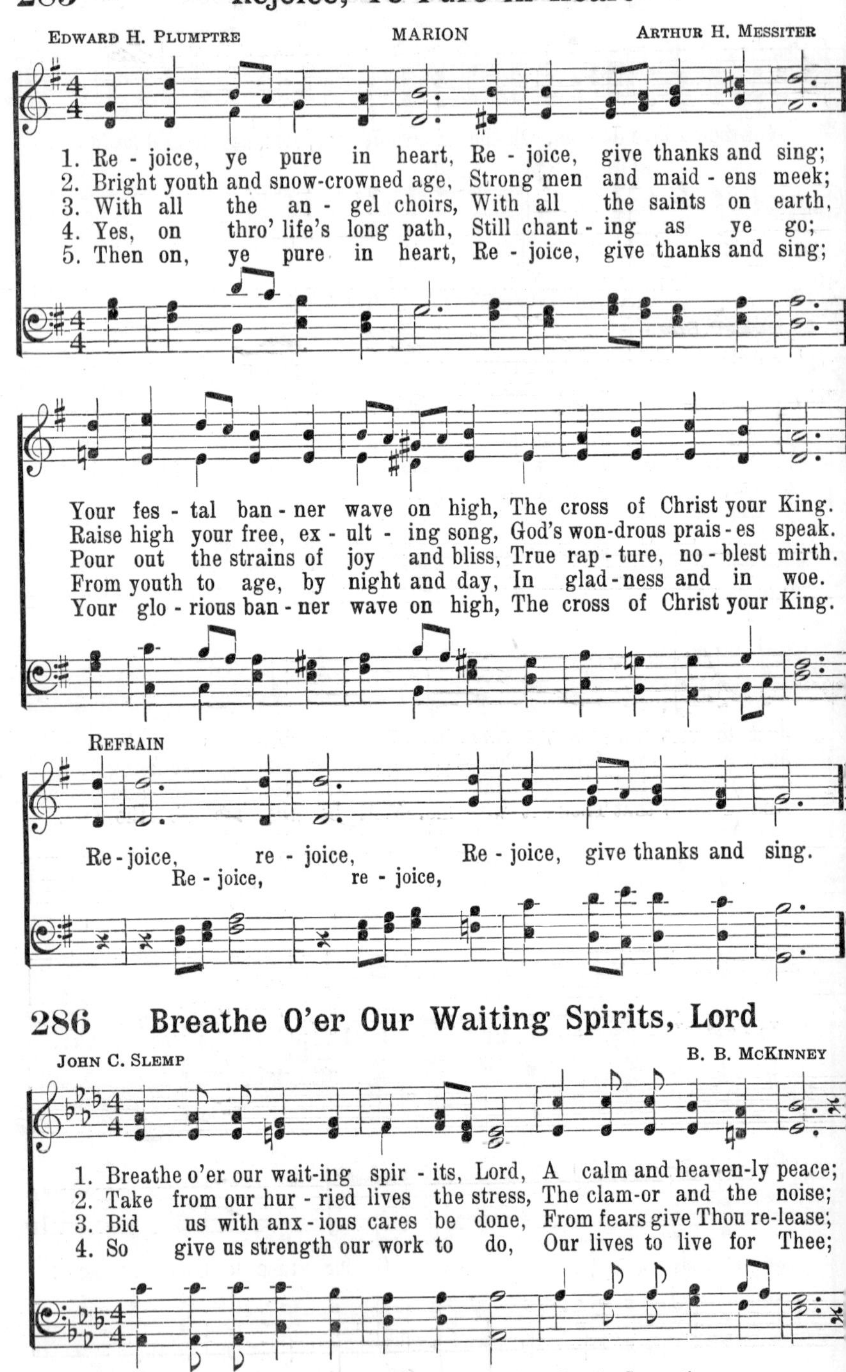
1. Re - joice, ye pure in heart, Re - joice, give thanks and sing;
2. Bright youth and snow-crowned age, Strong men and maid - ens meek;
3. With all the an - gel choirs, With all the saints on earth,
4. Yes, on thro' life's long path, Still chant - ing as ye go;
5. Then on, ye pure in heart, Re - joice, give thanks and sing;
Your fes - tal ban - ner wave on high, The cross of Christ your King.
Raise high your free, ex - ult - ing song, God's won-drous prais - es speak.
Pour out the strains of joy and bliss, True rap - ture, no - blest mirth.
From youth to age, by night and day, In glad - ness and in woe.
Your glo - rious ban - ner wave on high, The cross of Christ your King.
REFRAIN
Re - joice, re - joice, Re - joice, give thanks and sing.
Re - joice, re - joice,

286 Breathe O'er Our Waiting Spirits, Lord

JOHN C. SLEMP — B. B. McKINNEY

1. Breathe o'er our wait-ing spir - its, Lord, A calm and heaven-ly peace;
2. Take from our hur - ried lives the stress, The clam-or and the noise;
3. Bid us with anx - ious cares be done, From fears give Thou re-lease;
4. So give us strength our work to do, Our lives to live for Thee;

Breathe O'er Our Waiting Spirits, Lord
Make us at-ten-tive to Thy Word, Let all our striv-ings cease.
Re-fresh our souls in Sab-bath rest, Give us e-ter-nal joys.
Make us with Thee to be at one, Our fal-tering faith in-crease.
In wor-ship now our vows re-new— True Chris-tians let us be.
287
The Hem of His Garment
G. F. R.
Geo. F. Root
1. She on-ly touched the hem of His gar-ment As to His side she stole,
2. She came in fear and trem-bling be-fore Him, She knew her Lord had come;
3. He turned with "Daughter, be of good com-fort, Thy faith hath made thee whole!"
A-mid the crowd that gathered a-round Him, And straightway she was whole.
She felt that from Him vir-tue hath healed her, The might-y deed was done.
And peace that pass-eth all un-der-stand-ing With glad-ness filled her soul.
Chorus
Oh, touch the hem of His gar-ment! And thou, too, shalt be free!
His sav-ing power this ver-y hour Shall give new life to thee!

288 Depth of Mercy! Can There Be

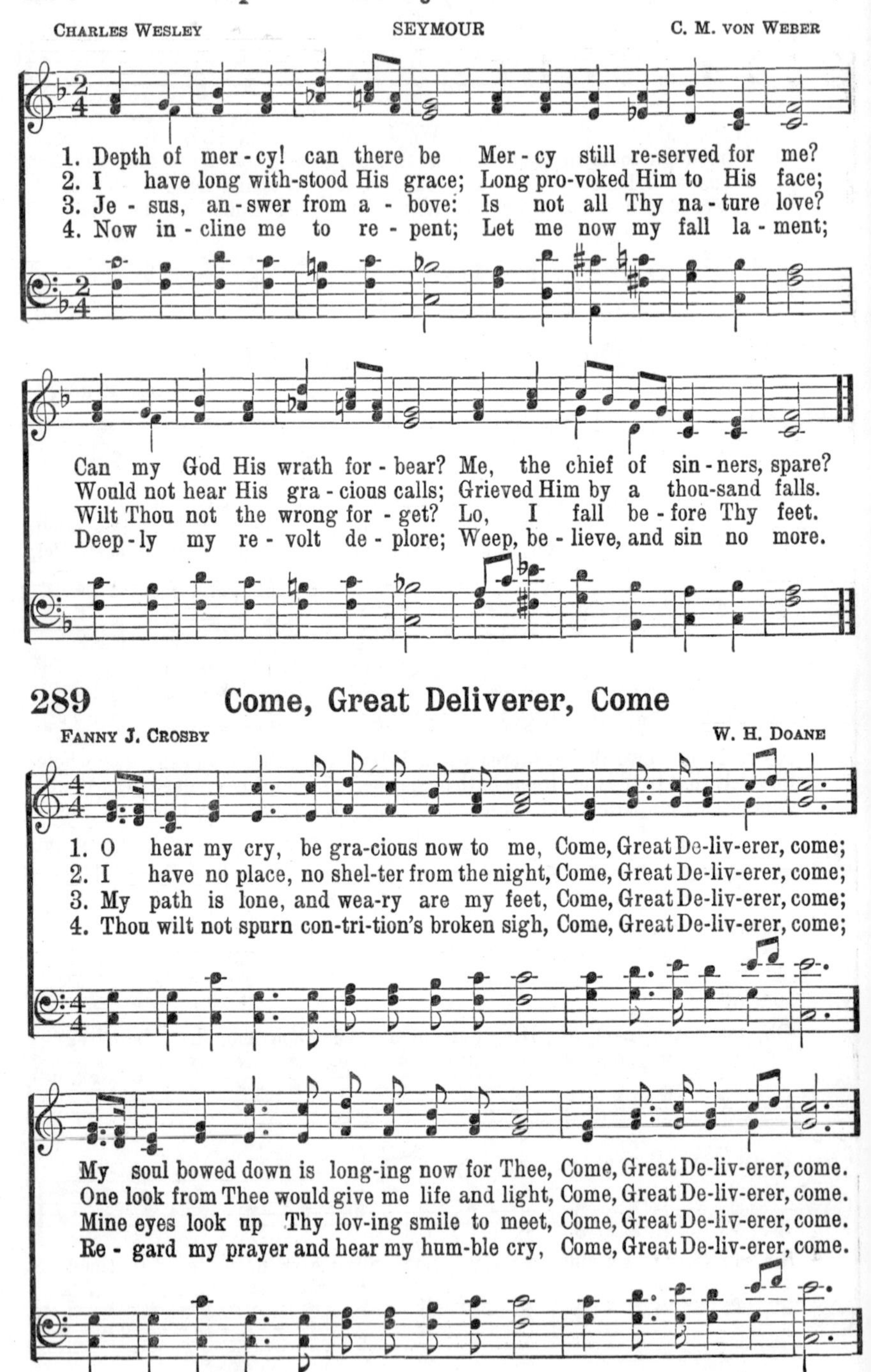

CHARLES WESLEY
SEYMOUR
C. M. VON WEBER
1. Depth of mer-cy! can there be Mer-cy still re-served for me?
2. I have long with-stood His grace; Long pro-voked Him to His face;
3. Je-sus, an-swer from a-bove: Is not all Thy na-ture love?
4. Now in-cline me to re-pent; Let me now my fall la-ment;
Can my God His wrath for-bear? Me, the chief of sin-ners, spare?
Would not hear His gra-cious calls; Grieved Him by a thou-sand falls.
Wilt Thou not the wrong for-get? Lo, I fall be-fore Thy feet.
Deep-ly my re-volt de-plore; Weep, be-lieve, and sin no more.
289 Come, Great Deliverer, Come
FANNY J. CROSBY
W. H. DOANE
1. O hear my cry, be gra-cious now to me, Come, Great De-liv-erer, come;
2. I have no place, no shel-ter from the night, Come, Great De-liv-erer, come;
3. My path is lone, and wea-ry are my feet, Come, Great De-liv-erer, come;
4. Thou wilt not spurn con-tri-tion's broken sigh, Come, Great De-liv-erer, come;
My soul bowed down is long-ing now for Thee, Come, Great De-liv-erer, come.
One look from Thee would give me life and light, Come, Great De-liv-erer, come.
Mine eyes look up Thy lov-ing smile to meet, Come, Great De-liv-erer, come.
Re-gard my prayer and hear my hum-ble cry, Come, Great De-liv-erer, come.

Come, Great Deliverer, Come
Chorus.
I've wandered far a-way o'er mountains cold, I've wandered far a-way from home;
O take me now, and bring me to Thy fold, Come, Great De-liv-erer, come.
290 Where Will You Spend Eternity?
Rev. E. A. Hoffman
J. H. Tenney
1. Where will you spend e-ter-ni-ty? This question comes to you and me!
2. Man-y are choos-ing Christ to-day, Turn-ing from all their sins a-way;
3. Leav-ing the strait and nar-row way, Go-ing the downward road to-day,
4. Re-pent, be-lieve, this ver-y hour, Trust in the Saviour's grace and power,
Tell me, what shall your an-swer be? Where will you spend e-ter-ni-ty?
Heaven shall their hap-py por-tion be; Where will you spend e-ter-ni-ty?
Sad will their fi-nal end-ing be,—Lost thro' a long e-ter-ni-ty!
Then will your joy-ous an-swer be, Saved thro' a long e-ter-ni-ty!
Refrain
1–2. E-ter-ni-ty! e-ter-ni-ty! Where will you spend e-ter-ni-ty?
3. E-ter-ni-ty! e-ter-ni-ty! Lost thro' a long e-ter-ni-ty!
4. E-ter-ni-ty! e-ter-ni-ty! Saved thro' a long e-ter-ni-ty!

291 Take Time to Be Holy

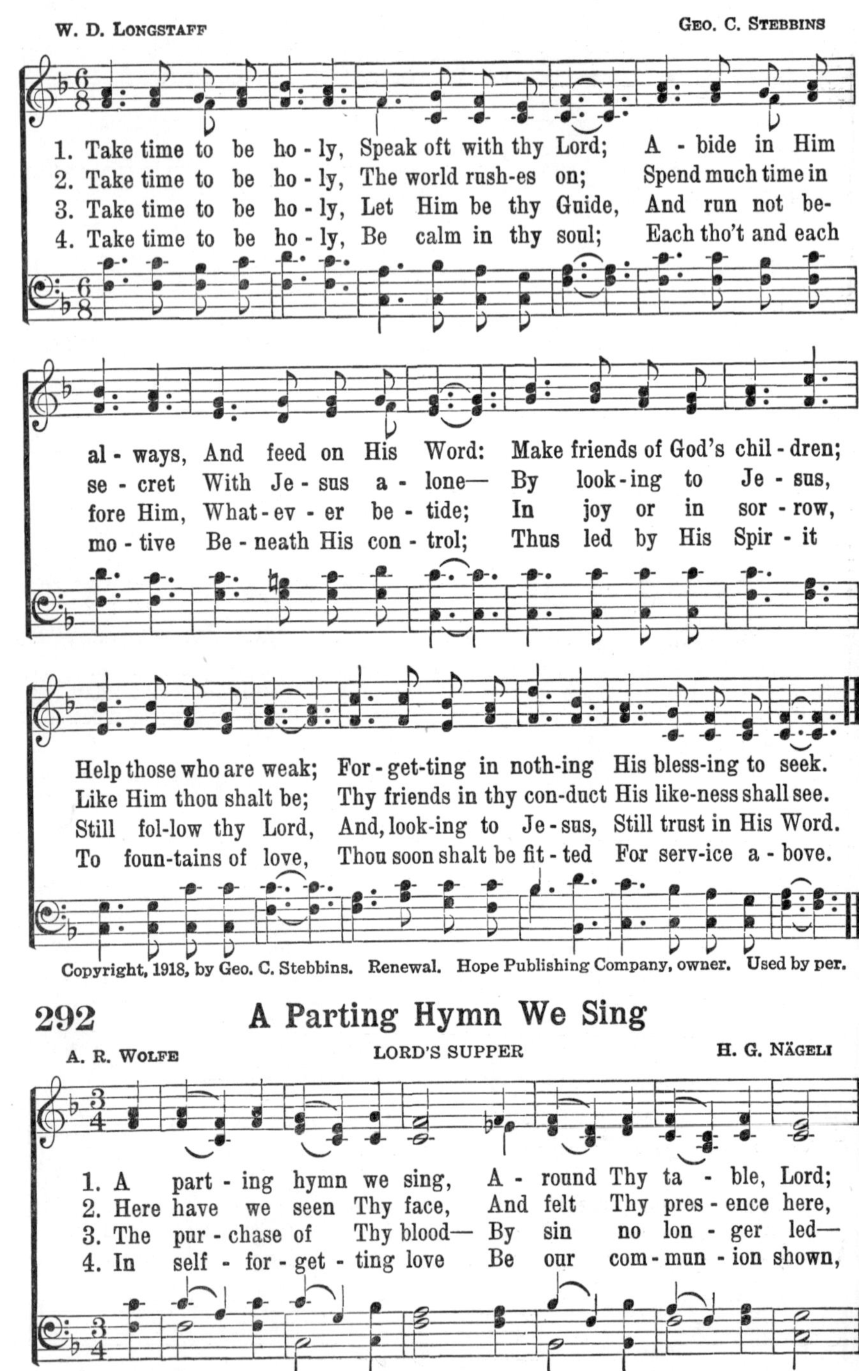

W. D. LONGSTAFF
GEO. C. STEBBINS
1. Take time to be ho-ly, Speak oft with thy Lord; A-bide in Him al-ways, And feed on His Word: Make friends of God's chil-dren; Help those who are weak; For-get-ting in noth-ing His bless-ing to seek.
2. Take time to be ho-ly, The world rush-es on; Spend much time in se-cret With Je-sus a-lone— By look-ing to Je-sus, Like Him thou shalt be; Thy friends in thy con-duct His like-ness shall see.
3. Take time to be ho-ly, Let Him be thy Guide, And run not be-fore Him, What-ev-er be-tide; In joy or in sor-row, Still fol-low thy Lord, And, look-ing to Je-sus, Still trust in His Word.
4. Take time to be ho-ly, Be calm in thy soul; Each tho't and each mo-tive Be-neath His con-trol; Thus led by His Spir-it To foun-tains of love, Thou soon shalt be fit-ted For serv-ice a-bove.
Copyright, 1918, by Geo. C. Stebbins. Renewal. Hope Publishing Company, owner. Used by per.
292 A Parting Hymn We Sing
A. R. WOLFE
LORD'S SUPPER
H. G. NÄGELI
1. A part-ing hymn we sing, A-round Thy ta-ble, Lord;
2. Here have we seen Thy face, And felt Thy pres-ence here,
3. The pur-chase of Thy blood— By sin no lon-ger led—
4. In self-for-get-ting love Be our com-mun-ion shown,

A Parting Hymn We Sing

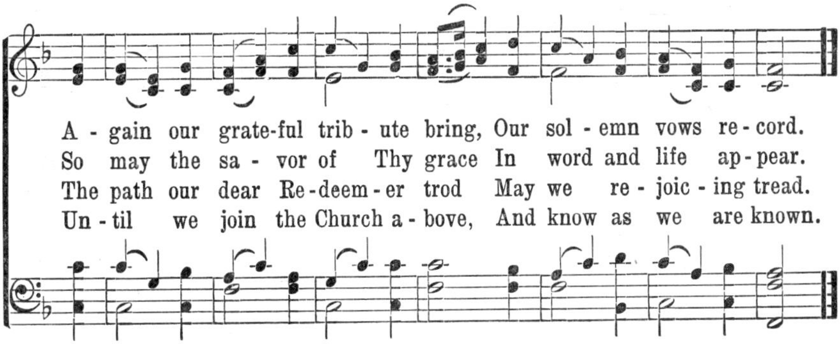

A - gain our grate-ful trib - ute bring, Our sol - emn vows re - cord.
So may the sa - vor of Thy grace In word and life ap - pear.
The path our dear Re - deem - er trod May we re - joic - ing tread.
Un - til we join the Church a - bove, And know as we are known.

293 Go Bury Thy Sorrow

MARY A. BACHELOR — P. P. BLISS

1. Go bur - y thy sor - row, the world hath its share; Go bur - y it deep - ly, go hide it with care: Go think of it calm - ly, when curtained by night; Go tell it to Je - sus, and all will be right.
2. Go tell it to Je - sus, He know-eth thy grief; Go tell it to Je - sus, He'll send thee re - lief; Go gath - er the sun - shine He sheds on the way; He'll lighten thy bur - den—go, wea-ry one, pray.
3. Hearts growing a - wea - ry with heav - i - er woe Now droop 'mid the dark - ness— go com - fort them, go! Go bur - y thy sor - row, let oth - ers be blest; Go give them the sun-shine, tell Je - sus the rest.

rit.

294 Near the Cross

FANNY J. CROSBY
W. H. DOANE
1. Je - sus, keep me near the cross, There a pre - cious foun - tain
2. Near the cross, a trem-bling soul, Love and mer - cy found me;
3. Near the cross! O Lamb of God, Bring its scenes be - fore me;
4. Near the cross I'll watch and wait, Hop - ing, trust - ing ev - er,
Free to all— a heal - ing stream, Flows from Cal-v'ry's moun - tain.
There the Bright and Morn - ing Star Sheds its beams a - round me.
Help me walk from day to day, With its shad - ows o'er me.
Till I reach the gold - en strand, Just be - yond the riv - er.
CHORUS
In the cross, in the cross, Be my glo - ry ev - er;
Till my rap - tured soul shall find Rest be - yond the riv - er.
295
'Tis Midnight
WILLIAM B. TAPPAN
OLIVE'S BROW
WILLIAM B. BRADBURY
1. 'Tis midnight; and on Ol - ive's brow The star is dimmed that late-ly shone:
2. 'Tis midnight; and from all removed, The Sav-iour wrestles lone with fears;
3. 'Tis midnight; and for oth - ers' guilt The Man of Sor-rows weeps in blood;
4. 'Tis midnight; and from ether-plains Is borne the song that an - gels know;

'Tis Midnight

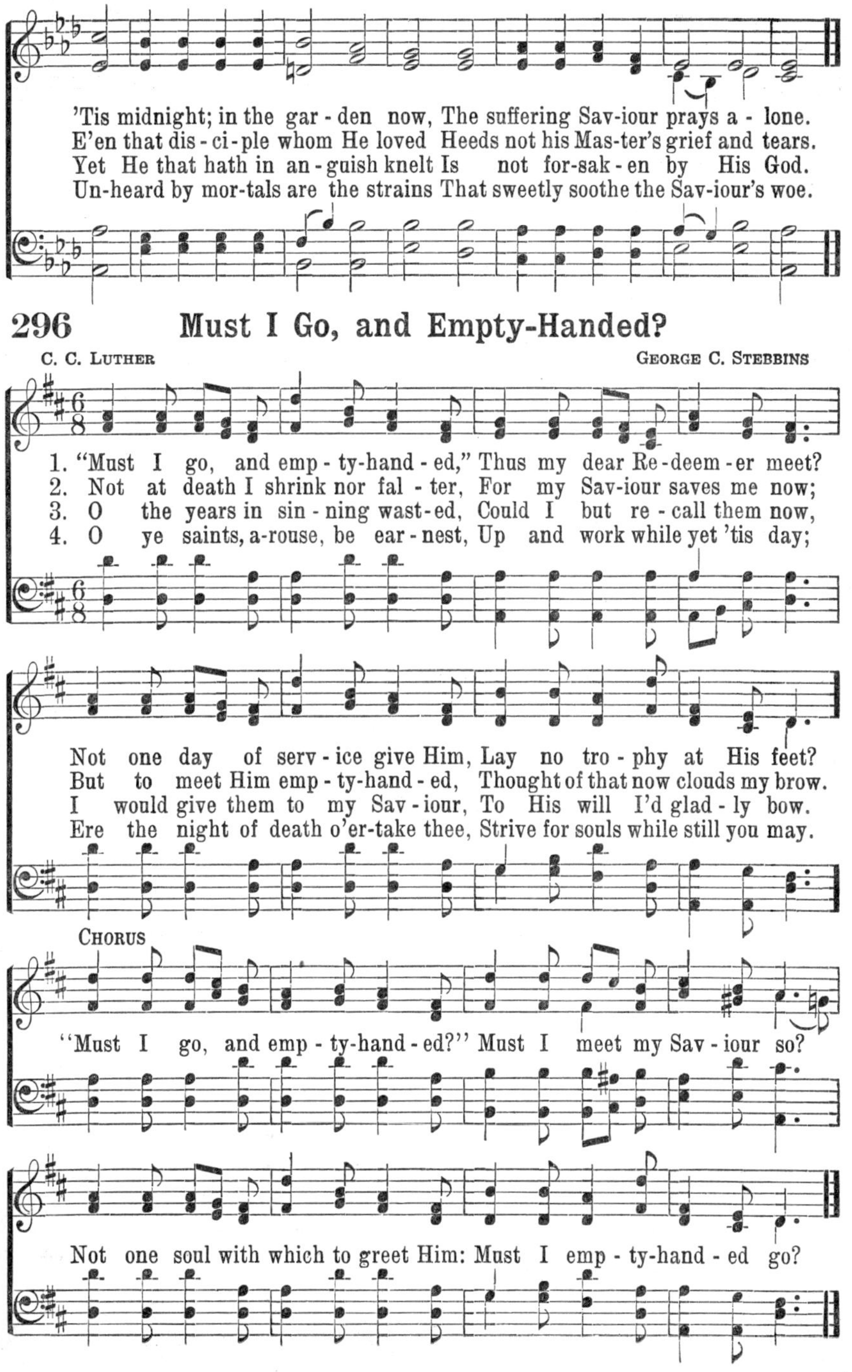
'Tis midnight; in the gar - den now, The suffering Sav-iour prays a - lone.
E'en that dis - ci - ple whom He loved Heeds not his Mas-ter's grief and tears.
Yet He that hath in an - guish knelt Is not for-sak - en by His God.
Un-heard by mor-tals are the strains That sweetly soothe the Sav-iour's woe.
296 Must I Go, and Empty-Handed?
C. C. Luther
George C. Stebbins
1. "Must I go, and emp - ty-hand - ed," Thus my dear Re-deem - er meet?
2. Not at death I shrink nor fal - ter, For my Sav-iour saves me now;
3. O the years in sin - ning wast-ed, Could I but re - call them now,
4. O ye saints, a-rouse, be ear - nest, Up and work while yet 'tis day;
Not one day of serv - ice give Him, Lay no tro - phy at His feet?
But to meet Him emp - ty-hand - ed, Thought of that now clouds my brow.
I would give them to my Sav - iour, To His will I'd glad - ly bow.
Ere the night of death o'er-take thee, Strive for souls while still you may.
Chorus
"Must I go, and emp - ty-hand - ed?" Must I meet my Sav - iour so?
Not one soul with which to greet Him: Must I emp - ty-hand - ed go?

297 Lord, I Hear of Showers of Blessing

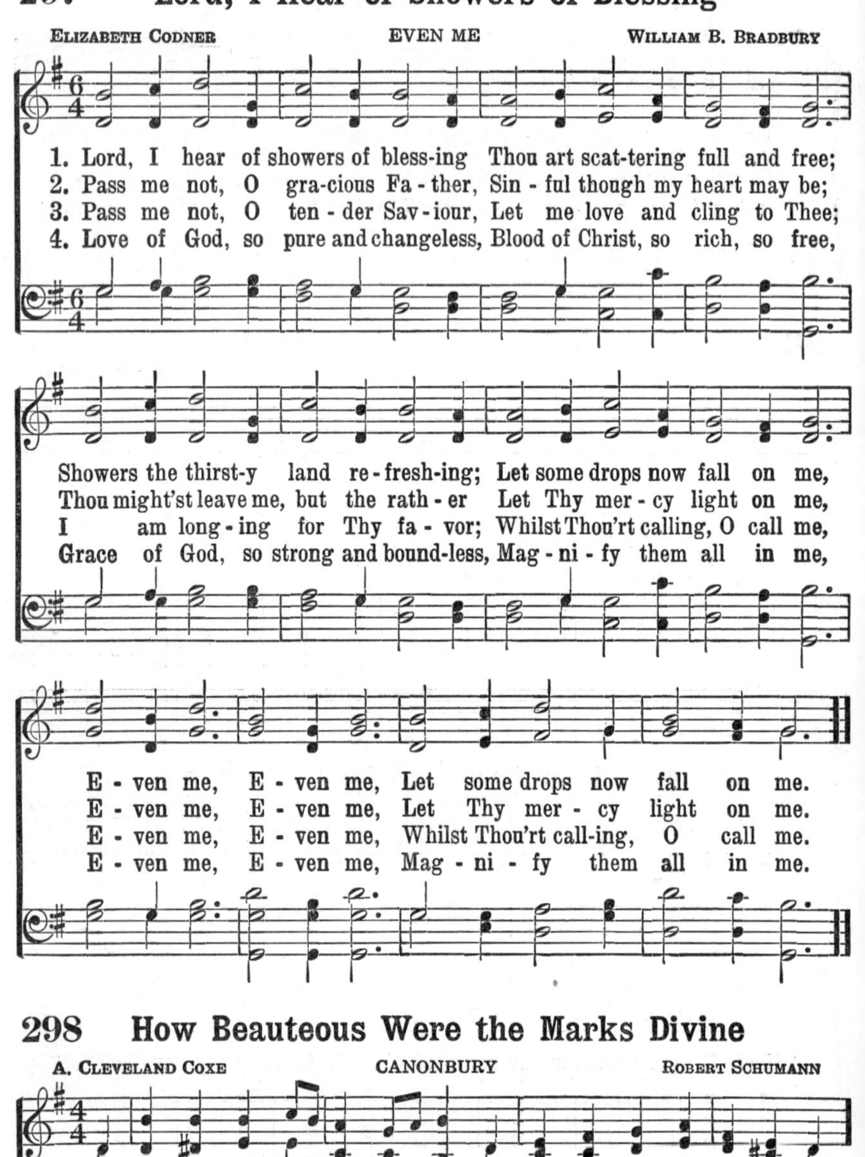

ELIZABETH CODNER
EVEN ME
WILLIAM B. BRADBURY
1. Lord, I hear of showers of bless-ing Thou art scat-tering full and free;
2. Pass me not, O gra-cious Fa - ther, Sin - ful though my heart may be;
3. Pass me not, O ten - der Sav - iour, Let me love and cling to Thee;
4. Love of God, so pure and changeless, Blood of Christ, so rich, so free,
Showers the thirst-y land re - fresh-ing; Let some drops now fall on me,
Thou might'st leave me, but the rath - er Let Thy mer - cy light on me,
I am long - ing for Thy fa - vor; Whilst Thou'rt calling, O call me,
Grace of God, so strong and bound-less, Mag - ni - fy them all in me,
E - ven me, E - ven me, Let some drops now fall on me.
E - ven me, E - ven me, Let Thy mer - cy light on me.
E - ven me, E - ven me, Whilst Thou'rt call-ing, O call me.
E - ven me, E - ven me, Mag - ni - fy them all in me.

298 How Beauteous Were the Marks Divine

A. CLEVELAND COXE — CANONBURY — ROBERT SCHUMANN

1. How beau-teous were the marks di - vine, That in Thy meek-ness used to shine,
2. O who like Thee, so calm, so bright, So pure, so made to live in light—
3. O who like Thee so hum - bly bore The scorn, the scoffs of men, be - fore?
4. O in Thy light be mine to go, Il - lum - ing all my way of woe:

How Beauteous Were the Marks Divine

That lit Thy lone-ly path-way, trod In won-drous love, O Son of God!
O who like Thee did ev - er go So pa-tient thro' a world of woe?
So meek, for-giv-ing, god-like, high, So glo-rious in hu-mil-i-ty?
And give me ev-er on the road To trace Thy foot-steps, Son of God.
299
Who will Our Pilot Be?
LIZZIE DEARMOND
OUR PILOT
IRA B. WILSON
In moderate time. Duet or Unison
1. We sail a-long toward the har-bor light, O-ver the great life sea;
2. We sail a-long in the morn-ing bright, Hap-py and glad are we;
3. We sail a-long, there are shoals, they say, Dangers from which to flee;
The breakers roar and the waves dash high, Who will our pi-lot be?
But still we ask, as the rocks draw near, Who will our pi-lot be?
We face the storm with a heav-y heart, Who will our pi-lot be?
CHORUS.
The Christ will our Pi-lot be, . . . A won-der-ful Guide is He; . . .
The Christ will our Pi-lot be, A won - der-ful Guide is He;
So we'll sail, sail, sail! . . . Christ will our Pi-lot be.
So we'll sail, yes, so we'll sail!

300 Ready

S E L. CHARLIE D. TILLMAN

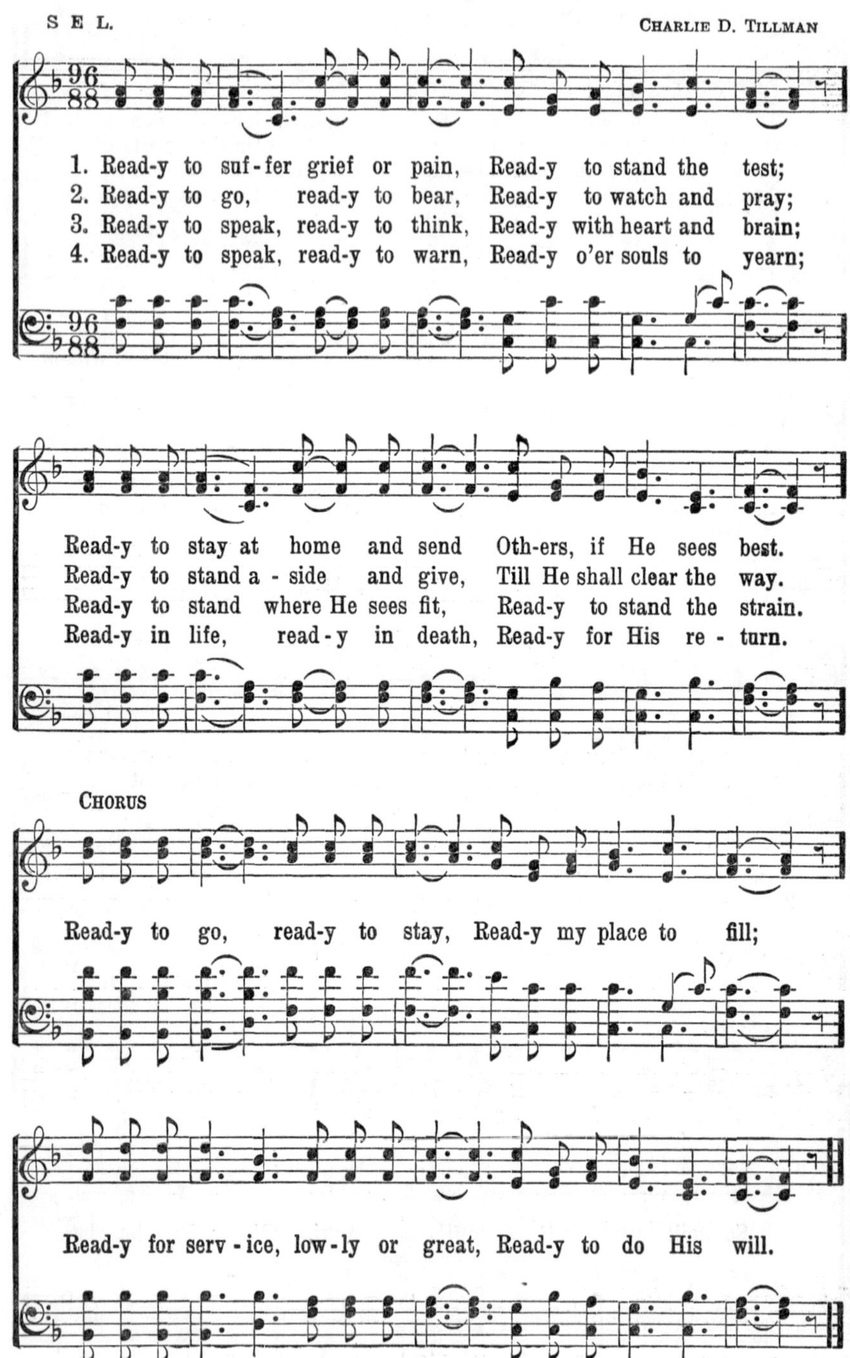

96
88
1. Read-y to suf-fer grief or pain, Read-y to stand the test;
2. Read-y to go, read-y to bear, Read-y to watch and pray;
3. Read-y to speak, read-y to think, Read-y with heart and brain;
4. Read-y to speak, read-y to warn, Read-y o'er souls to yearn;
Read-y to stay at home and send Oth-ers, if He sees best.
Read-y to stand a - side and give, Till He shall clear the way.
Read-y to stand where He sees fit, Read-y to stand the strain.
Read-y in life, read-y in death, Read-y for His re - turn.
CHORUS
Read-y to go, read-y to stay, Read-y my place to fill;
Read-y for serv-ice, low-ly or great, Read-y to do His will.

301 We Thank Thee, Lord

ALBERT H. HUTCHINSON — THANKSGIVING — ROBERT N. QUAILE

1. For all the bless-ings of the year, For all the friends we hold so
2. For life and health, those common things, Which ev-ery day and hour
3. For love of Thine, which nev - er tires, Which all our bet - ter thought in-
dear, For peace on earth, both far and near, We thank Thee, Lord.
brings, For home, where our af - fec - tion clings, We thank Thee, Lord.
spires, And warms our lives with heaven-ly fires, We thank Thee, Lord.
302 O God Eternal
JOHN C. SLEMP
B. B. McKINNEY
1. O God, E - ter - nal God! Thy name! Before the mountains were brought forth;
2. O God, in Christ we've seen Thy face—Up-on the cross He mirrored Thee:
3. O God, we come in rev-erent praise, We wor-ship Thee in joy - ful song;
rit.
Or ev - er Thou didst form the world, O God, Thou wert and art the same.
Thy ten-der heart, re-demp-tive love, O God, He told us of Thy grace.
We bow be-fore Thee hum - bly now, O God, we need Thee all our days.

303
Hold the Fort
P. P. B.
P. P. Bliss
1. Ho, my com-rades! see the sig - nal Wav - ing in the sky!
2. See the might - y host ad - vanc - ing, Sa - tan lead - ing on;
3. See the glo - rious ban - ner wav - ing! Hear the trump - et blow!
4. Fierce and long the bat - tle rag - es, But our help is near;
Re - in - force-ments now ap - pear - ing, Vic - to - ry is nigh.
Might - y men a - round us fall - ing, Cour - age al - most gone!
In our Lead - er's name we tri - umph O - ver ev - ery foe.
On - ward comes our great Com - mand - er, Cheer, my com - rades, cheer!
Chorus
"Hold the fort, for I am com - ing," Je - sus sig - nals still;
Wave the an - swer back to heav - en, "By Thy grace we will."
304
Draw Near
B. B. McK.
B. B. McKinney
Draw near, . . . Draw near, . . . The Mas - ter is here;
Draw near,
Draw near,

Draw Near

Keep si - lence, Keep si - lence, The Mas - ter is here.

305 In the Old-time Way

B. B. McK. B. B. McKinney

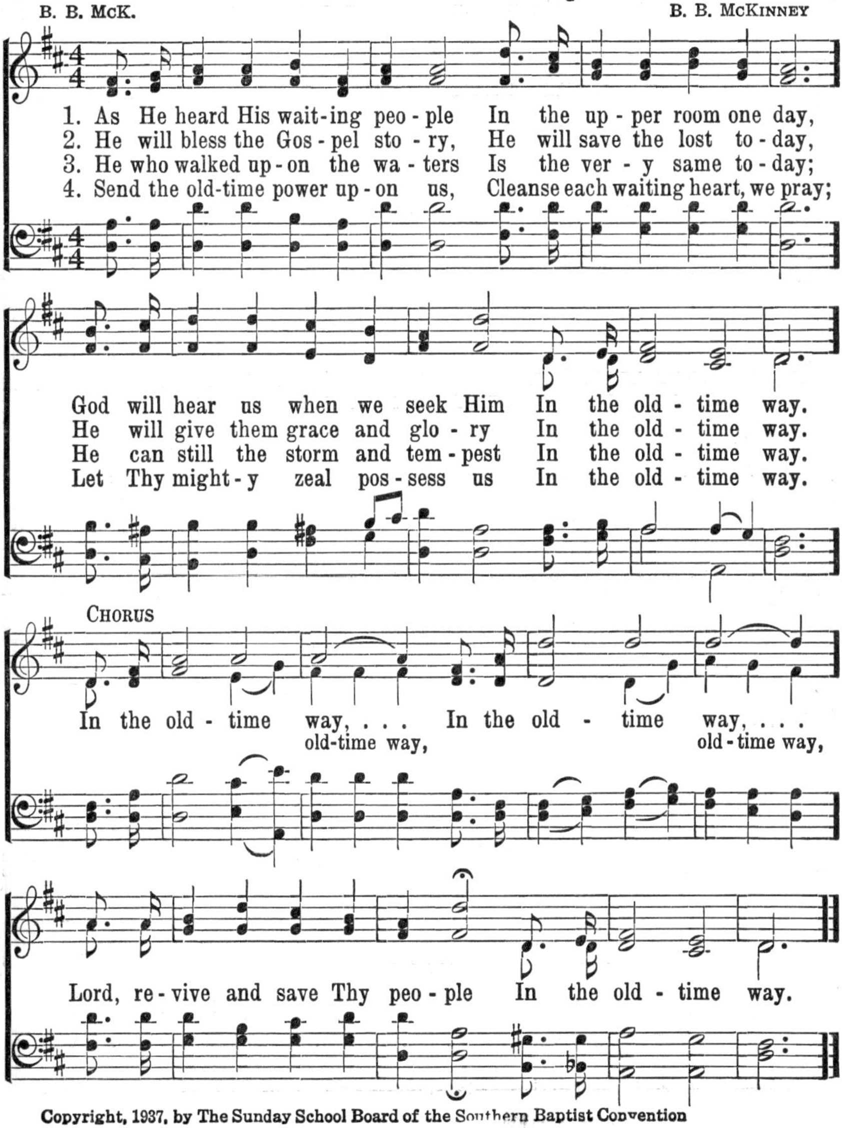

1. As He heard His wait-ing peo - ple In the up - per room one day,
God will hear us when we seek Him In the old - time way.
2. He will bless the Gos - pel sto - ry, He will save the lost to - day,
He will give them grace and glo - ry In the old - time way.
3. He who walked up - on the wa - ters Is the ver - y same to - day;
He can still the storm and tem - pest In the old - time way.
4. Send the old-time power up - on us, Cleanse each waiting heart, we pray;
Let Thy might - y zeal pos - sess us In the old - time way.

Chorus

In the old - time way, . . . (old-time way,) In the old - time way, . . . (old - time way,)
Lord, re - vive and save Thy peo - ple In the old - time way.

306 Praise Him, All Ye Little Children

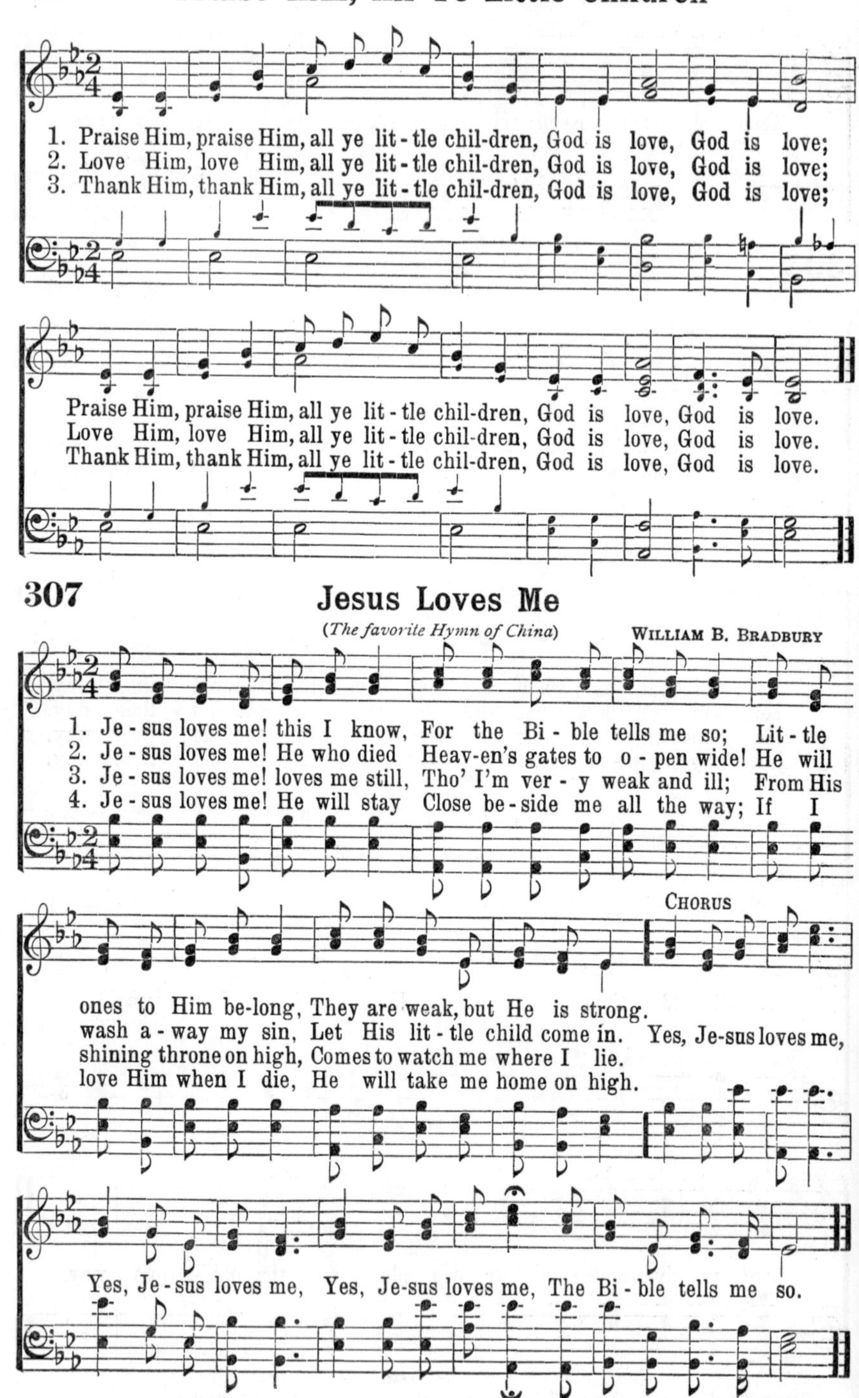

1. Praise Him, praise Him, all ye lit - tle chil-dren, God is love, God is love;
2. Love Him, love Him, all ye lit - tle chil-dren, God is love, God is love;
3. Thank Him, thank Him, all ye lit - tle chil-dren, God is love, God is love;
Praise Him, praise Him, all ye lit - tle chil-dren, God is love, God is love.
Love Him, love Him, all ye lit - tle chil-dren, God is love, God is love.
Thank Him, thank Him, all ye lit - tle chil-dren, God is love, God is love.
307
Jesus Loves Me
(The favorite Hymn of China)
WILLIAM B. BRADBURY
1. Je - sus loves me! this I know, For the Bi - ble tells me so; Lit - tle
2. Je - sus loves me! He who died Heav-en's gates to o - pen wide! He will
3. Je - sus loves me! loves me still, Tho' I'm ver - y weak and ill; From His
4. Je - sus loves me! He will stay Close be - side me all the way; If I
CHORUS
ones to Him be-long, They are weak, but He is strong.
wash a - way my sin, Let His lit - tle child come in. Yes, Je-sus loves me,
shining throne on high, Comes to watch me where I lie.
love Him when I die, He will take me home on high.
Yes, Je - sus loves me, Yes, Je-sus loves me, The Bi - ble tells me so.

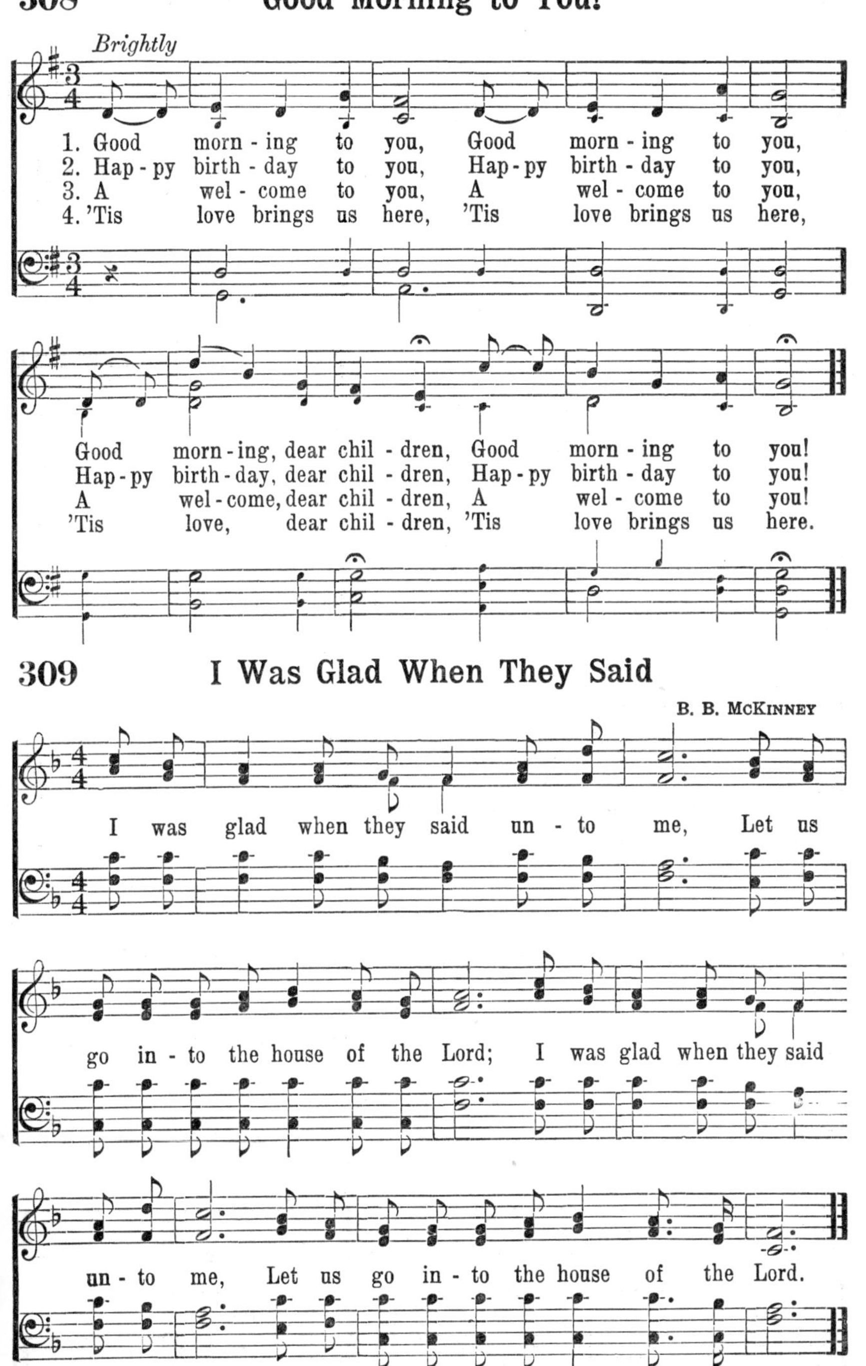
308 Good Morning to You!
Brightly
1. Good morn - ing to you, Good morn - ing to you,
2. Hap - py birth - day to you, Hap - py birth - day to you,
3. A wel - come to you, A wel - come to you,
4. 'Tis love brings us here, 'Tis love brings us here,
Good morn - ing, dear chil - dren, Good morn - ing to you!
Hap - py birth - day, dear chil - dren, Hap - py birth - day to you!
A wel - come, dear chil - dren, A wel - come to you!
'Tis love, dear chil - dren, 'Tis love brings us here.
309 I Was Glad When They Said
B. B. McKinney
I was glad when they said un - to me, Let us go in - to the house of the Lord; I was glad when they said un - to me, Let us go in - to the house of the Lord.

310 Child's Morning Hymn

REBECCA J. WESTON — D. BATCHELLOR

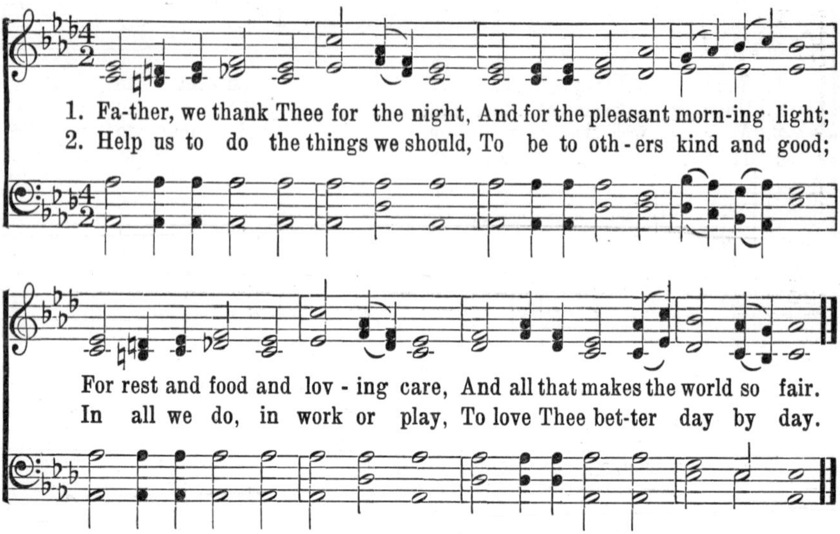

1. Fa-ther, we thank Thee for the night, And for the pleasant morn-ing light;
2. Help us to do the things we should, To be to oth - ers kind and good;

For rest and food and lov - ing care, And all that makes the world so fair.
In all we do, in work or play, To love Thee bet-ter day by day.

311 Jesus Loves the Little Children

Anonymous — GEO. F. ROOT

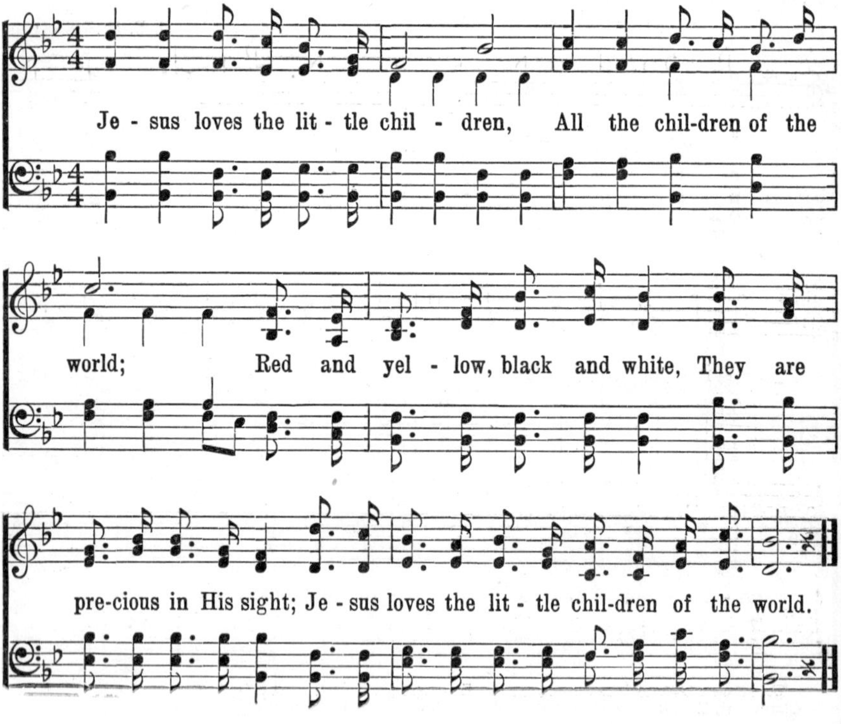

Je - sus loves the lit - tle chil - dren, All the chil-dren of the world; Red and yel - low, black and white, They are pre-cious in His sight; Je - sus loves the lit - tle chil-dren of the world.

312 The Happy Story Hour

AURORA M. SHUMATE — IDA T. TRUSS

In a happy manner

1. Ev - ery Sun-day eve - ning To the Church we go
For the hap - py Sto - ry Hour, And we love it so.

2. Here we have some sto - ries Of God's love and care—
Oth - ers tell us how to live And with peo-ple share.

3. How we like the sing - ing And the work and play!
Hap - py, hap - py Sto - ry Hour—We can-not stay a - way.

CHORUS

The Sto - ry Hour, the Sto - ry Hour, The hap-py Sto - ry Hour, We
sing and pray and lis - ten well, In the hap-py Sto - ry Hour.

313 Prayer Response

B. B. McKINNEY

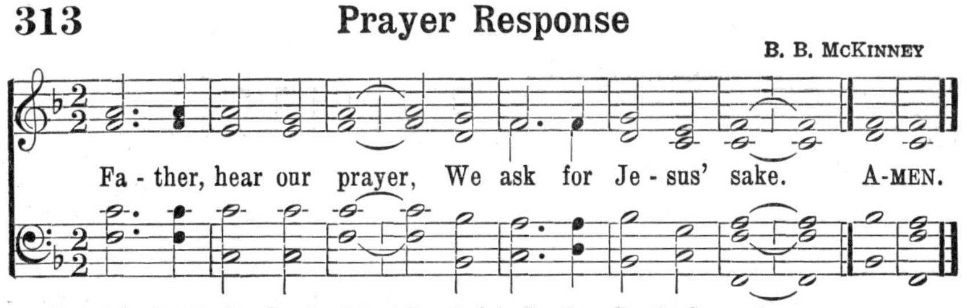
Fa - ther, hear our prayer, We ask for Je - sus' sake. A-MEN.

314 Away in a Manger

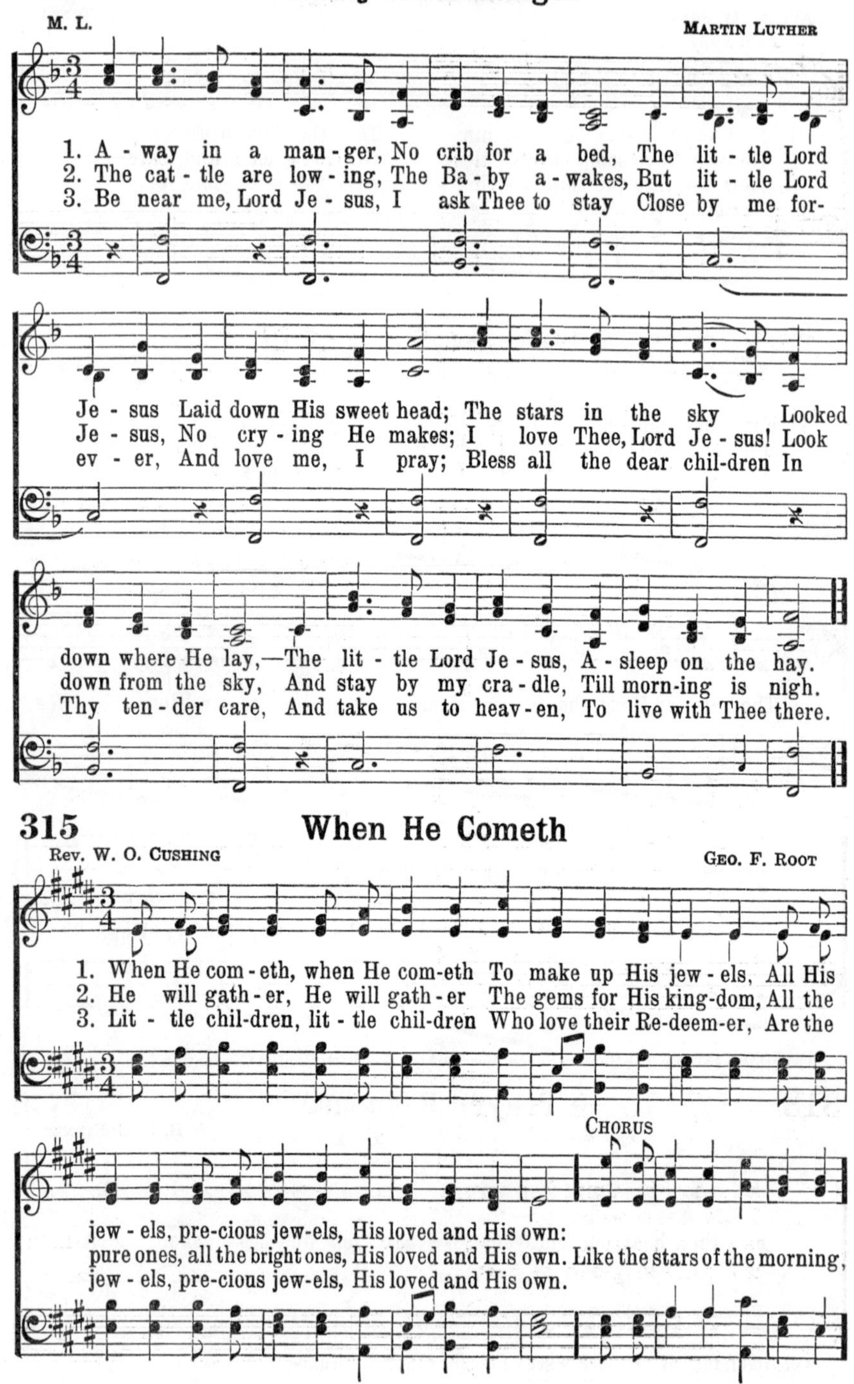
M. L.
Martin Luther
1. A - way in a man - ger, No crib for a bed, The lit - tle Lord
2. The cat - tle are low - ing, The Ba - by a - wakes, But lit - tle Lord
3. Be near me, Lord Je - sus, I ask Thee to stay Close by me for-
Je - sus Laid down His sweet head; The stars in the sky Looked
Je - sus, No cry - ing He makes; I love Thee, Lord Je - sus! Look
ev - er, And love me, I pray; Bless all the dear chil-dren In
down where He lay,—The lit - tle Lord Je - sus, A - sleep on the hay.
down from the sky, And stay by my cra - dle, Till morn-ing is nigh.
Thy ten - der care, And take us to heav - en, To live with Thee there.
315
When He Cometh
Rev. W. O. Cushing
Geo. F. Root
1. When He com - eth, when He com - eth To make up His jew - els, All His
2. He will gath - er, He will gath - er The gems for His king - dom, All the
3. Lit - tle chil-dren, lit - tle chil-dren Who love their Re - deem - er, Are the
Chorus
jew - els, pre - cious jew - els, His loved and His own:
pure ones, all the bright ones, His loved and His own. Like the stars of the morning,
jew - els, pre - cious jew - els, His loved and His own.

When He Cometh
His bright crown adorning, They shall shine in their beauty, Bright gems for His crown.
316 The Sweet Story of Old
Mrs. Jemima Luke
J. C. Englebrecht
1. I think when I read that sweet sto-ry of old When Je - sus was here
2. I wish that His hands had been placed on my head, That His arm had been thrown
3. Yet still to His foot-stool in prayer I may go, And ask for a share
4. In that beau-ti-ful place He is gone to pre-pare, For all that are washed
a - mong men, How He called lit-tle chil-dren as lambs to His fold, I should
a - round me; And that I might have seen His kind look when He said, "Let the
in His love; And if I now ear-nest - ly seek Him be - low, I shall
and for-given; And man - y dear chil-dren are gath-er-ing there, For "Of
Fine Refrain
D. S.
like to have been with them then. I should like to have been with them then;
lit - tle ones come un - to Me." "Let the lit-tle ones come un - to Me;"
see Him and hear Him a - bove. I shall see Him and hear Him a - bove;
such is the king-dom of heaven." For "Of such is the king-dom of heaven;"

317 Let the Beauty of Jesus
ALBERT ORSBORN
REV. TOM JONES
Let the beau-ty of Je-sus be seen in me, All His
won-der-ful pas-sion and pu-ri-ty; O Thou Spir-it di-vine,
All my na-ture re-fine, Till the beau-ty of Je-sus be seen in me.
Copyright property of Rev. Tom Jones
318 Only Believe
P. R.
PAUL RADER
On-ly be-lieve, on-ly be-lieve; All things are pos-si-ble, on-ly be-lieve;
On-ly be-lieve, on-ly be-lieve; All things are pos-si-ble, on-ly be-lieve.
Copyright, 1921, by Paul Rader

319 Jesus Loves Even Me

P. P. B. P. P. Bliss

1. I am so glad that our Father in heaven Tells of His love in the Book He has given; Wonderful things in the Bible I see: This is the dearest, that Jesus loves me.
2. Tho' I forget Him and wander away, Still He doth love me wherever I stray; Back to His dear loving arms would I flee, When I remember that Jesus loves me.
3. Oh, if there's only one song I can sing, When in His beauty I see the great King, This shall my song in eternity be: "Oh, what a wonder that Jesus loves me."
Chorus
I am so glad that Jesus loves me, Jesus loves me, Jesus loves me,
I am so glad that Jesus loves me, Jesus loves even me.

320 Dare to Be Brave, Dare to Be True

W. J. Rooper — Duncan Hume

1. Dare to be brave, dare to be true, Strive for the right, for the Lord is with you; Fight with sin brave - ly, fight and be strong, Christ is your Cap - tain, fear on - ly what's wrong.
2. Dare to be brave, dare to be true, God is your Fa - ther, He watch-es o'er you; He knows your tri - als; when your heart quails, Call Him to res - cue,—His grace nev - er fails.
3. Dare to be brave, dare to be true, God grant you cour - age to car - ry you through; Try to help oth - ers, ev - er be kind, Let the op - prest a strong friend in you find.
Refrain
Fight then, good sol-diers, fight and be brave; Christ is your Cap - tain, might-y to save.
rit
321 Into My Heart
H. D. C.
Harry D. Clarke
Sing prayerfully
In - to my heart, In - to my heart, Come in - to my heart, Lord Je - sus;

Into My Heart

322 Dare to Be a Daniel

P. P. B. P. P. Bliss

Come in to-day, Come in to stay, Come in-to my heart, Lord Je - sus.
1. Stand-ing by a pur-pose true, Heed-ing God's com-mand,
2. Man-y might-y men are lost, Dar-ing not to stand,
3. Man-y gi-ants, great and tall, Stalk-ing through the land,
4. Hold the Gos-pel ban-ner high! On to vic-tory grand!
Hon-or them, the faith-ful few! All hail to Dan-iel's Band!
Who for God had been a host, By join-ing Dan-iel's Band!
Head-long to the earth would fall, If met by Dan-iel's Band!
Sa-tan and his host de-fy, And shout for Dan-iel's Band!
Chorus
Dare to be a Dan-iel, Dare to stand a-lone,
Dare to have a pur-pose firm! Dare to make it known!

323 Lead Me to Some Soul Today

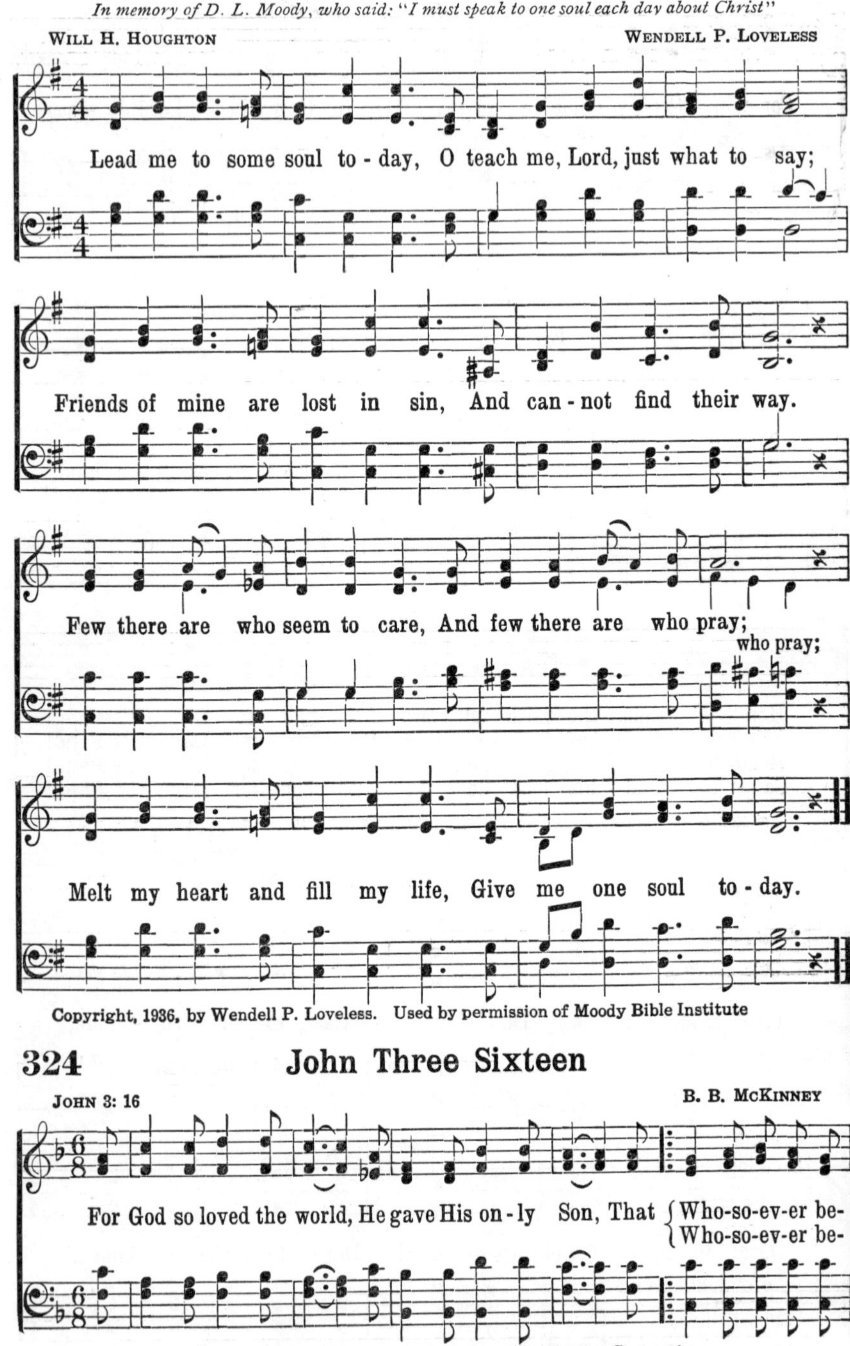
In memory of D. L. Moody, who said: "I must speak to one soul each day about Christ"
WILL H. HOUGHTON
WENDELL P. LOVELESS
Lead me to some soul to - day, O teach me, Lord, just what to say;
Friends of mine are lost in sin, And can - not find their way.
Few there are who seem to care, And few there are who pray;
who pray;
Melt my heart and fill my life, Give me one soul to - day.
Copyright, 1936, by Wendell P. Loveless. Used by permission of Moody Bible Institute
324 John Three Sixteen
JOHN 3: 16
B. B. MCKINNEY
For God so loved the world, He gave His on - ly Son, That
Who-so-ev-er be-
Who-so-ev-er be-
Copyright, 1937, by The Sunday School Board of the Southern Baptist Convention

John Three Sixteen

liev-eth on Him,
liev-eth on Him, Should not perish, should not perish, but have e-ter-nal life.
325 Sweeter Than the Day Before
Robert C. Loveless
Wendell P. Loveless
Ev-ery day with Je-sus Is sweet-er than the day be-fore;
Ev-ery day with Je-sus, I love Him more and more;
Je-sus saves and keeps me, And He's the One I'm liv-ing for:
Ev-ery day with Je-sus Is sweet-er than the day be-fore.

326 Be Ye Doers of the Word

BLANCHE LINTHICUM and
B. B. McK.
(Song for Juniors)
B. B. McKINNEY
1. Out of James one twen-ty-two Comes a call for Jun-iors true,
2. We would strive for Christ to live; Time and tal-ents we would give;
3. Kind to oth-ers we would be, Je-sus' like-ness they would see;
4. Let us serve with all our might; Let us stand for truth and right,
Who will live for Christ the ris-en Lord: Lis-ten to this trump-et call
We would fol-low Je-sus all the way: Tithes and offerings we would bring;
We would keep our bod-ies clean and strong: We would strive in school and play
Al-ways liv-ing for the ris-en Lord: Come and join our hap-py throng;
Ring-ing out to one and all, "Be ye do-ers of the Word."
We would work and pray and sing For the Mas-ter ev-ery day.
To learn les-sons and o-bey, Live for right and con-quer wrong.
Sing with us our joy-ous song, "Be ye do-ers of the Word."
CHORUS
"Be ye do-ers of the Word, Be ye do-ers of the Word, Be ye do-ers
of the Word, And not hearers, not hearers on-ly, Be ye do-ers of the Word."

327 Labor On

Dr. C. R. Blackall — W. H. Doane

Spirited
1. In the har - vest field there is work to do, For the grain is ripe, and the reap - ers few; And the Mas - ter's voice bids the work - ers true Heed the call that He gives to - day.
2. Crowd the gar - ner well with its sheaves all bright, Let the song be glad, and the heart be light, Fill the pre - cious hours, ere the shades of night Take the place of the gold - en day.
3. In the glean - er's path may be rich re - ward, Tho' the time seems long, and the la - bor hard; For the Mas - ter's joy, with His cho - sen shared, Drives the gloom from the dark - est day.
4. Lo! the Har - vest Home in the realms a - bove Shall be gained by each who has toiled and strove, When the Mas - ter's voice, in His words of love, Calls a - way to e - ter - nal day.
Chorus
La - bor on, La - bor on, la - bor on, la - bor on, Keep the bright re - ward in view, For the Mas - ter has said He will strength re - new; La - bor on till the close of day.

328 Trusting Jesus

E. Page
Ira D. Sankey
1. Sim - ply trust - ing ev - ery day, Trust - ing through a storm - y way;
2. Bright-ly doth His Spir - it shine In - to this poor heart of mine;
3. Sing - ing if my way is clear: Pray - ing if the path be drear;
4. Trust - ing Him while life shall last, Trust - ing Him till earth be past;
E - ven when my faith is small, Trust-ing Je - sus, that is all.
While He leads I can - not fall; Trust-ing Je - sus, that is all.
If in dan - ger, for Him call; Trust-ing Je - sus, that is all.
Till with - in the jas - per wall: Trust-ing Je - sus, that is all.
Chorus
Trust - ing as the mo - ments fly, Trust - ing as the days go by;
Trust - ing Him what-e'er be - fall, Trust - ing Je - sus, that is all.
329
Fall Fresh On Me
Arr. by B. B. McKinney
Spir - it of the liv - ing God, Fall fresh on me, Spir - it of the
D. S.—Spir - it of the

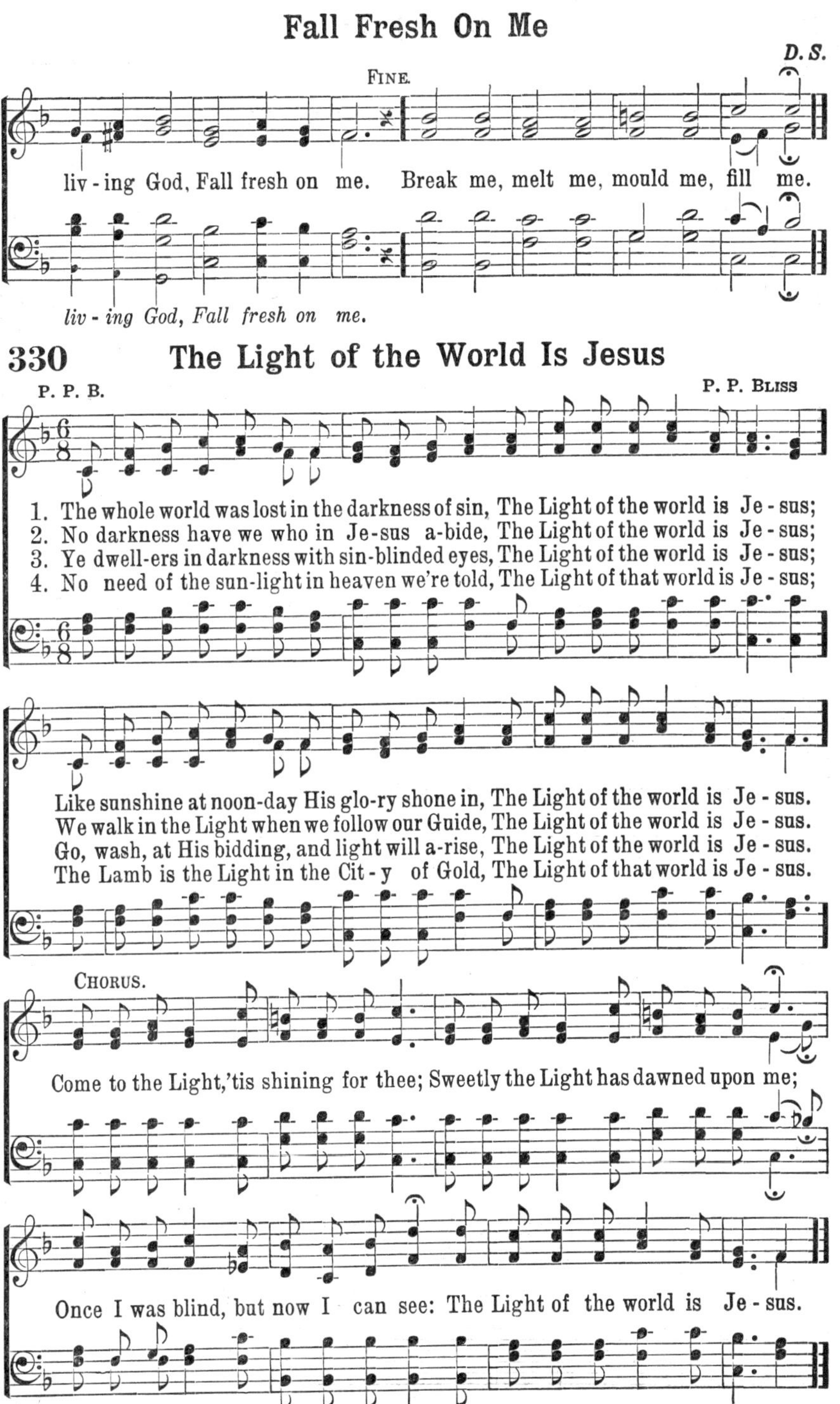
Fall Fresh On Me
D.S.
Fine.
liv - ing God, Fall fresh on me. Break me, melt me, mould me, fill me.
liv - ing God, Fall fresh on me.
330 The Light of the World Is Jesus
P. P. B.
P. P. Bliss
1. The whole world was lost in the darkness of sin, The Light of the world is Je - sus;
2. No darkness have we who in Je-sus a-bide, The Light of the world is Je - sus;
3. Ye dwell-ers in darkness with sin-blinded eyes, The Light of the world is Je - sus;
4. No need of the sun-light in heaven we're told, The Light of that world is Je - sus;
Like sunshine at noon-day His glo-ry shone in, The Light of the world is Je - sus.
We walk in the Light when we follow our Guide, The Light of the world is Je - sus.
Go, wash, at His bidding, and light will a-rise, The Light of the world is Je - sus.
The Lamb is the Light in the Cit - y of Gold, The Light of that world is Je - sus.
Chorus.
Come to the Light,'tis shining for thee; Sweetly the Light has dawned upon me;
Once I was blind, but now I can see: The Light of the world is Je - sus.

331 Seal Us, O Holy Spirit

I. H. M. *(Inscribed to my friend, Rev. J. F. Carson, D.D.)* I. H. MEREDITH

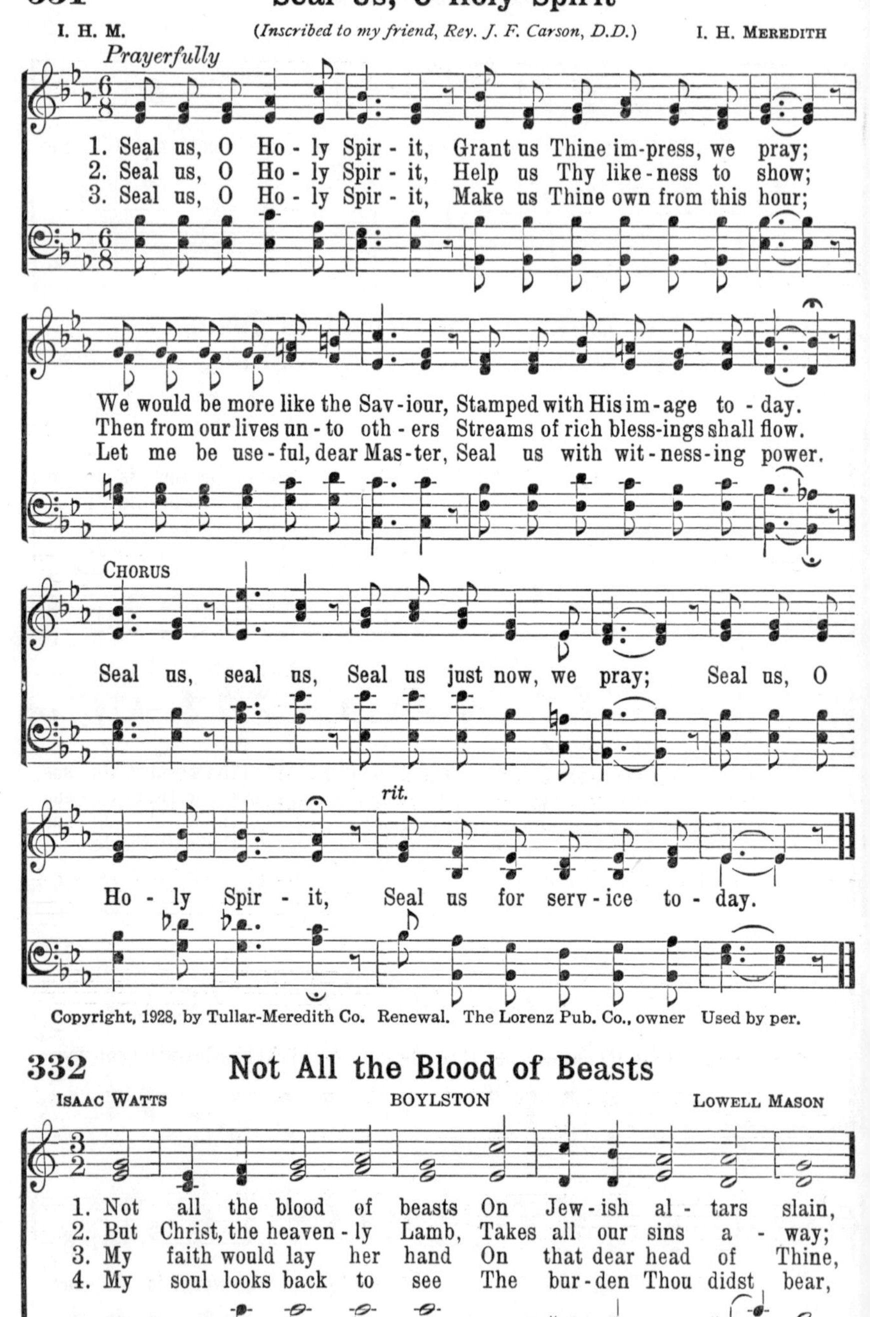

Prayerfully
1. Seal us, O Ho - ly Spir - it, Grant us Thine im-press, we pray;
2. Seal us, O Ho - ly Spir - it, Help us Thy like - ness to show;
3. Seal us, O Ho - ly Spir - it, Make us Thine own from this hour;
We would be more like the Sav - iour, Stamped with His im - age to - day.
Then from our lives un - to oth - ers Streams of rich bless-ings shall flow.
Let me be use - ful, dear Mas - ter, Seal us with wit - ness - ing power.
CHORUS
Seal us, seal us, Seal us just now, we pray; Seal us, O
rit.
Ho - ly Spir - it, Seal us for serv - ice to - day.

332 Not All the Blood of Beasts

ISAAC WATTS BOYLSTON LOWELL MASON

1. Not all the blood of beasts On Jew - ish al - tars slain,
2. But Christ, the heaven - ly Lamb, Takes all our sins a - way;
3. My faith would lay her hand On that dear head of Thine,
4. My soul looks back to see The bur - den Thou didst bear,

Not All the Blood of Beasts

Could give the guilt - y con-science peace, Or wash a - way the stain.
A sac - ri - fice of no - bler name And rich - er blood than they.
While like a pen - i - tent I stand, And there con-fess my sin.
While hang-ing on the curs - ed tree, And know my guilt was there.
333 There's a Great Day Coming
W. L. T.
Will L. Thompson
1. There's a great day coming, A great day coming, There's a great day coming by and by; When the saints and the sin-ners shall be part - ed right and left, Are you read-y for that day to come?
2. There's a bright day coming, A bright day coming, There's a bright day coming by and by; But its brightness shall on - ly come to them that love the Lord, Are you
3. There's a sad day coming, A sad day coming, There's a sad day coming by and by; When the sin - ner shall hear his doom, "De-part, I know ye not," Are you
Chorus
m
pp
Are you read-y? Are you read-y? Are you read-y for the judgment day? Are you read-y? Are you read-y for the judgment day?

334 Leave Your Burden At the Place of Prayer

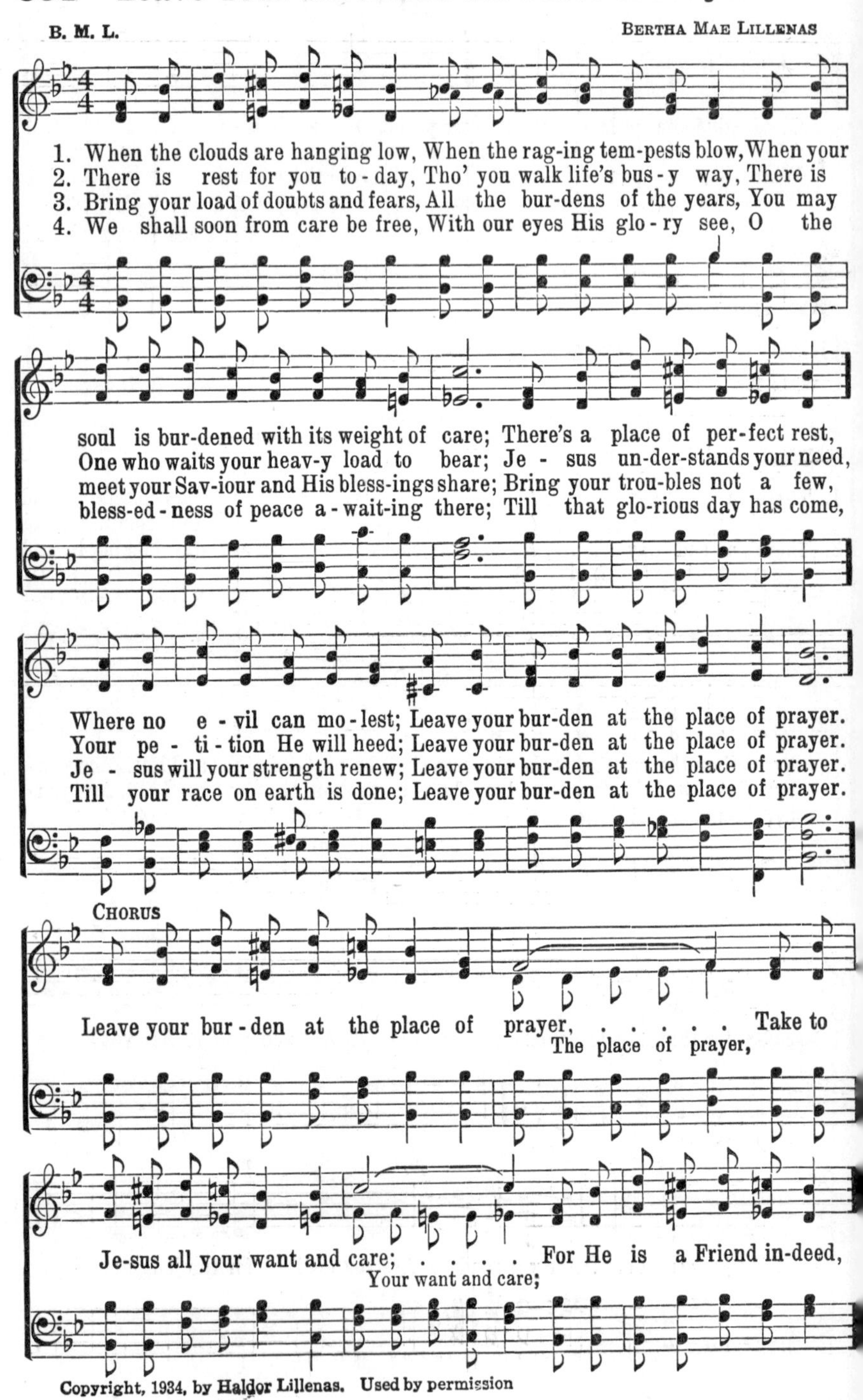
B. M. L.
BERTHA MAE LILLENAS
1. When the clouds are hanging low, When the rag-ing tem-pests blow, When your soul is bur-dened with its weight of care; There's a place of per-fect rest, Where no e - vil can mo-lest; Leave your bur-den at the place of prayer.
2. There is rest for you to - day, Tho' you walk life's bus - y way, There is One who waits your heav-y load to bear; Je - sus un-der-stands your need, Your pe - ti - tion He will heed; Leave your bur-den at the place of prayer.
3. Bring your load of doubts and fears, All the bur-dens of the years, You may meet your Sav-iour and His bless-ings share; Bring your trou-bles not a few, Je - sus will your strength renew; Leave your bur-den at the place of prayer.
4. We shall soon from care be free, With our eyes His glo - ry see, O the bless-ed - ness of peace a - wait-ing there; Till that glo-rious day has come, Till your race on earth is done; Leave your bur-den at the place of prayer.
CHORUS
Leave your bur - den at the place of prayer, ... Take to
The place of prayer,
Je-sus all your want and care; . . . . For He is a Friend in-deed,
Your want and care;

Leave Your Burden At the Place of Prayer

335 Did You Think to Pray?

Mrs. M. A. Kidder — W. O. Perkins

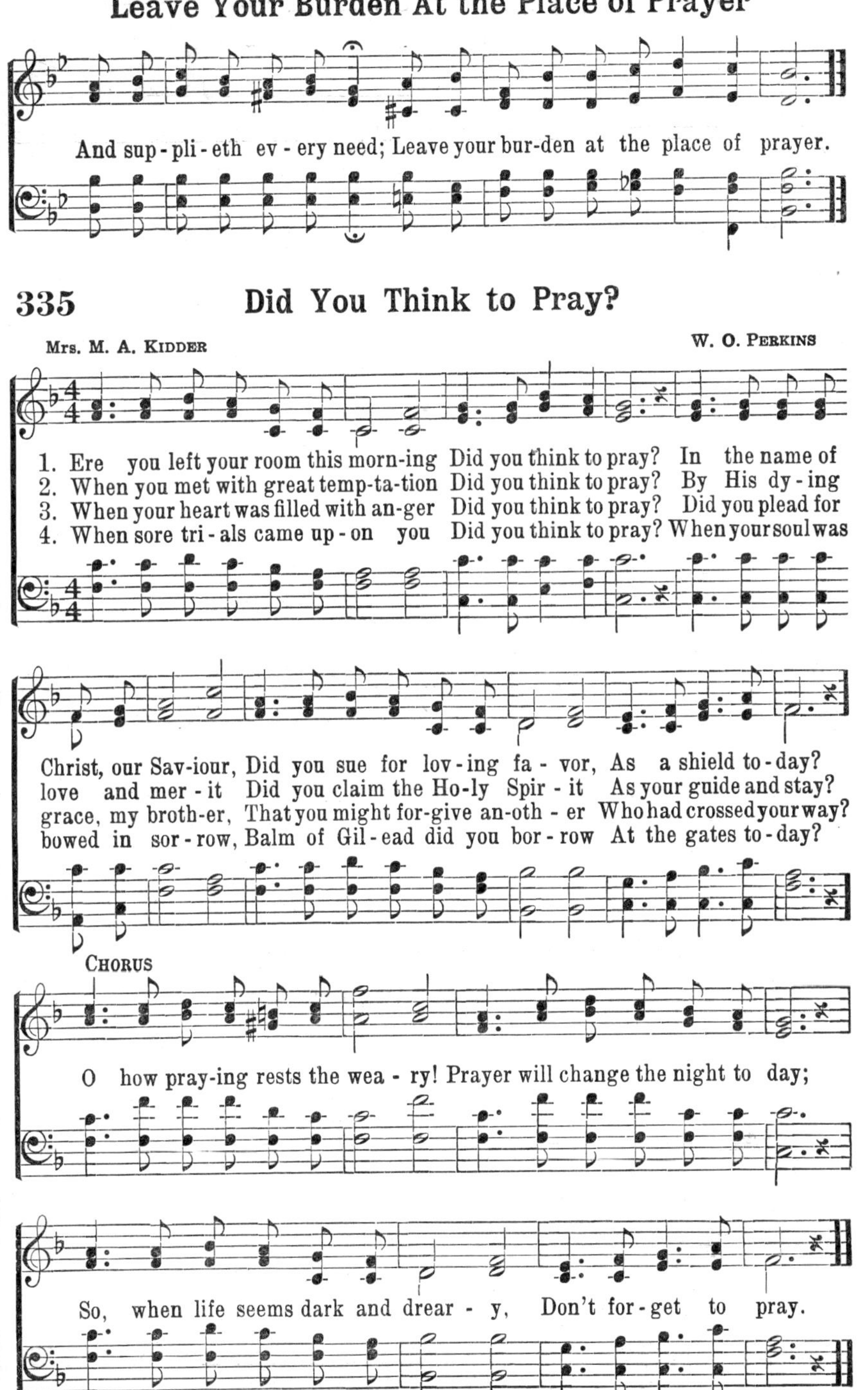
And sup-pli-eth ev-ery need; Leave your bur-den at the place of prayer.
1. Ere you left your room this morn-ing Did you think to pray? In the name of Christ, our Sav-iour, Did you sue for lov-ing fa-vor, As a shield to-day?
2. When you met with great temp-ta-tion Did you think to pray? By His dy-ing love and mer-it Did you claim the Ho-ly Spir-it As your guide and stay?
3. When your heart was filled with an-ger Did you think to pray? Did you plead for grace, my broth-er, That you might for-give an-oth-er Who had crossed your way?
4. When sore tri-als came up-on you Did you think to pray? When your soul was bowed in sor-row, Balm of Gil-ead did you bor-row At the gates to-day?
Chorus
O how pray-ing rests the wea-ry! Prayer will change the night to day;
So, when life seems dark and drear-y, Don't for-get to pray.

336 He Lives On High

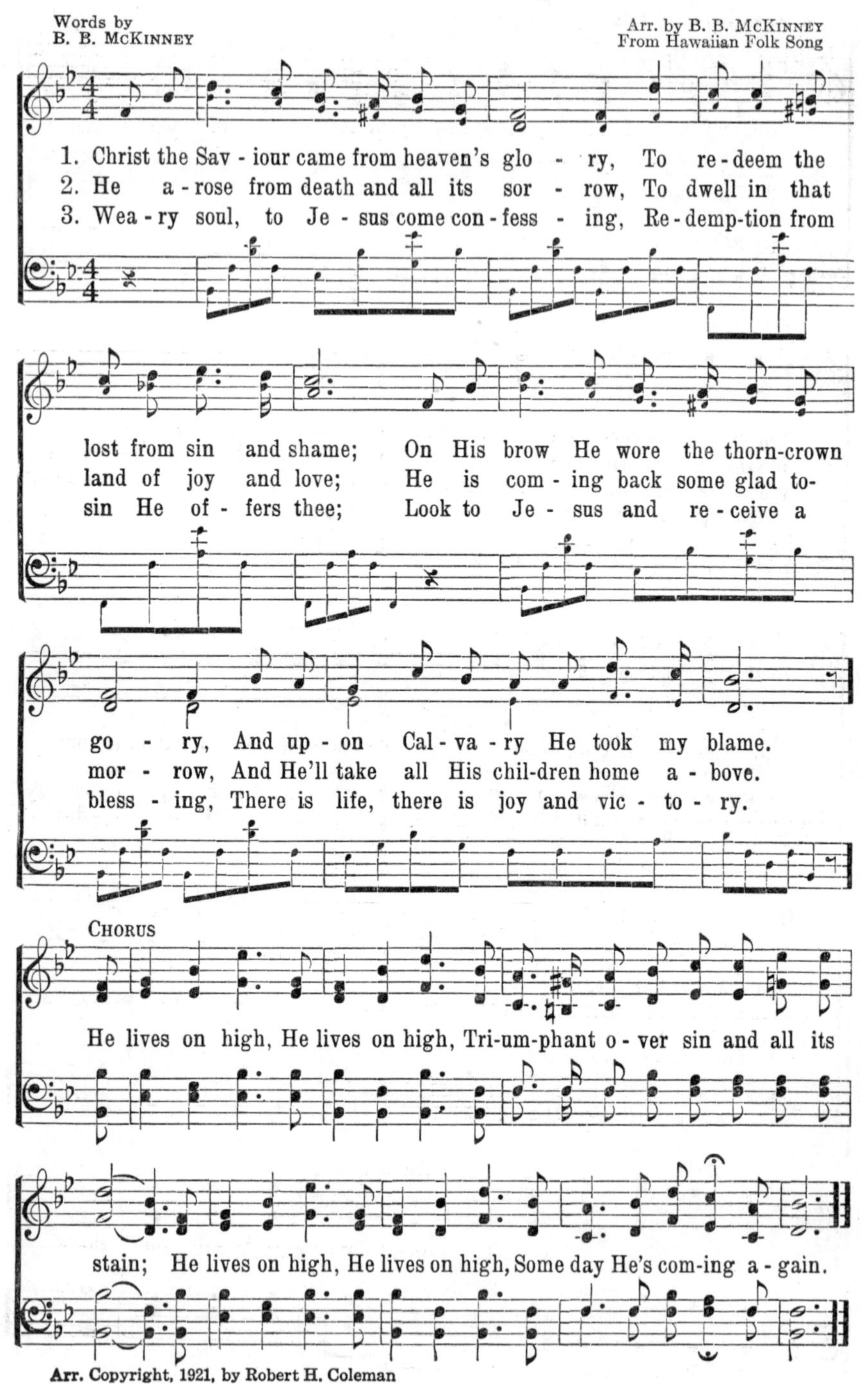
Words by
B. B. McKinney
Arr. by B. B. McKinney
From Hawaiian Folk Song
1. Christ the Sav - iour came from heaven's glo - ry, To re - deem the
2. He a - rose from death and all its sor - row, To dwell in that
3. Wea - ry soul, to Je - sus come con - fess - ing, Re - demp - tion from
lost from sin and shame; On His brow He wore the thorn-crown
land of joy and love; He is com - ing back some glad to-
sin He of - fers thee; Look to Je - sus and re - ceive a
go - ry, And up - on Cal - va - ry He took my blame.
mor - row, And He'll take all His chil - dren home a - bove.
bless - ing, There is life, there is joy and vic - to - ry.
Chorus
He lives on high, He lives on high, Tri - um - phant o - ver sin and all its
stain; He lives on high, He lives on high, Some day He's com - ing a - gain.

337 My Name's Written There

M. A. K. and B. B. McK.
Frank M. Davis
1. I am bought not with rich - es, Nei-ther sil - ver nor gold; But
2. My sins, they were man - y, Like the sands of the sea, But the
3. Oh! that beau-ti - ful cit - y, With its man-sions of light, With its
Christ hath redeemed me, I am safe in His fold; In the Book of His
blood of my Sav - iour Is suf - fi - cient for me; For His prom-ise is
glo - ri - fied be - ings, In pure gar-ments of white; Where no e - vil thing
king-dom, With its pag-es so fair, Through Je-sus my Sav-iour, My
writ - ten, In bright let-ters that glow, "Tho' your sins be as scar - let, I will
com - eth To de-spoil what is fair; Where the angels are watching, My
name's writ-ten there.
make them like snow." My name's writ-ten there, On the page white and fair;
name's writ-ten there.
Refrain
In the Book of God's king - dom, My name's writ - ten there.

Yield Not to Temptation

H. R. P.

Dr. H. R. Palmer

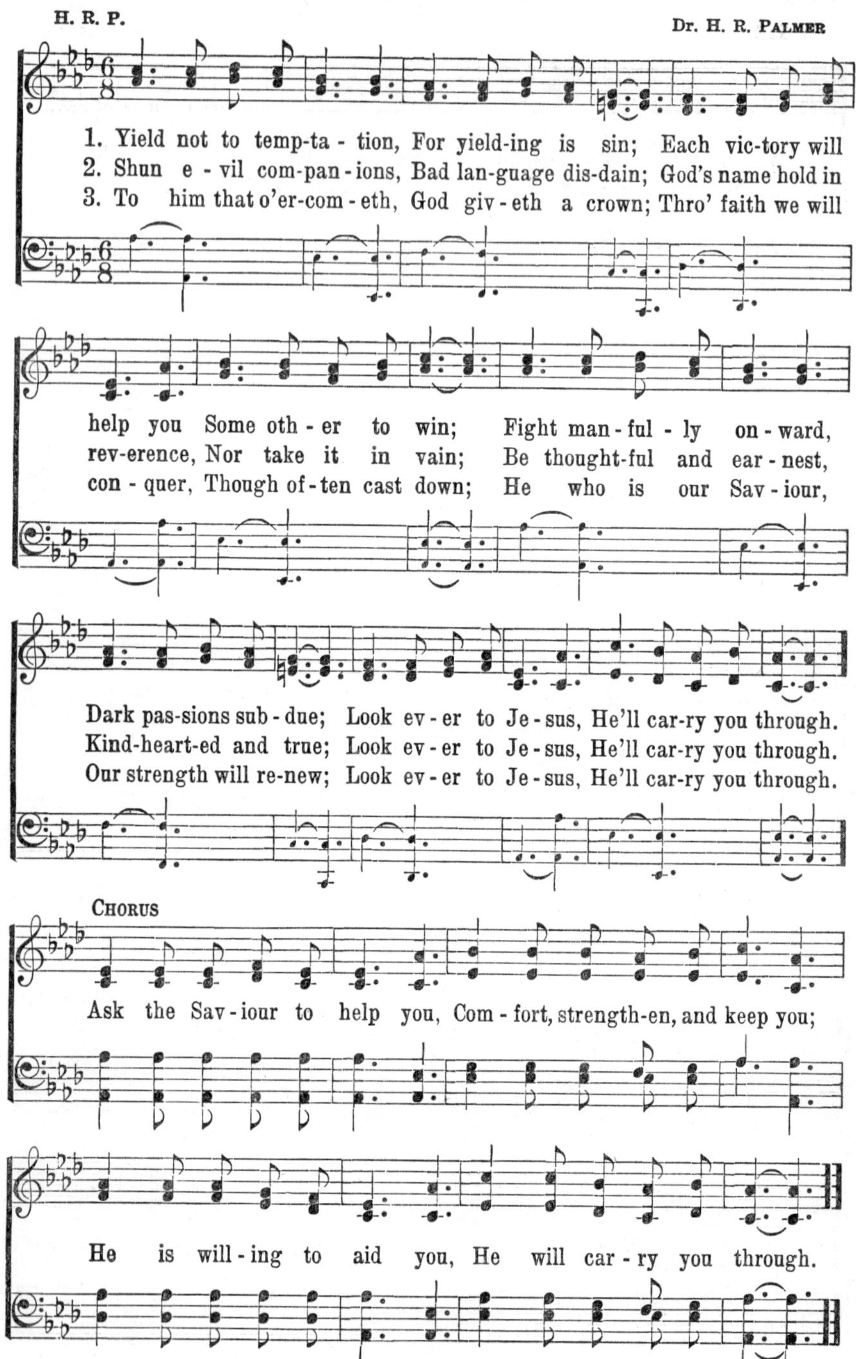
1. Yield not to temp-ta - tion, For yield-ing is sin; Each vic-tory will help you Some oth - er to win; Fight man-ful - ly on - ward, Dark pas-sions sub - due; Look ev - er to Je - sus, He'll car-ry you through.
2. Shun e - vil com-pan - ions, Bad lan-guage dis-dain; God's name hold in rev-erence, Nor take it in vain; Be thought-ful and ear - nest, Kind-heart-ed and true; Look ev - er to Je - sus, He'll car-ry you through.
3. To him that o'er-com - eth, God giv - eth a crown; Thro' faith we will con - quer, Though of - ten cast down; He who is our Sav - iour, Our strength will re-new; Look ev - er to Je - sus, He'll car-ry you through.
Chorus
Ask the Sav - iour to help you, Com - fort, strength-en, and keep you;
He is will - ing to aid you, He will car - ry you through.

339 Saved, Saved!

J. P. S. J. P. SCHOLFIELD

1. I've found a friend who is all to me, His love is ever true; . . . . . . I love to tell how He lifted me And what His grace can do for you. . . .
2. He saves me from every sin and harm, Secures my soul each day; . . . . . . I'm leaning strong on His mighty arm; I know He'll guide me all the way. . . .
3. When poor and needy and all alone, In love He said to me, ... "Come unto Me and I'll lead you home, To live with Me eternally." . . .
CHORUS
Saved . . . . by His power divine, Saved . . . . to new life sublime!
Saved by His power, Saved to new life,
cres. rit.
Life now is sweet and my joy is complete, For I'm saved, saved, saved!

340 Once for All

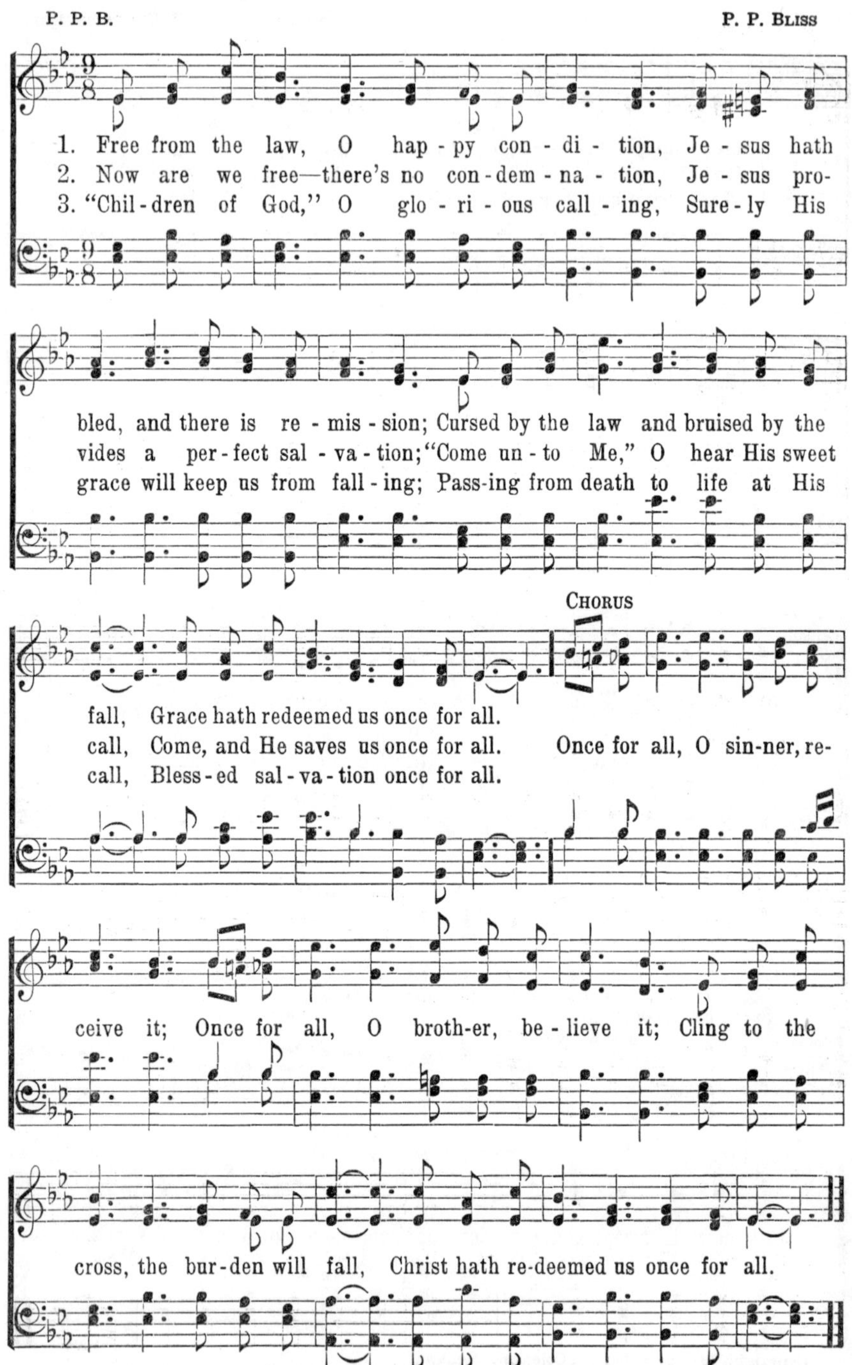
P. P. B.
P. P. Bliss
1. Free from the law, O hap-py con-di-tion, Je-sus hath bled, and there is re-mis-sion; Cursed by the law and bruised by the fall, Grace hath redeemed us once for all.
2. Now are we free—there's no con-dem-na-tion, Je-sus pro-vides a per-fect sal-va-tion; "Come un-to Me," O hear His sweet call, Come, and He saves us once for all.
3. "Chil-dren of God," O glo-ri-ous call-ing, Sure-ly His grace will keep us from fall-ing; Pass-ing from death to life at His call, Bless-ed sal-va-tion once for all.
Chorus
Once for all, O sin-ner, re-ceive it; Once for all, O broth-er, be-lieve it; Cling to the cross, the bur-den will fall, Christ hath re-deemed us once for all.

341 That Will Be Glory for Me

P. P. Bliss
Arr. from James McGranahan
by B. B. McKinney
1. I know not the hour when my Lord will come To take me a - way to His
2. I know not the song that the an - gels sing, I know not the sound of the
3. I know not the form of my man-sion fair, I know not the name that I
own dear home; But I know that His pres-ence will light-en the gloom, And
harp's glad ring; But I know there'll be prais-es to Je - sus our King, And
then shall bear; But I know that my Sav-iour will wel-come me there, And
Chorus
that will be glo - ry for me. And that will be glo - ry for me, ...
that will be glo - ry for me.
that will be glo - ry for me. And that will be glo - ry, be glo - ry for me,
Oh, that will be glo - ry for me; . . . . . When I stand in His
Oh, that will be glo - ry, be glo - ry for me;
rit.
pres-ence, and like Him shall be, Oh, that will be glo - ry for me.

342 The Beautiful Garden of Prayer

ELEANOR ALLEN SCHROLL — J. H. FILLMORE

1. There's a gar-den where Je - sus is wait - ing, There's a place that is won-drous-ly fair; For it glows with the light of His pres-ence, 'Tis the beau - ti - ful gar - den of prayer.
2. There's a gar-den where Je - sus is wait - ing, And I go with my bur - den and care, Just to learn from His lips words of com - fort, In the beau - ti - ful gar - den of prayer.
3. There's a gar-den where Je - sus is wait - ing, And He bids you to come meet Him there, Just to walk and to talk with my Sav - iour, In the beau - ti - ful gar - den of prayer.
REFRAIN
O the beau - ti - ful gar-den, the gar-den of prayer, O the beau-ti - ful gar-den of prayer; There my Sav-iour a- waits, and He o - pens the gates To the beau-ti - ful gar-den of prayer.
poco rit.

343

Our Best

S. C. Kirk

Grant Colfax Tullar

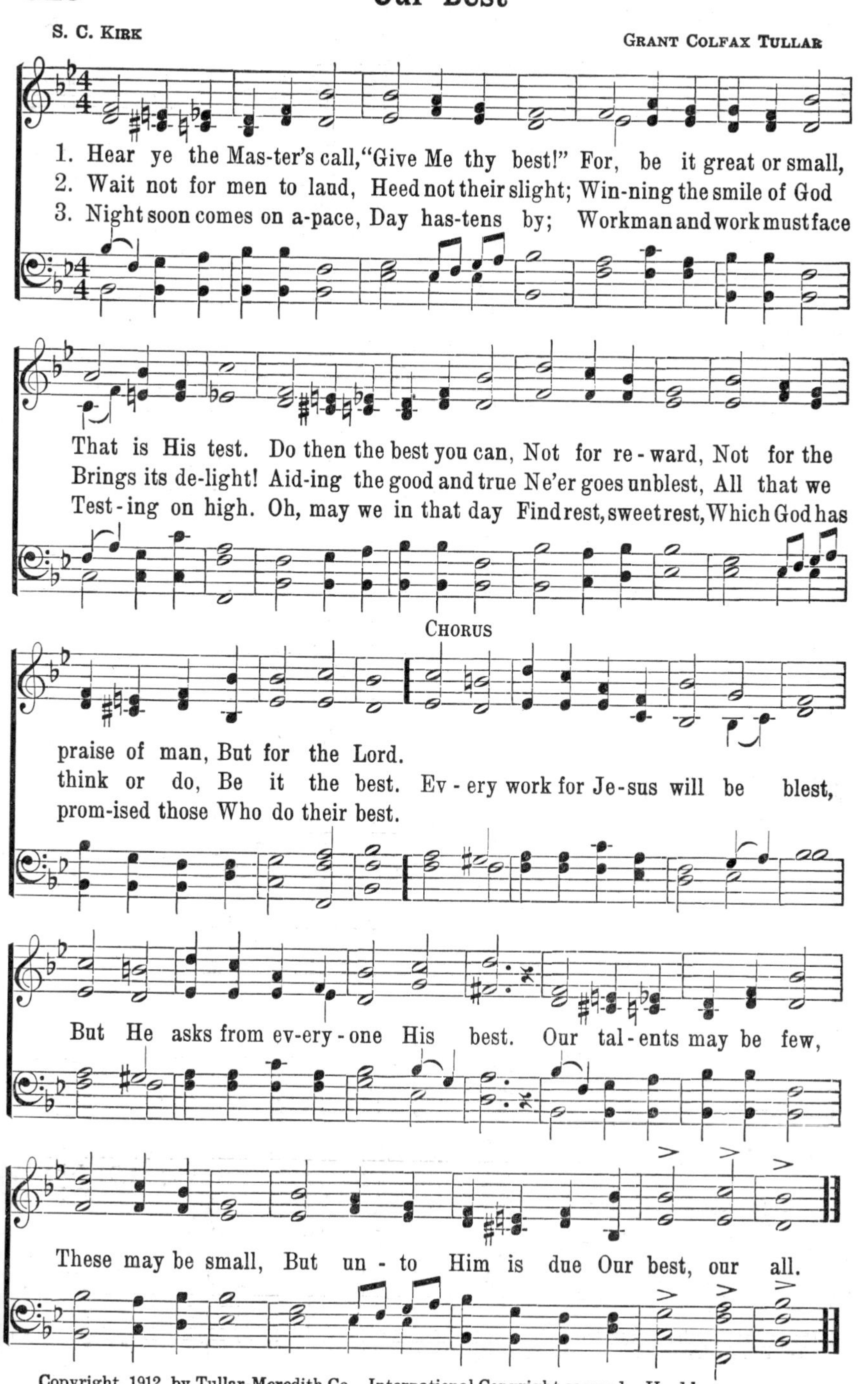
1. Hear ye the Mas-ter's call, "Give Me thy best!" For, be it great or small, That is His test. Do then the best you can, Not for re-ward, Not for the praise of man, But for the Lord.
2. Wait not for men to laud, Heed not their slight; Win-ning the smile of God Brings its de-light! Aid-ing the good and true Ne'er goes unblest, All that we think or do, Be it the best.
3. Night soon comes on a-pace, Day has-tens by; Workman and work must face Test-ing on high. Oh, may we in that day Find rest, sweet rest, Which God has prom-ised those Who do their best.
Chorus
Ev-ery work for Je-sus will be blest, But He asks from ev-ery-one His best. Our tal-ents may be few, These may be small, But un-to Him is due Our best, our all.

344

Sweet By and By

S. F. Bennett
J. P. Webster
1. There's a land that is fair - er than day, And by faith we can
2. We shall sing on that beau - ti - ful shore The me - lo - di - ous
3. To our boun - ti - ful Fa - ther a - bove, We will of - fer the
see it a - far; For the Fa - ther waits o - ver the way, To pre-
songs of the blest, And our spir - its shall sor - row no more, Not a
trib - ute of praise, For the glo - ri - ous gift of His love, And the
pare us a dwell - ing-place there.
sigh for the bless - ing of rest.
bless-ings that hal - low our days.
Chorus
In the sweet by and by,
In the sweet by and by,
We shall meet on that beau - ti - ful shore;
by and by;
In the sweet by and by,
In the sweet by and by,
We shall meet on that beau-ti-ful shore.

345 Nailed to the Cross

Mrs. Frank A. Breck — Grant Colfax Tullar

Duet. ad lib.
1. There was One who was will-ing to die in my stead, That a soul so un-wor-thy might live, And the path to the cross He was will-ing to tread, All the sins of my life to for-give.
2. He is ten-der and lov-ing and pa-tient with me, While He cleans-es my heart of its dross; But "there's no con-dem-na-tion," I know I am free, For my sins are all nailed to the cross.
3. I will cling to my Sav-iour and nev-er de-part—I will joy-ful-ly jour-ney each day, With a song on my lips and a song in my heart, That my sins have been tak-en a-way.
Refrain
pp
They are nailed to the cross, They are nailed to the cross, O how much He was will-ing to bear! With what an-guish and loss, Jesus went to the cross! But He carried my sins with Him there.
rit.

346 Jesus My Lord Is Real to Me

I. E. R. I. E. Reynolds

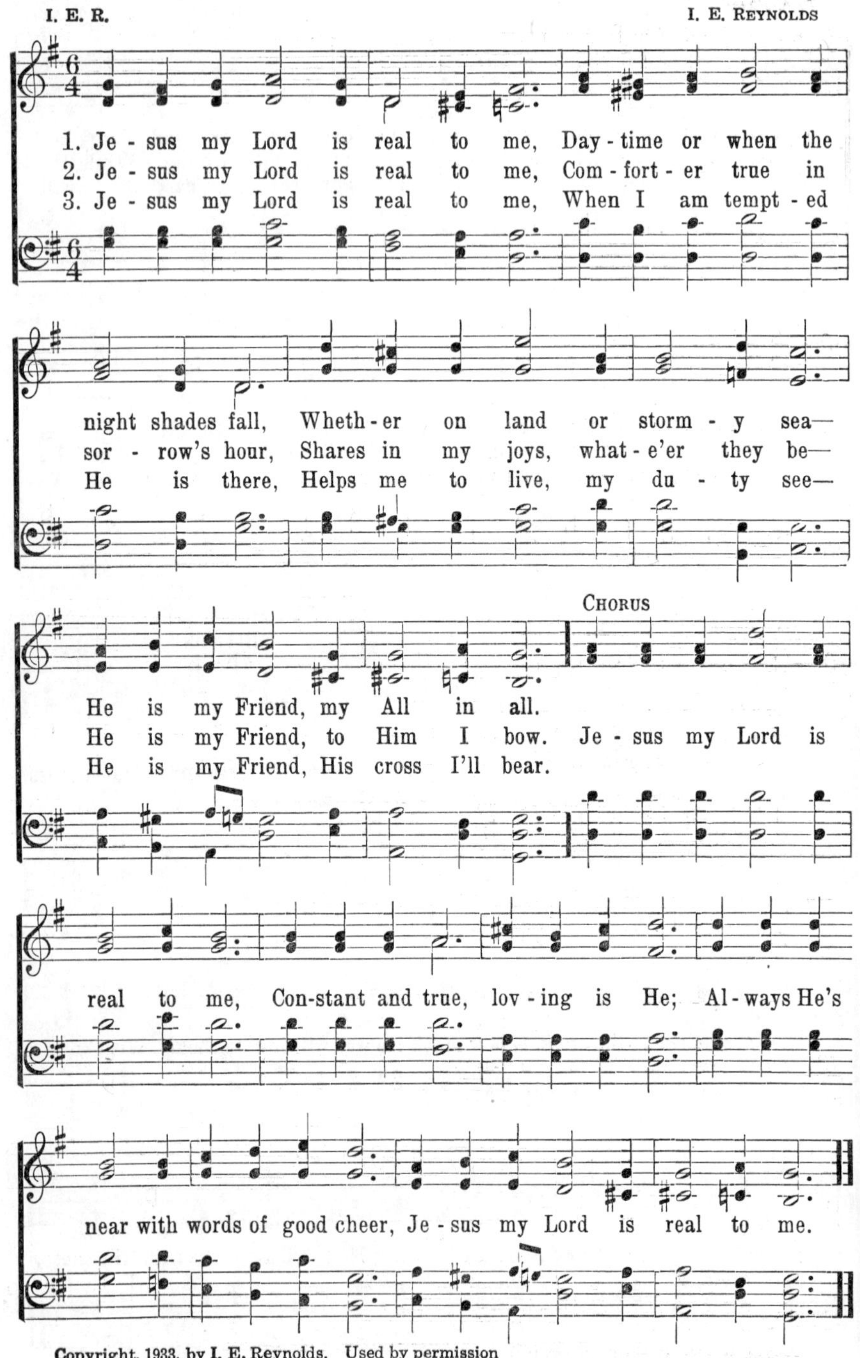

1. Je - sus my Lord is real to me, Day - time or when the night shades fall, Wheth - er on land or storm - y sea— He is my Friend, my All in all.
2. Je - sus my Lord is real to me, Com - fort - er true in sor - row's hour, Shares in my joys, what - e'er they be— He is my Friend, to Him I bow.
3. Je - sus my Lord is real to me, When I am tempt - ed He is there, Helps me to live, my du - ty see— He is my Friend, His cross I'll bear.
Chorus
Je - sus my Lord is real to me, Con-stant and true, lov - ing is He; Al - ways He's near with words of good cheer, Je - sus my Lord is real to me.

347 Serve the Lord with Gladness

B. B. McK.
B. B. McKinney
1. "Serve the Lord with gladness" In our works and ways, Come be-fore His pres-ence
2. "Serve the Lord with gladness," Thankful all the while For His ten-der mer-cies,
3. "Serve the Lord with gladness," This shall be our theme, As we walk to-geth - er
With our songs of praise; Un - to Him our Mak-er We would pledge anew (a-new),
For His lov - ing smile. Bless-ed truth en-dur - ing, Always just the same (the same),
In His love su - preme. Listening, ev - er lis-tening, For the still small voice (His voice),
Life's supreme de-vo-tion To serv-ice true.
We will serve with gladness And praise His name.
His sweet will so precious Will be our choice.
CHORUS
"Serve Him with gladness," Enter His courts with song (with song); To our Cre - a - tor True praises be-long (belong). Great is His mer-cy,
rit.
Won-der-ful is His name (His name), We glad-ly serve Him, His great love proclaim (proclaim).

348 Where We'll Never Grow Old

Jas. C. Moore
(Dedicated to my Father and Mother)
Jas. C. Moore
Effectively
1. I have heard of a land on the far-a-way strand, 'Tis a beau-ti-ful home of the soul; Built by Je-sus on high, there we nev-er shall die, 'Tis a land where we nev-er grow old.
2. In that beau-ti-ful home where we'll nev-er-more roam, We shall be in the sweet by and by; Hap-py praise to the King through e-ter-ni-ty sing, 'Tis a land where we nev-er shall die.
3. When our work here is done and the life-crown is won, And our trou-bles and tri-als are o'er, All our sor-row will end, and our voic-es will blend With the loved ones who've gone on be-fore.
Chorus
Nev-er grow old, nev-er grow old, In a land where we'll never grow old;
Where we'll
Nev-er grow old, nev-er grow old, In a land where we'll never grow old.
Where we'll
Jas. C. Moore, owner

349 Wonderful Story of Love

J. M. D. — Rev. J. M. Driver

1. Won-der-ful sto-ry of love; Tell it to me a-gain; Won-der-ful
2. Won-der-ful sto-ry of love; Tho' you are far a-way; Won-der-ful
3. Won-der-ful sto-ry of love; Je-sus pro-vides a rest; Won-der-ful
sto-ry of love; Wake the im-mor-tal strain! An-gels with rapture announce it,
sto-ry of love; Still He doth call to-day; Call-ing from Cal-va-ry's mountain,
sto-ry of love; For all the pure and blest, Rest in those mansions a-bove us,
Shepherds with won-der re-ceive it; Sin-ner, O won't you be-lieve it?
Down from the crys-tal bright foun-tain, E'en from the dawn of cre-a-tion,
With those who've gone on be-fore us, Sing-ing the rap-tur-ous cho-rus,
Won-der-ful sto-ry of love.
Chorus
Won-der-ful! Won-der-ful! Won-der-ful! Won-der-ful sto-ry of love!
Won-der-ful sto-ry of love; Won-der-ful sto-ry of love; Won-der-ful sto-ry of love;

350 Though Your Sins Be as Scarlet

FANNY J. CROSBY
W. H. DOANE
DUET Gently
1. "Tho' your sins be as scar-let, They shall be as white as snow;
2. Hear the voice that en-treats you, O re-turn ye un-to God!
3. He'll for-give your trans-gres-sions, And re-mem-ber them no more;
Tho' your sins be as scar-let, They shall be as white as snow;
Hear the voice that en-treats you, O re-turn ye un-to God!
He'll for-give your trans-gres-sions, And re-mem-ber them no more;
QUARTET
Tho' they be red . . . . . like crim-son, They shall be as wool!"
He is of great . . . . com-pas-sion, And of won-drous love;
"Look un-to Me, ... ye peo-ple," Saith the Lord your God!
1. Tho' they be red
DUET p
QUARTET f
"Tho' your sins be as scar-let, Tho' your sins be as scar-let,
Hear the voice that en-treats you, Hear the voice that en-treats you,
He'll for-give your trans-gres-sions, He'll for-give your trans-gres-sions,
p rit.
They shall be as white as snow, They shall be as white as snow."
O re-turn ye un-to God! O re-turn ye un-to God!
And re-mem-ber them no more, And re-mem-ber them no more.

351 Open My Eyes, That I May See

C. H. S. — Chas. H. Scott

1. O - pen my eyes, that I may see Glimps-es of truth Thou hast for me;
2. O - pen my ears, that I may hear Voic - es of truth Thou send-est clear;
3. O - pen my mouth, and let me bear Glad - ly the warm truth ev-ery-where;
Place in my hands the won-der-ful key That shall un-clasp, and set me free.
And while the wave-notes fall on my ear, Ev - ery-thing false will dis - ap-pear.
O - pen my heart, and let me pre-pare Love with Thy chil-dren thus to share.
Si - lent - ly now I wait for Thee, Read-y, my God, Thy will to see;
Si - lent - ly now I wait for Thee, Read-y, my God, Thy will to see;
Si - lent - ly now I wait for Thee, Read-y, my God, Thy will to see;
O - pen my eyes, il - lu - mine me, Spir - it di - vine!
O - pen my ears, il - lu - mine me, Spir - it di - vine!
O - pen my heart, il - lu - mine me, Spir - it di - vine!

352 Love Lifted Me

JAMES ROWE
HOWARD E. SMITH
1. I was sink-ing deep in sin, Far from the peaceful shore, Ver - y deep-ly stained with-in, Sink-ing to rise no more; But the Mas-ter of the sea Heard my de-spair-ing cry, From the wa-ters lift - ed me, Now safe am I.
2. All my heart to Him I give, Ev - er to Him I'll cling, In His bless-ed pres - ence live, Ev - er His prais-es sing. Love so might-y and so true Mer - its my soul's best songs; Faith-ful, lov-ing serv-ice, too, To Him be - longs.
3. Souls in dan-ger, look a-bove, Je - sus com-plete-ly saves; He will lift you by His love Out of the an - gry waves. He's the Mas-ter of the sea, Bil - lows His will o - bey; He your Sav-iour wants to be—Be saved to - day.
CHORUS
Love lift - ed me! . . . . Love lift - ed me! . . . . When noth-ing else could help, Love lift - ed me. Love lift - ed me.
e - ven me! e - ven me!
1
2

353 Safe in the Arms of Jesus

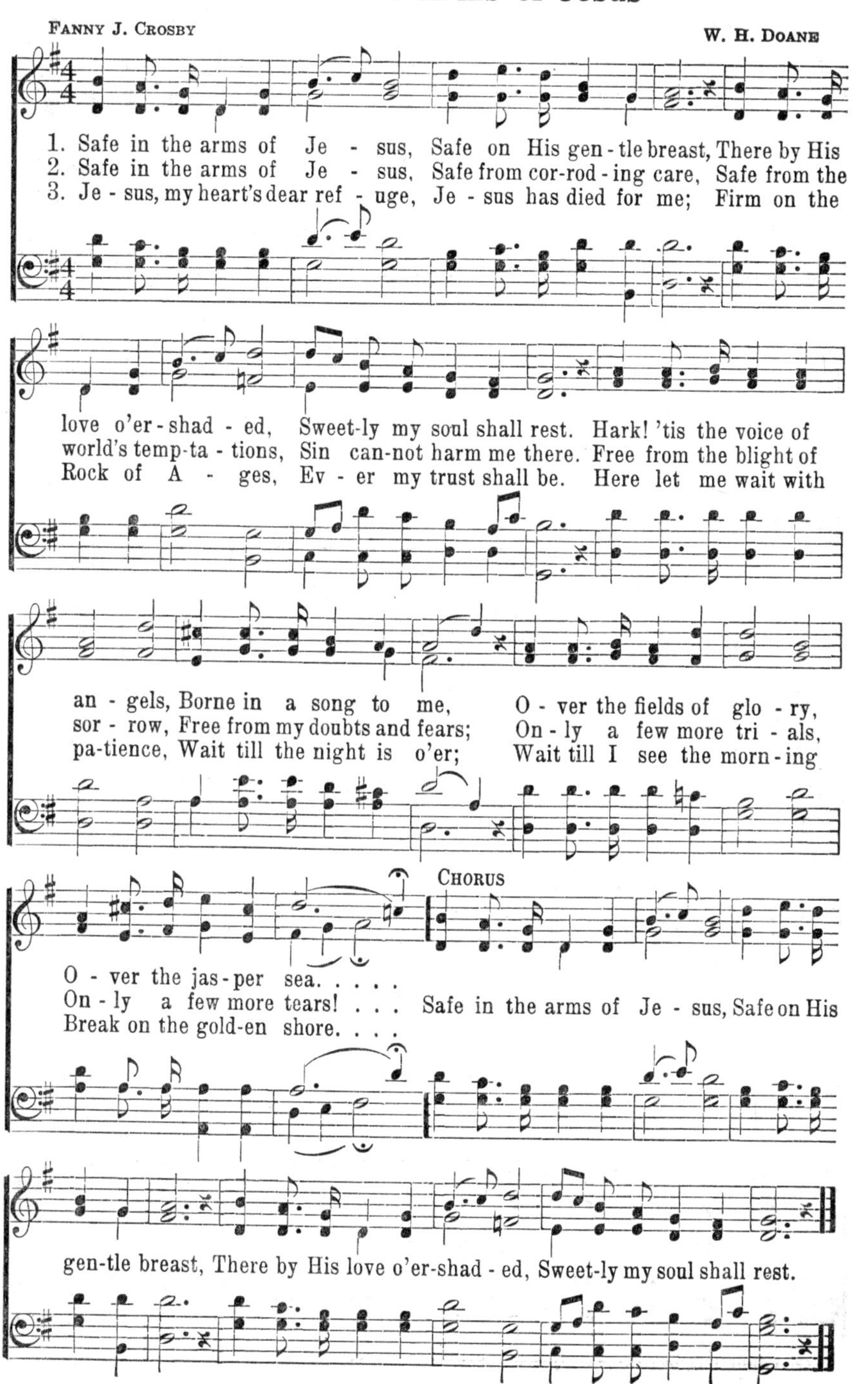
FANNY J. CROSBY
W. H. DOANE
1. Safe in the arms of Je - sus, Safe on His gen - tle breast, There by His love o'er - shad - ed, Sweet-ly my soul shall rest. Hark! 'tis the voice of an - gels, Borne in a song to me, O - ver the fields of glo - ry, O - ver the jas - per sea. . . . .
2. Safe in the arms of Je - sus, Safe from cor-rod - ing care, Safe from the world's temp-ta - tions, Sin can-not harm me there. Free from the blight of sor - row, Free from my doubts and fears; On - ly a few more tri - als, On - ly a few more tears! . . .
3. Je - sus, my heart's dear ref - uge, Je - sus has died for me; Firm on the Rock of A - ges, Ev - er my trust shall be. Here let me wait with pa-tience, Wait till the night is o'er; Wait till I see the morn - ing Break on the gold-en shore. . . .
CHORUS
Safe in the arms of Je - sus, Safe on His gen-tle breast, There by His love o'er-shad - ed, Sweet-ly my soul shall rest.

354 When the Mists Have Rolled Away

ANNIE HERBERT. Arr.
IRA D. SANKEY
1. When the mists have rolled in splendor From the beau-ty of the hills, And the
2. Oft we tread the path be-fore us With a wea-ry burdened heart; Oft we
3. We shall come with joy and gladness, We shall gather round the throne; Face to
sun-light falls in gladness On the riv - er and the rills, We re - call our
toil a - mid the shadows, And our fields are far a - part; But the Sav-iour's
face with those that love us, We shall know as we are known: And the song of
D. S.—In the dawn-ing
Fa-ther's promise In the rain-bow of the spray: We shall know each oth-er
"Come, ye blessed" All our la - bor will re - pay, When we gath-er in the
our re-demp-tion Shall resound thro' endless day When the shadows have de-
of the morn-ing Of that bright and hap - py day, We shall know each oth - er
rit.
FINE CHORUS
bet - ter When the mists have rolled a-way. We shall know . . . as we are
morning Where the mists have rolled a-way.
part - ed, And the mists have rolled a-way.
We shall know
bet-ter When the mists have rolled a - way.
D. S.
known, ... Nev-er - more . . . . to walk a - lone; . . . .
as we are known, Nev - er-more to walk a-lone;

355 Praise Him! Praise Him!

Fanny J. Crosby

Chester G. Allen

1. Praise Him! praise Him! Je-sus, our bless-ed Re-deem-er! Sing, O Earth, His
2. Praise Him! praise Him! Je-sus, our bless-ed Re-deem-er! For our sins He
3. Praise Him! praise Him! Je-sus, our bless-ed Re-deem-er! Heavenly por-tals
won-der-ful love pro-claim! Hail Him! hail Him! highest archangels in glo-ry;
suffered, and bled, and died; He our Rock, our hope of e-ter-nal sal-va-tion,
loud with ho-san-nas ring! Je-sus, Sav-iour, reigneth for-ev-er and ev-er;
Strength and hon-or give to His ho-ly name! Like a shep-herd, Je-sus will
Hail Him! hail Him! Je-sus the Cru-ci-fied. Sound His prais-es! Je-sus who
Crown Him! crown Him! Prophet, and Priest, and King! Christ is com-ing! o-ver the
Refrain
guard His children, In His arms He carries them all day long:
bore our sor-rows, Love unbounded, wonderful, deep and strong: Praise Him! praise Him!
world vic-to-rious, Power and glo-ry un-to the Lord be-long:
tell of His ex-cel-lent greatness: Praise Him! praise Him! ev-er in joy-ful song!

356 In the Garden

C. A. M.
C. Austin Miles
1. I come to the gar-den a - lone, While the dew is still on the
2. He speaks, and the sound of His voice Is so sweet the birds hush their
3. I'd stay in the gar-den with Him Though the night a-round me be
ros - es, And the voice I hear, Fall-ing on my ear, The
sing - ing, And the mel - o - dy That He gave to me, With-
fall - ing, But He bids me go; Thro' the voice of woe His
Son of God dis - clos - es.
in my heart is ring - ing.
voice to me is call - ing.
Chorus
And He walks with me, and He
talks with me, And He tells me I am His own; And the
joy we share as we tar - ry there, None oth-er has ev - er known.

357 Look to Jesus

G. K. K. G. Kearnie Keegan

1. Are you tired of the life you're now liv - ing? Are you wea - ry of sin and its snares? Are you seek-ing for that which is last - ing? Look to Je - sus; you'll find that He cares. . .
2. Are you long-ing to know His for-give-ness? Do you yearn to be free from all sin? Does your lone-ly heart leap when you wit-ness God's won-der-ful love for all men? . .
3. Look to Je - sus the bless-ed Re-deem-er, Give your heart, and your all to the Lord; To His o-pen arms run for sal-va - tion, He has prom-ised it all in His Word. . .
Chorus
He is watch - ing, He is wait - ing, He is long-ing your soul to set free; . . . . Wea-ry one, give your heart to the Sav - iour, Live with Him thro' e - ter - ni - ty.
He is watch-ing for you, He is wait-ing for you, to set free;

358 May God Depend on You?

W. C. Martin
Ira B. Wilson
In march time
1. In the war-fare that is wag-ing For the truth and for the right,
2. See, they come on sa - ble pin-ions, Come in strong Sa-tan-ic might,—
3. From His throne the Fa - ther sees us; An-gels help us to pre - vail;
When the con-flict fierce is rag-ing With the pow-ers of the night,
Pow - ers come and dark do-min-ions From the re-gions of the night.
And our lead-er true is Je - sus, And we shall not, can-not fail.
God needs peo-ple brave and true; May He then de-pend on you?
God re-quires the brave and true; May He then de-pend on you?
Triumph crowns the brave and true; May the Lord de-pend on you?
(1) God needs peo - ple brave and true;
Chorus
May the Lord . . . de-pend on you? . . . Loy-al-ty . . . . is but His due; . . .
May the Lord de - pend on you? Loy-al-ty is but His due;
Say, O spir - it brave and true, That He may de-pend on you!
Say, O spir - it brave and true,

359 Bringing In the Sheaves

KNOWLES SHAW
GEORGE A. MINOR
1. Sow-ing in the morn-ing, sow-ing seeds of kind-ness, Sow-ing in the noon-tide and the dew-y eve; Wait-ing for the har-vest, and the time of reap-ing, We shall come re-joic-ing, bring-ing in the sheaves.
2. Sow-ing in the sun-shine, sow-ing in the shad-ows, Fear-ing nei-ther clouds nor win-ter's chill-ing breeze; By and by the har-vest and the la-bor end-ed, We shall come re-joic-ing, bring-ing in the sheaves.
3. Go-ing forth with weep-ing, sow-ing for the Mas-ter, Tho' the loss sus-tained our spir-it of-ten grieves; When our weep-ing's o-ver, He will bid us wel-come, We shall come re-joic-ing, bring-ing in the sheaves.
CHORUS
Bring-ing in the sheaves, bring-ing in the sheaves, We shall come re-joic-ing, bring-ing in the sheaves;
Bring-ing in the sheaves, bring-ing in the sheaves, We shall come re-joic-ing, bring-ing in the sheaves.
1
2

360 When They Ring the Golden Bells

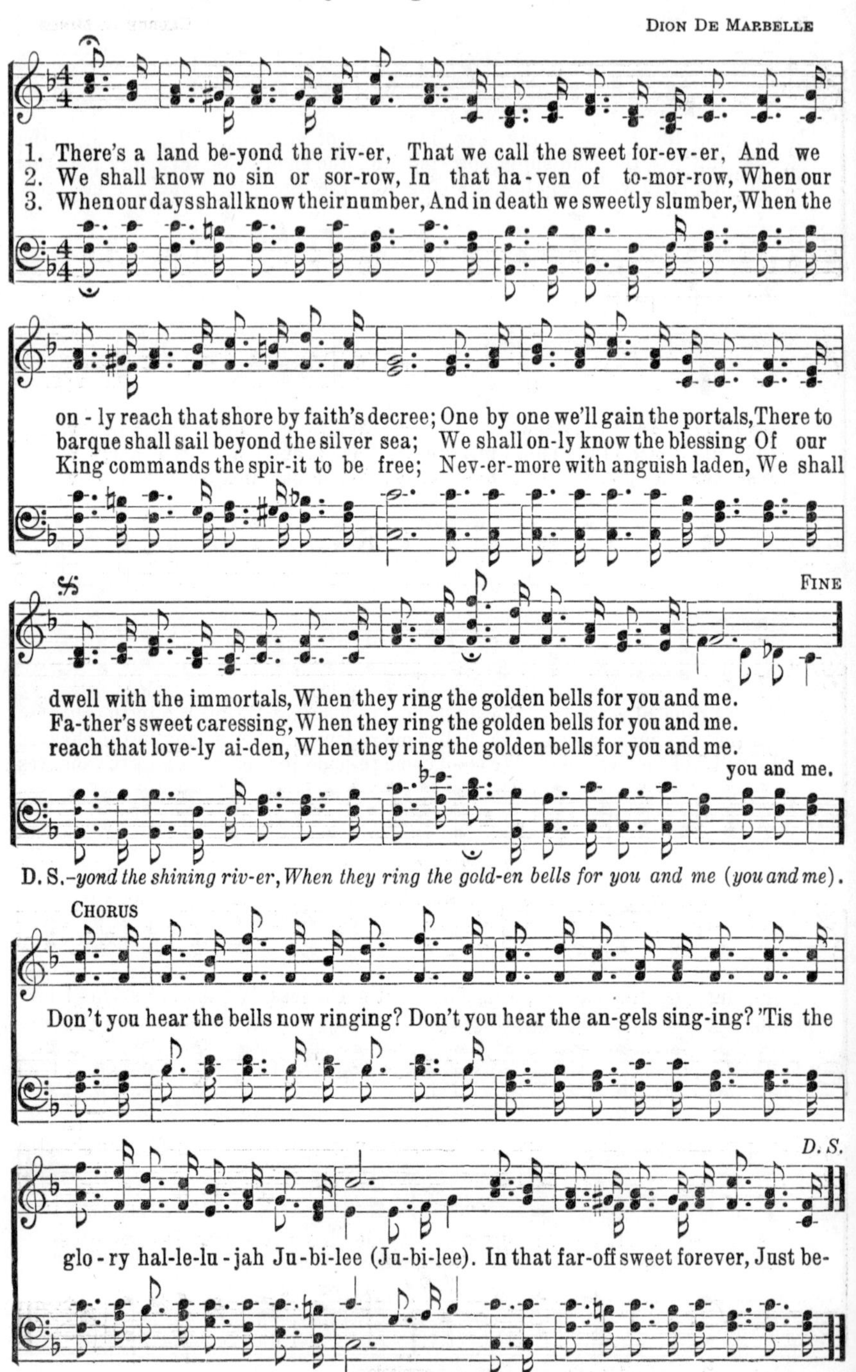
Dion De Marbelle
1. There's a land be-yond the riv-er, That we call the sweet for-ev-er, And we
2. We shall know no sin or sor-row, In that ha-ven of to-mor-row, When our
3. When our days shall know their number, And in death we sweetly slumber, When the
on - ly reach that shore by faith's decree; One by one we'll gain the portals, There to
barque shall sail beyond the silver sea; We shall on-ly know the blessing Of our
King commands the spir-it to be free; Nev-er-more with anguish laden, We shall
dwell with the immortals, When they ring the golden bells for you and me.
Fa-ther's sweet caressing, When they ring the golden bells for you and me.
reach that love-ly ai-den, When they ring the golden bells for you and me.
Fine
you and me.
D. S.-yond the shining riv-er, When they ring the gold-en bells for you and me (you and me).
Chorus
Don't you hear the bells now ringing? Don't you hear the an-gels sing-ing? 'Tis the
glo-ry hal-le-lu-jah Ju-bi-lee (Ju-bi-lee). In that far-off sweet forever, Just be-
D. S.

361 The Peace That Jesus Gives

H. L.
HALDOR LILLENAS
1. Like the sun-shine aft-er rain, Like a rest that fol-fows pain;
2. Like the soft, re-fresh-ing dew, Like a ros-y day-break new,
3. Like a riv-er deep and long, With its cur-rent, cease-less, strong,
Like a hope re-turned a-gain, Is the peace that Je-sus gives.
Like a friend-ship ten-der, true, Is the peace that Je-sus gives.
Like the ca-dence of a song, Is the peace that Je-sus gives.
CHORUS
Oh, the peace that Je-sus gives . . . Nev-er dies, it al-ways lives; . . .
Je-sus gives,
ev-er lives;
Like the mu-sic of a psalm, Like a glad, e-ter-nal calm,
Is the peace that Je-sus gives, . . . Is the peace that Je-sus gives.
Je-sus gives,

362 Great Redeemer!

John Roy Harris — Paolo Conte

1. Great Re-deem-er, we a-dore Thee, God of mer-cy, love, and grace;
2. Great Re-deem-er, we im-plore Thee, Drive our doubts and fears a-way;
3. Life and love from Thee are beam-ing, Sin and sor-row melt a-way;
4. When we see Thee in Thy beau-ty, As Thou art, so we shall be;
Warm our hearts with Thine own be-ing, May we see Thy kind-ly face!
Cause Thy face to smile up-on us, Shine on us Thy light to-day!
King of kind-ness, God of glo-ry, Fill us with Thy-self to-day!
In Thy im-age Thou hast made us, Great Re-deem-er, we love Thee!
Great Re-deem-er, we a-dore Thee, God's great love to man Thou art;
Great Re-deem-er, we a-dore Thee, High-est hills pro-claim Thy fame;
Great Re-deem-er, we a-dore Thee, Life and lib-er-ty are Thine;
Great Re-deem-er, we a-dore Thee, In Thy like-ness we shall be;
We a-dore Thee, Great Re-deem-er, Reign su-preme in ev-ery heart.
We a-dore Thee, Great Re-deem-er, Men and an-gels praise Thy name.
We a-dore Thee, Great Re-deem-er, Fill us with Thy love di-vine.
We a-dore Thee, Great Re-deem-er, God of life e-ter-nal-ly.

363 The Lily of the Valley

English Melody

1. I have found a friend in Je - sus, He's ev - ery-thing to me, He's the
2. He all my griefs has tak - en, and all my sor-rows borne; In temp-
3. He will nev - er, nev - er leave me, nor yet for - sake me here, While I
fair-est of ten thou-sand to my soul; The Lil - y of the Val-ley,
ta - tion He's my strong and mighty tower; I have all for Him for-sak - en,
live by faith and do His bless-ed will; A wall of fire a-bout me,
D. S.—Lil - y of the Val - ley,
FINE.
in Him a-lone I see All I need to cleanse and make me ful-ly whole.
and all my i - dols torn From my heart, and now He keeps me by His power.
I've noth-ing now to fear, With His man-na He my hun-gry soul shall fill.
the Bright and Morn-ing Star, He's the fair - est of ten thou-sand to my soul.
In sor - row He's my com - fort, in trou - ble He's my stay,
Though all the world for - sake me, and Sa - tan tempt me sore,
Then sweep-ing up to glo - ry to see His bless - ed face,
D. S.
He tells me ev - ery care on Him to roll: He's the
Through Je - sus I shall safe - ly reach the goal: He's the
Where riv - ers of de - light shall ev - er roll: He's the

364 Zion Stands with Hills Surrounded

THOMAS KELLY

DR. THOS. HASTINGS

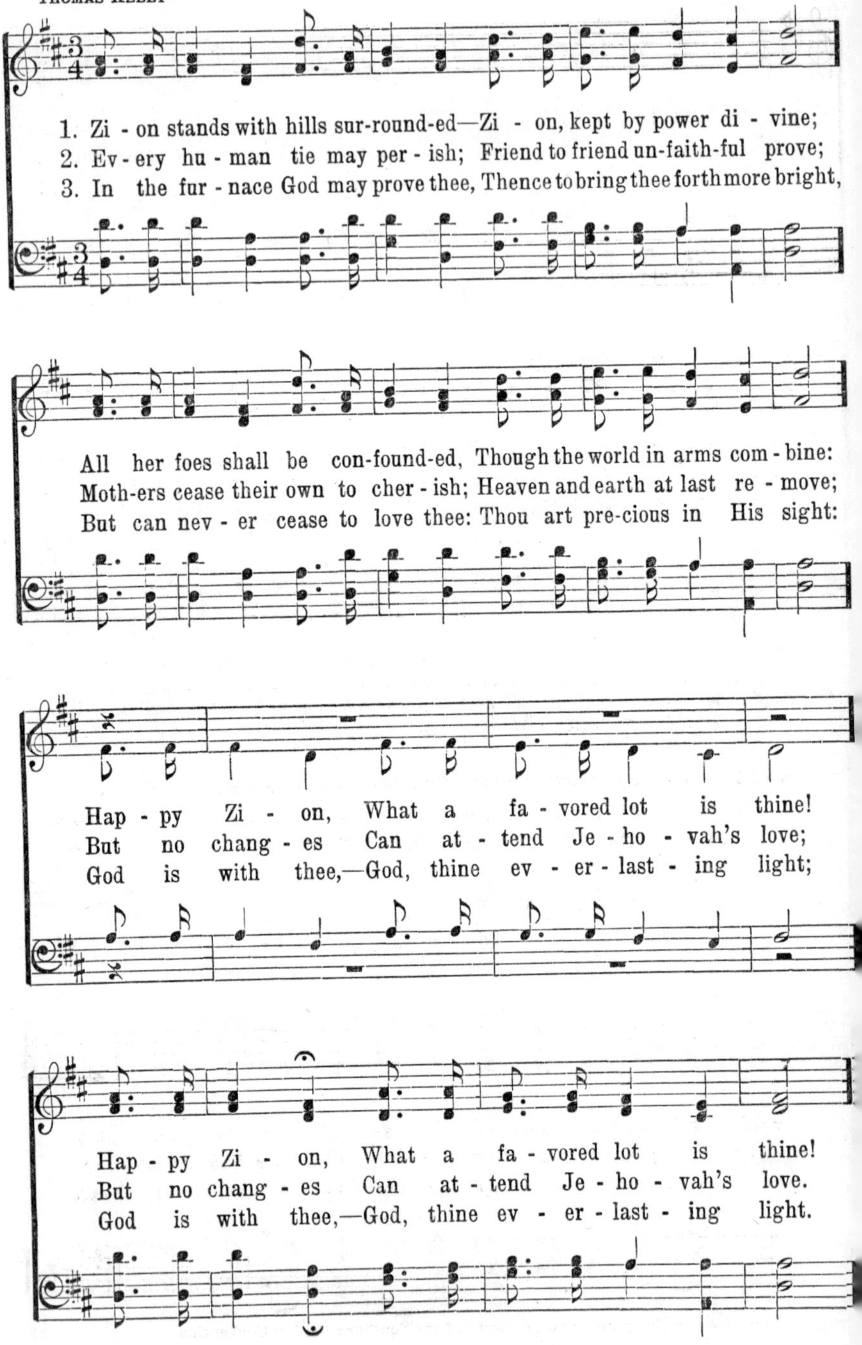

1. Zi - on stands with hills sur-round-ed—Zi - on, kept by power di - vine;
2. Ev - ery hu - man tie may per - ish; Friend to friend un-faith-ful prove;
3. In the fur - nace God may prove thee, Thence to bring thee forth more bright,

All her foes shall be con-found-ed, Though the world in arms com - bine:
Moth-ers cease their own to cher - ish; Heaven and earth at last re - move;
But can nev - er cease to love thee: Thou art pre-cious in His sight:

Hap - py Zi - on, What a fa - vored lot is thine!
But no chang - es Can at - tend Je - ho - vah's love;
God is with thee,—God, thine ev - er - last - ing light;

Hap - py Zi - on, What a fa - vored lot is thine!
But no chang - es Can at - tend Je - ho - vah's love.
God is with thee,—God, thine ev - er - last - ing light.

365 In Thy Holy Temple

B. B. McKinney, Sr. — B. B. McKinney, Jr.

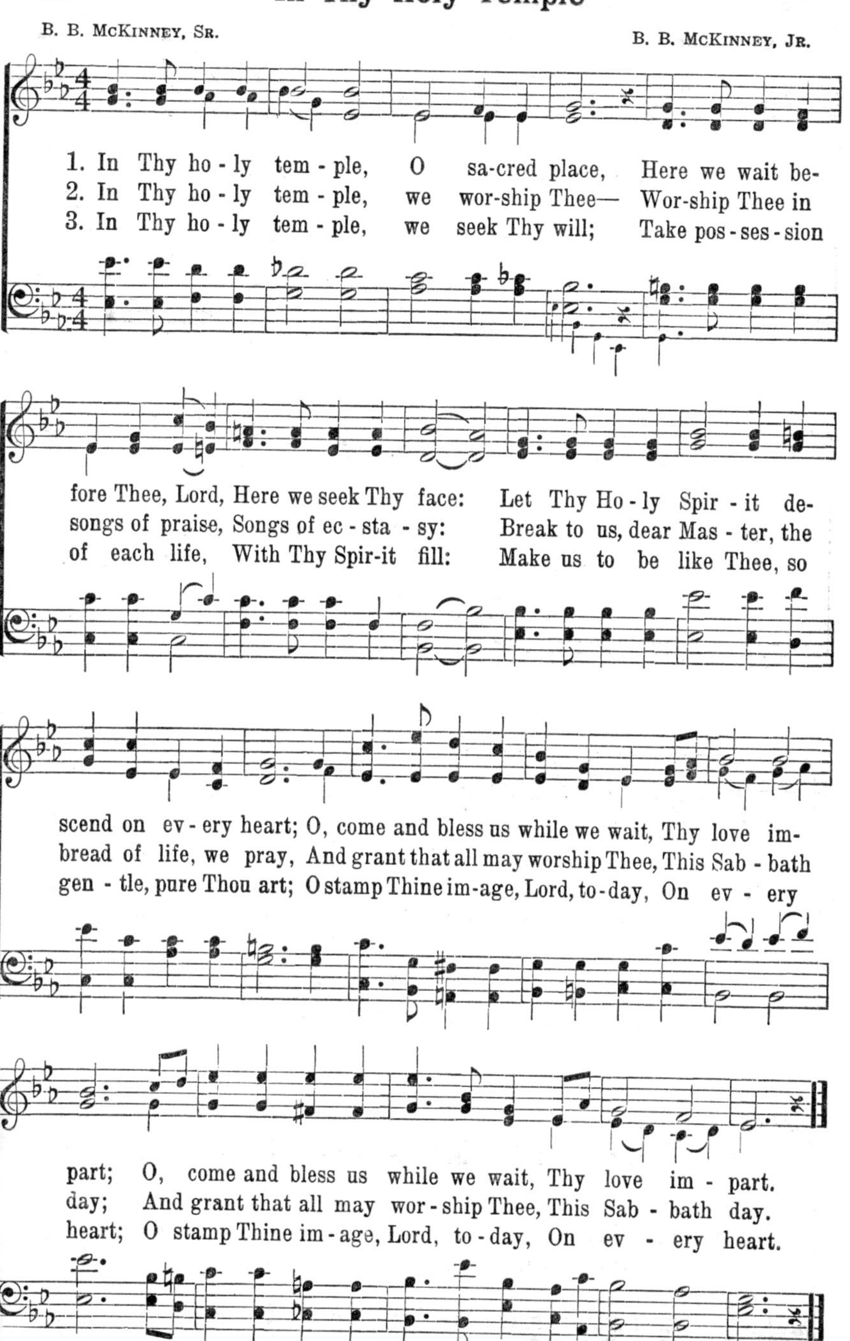
1. In Thy ho - ly tem - ple, O sa-cred place, Here we wait be-
2. In Thy ho - ly tem - ple, we wor-ship Thee— Wor-ship Thee in
3. In Thy ho - ly tem - ple, we seek Thy will; Take pos - ses - sion
fore Thee, Lord, Here we seek Thy face: Let Thy Ho - ly Spir - it de-
songs of praise, Songs of ec - sta - sy: Break to us, dear Mas - ter, the
of each life, With Thy Spir-it fill: Make us to be like Thee, so
scend on ev - ery heart; O, come and bless us while we wait, Thy love im-
bread of life, we pray, And grant that all may worship Thee, This Sab - bath
gen - tle, pure Thou art; O stamp Thine im-age, Lord, to-day, On ev - ery
part; O, come and bless us while we wait, Thy love im - part.
day; And grant that all may wor - ship Thee, This Sab - bath day.
heart; O stamp Thine im - age, Lord, to - day, On ev - ery heart.

Give of Your Best to the Master

H. B. G.
BARNARD
Mrs. CHARLES BARNARD
1. Give of your best to the Mas - ter; Give of the strength of your youth;
2. Give of your best to the Mas - ter; Give Him first place in your heart;
3. Give of your best to the Mas - ter; Naught else is wor-thy His love;
REF.—Give of your best to the Mas - ter; Give of the strength of your youth;
FINE
Throw your soul's fresh, glowing ar - dor In - to the bat-tle for truth.
Give Him first place in your serv - ice, Con-se-crate ev - 'ry part.
He gave Him-self for your ran - som, Gave up His glo - ry a - bove:
Clad in sal - va-tion's full ar - mor, Join in the bat - tle for truth.
Je - sus has set the ex - am - ple; Dauntless was He, young and brave;
Give, and to you shall be giv - en; God His be-lov - ed Son gave;
Laid down His life with-out mur - mur, You from sin's ru - in to save;
rall.
D.C. Ref.
Give Him your loy - al de - vo - tion, Give Him the best that you have. . .
Grate-ful - ly seek-ing to serve Him, Give Him the best that you have. . .
Give Him your heart's ad-o - ra - tion, Give Him the best that you have. . .

367

Tell Me the Story of Jesus

Fanny J. Crosby — Jno. R. Sweney

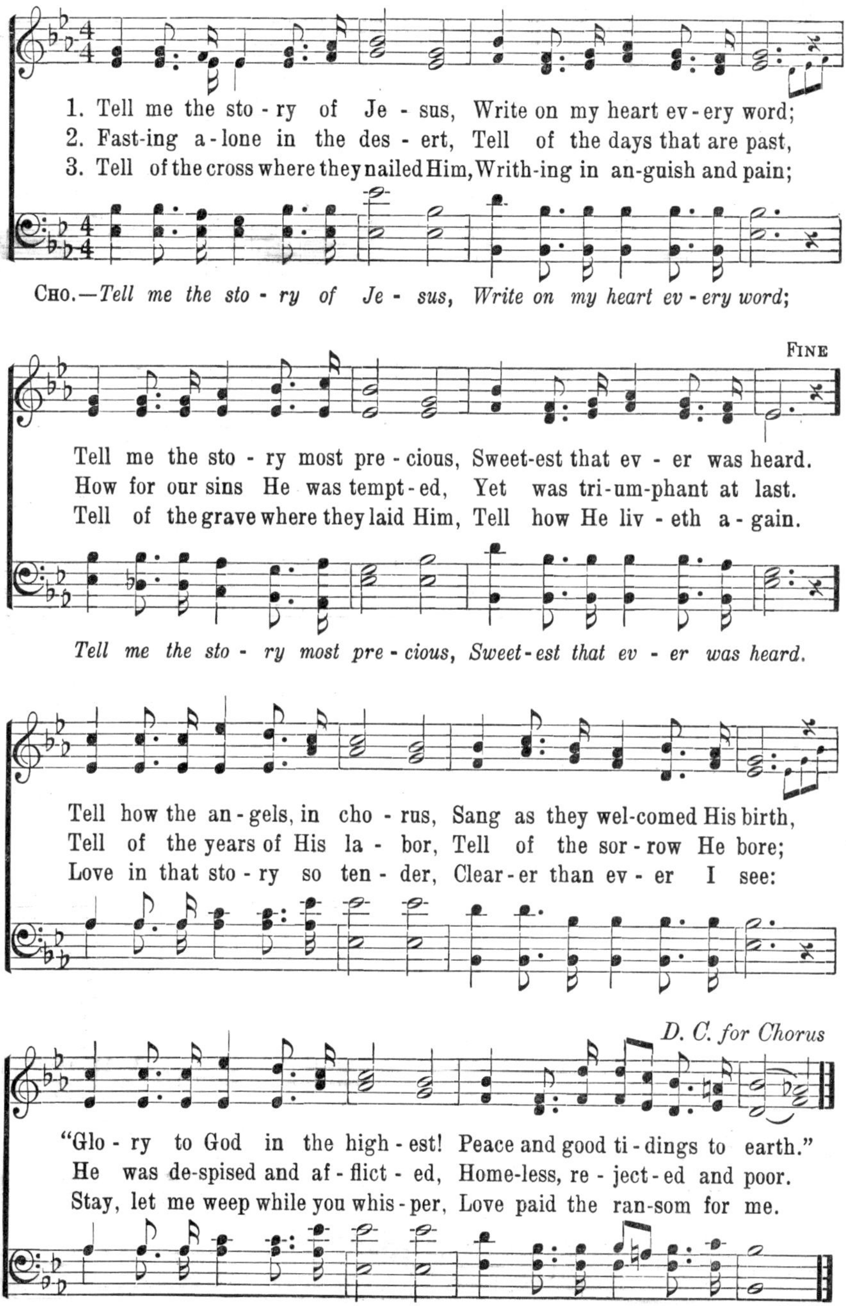

1. Tell me the story of Jesus, Write on my heart every word;
Tell me the story most precious, Sweetest that ever was heard.
Tell how the angels, in chorus, Sang as they welcomed His birth,
"Glory to God in the highest! Peace and good tidings to earth."

2. Fasting alone in the desert, Tell of the days that are past,
How for our sins He was tempted, Yet was triumphant at last.
Tell of the years of His labor, Tell of the sorrow He bore;
He was despised and afflicted, Homeless, rejected and poor.

3. Tell of the cross where they nailed Him, Writhing in anguish and pain;
Tell of the grave where they laid Him, Tell how He liveth again.
Love in that story so tender, Clearer than ever I see:
Stay, let me weep while you whisper, Love paid the ransom for me.

Cho.—*Tell me the story of Jesus, Write on my heart every word;*
Tell me the story most precious, Sweetest that ever was heard.

Fine

D. C. for Chorus

368

I Would Be True

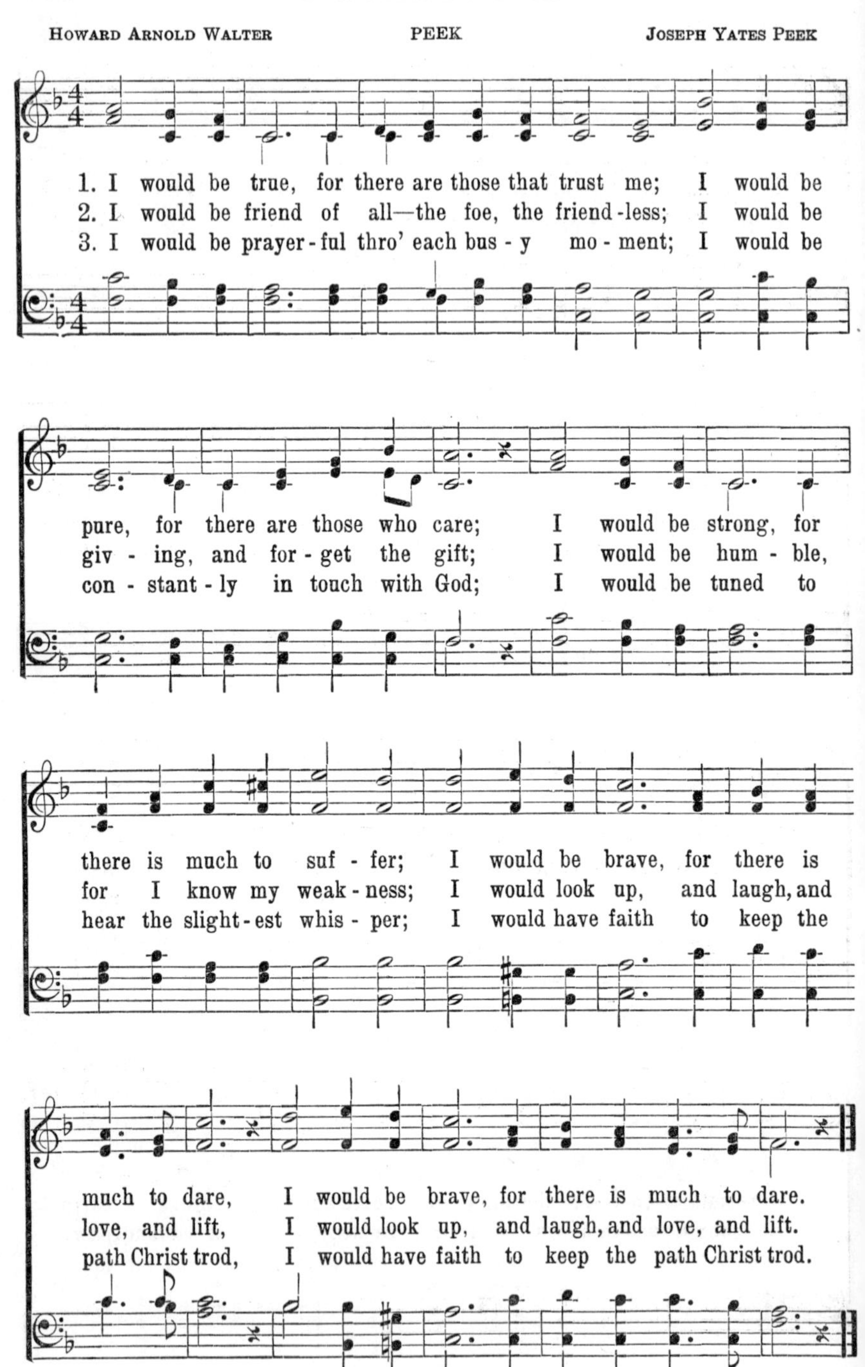
HOWARD ARNOLD WALTER
PEEK
JOSEPH YATES PEEK
1. I would be true, for there are those that trust me; I would be
2. I would be friend of all—the foe, the friend-less; I would be
3. I would be prayer-ful thro' each bus-y mo-ment; I would be
pure, for there are those who care; I would be strong, for
giv-ing, and for-get the gift; I would be hum-ble,
con-stant-ly in touch with God; I would be tuned to
there is much to suf-fer; I would be brave, for there is
for I know my weak-ness; I would look up, and laugh, and
hear the slight-est whis-per; I would have faith to keep the
much to dare, I would be brave, for there is much to dare.
love, and lift, I would look up, and laugh, and love, and lift.
path Christ trod, I would have faith to keep the path Christ trod.

369 All the Way My Saviour Leads Me

FANNY J. CROSBY ROBERT LOWRY

1. All the way my Sav-iour leads me; What have I to ask be-side?
2. All the way my Sav-iour leads me, Cheers each wind-ing path I tread,
3. All the way my Sav-iour leads me; Oh, the full-ness of His love!
Can I doubt His ten-der mer-cy, Who through life has been my Guide?
Gives me grace for ev-ery tri-al, Feeds me with the liv-ing bread.
Per-fect rest to me is prom-ised In my Fa-ther's house a-bove.
Heaven-ly peace, di-vin-est com-fort, Here by faith in Him to dwell!
Though my wea-ry steps may fal-ter, And my soul a-thirst may be,
When my spir-it, clothed im-mor-tal, Wings its flight to realms of day,
For I know, what-e'er be-fall me, Je-sus do-eth all things well; well.
Gushing from the Rock be-fore me, Lo! a spring of joy I see; see.
This my song thro' end-less a-ges: Je-sus led me all the way; way.
1
2

370 Tell Me the Old, Old Story

Kate Hankey
W. H. Doane
1. Tell me the Old, Old Sto - ry, Of un-seen things a - bove, Of Je - sus
2. Tell me the sto - ry slow - ly, That I may take it in— That won-der-
3. Tell me the sto - ry soft - ly, With ear-nest tones and grave; Re - mem-ber
4. Tell me the same old sto - ry, When you have cause to fear That this world's
and His glo - ry, Of Je - sus and His love; Tell me the sto - ry
ful re - demp-tion, God's rem - e - dy for sin; Tell me the sto - ry
I'm the sin - ner Whom Je - sus came to save; Tell me the sto - ry
emp-ty glo - ry Is cost - ing me too dear; Yes, and when that world's
sim - ply, As to a lit - tle child, For I am weak and wea - ry,
of - ten, For I for-get so soon, The "ear - ly dew" of morn-ing
al - ways, If you would real-ly be, In an - y time of trou - ble,
glo - ry Is dawn-ing on my soul, Tell me the Old, Old Sto - ry:
And help - less and de - filed.
Has passed a - way at noon.
A com - fort - er to me.
"Christ Je - sus makes thee whole."
Chorus
Tell me the Old, Old Sto - ry, Tell me the
Old, Old Sto - ry, Tell me the Old, Old Sto - ry Of Je - sus and His love.

371 I Love to Tell the Story

CATHERINE HANKEY | WILLIAM G. FISCHER

1. I love to tell the sto - ry Of un - seen things a - bove, Of
2. I love to tell the sto - ry, More won - der - ful it seems Than
3. I love to tell the sto - ry, 'Tis pleas - ant to re - peat What
4. I love to tell the sto - ry, For those who know it best Seem
Je - sus and His glo - ry, Of Je - sus and His love. I love to
all the gold - en fan - cies Of all our gold - en dreams. I love to
seems, each time I tell it, More won - der - ful - ly sweet. I love to
hun - ger - ing and thirst - ing To hear it like the rest. And when, in
tell the sto - ry, Be - cause I know 'tis true; It sat - is - fies my
tell the sto - ry, It did so much for me; And that is just the
tell the sto - ry, For some have nev - er heard The mes - sage of sal-
scenes of glo - ry, I sing the new, new song, 'Twill be the old, old
long - ings As noth - ing else can do.
rea - son I tell it now to thee.
va - tion From God's own ho - ly Word.
sto - ry That I have loved so long.
CHORUS
I love to tell the sto - ry, 'Twill
be my theme in glo - ry To tell the old, old sto - ry Of Je - sus and His love.

372 The Cross Is Not Greater

B. B. BALLINGTON BOOTH

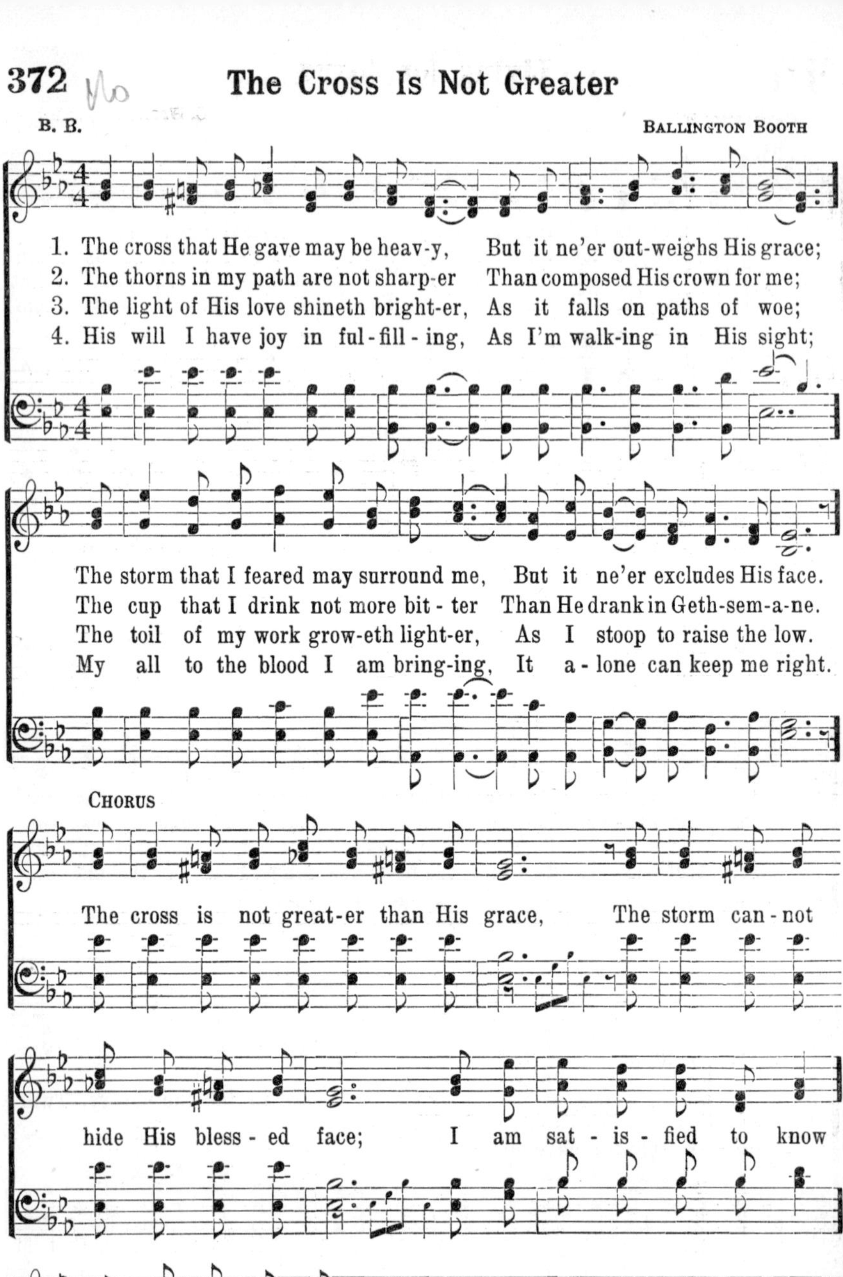
1. The cross that He gave may be heav-y, But it ne'er out-weighs His grace;
2. The thorns in my path are not sharp-er Than composed His crown for me;
3. The light of His love shineth bright-er, As it falls on paths of woe;
4. His will I have joy in ful-fill-ing, As I'm walk-ing in His sight;
The storm that I feared may surround me, But it ne'er excludes His face.
The cup that I drink not more bit-ter Than He drank in Geth-sem-a-ne.
The toil of my work grow-eth light-er, As I stoop to raise the low.
My all to the blood I am bring-ing, It a-lone can keep me right.
CHORUS
The cross is not great-er than His grace, The storm can-not
hide His bless-ed face; I am sat-is-fied to know
That with Je-sus here be-low, I can con-quer ev-ery foe.

373 Living for Jesus

T. O. Chisholm — C. Harold Lowden

Not fast
1. Liv-ing for Je-sus a life that is true, Striv-ing to please Him in all that I do,
2. Liv-ing for Je-sus who died in my place, Bear-ing on Cal-v'ry my sin and dis-grace,
3. Liv-ing for Je-sus wher-ev-er I am, Do-ing each du-ty in His ho-ly name,
4. Liv-ing for Je-sus thro' earth's lit-tle while, My dear-est treas-ure, the light of His smile,
Yield-ing al-le-giance, glad-heart-ed and free, This is the path-way of bless-ing for me.
Such love constrains me to an-swer His call, Fol-low His lead-ing and give Him my all.
Will-ing to suf-fer af-flic-tion or loss, Deem-ing each tri-al a part of my cross.
Seek-ing the lost ones He died to re-deem, Bring-ing the wea-ry to find rest in Him.
*Chorus Unison. A little slower
O Je-sus, Lord and Sav-iour, I give my-self to Thee; For Thou, in Thy a-tone-ment, Didst give Thy-self for me; I own no oth-er Mas-ter, My heart shall be Thy throne, My life I give, henceforth to live, O Christ, for Thee a-lone.
rit.

*Melody in lower notes. A two-part effect may be had by having the men sing the melody, the women taking the middle notes.

374

Loyalty to Christ

Dr. E. T. Cassel
Flora H. Cassel
1. From o - ver hill and plain There comes the signal strain, 'Tis loy-al-ty, loy-al-ty,
2. O hear, ye brave, the sound That moves the earth around, 'Tis loy-al-ty, loy-al-ty,
3. Come, join our loy-al throng, We'll rout the gi-ant wrong, 'Tis loy-al-ty, loy-al-ty,
4. The strength of youth we lay At Je - sus' feet to - day, 'Tis loy-al-ty, loy-al-ty,
loy - al - ty to Christ; Its mu - sic rolls a - long, The hills take up the song,
loy - al - ty to Christ; A - rise to dare and do, Ring out the watch-word true,
loy - al - ty to Christ; Where Satan's banners float We'll send the bu - gle note,
loy - al - ty to Christ; His Gos - pel we'll pro-claim Thro'-out the world's do-main,
Of loy-al - ty, loy-al-ty, Yes, loy-al - ty to Christ.
Chorus
"On to vic - to - ry! On to vic-to-ry!" Cries our great Commander, "On!" . . . We'll move at His command,
great Commander, "On!"
We'll soon possess the land, Thro' loy-al-ty, loy - al-ty, Yes, loy-al - ty to Christ.

375

Satisfied with Jesus

B. B. McK.
B. B. McKinney
Slowly
1. I am sat-is-fied with Je-sus, He has done so much for me,
2. He is with me in my tri-als, Best of friends of all is He;
3. I can hear the voice of Je-sus Call-ing out so plead-ing-ly,
4. When my work on earth is end-ed, And I cross the mys-tic sea,
He has suf-fered to re-deem me, He has died to set me free.
I can al-ways count on Je-sus, Can He al-ways count on me?
"Go and win the lost and stray-ing;" Is He sat-is-fied with me?
Oh, that I could hear Him say-ing, "I am sat-is-fied with thee."
Chorus
I am sat-is-fied, I am sat-is-fied, I am sat-is-fied with Je-sus, But the ques-tion comes to me, As I think of Cal-va-ry, Is my Mas-ter sat-is-fied with me?
rit.

376 Sunlight

J. W. Van DeVenter W. S. Weeden

1. I wan-dered in the shades of night, Till Je - sus came to me,
2. Tho' clouds may gath - er in the sky, And bil - lows round me roll,
3. While walk-ing in the light of God, I sweet com-mun - ion find;
4. I cross the wide - ex - tend - ed fields, I jour - ney o'er the plain,
5. Soon I shall see Him as He is, The light that came to me,
And with the sun - light of His love Bid all my dark - ness flee.
How - ev - er dark the world may be, I've sun - light in my soul.
I press with ho - ly vig - or on, And leave the world be - hind.
And in the sun - light of His love I reap the gold - en grain.
Be - hold the bright-ness of His face, Thro'-out e - ter - ni - ty.
Chorus
Sun-light, sun - light in my soul to - day,
to - day, yes,
Sun-light, sun-light all a - long the way;
nar - row way;
Since the Sav - iour found me, Took a-way my sin,
load of sin;
I have had the sun-light of His love with - in.

377 I Will Sing the Wondrous Story

F. H. Rowley
Peter P. Bilhorn
1. I will sing the won-drous sto - ry Of the Christ who died for me,
2. I was lost, but Je - sus found me, Found the sheep that went a - stray,
3. I was bruised, but Je - sus healed me; Faint was I from man-y a fall;
4. Days of dark-ness still come o'er me, Sor-row's paths I of - ten tread,
5. He will keep me till the riv - er Rolls its wa - ters at my feet;
How He left His home in glo - ry For the cross of Cal - va - ry.
Threw His lov - ing arms a - round me, Drew me back in - to His way.
Sight was gone, and fears pos-sessed me, But He freed me from them all.
But the Sav - iour still is with me; By His hand I'm safe - ly led.
Then He'll bear me safe - ly o - ver, Where the loved ones I shall meet.
Chorus
Yes, I'll sing . . . . the won-drous sto - ry Of the
Yes, I'll sing the won-drous sto - ry
Christ . . . who died for me, ... Sing it with . . . . the saints in
Of the Christ who died for me, Sing it with
glo - - ry, Gath-ered by . . . . the crys-tal sea.
the saints in glo - ry, Gath-ered by the crys-tal sea.

378

Tell It Again

Mrs. M. B. C. Slade
R. M. McIntosh
1. In - to the tent where a gip - sy boy lay, Dy - ing a - lone at the close of the day, News of sal - va - tion we car - ried, said he: "No - bod - y ev - er has told it to me!"
2. "Did He so love me, a poor lit - tle boy? Send un - to me the good ti - dings of joy? Need I not per - ish? my hand will He hold? No - bod - y ev - er the sto - ry has told!"
3. Bend-ing we caught the last words of his breath, Just as he en-tered the val - ley of death: "God sent His Son!" "Who-so - ev - er," said He: "Then I am sure that He sent Him for me!"
4. Smil - ing, he said, as his last sigh he spent, "I am so glad that for me He was sent!" Whis-pered, while low sank the sun in the west, "Lord, I be - lieve, tell it now to the rest!"
Refrain
Tell it a - gain! Tell it a - gain! Sal-va-tion's sto - ry re-peat o'er and o'er, Till none can say of the chil-dren of men, "No-bod - y ev - er has told me be - fore."

379 We've a Story to Tell

Colin Sterne H. E. Nichol

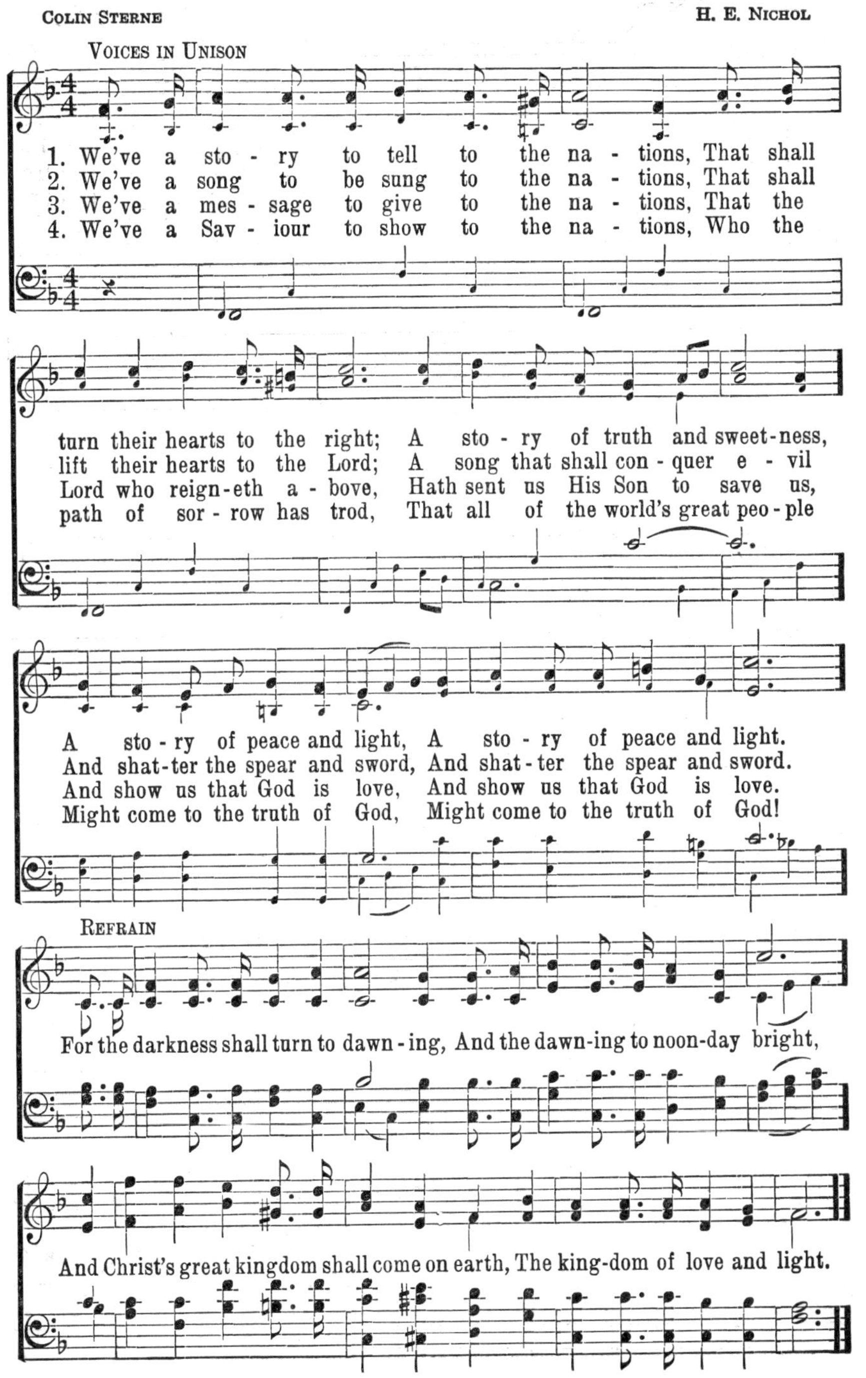

Voices in Unison
1. We've a sto - ry to tell to the na - tions, That shall turn their hearts to the right; A sto - ry of truth and sweet-ness, A sto - ry of peace and light, A sto - ry of peace and light.
2. We've a song to be sung to the na - tions, That shall lift their hearts to the Lord; A song that shall con - quer e - vil And shat-ter the spear and sword, And shat - ter the spear and sword.
3. We've a mes - sage to give to the na - tions, That the Lord who reign-eth a - bove, Hath sent us His Son to save us, And show us that God is love, And show us that God is love.
4. We've a Sav - iour to show to the na - tions, Who the path of sor - row has trod, That all of the world's great peo - ple Might come to the truth of God, Might come to the truth of God!
Refrain
For the darkness shall turn to dawn - ing, And the dawn-ing to noon-day bright,
And Christ's great kingdom shall come on earth, The king-dom of love and light.

380

My Mother's Bible

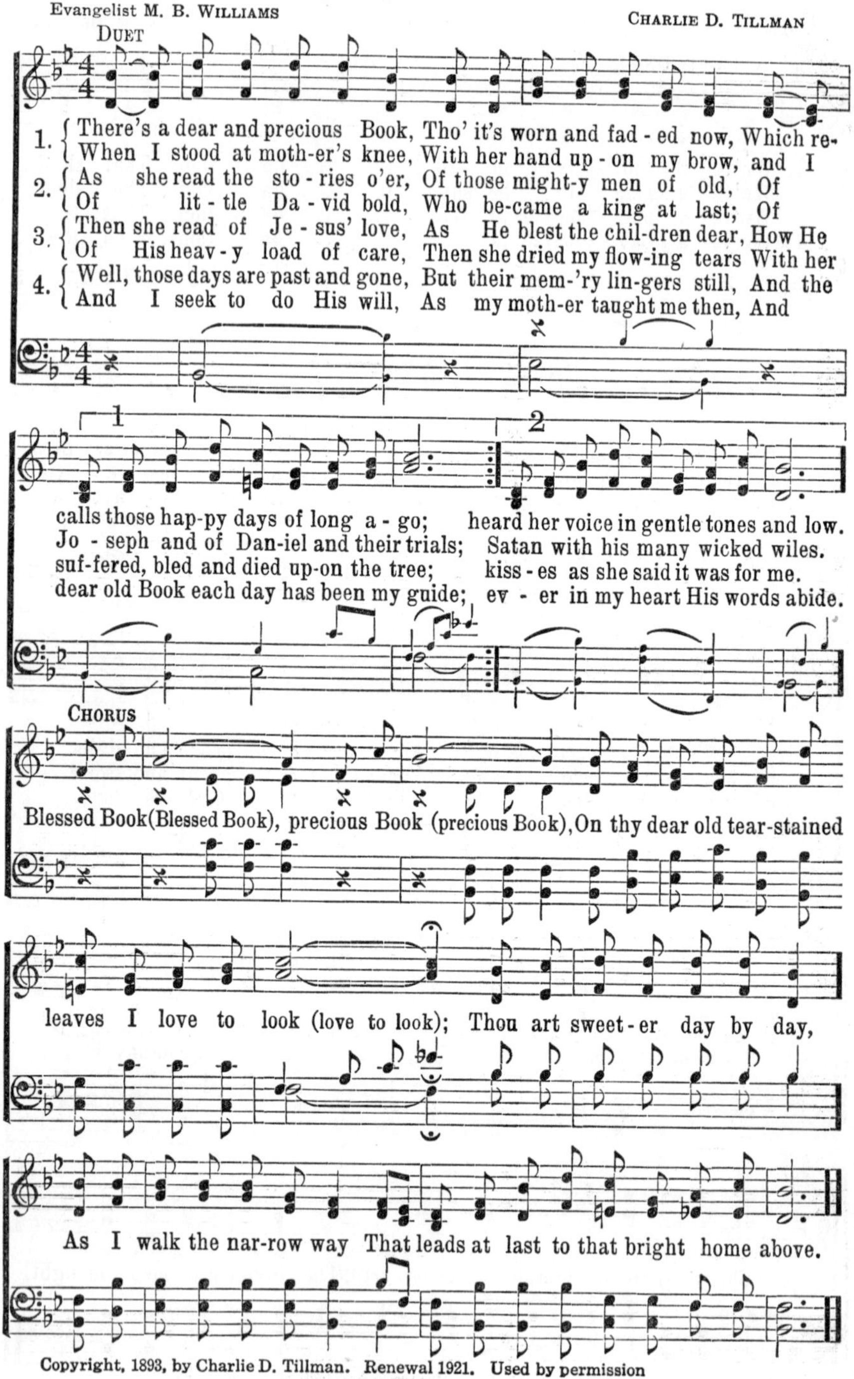
Evangelist M. B. WILLIAMS
CHARLIE D. TILLMAN
DUET
1. { There's a dear and precious Book, Tho' it's worn and fad - ed now, Which re-
{ When I stood at moth-er's knee, With her hand up - on my brow, and I
2. { As she read the sto - ries o'er, Of those might-y men of old, Of
{ Of lit - tle Da - vid bold, Who be-came a king at last; Of
3. { Then she read of Je - sus' love, As He blest the chil-dren dear, How He
{ Of His heav - y load of care, Then she dried my flow-ing tears With her
4. { Well, those days are past and gone, But their mem-'ry lin-gers still, And the
{ And I seek to do His will, As my moth-er taught me then, And
1
2
calls those hap-py days of long a - go; heard her voice in gentle tones and low.
Jo - seph and of Dan-iel and their trials; Satan with his many wicked wiles.
suf-fered, bled and died up-on the tree; kiss - es as she said it was for me.
dear old Book each day has been my guide; ev - er in my heart His words abide.
CHORUS
Blessed Book (Blessed Book), precious Book (precious Book), On thy dear old tear-stained
leaves I love to look (love to look); Thou art sweet - er day by day,
As I walk the nar-row way That leads at last to that bright home above.

381 Sweet Peace, the Gift of God's Love
P. P. B.
P. P. BILHORN
1. There comes to my heart one sweet strain (sweet strain), A
2. Through Christ on the cross peace was made (was made), My
3. When Je - sus as Lord I had crowned (had crowned), My
4. In Je - sus for peace I a - bide (a - bide), And
glad and a joy - ous re - frain (re - frain); I sing it a-
debt by His death was all paid (all paid); No oth - er foun-
heart with this peace did a - bound (a - bound); In Him the rich
as I keep close to His side (His side), There's noth-ing but
gain and a - gain, Sweet peace, the gift of God's love.
da - tion is laid For peace, the gift of God's love.
bless-ing I found, Sweet peace, the gift of God's love.
peace doth be - tide, Sweet peace, the gift of God's love.
CHORUS
Peace, peace, sweet peace! Won - der - ful gift from a - bove (a-bove)! Oh,
cres.
won - der-ful, won-der-ful peace! Sweet peace, the gift of God's love!
Copyright, 1914, by P. P. Bilhorn, Renewal. Nazarene Publishing House, owner

382 He Ransomed Me

Julia H. Johnston — J. W. Henderson

1. There's a sweet and bless-ed sto - ry Of the Christ who came from glo - ry,
2. From the depth of sin and sad - ness To the heights of joy and glad-ness
3. From the throne of heaven-ly glo - ry— Oh, the sweet and bless - ed sto - ry!
4. By and by with joy in - creas-ing, And with grat - i - tude un - ceas - ing,
Just to res-cue me from sin and mis-er - y; He in lov-ing-kindness sought me,
Je - sus lift - ed me, in mer-cy full and free; With His precious blood He bo't me,
Je - sus came to lift the lost in sin and woe In - to lib - er - ty all - glo - rious,
Lift - ed up with Christ for-ev-er-more to be; I will join the hosts there sing-ing,
ad lib.
And from sin and shame hath bro't me, Hal - le - lu - jah! Je - sus ran-somed me.
When I knew Him not, He sought me, And in love di - vine He ran-somed me.
Tro-phies of His grace vic - to - rious, Ev - er-more re - joic-ing here be - low.
In the an-them ev - er ring-ing, To the King of Love who ran-somed me.
Chorus
Hal - le - lu - jah, what a Sav-iour! Who can take a poor lost sin-ner, Lift him
from the mir - y clay and set him free; (Hal-le-lu-jah!) I will ev - er tell the sto - ry,

He Ransomed Me

ad lib.
Shout-ing glo-ry, glo-ry, glo-ry, Hal-le-lu-jah! Je-sus ran-somed me.

383 He Died of a Broken Heart

T. D.

T. DENNIS
Arr. by B. B. McKINNEY

DUET Slowly
1. Have you read the sto-ry of the Cross, Where Je-sus bled and died;
2. Have you read how they placed the crown of thorns Up-on His brow for you,
3. Have you read how He saved the dy-ing thief, When hanging on the tree,
4. Have you read that He looked to heaven and said, "'Tis finished?" 'Twas for thee!
Where your debt was paid by His precious blood That flowed from His wounded side?
When He prayed, "For-give them, oh, for-give; They know not what they do?"
When He looked with plead-ing eyes and said, "Dear Lord, re-mem-ber Me?"
Have you ev-er said, "I thank Thee, Lord, For giv-ing Thy life for me?"
CHORUS
He died of a bro-ken heart for you, He died of a bro-ken heart;
Up-on a tree, for you, for me, He died of a bro-ken heart.

384 He Just Put Himself In My Place

Author unknown
Arr. J. M. G.

HOMER HAMMONTREE

1. Shall I tell you what brought me to Je - sus, What caused me to seek His bless - ed face? It was this, that, to save and to cleanse me, He just put Him - self in my place. . . .
2. O, He felt all my load in the gar - den, My guilt He did car - ry to the tree; I was lost, and con-demned un - to judg - ment, But my Lord Him - self died for me. . . . .
3. Soon He's com - ing a - gain from the glo - ry,—The proph - ets of God on this a - gree; And till then this to oth - ers I'm tell - ing, That for them He died as for me. . . . .
CHORUS
He just put Him - self in my place, (O bless His name!) He just put Him - self in my place; (O bless His name!) This is the Gos - pel sto - ry,

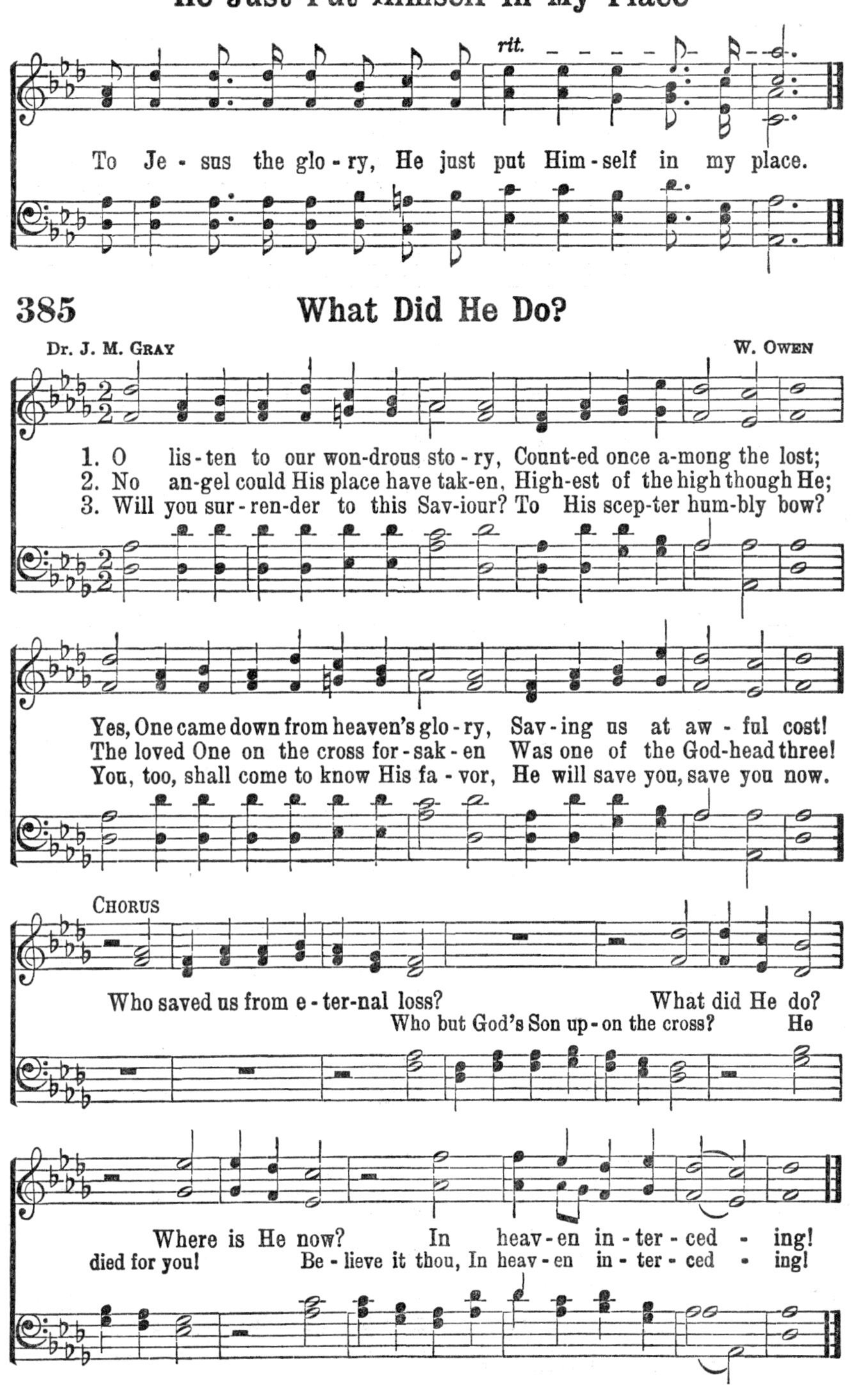
He Just Put Himself In My Place
rit.
To Je - sus the glo - ry, He just put Him - self in my place.
385
What Did He Do?
Dr. J. M. Gray
W. Owen
1. O lis-ten to our won-drous sto - ry, Count-ed once a-mong the lost;
2. No an-gel could His place have tak-en, High-est of the high though He;
3. Will you sur-ren-der to this Sav-iour? To His scep-ter hum-bly bow?
Yes, One came down from heaven's glo - ry, Sav-ing us at aw - ful cost!
The loved One on the cross for - sak - en Was one of the God-head three!
You, too, shall come to know His fa - vor, He will save you, save you now.
Chorus
Who saved us from e - ter-nal loss?
Who but God's Son up - on the cross?
What did He do?
He died for you!
Where is He now?
Be - lieve it thou,
In heav - en in - ter - ced - ing!

386 Not Half Has Ever Been Told

Rev. J. B. ATCHINSON
O. F. PRESBREY
Effective as a Solo
1. I have read of a beau-ti-ful cit - y, Far a-way in the kingdom of God;
2. I have read of bright mansions in heaven, Which the Saviour has gone to prepare;
3. I have read of white robes for the righteous, Of bright crowns which the glorified wear,
4. I have read of a Christ so for-giv-ing, That vile sinners may ask and re-ceive
I have read how its walls are of jas - per, How its streets are all golden and broad.
And the saints who on earth have been faithful, Rest for-ev - er with Christ o-ver there;
When our Father shall bid them "Come, enter, And My glo-ry e-ter-nal-ly share;"
Peace and pardon from every transgression, If when ask-ing they on-ly be - lieve.
In the midst of the street is life's riv-er, Clear as crys-tal and pure to be - hold;
There no sin ev - er en-ters, nor sor-row, The in-hab - it-ants nev-er grow old;
How the righteous are ev-er-more bless-ed As they walk thro' the streets of pure gold;
I have read how He'll guide and protect us, If for safe-ty we en - ter His fold;
But not half of that cit - y's bright glo - ry To mor-tals has ev-er been told.
But not half of the joys that a - wait them To mor-tals has ev-er been told.
But not half of the won-der-ful sto - ry To mor-tals has ev-er been told.
But not half of His goodness and mer - cy To mor-tals has ev-er been told.
CHORUS
Not half has ev-er been told (been told); Not half has ev-er been told (been told);

Not Half Has Ever Been Told

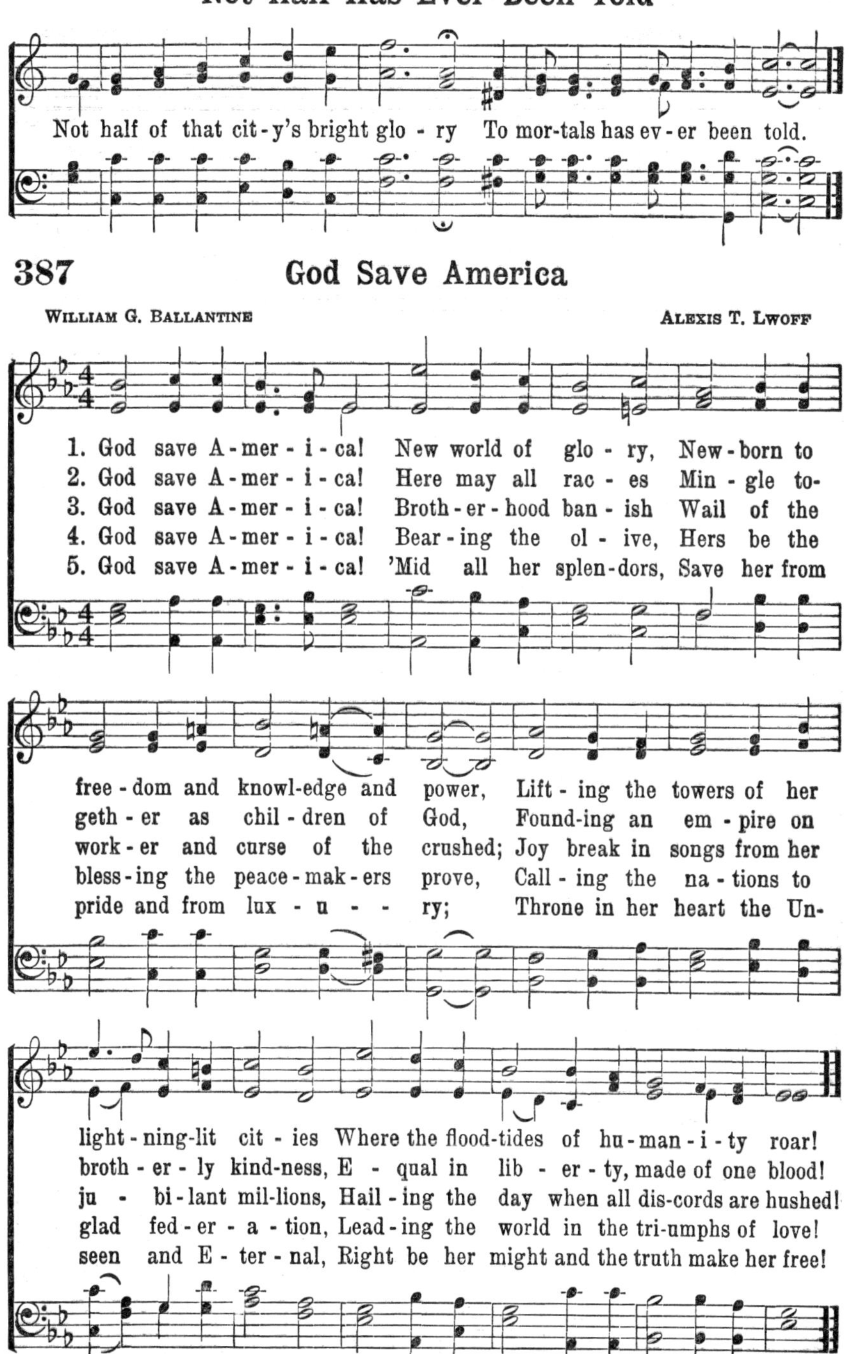
Not half of that cit-y's bright glo - ry To mor-tals has ev - er been told.
387 God Save America
WILLIAM G. BALLANTINE
ALEXIS T. LWOFF
1. God save A-mer-i-ca! New world of glo-ry, New-born to free-dom and knowl-edge and power, Lift-ing the towers of her light-ning-lit cit-ies Where the flood-tides of hu-man-i-ty roar!
2. God save A-mer-i-ca! Here may all rac-es Min-gle to-geth-er as chil-dren of God, Found-ing an em-pire on broth-er-ly kind-ness, E-qual in lib-er-ty, made of one blood!
3. God save A-mer-i-ca! Broth-er-hood ban-ish Wail of the work-er and curse of the crushed; Joy break in songs from her ju-bi-lant mil-lions, Hail-ing the day when all dis-cords are hushed!
4. God save A-mer-i-ca! Bear-ing the ol-ive, Hers be the bless-ing the peace-mak-ers prove, Call-ing the na-tions to glad fed-er-a-tion, Lead-ing the world in the tri-umphs of love!
5. God save A-mer-i-ca! 'Mid all her splen-dors, Save her from pride and from lux-u-ry; Throne in her heart the Un-seen and E-ter-nal, Right be her might and the truth make her free!

388 My Redeemer

P. P. Bliss
James McGranahan
1. I will sing of my Re-deem-er And His won-drous love to me;
2. I will tell the won-drous sto-ry, How my lost es-tate to save,
3. I will praise my dear Re-deem-er, His tri-um-phant power I'll tell,
4. I will sing of my Re-deem-er, And His heaven-ly love to me;
On the cru-el cross He suf-fered, From the curse to set me free.
In His bound-less love and mer-cy, He the ran-som free-ly gave.
How the vic-to-ry He giv-eth O-ver sin, and death, and hell.
He from death to life hath brought me, Son of God, with Him to be.
Chorus
Sing, oh, sing . . . . of my Re-deem-er, With His
Sing, oh, sing of my Re-deem-er, Sing, oh, sing of my Re-deem-er, With His
blood . . . . He pur-chased me, ... On the cross . . . . He sealed my
blood He purchased me, With His blood He purchased me, On the cross He sealed my pardon, On the
Repeat pp after last verse
par-don, Paid the debt . . . . and made me free. . . .
cross He sealed my par-don, Paid the debt and made me free, and made me free.

389 Thy Word Have I Hid In My Heart

Adapted by E. O. S. | E. O. SELLERS

1. Thy Word is a lamp to my feet, A light to my path al-way;
2. For-ev-er, O Lord, is Thy Word Es-tab-lished and fixed on high;
3. At morn-ing, at noon, and at night I ev-er will give Thee praise;
4. Thro' Him whom Thy Word hath foretold, The Sav-iour and Morn-ing Star,
To guide and to save me from sin, And show me the heaven-ly way.
Thy faith-ful-ness un-to all men A-bid-eth for-ev-er nigh.
For Thou art my por-tion, O Lord, And shall be through all my days!
Sal-va-tion and peace have been bro't To those who have strayed a-far.
CHORUS—Ps. 119: 11
Thy Word have I hid in my heart, ... That I might not
in my heart,
sin a-gainst Thee, ... That I might not sin, That
a-gainst Thee,
ad lib.
I might not sin, Thy Word have I hid in my heart.

390 Trust and Obey

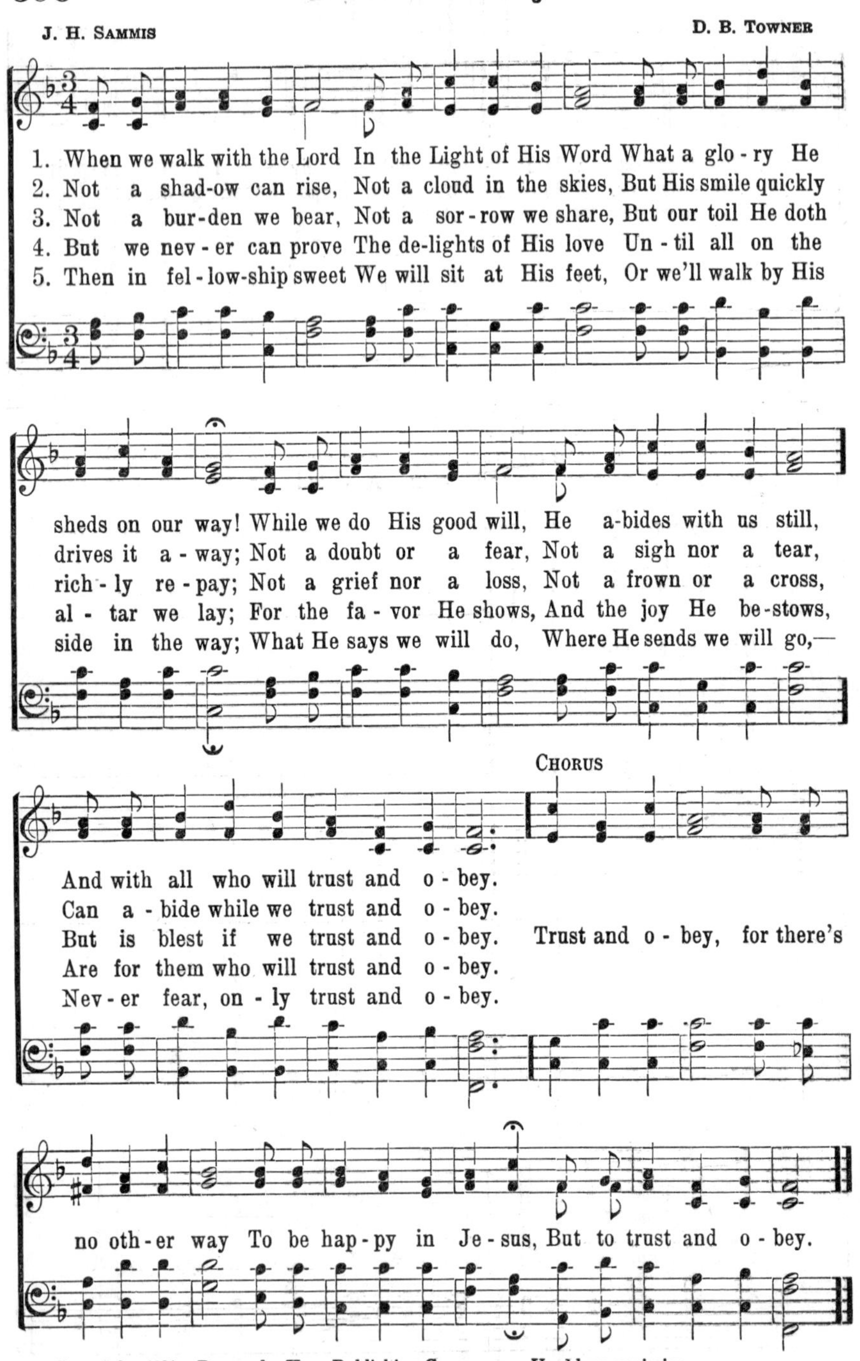
J. H. Sammis
D. B. Towner
1. When we walk with the Lord In the Light of His Word What a glo - ry He sheds on our way! While we do His good will, He a-bides with us still, And with all who will trust and o - bey.
2. Not a shad-ow can rise, Not a cloud in the skies, But His smile quickly drives it a - way; Not a doubt or a fear, Not a sigh nor a tear, Can a - bide while we trust and o - bey.
3. Not a bur-den we bear, Not a sor - row we share, But our toil He doth rich - ly re - pay; Not a grief nor a loss, Not a frown or a cross, But is blest if we trust and o - bey.
4. But we nev - er can prove The de-lights of His love Un - til all on the al - tar we lay; For the fa - vor He shows, And the joy He be-stows, Are for them who will trust and o - bey.
5. Then in fel - low-ship sweet We will sit at His feet, Or we'll walk by His side in the way; What He says we will do, Where He sends we will go,— Nev - er fear, on - ly trust and o - bey.
Chorus
Trust and o - bey, for there's no oth - er way To be hap - py in Je - sus, But to trust and o - bey.

391 He Keeps Me Singing

L. B. B. L. B. Bridgers

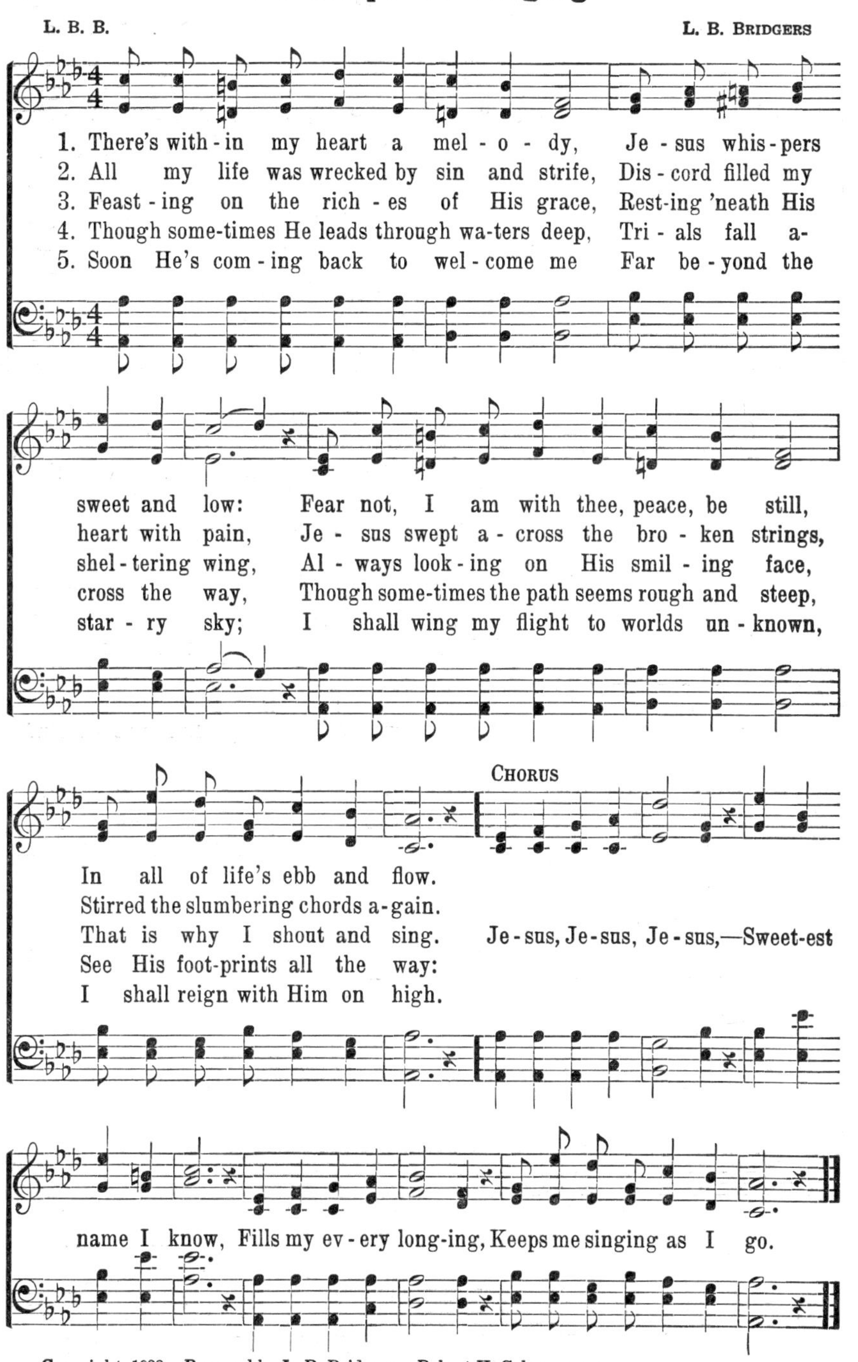
L. B. B.
L. B. Bridgers
1. There's with - in my heart a mel - o - dy, Je - sus whis - pers
2. All my life was wrecked by sin and strife, Dis - cord filled my
3. Feast - ing on the rich - es of His grace, Rest-ing 'neath His
4. Though some-times He leads through wa-ters deep, Tri - als fall a-
5. Soon He's com - ing back to wel - come me Far be - yond the
sweet and low: Fear not, I am with thee, peace, be still,
heart with pain, Je - sus swept a - cross the bro - ken strings,
shel - tering wing, Al - ways look - ing on His smil - ing face,
cross the way, Though some-times the path seems rough and steep,
star - ry sky; I shall wing my flight to worlds un - known,
In all of life's ebb and flow.
Stirred the slumbering chords a - gain.
That is why I shout and sing.
See His foot-prints all the way:
I shall reign with Him on high.
Chorus
Je - sus, Je - sus, Je - sus,—Sweet-est
name I know, Fills my ev - ery long-ing, Keeps me singing as I go.

392 We Have An Anchor

PRISCILLA J. OWENS
WM. J. KIRKPATRICK
1. Will your an - chor hold in the storms of life, When the
2. It is safe - ly moored, 'twill the storm with - stand, For 'tis
3. When our eyes be - hold through the gath - ering night The
clouds un - fold their wings of strife? When the strong tides lift, and the
well se - cured by the Sav-iour's hand; Though the tem-pest rage and the
cit - y of gold, our har - bor bright, We shall an - chor fast by the
ca - bles strain, Will your an - chor drift, or firm re - main?
wild winds blow, Not an an - gry wave shall our bark o'er - flow.
heaven-ly shore, With the storms all past for - ev - er - more.
REFRAIN
We have an an-chor that keeps the soul Steadfast and sure while the bil-lows roll,
Fastened to the Rock which cannot move, Grounded firm and deep in the Saviour's love.

393 Trust, Try, and Prove Me

L. S. L.
Lida Shivers Leech
1. Bring ye all the tithes in-to the store-house, All your mon-ey, tal-ents, time and love; Con-se-crate them all up-on the al-tar; While your Sav-iour from a-bove speaks sweet-ly,
2. When my wa-vering faith in tri-als fal-ter, When His guid-ing hand I can-not see, Then in won-drous love and ten-der mer-cy, Through His Word He says to me, My child, just
3. I have yield-ed Him my life for-ev-er, All I am, or have, or hope to be; Naught on earth my hold on Him can sev-er, While I hear Him say to me, My child, just
rit.
Refrain
Trust Me, try Me, prove Me, saith the Lord of hosts, and see
Trust Me, yes, then try Me, prove Me,
If a bless-ing, un-meas-ured bless-ing, I will not pour out on thee.

While the Days Are Going By

George Cooper — Ira D. Sankey

1. There are lone - ly hearts to cher - ish, While the days are go - ing by;
There are wea - ry souls who per - ish, While the days are go - ing by;
2. There's no time for i - dle scorn - ing, While the days are go - ing by;
Let your face be like the morn - ing, While the days are go - ing by;
3. All the lov - ing links that bind us, While the days are go - ing by;
One by one we leave be - hind us, While the days are go - ing by;
If a smile we can re - new, As our jour - ney we pur - sue,
Oh, the world is full of sighs, Full of sad and weep - ing eyes;
But the seeds of good we sow, Both in shade and shine will grow,
Oh, the good we all may do, While the days are go - ing by.
Help your fall - en broth - er rise, While the days are go - ing by.
And will keep our hearts a - glow, While the days are go - ing by.
Refrain
Go - ing by, go - ing by, Go - ing by, go - ing by,
Go - ing by, go - ing by, Go - ing by, go - ing by,
Oh, the good we all may do, While the days are go-ing by.

395 When the Battle's Over

Isaac Watts, D.D.
English. Arr. by Wm. B. Blake
1. Am I a soldier of the cross, A follower of the Lamb.
And shall I fear to own His cause, Or blush to speak His name?
2. Must I be carried to the skies On flowery beds of ease,
While others fought to win the prize, And sailed thro' blood-y seas?
3. Sure I must fight if I would reign, Increase my courage, Lord;
I'll bear the toil, endure the pain, Supported by Thy Word.
Chorus
And when the battle's over we shall wear a crown! Yes, we shall wear a crown! Yes, we shall wear a crown! And when the battle's over we shall wear a crown In the new Jerusalem.
Fine.
Wear a crown, wear a crown, Wear a bright and shining crown;
Wear a crown, wear a crown,
D. S.

396 "Are Ye Able," Said the Master

Earl Marlatt — Harry S. Mason

1. "Are ye a - ble," said the Mas - ter, "To be cru - ci - fied with Me?"
2. "Are ye a - ble," to re-mem - ber, When a thief lifts up his eyes,
3. "Are ye a - ble," when the shad-ows Close a-round you with the sod,
4. "Are ye a - ble," still the Mas - ter Whis-pers down e - ter - ni - ty,
"Yea," the conquering Christians answered, "To the death we fol - low Thee."
That his par-doned soul is wor - thy Of a place in Par - a - dise?
To be - lieve that spir - it tri-umphs, To com-mend your soul to God?
And he - ro - ic spir - its an - swer, Now, as then in Gal - i - lee.
Refrain
"Lord, we are a - ble," Our spir - its are Thine, Re - mold them,
make us like Thee, di - vine: Thy guid - ing ra-diance a - bove
rit
us shall be A bea - con to God, To love and loy - al - ty.

397 The Nail-Scarred Hand

B. B. McK. — B. B. McKinney

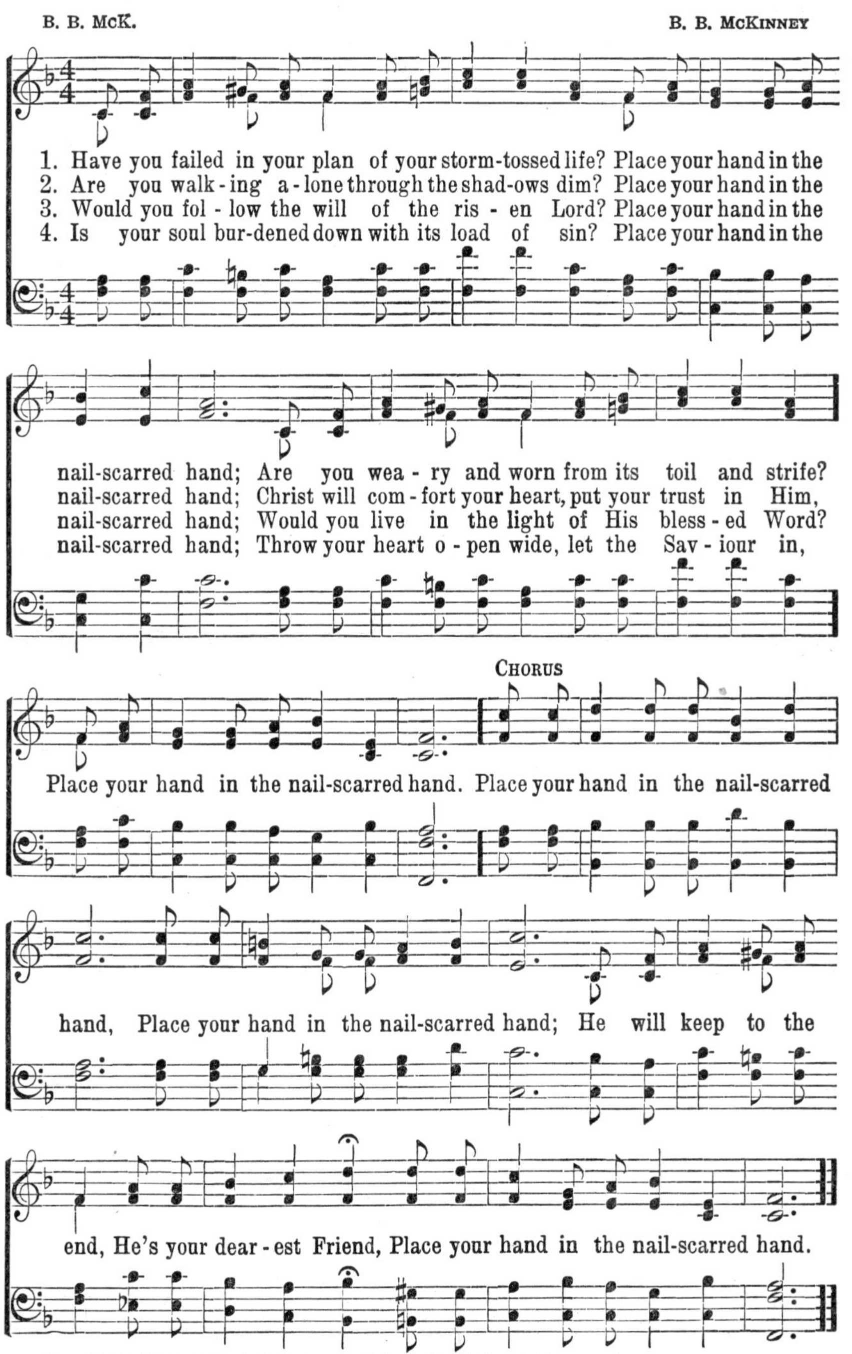
1. Have you failed in your plan of your storm-tossed life? Place your hand in the
2. Are you walk-ing a-lone through the shad-ows dim? Place your hand in the
3. Would you fol-low the will of the ris-en Lord? Place your hand in the
4. Is your soul bur-dened down with its load of sin? Place your hand in the
nail-scarred hand; Are you wea-ry and worn from its toil and strife?
nail-scarred hand; Christ will com-fort your heart, put your trust in Him,
nail-scarred hand; Would you live in the light of His bless-ed Word?
nail-scarred hand; Throw your heart o-pen wide, let the Sav-iour in,
Place your hand in the nail-scarred hand.
CHORUS
Place your hand in the nail-scarred hand, Place your hand in the nail-scarred hand; He will keep to the end, He's your dear-est Friend, Place your hand in the nail-scarred hand.

398 'Neath the Old Olive Trees

B. B. McK.
B. B. McKinney
Duet Slowly
1. 'Neath the stars of the night Walked the Saviour of light, In the gar-den of dew-la-dened breeze; Where no light could be found, Je-sus knelt on the ground, There He prayed 'neath the old ol-ive trees.
2. All the sin of the world On the Sav-iour was hurled, As He knelt in the gar-den a-lone; Hear His soul-burdened plea, Let this cup pass from Me, "E-ven so, not My will, Thine be done."
3. May my song ev-er be Of the love prof-fered me, By my Lord all a-lone on His knees: Praise His won-der-ful name, He who bore all my blame, As He knelt 'neath the old ol-ive trees.
Chorus
'Neath the old ol-ive trees, 'Neath the old ol-ive trees, Went the Sav-iour a-lone on His knees: "Not My will, Thine be done," Cried the Fa-ther's own Son, As He knelt 'neath the old ol-ive trees.

399 Scattering Precious Seed

W. A. Ogden — Geo. C. Hugg

1. Scat-ter-ing precious seed by the way-side, Scat-ter-ing precious seed by the hill-side; Scat-ter-ing precious seed o'er the field, wide, Scat-ter-ing precious seed by the way.
2. Scat-ter-ing precious seed for the grow-ing, Scat-ter-ing precious seed, free-ly sow-ing, Scat-ter-ing precious seed, trusting, knowing, Sure-ly the Lord will send it the rain.
3. Scat-ter-ing precious seed, doubting never, Scat-ter-ing precious seed, trusting ev-er; Sow-ing the word with prayer and en-deav-or, Trusting the Lord for growth and for yield.
Chorus
Sow - ing in the morn - ing,
Sow-ing the precious seed, Sow-ing the precious seed,
Sow - ing at the noon - tide;
Sowing the seed at noontide, Sowing the precious seed;
Sow - ing in the eve - ning,
Sowing the precious seed, Sowing the precious seed,
Sow-ing the pre-cious seed by the way. . . . .
by the way.
pp

Never Alone

Anonymous
Arr. by B. B. McKinney
1. I've seen the light - ning flash - ing, And heard the thun-der roll,
2. The world's fierce winds are blow - ing, Temp-ta-tions are sharp and keen;
3. When in af - flic - tion's val - ley, I'm tread-ing the road of care,
4. He died for me on the moun-tain, For me they pierced His side,
I've felt sin's break - ers dash - ing, Try-ing to con-quer my soul;
I feel a peace in know-ing My Sav - iour stands be - tween;
My Sav-iour helps me to car - ry My cross when heav-y to bear,
For me He o-pened that foun-tain, The crim - son, cleans-ing tide;
I've heard the voice of Je - sus, Tell-ing me still to fight on,
He stands to shield me from dan - ger, When earth-ly friends are gone,
My feet en-tan-gled with bri - ars, Read-y to cast me down;
For me He wait-eth in glo - ry, Seat-ed up-on His throne;
He prom-ised nev-er to leave me, Nev-er to leave me a - lone.
He prom-ised nev-er to leave me, Nev-er to leave me a - lone.
My Sav-iour whis-pered His prom-ise, Nev-er to leave me a - lone.
He prom-ised nev-er to leave me, Nev-er to leave me a - lone.

Never Alone

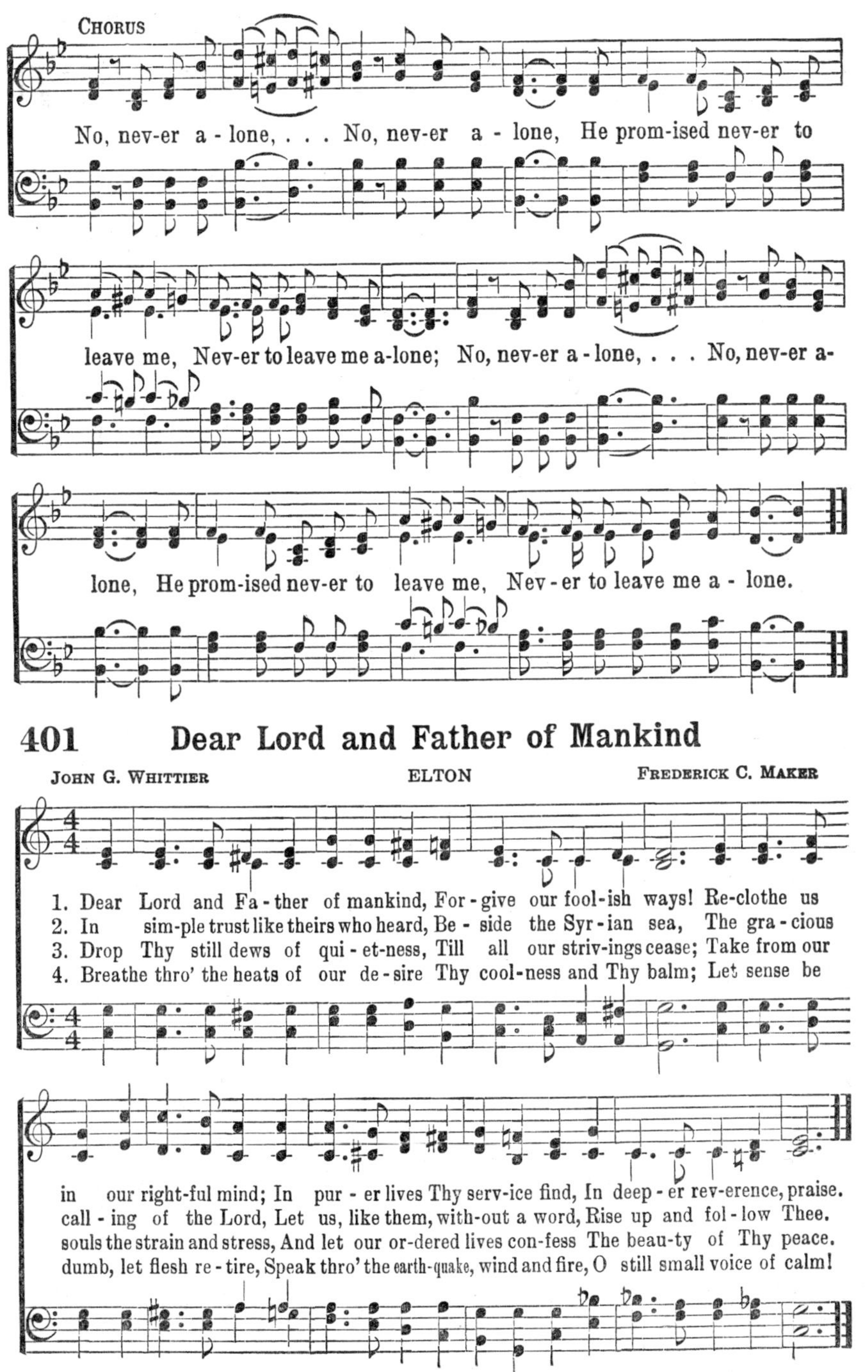

CHORUS
No, nev-er a - lone, . . . No, nev-er a - lone, He prom-ised nev-er to
leave me, Nev-er to leave me a-lone; No, nev-er a - lone, . . . No, nev-er a-
lone, He prom-ised nev-er to leave me, Nev - er to leave me a - lone.

401 Dear Lord and Father of Mankind

JOHN G. WHITTIER — ELTON — FREDERICK C. MAKER

1. Dear Lord and Fa - ther of mankind, For - give our fool-ish ways! Re-clothe us in our right-ful mind; In pur - er lives Thy serv-ice find, In deep - er rev-erence, praise.
2. In sim-ple trust like theirs who heard, Be - side the Syr - ian sea, The gra - cious call - ing of the Lord, Let us, like them, with-out a word, Rise up and fol - low Thee.
3. Drop Thy still dews of qui - et-ness, Till all our striv-ings cease; Take from our souls the strain and stress, And let our or-dered lives con-fess The beau-ty of Thy peace.
4. Breathe thro' the heats of our de - sire Thy cool-ness and Thy balm; Let sense be dumb, let flesh re - tire, Speak thro' the earth-quake, wind and fire, O still small voice of calm!

402 The Fight Is On

Mrs. C. H. M. — Mrs. C. H. Morris

1. The fight is on, the trump-et sound is ring - ing out, The cry "To
2. The fight is on, a - rouse, ye sol-diers brave and true! Je - ho - vah
3. The Lord is lead - ing on to cer - tain vic - to - ry; The bow of
arms!" is heard a - far and near; The Lord of hosts is march-ing on to
leads, and vic - tory will as-sure; Go buck - le on the ar - mor God has
prom - ise spans the east-ern sky; His glo-rious name in ev - ery land shall
vic - to - ry, The tri - umph of the Christ will soon ap - pear.
giv - en you, And in His strength un - to the end en - dure.
hon - ored be; The morn will break, the dawn of peace is nigh.
Chorus Unison
The fight is on, O Chris-tian sol-dier, And face to face in stern ar - ray, With
ar-mor gleaming, and col-ors streaming, The right and wrong engage to-day!

The Fight Is On
Harmony
The fight is on, but be not wea - ry; Be strong and in His might hold fast;
If God be for us, His ban-ner o'er us, We'll sing the victor's song at last!
Vic-tory! Vic-tory!
403 O Brother Man, Fold to Thy Heart
JOHN G. WHITTIER
STRENGTH AND STAY
JOHN B. DYKES
1. O broth-er man, fold to thy heart thy broth-er; Where pit-y dwells, the peace of God is there; To wor-ship right-ly is to love each oth-er, Each smile a hymn, each kind-ly deed a prayer.
2. For one whom Je-sus loved has tru-ly spo-ken,—The ho-lier wor-ship which He deigns to bless Re-stores the lost and binds the spir-it bro-ken, And feeds the wid-ow and the fa-ther-less.
3. Fol-low with rev-erent steps the great ex-am-ple Of Him whose ho-ly work was "do-ing good;" So shall the wide earth seem our Fa-ther's tem-ple, Each lov-ing life a psalm of grat-i-tude.

404 What Shall the Harvest Be?

EMILY S. OAKLEY | P. P. BLISS

1. Sow-ing the seed by the day-light fair, Sow-ing the seed by the noon-day glare,
2. Sow-ing the seed by the way-side high, Sow-ing the seed on the rocks to die,
3. Sow-ing the seed with an aching heart, Sow-ing the seed while the teardrops start,
Sow-ing the seed by the fad-ing light, Sowing the seed in the sol-emn night:
Sow-ing the seed where the thorns will spoil, Sowing the seed in the fer-tile soil:
Sow-ing in hope till the reap-ers come Glad-ly to gath-er the har-vest home:
O what shall the har-vest be? . . . O what shall the har-vest be?
CHORUS
Sown . . . . in the dark - - ness or sown . . . . in the
Sown in the dark-ness or sown in the light, Sown in the dark-ness or
light, ... Sown . . . . in our weak - - ness or
sown in the light, Sown in our weak-ness or sown in our might,

What Shall the Harvest Be?

sown . . . . in our might, ... Gath - ered in time or e-
sown in our weak-ness or sown in our might, Gath-ered in time or e-
ter - ni - ty, Sure, ah, sure will the har - vest be. . . .
ter - ni - ty, Sure, ah, sure will the har - vest, har-vest be.

405 Where Cross the Crowded Ways of Life

FRANK MASON NORTH GERMANY WILLIAM GARDINER

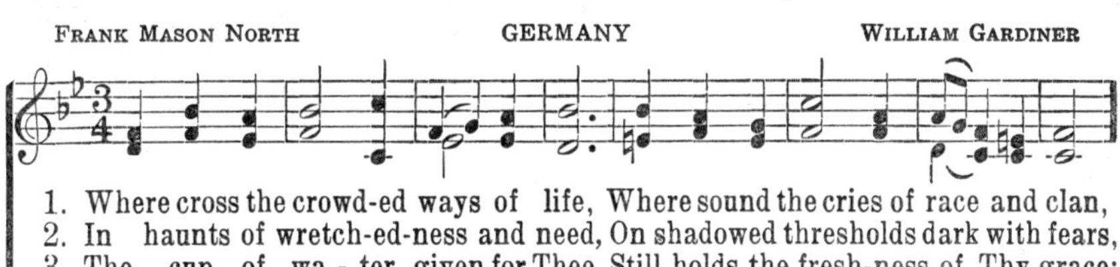
1. Where cross the crowd-ed ways of life, Where sound the cries of race and clan,
2. In haunts of wretch-ed-ness and need, On shadowed thresholds dark with fears,
3. The cup of wa - ter given for Thee Still holds the fresh-ness of Thy grace;
4. O Mas-ter from the moun-tain side, Make haste to heal those hearts of pain;
5. Till sons of men shall learn Thy love, And fol-low where Thy feet have trod;

A - bove the noise of self - ish strife, We hear Thy voice, O Son of Man!
From paths where hide the lures of greed, We catch the vi - sion of Thy tears.
Yet long these mul - ti - tudes to see The sweet com-pas-sion of Thy face.
A-mong these rest-less throngs a - bide, Oh, tread the cit - y's streets a-gain;
Till glo - rious, from Thy heaven a-bove, Shall come the cit - y of our God.

406 The Church's One Foundation

SAMUEL J. STONE
SAMUEL S. WESLEY
1. The Church-'s one foun - da - tion Is Je - sus Christ her Lord;
2. E - lect from ev - ery na - tion, Yet one o'er all the earth,
3. 'Mid toil and trib - u - la - tion, And tu - mult of her war,
4. Yet she on earth hath un - ion With God the Three in One,
She is His new cre - a - tion By Spir - it and the Word:
Her char - ter of sal - va - tion, One Lord, one faith, one birth;
She waits the con - sum - ma - tion Of peace for - ev - er - more;
And mys - tic sweet com - mun - ion With those whose rest is won:
From heaven He came and sought her To be His ho - ly bride;
One ho - ly name she bless - es, Par - takes one ho - ly food,
Till, with the vi - sion glo - rious, Her long - ing eyes are blest,
O hap - py ones and ho - ly! Lord, give us grace that we,
With His own blood He bought her, And for her life He died.
And to one hope she press - es, With ev - ery grace en - dued.
And the great Church vic - to - rious Shall be the Church at rest.
Like them, the meek and low - ly, On high may dwell with Thee.

407 "Here Am I; Send Me"

DANIEL MARCH
ELLESDIE
WOLFGANG A. MOZART
1. Hark, the voice of Je - sus call - ing,"Who will go and work to - day?
2. If you can - not cross the o - cean And the hea-then lands ex-plore,
3. If you can - not sing like an - gels, If you can-not preach like Paul,
4. Let none hear you i - dly say - ing,"There is noth-ing I can do,"
Fields are white, and har - vest wait-ing, Who will bear the sheaves a - way?"
You can find the need - y near-er, You can help those at your door;
You can tell the love of Je - sus, You can say He died for all;
While the souls of men are dy - ing, And the Mas - ter calls for you;
Loud and long the Mas - ter call - eth, Rich re-ward He of - fers free;
If you can - not give the thousands, You can give the wid-ow's mite,
If you can - not rouse the wick - ed, With the judgment's dread a - larms,
Take the task He gives you glad - ly, Let His work your pleas-ure be,
Who will an - swer, glad - ly say - ing, "Here am I, send me, send me?"
And the least you do for Je - sus Will be pre - cious in His sight.
You can lead the lit - tle chil-dren To the Sav-iour's wait-ing arms.
An - swer quick-ly while He call - eth, "Here am I, send me, send me."

408 A Clean Heart

Rev. Walter C. Smith   Fred H. Byshe

1. One thing I of the Lord de-sire, For all my path hath mir-y been,
2. If clear-er vi-sion Thou im-part, Grate-ful and glad my soul shall be;
3. Yea, on-ly as this heart is clean May larg-er vi-sion yet be mine,
4. I watch to shun the mir-y way, And stanch the springs of guilt-y thought,
Be it by wa-ter or by fire, O make me clean, O make me clean.
But yet to have a pur-er heart Is more to me, Is more to me.
For mir-rored in its depths are seen The things di-vine, The things divine.
But, watch and strug-gle as I may, Pure I am not, Pure I am not.
rit.
Refrain
So wash me, Thou, with-out, with-in, Or purge with fire, if that must be,
Wash me, Thou, with-out, with-in, Or purge with fire, if that must be,
No mat-ter how, if on-ly sin Die out in me, Die out in me.
An-y-how, if on-ly sin Die out in me, Die out, die out in me.
Die in me.

409 He Will Hide Me

Miss M. E. Servoss
James McGranahan
1. When the storms of life are rag - ing, Tem-pests wild on sea and land,
2. Tho' He may send some af - flic - tion, 'Twill but make me long for home;
3. En - e - mies may strive to in - jure, Sa - tan all his arts em - ploy;
4. So, while here the cross I'm bear-ing, Meet-ing storms and bil - lows wild,
I will seek a place of ref - uge In the shad - ow of God's hand.
For in love and not in an - ger, All His chas - ten - ings will come.
He will turn what seems to harm me In - to ev - er - last - ing joy.
Je - sus for my soul is car - ing, Naught can harm His Fa-ther's child.
Chorus.
He will hide me, He will hide me, Where no harm can e'er be-tide me;
He will hide me, He will hide me, Where no harm can e'er be-tide me;
He will hide me, safe-ly hide me, In the shad - ow of His hand.
He will hide me, safe - ly hide me, In the shad-ow of His hand.

410 He Died for Me

JOHN NEWTON — B. B. MCKINNEY

DUET *Slowly*

1. I saw One hang-ing on a tree, In ag-o-ny and blood; He fixed His lan-guid eyes on me, As near His cross I stood.
2. Sure, nev-er, till my lat-est breath, Can I for-get that look: It seemed to charge me with His death, Tho' not a word He spoke.
3. My con-science felt and owned the guilt, And plunged me in de-spair; I saw my sins His blood had spilt, And helped to nail Him there.
4. A sec-ond look He gave, which said, "I free-ly all for-give: This blood is for thy ran-som paid, I die that thou may'st live."
CHORUS
It was for me, up-on a tree He died in ag-o-ny,
rit.
And now I give my life to live, For Him who died for me.

411 Just As I Am, Thine Own to Be

MARIANNE HEARN — JUST AS I AM — JOSEPH BARNBY

1. Just as I am, Thine own to be, Friend of the young, who lov-est me,
2. In the glad morn-ing of my day, My life to give, my vows to pay,
3. I would live ev-er in the light; I would work ev-er for the right;
4. Just as I am, young, strong, and free, To be the best that I can be

Just As I Am, Thine Own to Be
Unison
To con-se-crate my-self to Thee, O Je-sus Christ, I come.
With no re-serve and no de-lay, With all my heart I come.
I would serve Thee with all my might; There-fore, to Thee I come.
For truth, and right-eous-ness, and Thee, Lord of my life, I come.
412
We'll Never Say Good-By
Mrs. E. W. Chapman
J. H. Tenney
1. With friends on earth we meet in glad-ness, While swift the mo-ments fly,
2. How joy-ful is the hope that lin-gers, When loved ones cross death's sea,
3. No part-ing words shall e'er be spo-ken In yon-der home so fair,
Yet ev-er comes the tho't of sad-ness, That we must say, "Good-by."
That we, when all earth's toils are end-ed, With them shall ev-er be.
But songs of joy, and peace, and glad-ness, We'll sing for-ev-er there.
Chorus
We'll nev-er say good-by in heaven, We'll nev-er say good-by, ...
good-by,
Repeat Chorus pp.
For in that land of joy and song We'll nev-er say good-by.

413 I Know That My Redeemer Liveth

Jessie Brown Pounds — J. H. Fillmore

1. I know that my Redeemer liv-eth, And on the earth a-gain shall stand;
2. I know His promise nev-er faileth, The word He speaks, it can-not die;
3. I know my mansion He prepareth, That where He is there I may be;
1. And on the earth again shall stand;
I know e-ter-nal life He giv-eth, That grace and power are in His hand.
Tho' cru-el death my flesh assaileth, Yet I shall see . . . Him by and by.
O wondrous tho't, for me He car-eth, And He at last . . . will come for me.
That grace and power are in His hand.
Chorus
I know, I know . . . . that Je-sus liv-eth, And on the
I know, I know
earth . . . . a-gain shall stand; I know, I know . . . .
And on the earth
I know, I know
that life He giv-eth, That grace and power . . . . are in His hand.
That grace and power

414 It Pays to Serve Jesus

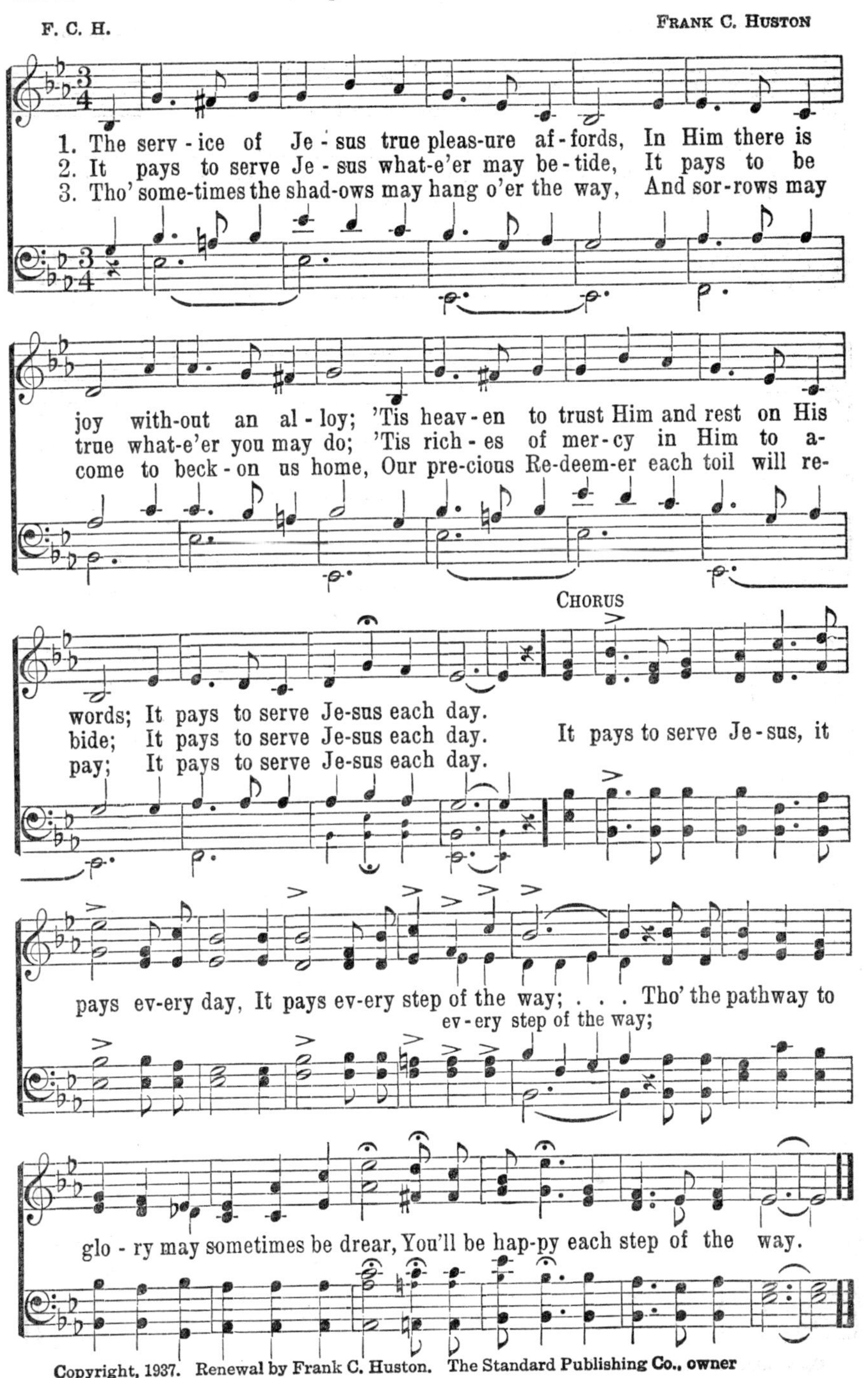
F. C. H.
FRANK C. HUSTON
1. The serv-ice of Je-sus true pleas-ure af-fords, In Him there is joy with-out an al-loy; 'Tis heav-en to trust Him and rest on His words; It pays to serve Je-sus each day.
2. It pays to serve Je-sus what-e'er may be-tide, It pays to be true what-e'er you may do; 'Tis rich-es of mer-cy in Him to a-bide; It pays to serve Je-sus each day.
3. Tho' some-times the shad-ows may hang o'er the way, And sor-rows may come to beck-on us home, Our pre-cious Re-deem-er each toil will re-pay; It pays to serve Je-sus each day.
CHORUS
It pays to serve Je-sus, it pays ev-ery day, It pays ev-ery step of the way; . . . Tho' the pathway to glo-ry may sometimes be drear, You'll be hap-py each step of the way.
ev-ery step of the way;

415 Speak to My Heart

Gene Routh | B. B. McKinney

1. Speak to my heart, Lord Je - sus, Speak that my soul may hear;
2. Speak to my heart, Lord Je - sus, Purge me from ev - ery sin;
3. Speak to my heart, Lord Je - sus, It is no lon - ger mine;

Speak to my heart, Lord Je - sus, Calm ev - ery doubt and fear.
Speak to my heart, Lord Je - sus, Help me the lost to win.
Speak to my heart, Lord Je - sus, I would be whol - ly Thine.

Chorus
Speak to my heart, oh, speak to my heart, Speak to my heart, I pray;
Yield - ed and still, seek - ing Thy will, Oh, speak to my heart to - day.

416 Forgive

Corinne Williams — B. B. McKinney

Solo Moderato
1. For-give the things I've said in haste, O Lord, to-day, Ere eve-ning shad-ows fold a-gain The light a-way; O take a-way the sting and hurt From hearts, I pray; And heal the wounded spir-its, Lord, In Thine own way!
2. For-give me for the man-y things I've left un-done–Some soul now wandering, lost in sin, I might have won; O may Thy Spir-it strive and win That err-ing one; And in the lives of all, O Lord, Thy will be done!
3. For-give me for the man-y things A-gainst Thy will I've done this day, O Lord, I pray, And love me still; O may Thy Ho-ly Spir-it, Lord, Come now and fill My yield-ed life, my Lord, my God, With Thine own will!
4. For-give me for the sake of Him Who died for me, Who gave Him-self that I might live In heaven with Thee, And lives to-day at Thy right hand To plead for me; For-give me for the sake of Him Who died for me!

417 Breathe On Me

EDWIN HATCH — B. B. MCKINNEY

1. Ho - ly Spir - it, breathe on me, Un - til my heart is clean;
2. Ho - ly Spir - it, breathe on me, My stub-born will sub - due;
3. Ho - ly Spir - it, breathe on me, Fill me with power di - vine;
4. Ho - ly Spir - it, breathe on me, Till I am all Thine own,
Let sun-shine fill its in - most part, With not a cloud be - tween.
Teach me in words of liv - ing flame What Christ would have me do.
Kin-dle a flame of love and zeal With - in this heart of mine.
Un - til my will is lost in Thine, To live for Thee a - lone.
CHORUS
Breathe on me, breathe on me, Ho - ly Spir - it, breathe on me;
Take Thou my heart, cleanse ev-ery part, Ho - ly Spir - it, breathe on me.

418 Jesus, Revealed in Me

(As sung by Gipsy Smith on Columbia Record)

GIPSY SMITH E. EDWIN YOUNG

1. Christ, the Trans-form-ing Light, Touch-es this heart of mine,
2. Here, Lord, I bring my heart, My love, my strength, my will;
3. Life is no lon-ger mine, I yield it all to Thee;
4. Tri-um-phant peace is mine, Now Je-sus reigns with-in;
Pierc-ing the dark-est night, Mak-ing His glo-ry shine.
Cleanse me in ev-ery part, With all Thy Spir-it fill.
Fill me that I may shine Un-til Thy face I see.
He giv-eth joy di-vine, And vic-tory o-ver sin.
CHORUS
Oh, to re-flect His grace, ... Caus-ing the world to see, ...
His grace, to see,
Love that will glow Till oth-ers shall know Je-sus, re-vealed in me.

419 Forward Through the Ages

FREDERICK L. HOSMER — ST. GERTRUDE — ARTHUR S. SULLIVAN

1. For-ward through the a - ges, In un - bro - ken line,
2. Wid - er grows the king - dom, Reign of love and light;
3. Not a - lone we con - quer, Not a - lone we fall;
Move the faith - ful spir - its At the call di - vine: Gifts in
For it we must la - bor, Till our faith is sight. Proph-ets
In each loss or tri - umph Lose or tri-umph all. Bound by
dif - fering meas - ure, Hearts of one ac - cord, Man - i - fold the
have pro - claimed it, Mar - tyrs tes - ti - fied, Po - ets sung its
God's far pur - pose In one liv - ing whole, Move we on to-
serv - ice, One the sure re - ward.
glo - ry, He - roes for it died.
geth - er To the shin - ing goal!
REFRAIN
For-ward thro' the a - ges,
In un-bro - ken line, Move the faith-ful spir - its At the call di - vine.

420 Into the Woods My Master Went

SIDNEY LANIER | B. B. MCKINNEY

SOLO *With tender expression*
1. In - to the woods my Mas - ter went, Clean for-spent, for - spent;
2. Out of the woods my Mas - ter went. And He was well con - tent;
In - to the woods my Mas - ter came, For-spent with love and shame.
Out of the woods my Mas - ter came, Con - tent with death and shame.
But the ol - ives were not blind to Him, The lit-tle gray leaves were kind to Him,
When death and shame would woo Him last, From under the trees they drew Him last,
The thorn-tree had a mind to Him, When in-to the woods He came.
'Twas on a tree they slew Him last, When out of the woods He came.

421 If You Only Knew Him

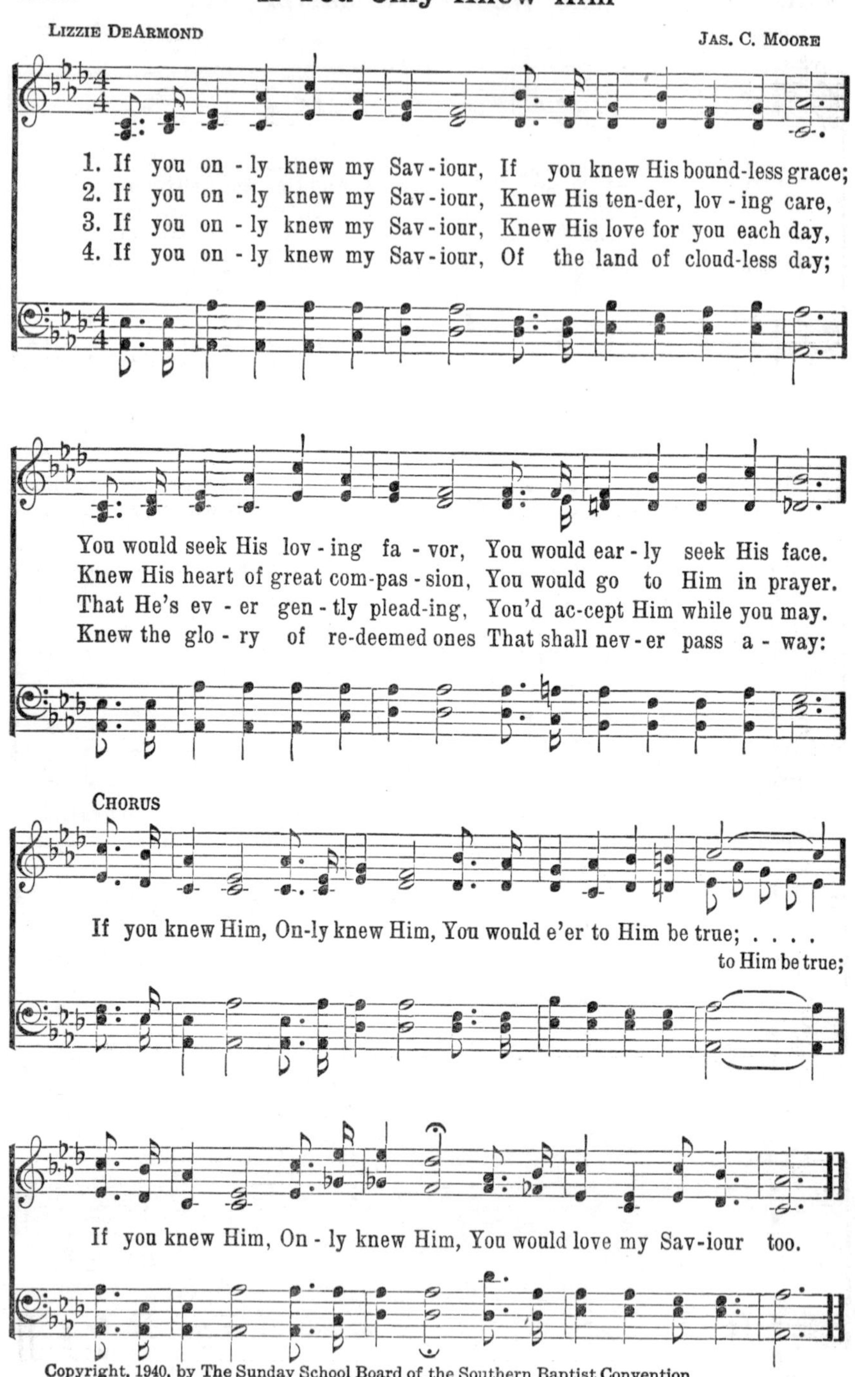
LIZZIE DEARMOND
JAS. C. MOORE
1. If you on - ly knew my Sav - iour, If you knew His bound-less grace;
2. If you on - ly knew my Sav - iour, Knew His ten-der, lov - ing care,
3. If you on - ly knew my Sav - iour, Knew His love for you each day,
4. If you on - ly knew my Sav - iour, Of the land of cloud-less day;
You would seek His lov - ing fa - vor, You would ear - ly seek His face.
Knew His heart of great com-pas - sion, You would go to Him in prayer.
That He's ev - er gen - tly plead-ing, You'd ac-cept Him while you may.
Knew the glo - ry of re-deemed ones That shall nev - er pass a - way:
CHORUS
If you knew Him, On-ly knew Him, You would e'er to Him be true; . . . .
to Him be true;
If you knew Him, On - ly knew Him, You would love my Sav-iour too.

422 He Leadeth Me

JOSEPH H. GILMORE — WILLIAM B. BRADBURY

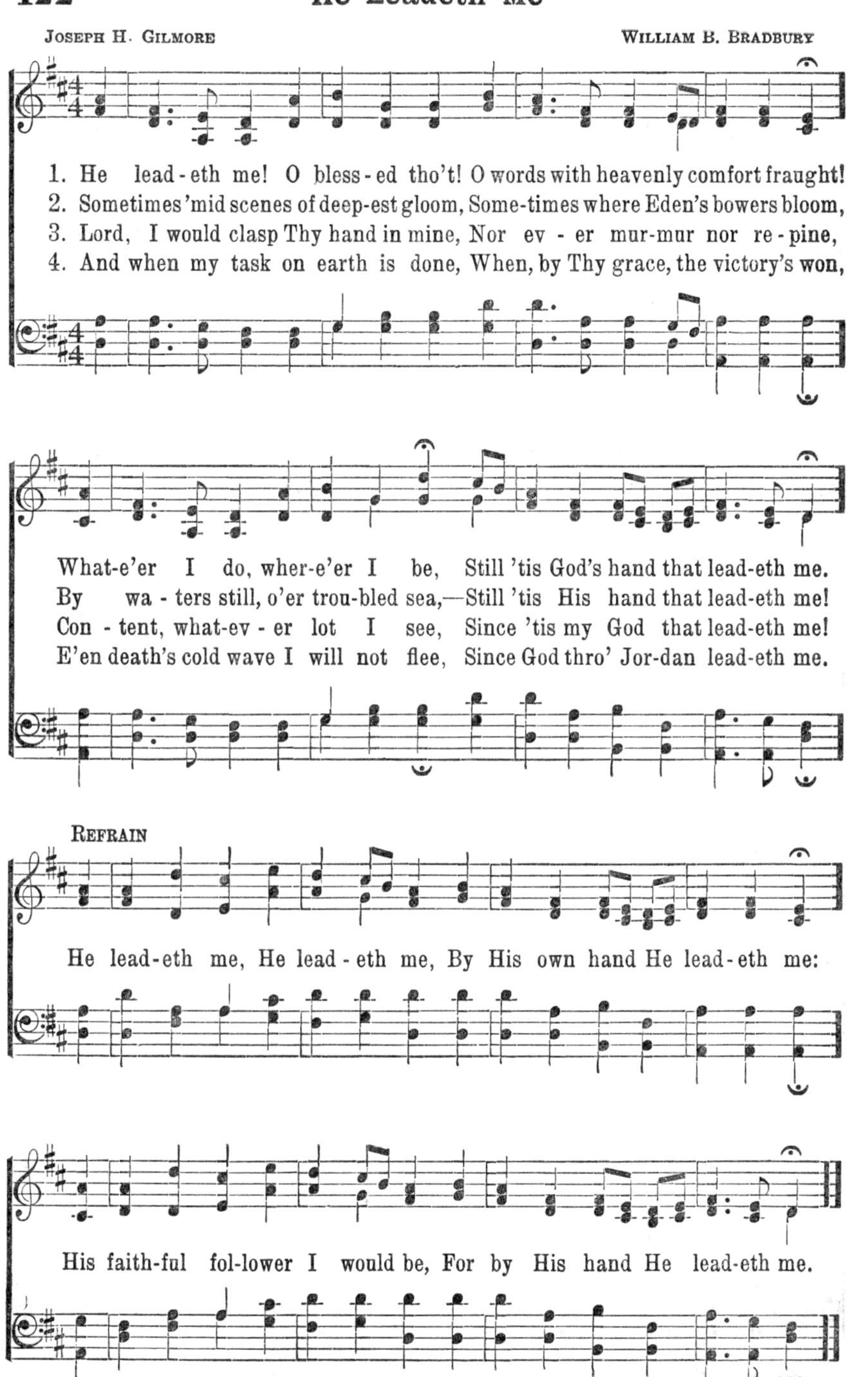
1. He lead-eth me! O bless-ed tho't! O words with heavenly comfort fraught!
2. Sometimes 'mid scenes of deep-est gloom, Some-times where Eden's bowers bloom,
3. Lord, I would clasp Thy hand in mine, Nor ev - er mur-mur nor re-pine,
4. And when my task on earth is done, When, by Thy grace, the victory's won,
What-e'er I do, wher-e'er I be, Still 'tis God's hand that lead-eth me.
By wa - ters still, o'er trou-bled sea,—Still 'tis His hand that lead-eth me!
Con - tent, what-ev - er lot I see, Since 'tis my God that lead-eth me!
E'en death's cold wave I will not flee, Since God thro' Jor-dan lead-eth me.
REFRAIN
He lead-eth me, He lead - eth me, By His own hand He lead-eth me:
His faith-ful fol-lower I would be, For by His hand He lead-eth me.

423 Let Others See Jesus in You

B. B. McK. B. B. McKinney

1. While pass-ing thro' this world of sin, And oth - ers your life shall view,
2. Your life's a book be - fore their eyes, They're reading it thro' and thro';
3. What joy 'twill be at set of sun, In man-sions be-yond the blue,
4. Then live for Christ both day and night, Be faith - ful, be brave and true,
Be clean and pure with-out, with-in, Let oth - ers see Je - sus in you.
Say, does it point them to the skies, Do oth - ers see Je - sus in you?
To find some souls that you have won; Let oth - ers see Je - sus in you.
And lead the lost to life and light; Let oth - ers see Je - sus in you.
Chorus
Let oth-ers see Je-sus in you, . . . Let oth-ers see Je - sus in you; . . .
in you,
in you;
Keep tell-ing the sto-ry, be faithful and true, Let oth-ers see Je - sus in you.

424 Take the Name of Jesus with You

Mrs. Lydia Baxter

W. H. Doane

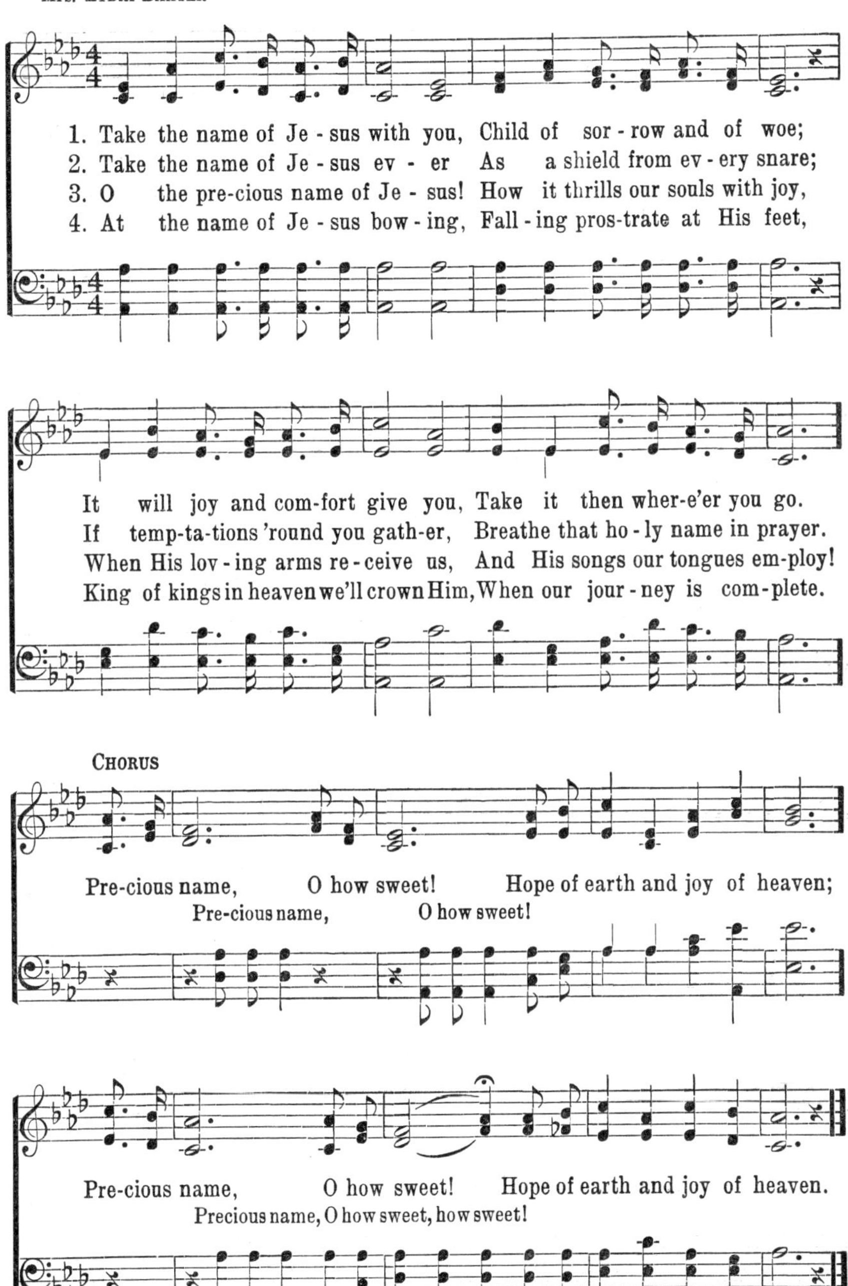
1. Take the name of Je - sus with you, Child of sor - row and of woe;
2. Take the name of Je - sus ev - er As a shield from ev - ery snare;
3. O the pre-cious name of Je - sus! How it thrills our souls with joy,
4. At the name of Je - sus bow - ing, Fall - ing pros-trate at His feet,
It will joy and com-fort give you, Take it then wher-e'er you go.
If temp-ta-tions 'round you gath-er, Breathe that ho - ly name in prayer.
When His lov - ing arms re - ceive us, And His songs our tongues em-ploy!
King of kings in heaven we'll crown Him, When our jour - ney is com-plete.
Chorus
Pre-cious name, O how sweet! Hope of earth and joy of heaven;
Pre-cious name, O how sweet!
Pre-cious name, O how sweet! Hope of earth and joy of heaven.
Precious name, O how sweet, how sweet!

425 Crown Him

Thomas Kelly
Arr. from Welsh by B. B. McKinney
1. Look, ye saints, the sight is glo-rious; See the Man of Sor-rows now;
2. Crown the Sav-iour, an-gels, crown Him; Rich the tro-phies Je-sus brings;
3. Sin-ners in de-ris-ion crowned Him, Mock-ing thus the Sav-iour's claim;
4. Hark! the bursts of ac-cla-ma-tion! Hark! these loud triumphant chords!
From the fight re-turned vic-to-rious, Ev-ery knee to Him shall bow.
In the seat of power en-throne Him, While the vault of heav-en rings.
Saints and an-gels crowd a-round Him, Own His ti-tle, praise His name.
Je-sus takes the high-est sta-tion, Oh, what joy the sight af-fords.
Chorus
Crown Him, crown Him, an-gels, crown Him, Crown the
Sav-iour King of kings (King of kings); Crown the Sav-iour King of kings.
Arr. Copyright, 1940, by The Sunday School Board of the Southern Baptist Convention
426 Art Thou Weary?
John M. Neale
STEPHANOS
Henry W. Baker
1. Art thou wea-ry, art thou lan-guid, Art thou sore dis-trest?
2. Hath He marks to lead me to Him, If He be my Guide?
3. If I still hold close-ly to Him, What hath He at last?
4. If I ask Him to re-ceive me, Will He say me nay?

Art Thou Weary?
"Come to Me," saith One, "and, com - ing, Be at rest."
"In His feet and hands are wound-prints, And His side."
"Sor - row van - quished, la - bor end - ed, Jor - dan passed."
"Not till earth and not till heav - en Pass a - way."
427
It Is Finished
E. L. C.
Ellis L. Carnett
1. "It is fin - ished," said my Sav - iour, As He hung on Cal - va - ry;
2. "It is fin - ished," said my Sav - iour, He had wrought sal-va-tion's plan;
3. "It is fin - ished," said my Sav - iour, Won't you trust this Sav-iour now?
Oh, the aw - ful pain and an - guish, Suf-f'ring there for you and me.
See Him, as by God for - sak - en, Hang-ing there for sin - ful man.
Turn from all your sins to Je - sus, At His feet, come, hum-bly bow.
Chorus
"It is fin - ished," "It is fin - ished," My sal - va - tion full and free;
Je - sus paid the debt for sin - ners, When He died on Cal - va - ry.

428 Blessed Redeemer

AVIS BURGESON CHRISTIANSEN
HARRY DIXON LOES
1. Up Cal-vary's mountain one dreadful morn, Walked Christ my Saviour, weary and worn;
2. "Fa-ther, forgive them!" thus did He pray, E'en while His life-blood flowed fast a-way;
3. O how I love Him, Sav-iour and Friend, How can my prais-es ev - er find end!
Fac - ing for sin-ners death on the cross, That He might save them from endless loss.
Pray-ing for sin-ners while in such woe— No one but Je - sus ev - er loved so.
Thro' years un-num-bered on heaven's shore, My tongue shall praise Him for-ev-er-more.
CHORUS
Bless-ed Re-deem - er! pre-cious Re-deem - er! Seems now I
Bless-ed Re-deem-er! bless - ed Re-deem - er!
see Him on Cal - va - ry's tree; Wound-ed and bleed - ing, for sin-ners
Wound-ed and bleed-ing,
plead - ing— Blind and un - heed - - ing— dy - ing for me!
for sin-ners plead - ing— Blind and un-heed - ing—

429 When the Shadows Flee

JAMES ROWE E. O. SELLERS

1. Smil-ing skies will bend a-bove us, When the shad-ows flee; Hearts now
2. Fet-ters nev-er-more will bind us, When the shad-ows flee; This dark
3. We shall view our home su-per-nal, When the shad-ows flee; We shall
cold a-gain will love us, When the shad-ows flee; We shall lose our care and
vale will be be-hind us, When the shad-ows flee; There will be no tem-pest
meet our King e-ter-nal, When the shad-ows flee; There, where death will reach us
sor-row, Trou-ble nev-er-more to bor-row, On that bless-ed, peace-ful mor-row,
sweeping, In our lov-ing Fa-ther's keep-ing We shall wake, where none are weeping,
nev-er, There, where naught our hearts shall sever, We shall dwell with Christ for-ev-er,
When the shad-ows flee.
CHORUS
With e-ter-nal day be-fore us, And our Sav-iour
watch-ing o'er us, We shall join the end-less cho-rus, When the shad-ows flee.
rit.

430 Oh, Where Are the Reapers?

Eben E. Rexford
Geo. F. Root
1. Oh, where are the reap - ers that gar - ner in The sheaves of the
2. Go out in the by - ways and search them all; The wheat may be
3. The fields are all rip - ening, and far and wide The world now is
4. So come with your sick - les, ye sons of men, And gath - er to-
good from the fields of sin; With sick-les of truth must the work be done,
there, tho' the weeds are tall; Then search in the high-way, and pass none by,
wait - ing the har - vest-tide: But reap - ers are few, and the work is great,
geth - er the gold - en grain; Toil on till the Lord of the har-vest come,
And no one may rest till the "har-vest home."
But gath - er from all for the home on high.
And much will be lost should the har-vest wait.
Then share ye His joy in the "har-vest home."
Chorus
Where are the reap-ers! Oh,
who will come And share in the glo - ry of the "har-vest home?" Oh,
who will help us to gar-ner in The sheaves of good from the fields of sin?

431 I'll Stand By

W. W. D.
JAMES MCGRANAHAN
1. Fierce and wild the storm is rag - ing Round a help - less bark,
2. Wea - ry, help-less, hope-less sea - men Faint - ing on the deck,
3. On a wild and storm - y o - cean, Sink - ing 'neath the wave,
4. Dar - ing death thy soul to res - cue, He in love has come;
On to doom 'tis swift - ly driv - ing, O'er the wa - ters dark!
With what joy they hail their Sav - iour, As He hails the wreck!
Souls that per - ish heed the mes - sage, Christ has come to save!
Leave the wreck, and in Him trust - ing Thou shalt reach thy home!
CHORUS
Joy, . . . be-hold the Sav - iour, Joy, . . . the mes-sage hear:
Joy, O joy, be - hold the Sav-iour, Joy, O joy, the mes-sage hear:
"I'll stand by un-til the morn-ing, I've come to save you, do not fear;" Yes,
"I'll stand by un-til the morn-ing, I've come to save you, do not fear."
do not fear.

432 Only a Step

FANNY J. CROSBY
W. H. DOANE
1. On-ly a step to Je-sus! Then why not take it now?
2. On-ly a step to Je-sus! Be-lieve, and thou shalt live;
3. On-ly a step to Je-sus! A step from sin to grace;
4. On-ly a step to Je-sus! O why not come and say:
Come, and thy sin con-fess-ing, To Him, thy Sav-iour, bow.
Lov-ing-ly now He's wait-ing, And read-y to for-give.
What has thy heart de-cid-ed— The mo-ments fly a-pace?
"Glad-ly to Thee my Sav-iour, I give my-self a-way?"
CHORUS
On-ly a step, on-ly a step; Come, He waits for thee;
Come, and thy sin con-fess-ing, Thou shalt re-ceive a bless-ing;
Do not re-ject the mer-cy He free-ly of-fers thee.

433 Don't Turn Him Away

H. L. — Haldor Lillenas, Chorus arranged

1. Pa - tient-ly, ten-der - ly plead - ing, Je - sus is stand-ing to - day;
2. Gra-cious, com-pas-sion-ate mer - cy Bro't Him from mansions a - bove;
3. Can you not now hear Him call - ing? Do not ill-treat such a Friend;
4. Now is the time to re - ceive Him, Grant Him ad-mis-sion to - day;
At your heart's door He knocks as be-fore, Oh, turn Him no lon-ger a - way.
Caused Him to wait Just outside your gate, Oh, yield to His won-der-ful love.
Give up your sin, Oh, let Him come in, Lo! He will be true to the end.
Grieve Him no more, But o - pen your door, And turn Him no lon-ger a - way.
Chorus
Don't turn Him a-way, don't turn Him a-way, He has come back to your heart a-gain,
Al-though you've gone a - stray; Oh, how you'll need Him to plead your cause On that e-
ter - nal day! Don't turn the Saviour away from your heart, Don't turn Him a-way.

434 Shall We Gather at the River?

R. L. Rev. Robert Lowry

1. Shall we gath-er at the riv - er, Where bright an-gel feet have trod;
2. On the mar-gin of the riv - er, Wash-ing up its sil - ver spray,
3. Ere we reach the shin-ing riv - er, Lay we ev - ery bur-den down;
4. Soon we'll reach the shin-ing riv - er, Soon our pil-grim-age will cease,
With its crys - tal tide for - ev - er Flow-ing by the throne of God?
We will walk and wor-ship ev - er, All the hap - py gold - en day.
Grace our spir - its will de - liv - er, And pro-vide a robe and crown.
Soon our hap - py hearts will quiv - er With the mel - o - dy of peace.
Chorus
Yes, we'll gath-er at the riv - er, The beau-ti - ful, the beau-ti - ful riv - er;
Gath-er with the saints at the riv - er That flows by the throne of God.
435 O God, Our Help in Ages Past
Isaac Watts
St. Anne
William Croft
1. O God, our help in a - ges past, Our hope for years to come,
2. Un - der the shad - ow of Thy throne Still may we dwell se - cure;
3. Be - fore the hills in or - der stood, Or earth re - ceived her frame,
4. O God, our help in a - ges past, Our hope for years to come;

O God, Our Help in Ages Past
Our shel-ter from the storm-y blast, And our e-ter-nal home!
Suf-fi-cient is Thine arm a-lone, And our de-fense is sure.
From ev-er-last-ing Thou art God, To end-less years the same.
Be Thou my guide while life shall last, And our e-ter-nal home.
436
Come Home
MABEL FROST
B. B. MCKINNEY
1. O soul in the far-a-way coun-try, A-wea-ry, and famished, and sad,
2. A-rise and come back to thy Fa-ther, He'll meet thee while yet on the way;
3. Although thou hast sinned against heaven, And weak and unworthy may be,
There's rest in the home of thy Fa-ther, His welcome will make thy heart glad.
As-sured of His ten-der com-pas-sion, Oh, why wilt thou lon-ger de-lay?
He of-fers thee full res-to-ra-tion, And par-don a-bun-dant and free.
CHORUS.
Come home, . . come home, . . Oh, why will you lon-ger roam? . .
Come home, come home, why roam?
Come home, . . come home, . . O prod-i-gal child, come home.
Come home, come home,

437 Memories of Galilee

ROBERT MORRIS H. R. PALMER

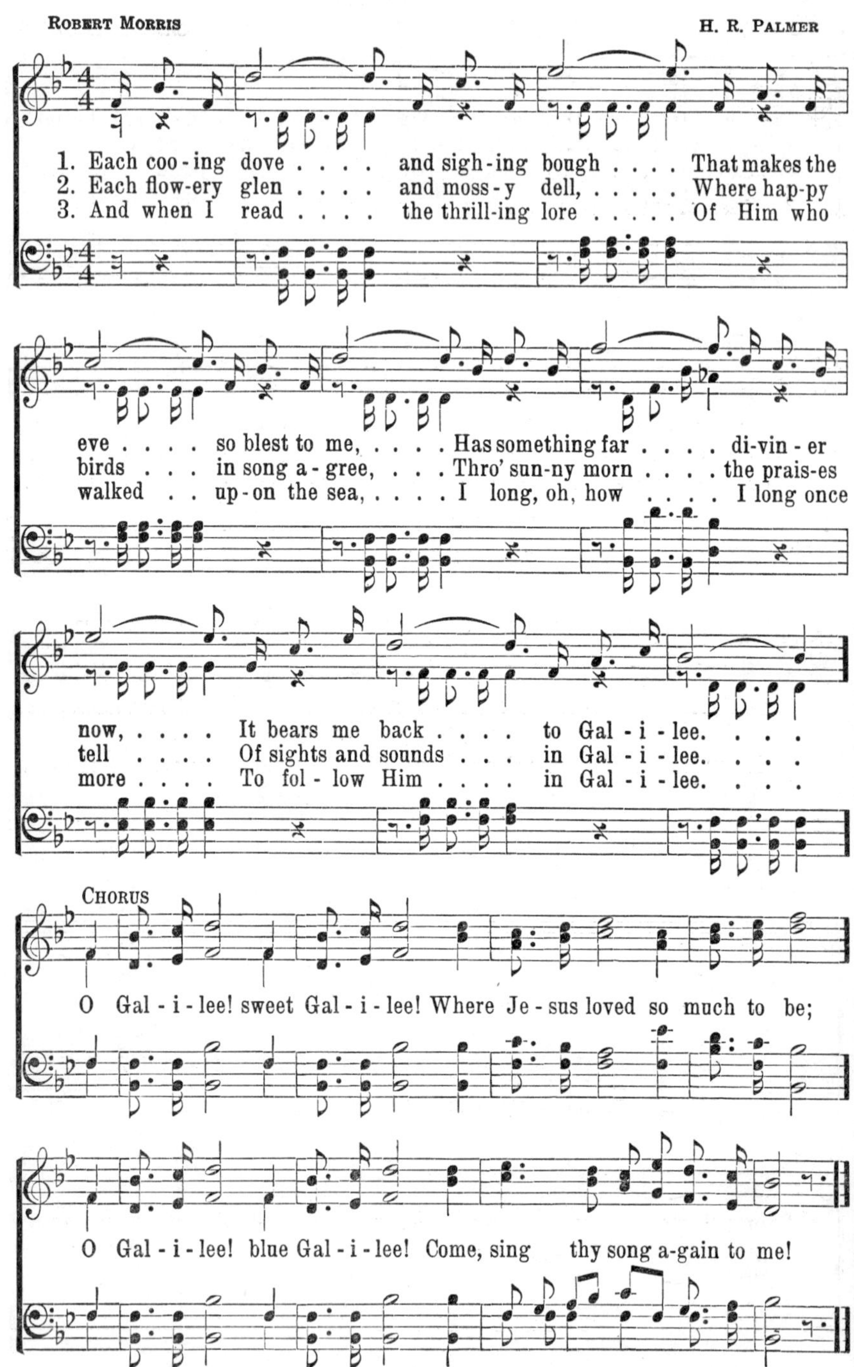
1. Each coo-ing dove . . . . and sigh-ing bough . . . . That makes the eve . . . . so blest to me, ... Has something far . . . . di-vin-er now, ... It bears me back . . . . to Gal-i-lee. . . .
2. Each flow-ery glen . . . . and moss-y dell, ... Where hap-py birds . . . in song a-gree, . . . Thro' sun-ny morn . . . . the prais-es tell . . . . Of sights and sounds . . . in Gal-i-lee. . . .
3. And when I read . . . . the thrill-ing lore . . . . . Of Him who walked . . up-on the sea, ... I long, oh, how . . . . I long once more . . . . To fol-low Him . . . . in Gal-i-lee. . . .
CHORUS
O Gal-i-lee! sweet Gal-i-lee! Where Je-sus loved so much to be;
O Gal-i-lee! blue Gal-i-lee! Come, sing thy song a-gain to me!

438 I Will Not Forget Thee

C. H. G.
Chas. H. Gabriel
1. Sweet is the prom-ise—"I will not for-get thee," Noth-ing can mo-lest or
2. Trusting the prom-ise—"I will not for-get thee," On-ward will I go with
3. When at the gold-en por-tals I am stand-ing, All my trib-u-la-tions,
turn my soul a-way; E'en tho' the night be dark with-in the val-ley,
songs of joy and love; Tho' earth de-spise me, tho' my friends for-sake me,
all my sor-rows past, How sweet to hear the bless-ed proc-la-ma-tion,
Just be-yond is shin-ing one e-ter-nal day.
I shall be re-mem-bered in my home a-bove.
"En-ter, faithful servant, welcome home at last!"
Chorus
I . . . . will not for-get thee or
I will not for-get thee, I will nev-er
leave thee; In My hands I'll hold thee, in My arms I'll fold thee; I . . . . will
leave thee;
I will not for-get
not for-get thee or leave thee; I am thy Re-deem-er, I will care for thee.
thee, for-get

439 Calvary

Rev. W. M'K. Darwood — Jno. R. Sweney

1. On Cal-vary's brow . . . . . my Sav-iour died, ... 'Twas there my
2. 'Mid rend-ing rocks . . . . . and darkening skies . . . . My Sav - iour
3. O Je-sus, Lord, ... how can it be . . . . . That Thou shouldst
(1) On Cal-vary's brow my Sav-iour died,
Lord . . . . . was cru-ci-fied; . . . . . 'Twas on the cross . . . .
bows . . . . . His head and dies; . . . . . The ope-ning veil . . . .
give . . . . . Thy life for me, ... To bear the cross . . . .
'Twas there my Lord was cru-ci-fied; 'Twas on the cross
He bled for me, ... And purchased there . . . my par-don free.
re-veals the way . . . . . To heav-en's joys . . . . . and end-less day.
and ag-o-ny . . . . . In that dread hour . . . . . on Cal-va-ry!
He bled for me, And purchased there
mf Refrain p m p pp
O Cal-va-ry! dark Cal-va-ry! Where Je-sus shed His blood for me (for me);
mf ff mf rit. p
O Cal-va-ry! blest Cal-va-ry! 'Twas there my Sav-iour died for me

440 Wait, and Murmur Not

W. H. Bellamy

Wm. J. Kirkpatrick

1. O trou-bled heart, there is a home, Be-yond the reach of toil and care;
2. Yet when bowed down beneath the load By heaven al-lowed, thine earth-ly lot;
3. Toil on, nor deem, tho' sore it be, One sigh un-heard, one prayer for-got;
A home where chang-es nev-er come: Who would not fain be rest-ing there?
Look up! thou'lt reach that blest a-bode; Wait, meek-ly wait, and mur-mur not.
The day of rest will dawn for thee; Wait, meek-ly wait, and mur-mur not.
Chorus
O wait, meek-ly wait, and mur-mur not, O
meek-ly wait,
wait, meek-ly wait, and mur-mur not, O wait,
meek-ly wait, meek-ly wait,
O wait, O wait, and mur-mur not.
meek-ly wait, O mur-mur not.

441 Open Our Eyes, Thy Glory Beholding

E. O. S.
Ernest O. Sellers
1. Lord, un-to Thee we look for sal-va-tion, Un-to Thy like-ness ev-er would grow;
2. Un - to all men Thy love and compassion Ev-er is seek-ing from shore to shore,
3. We would be Thine, Lord, to serve forever, Filled with Thy Spirit, lost in Thy love;
Be Thou our strength, our closest companion, Thus day by day Thy love ful-ly know.
List! He is call - ing, in love entreats you, "Come un-to Me, and live ev - er-more."
From Thy deep wells of grace and salvation, Send streams of power and strength from above.
rit.
Chorus
O - pen our eyes, Thy glo - ry be - hold - ing,
O - pen our eyes, Thy glo - ry be - hold - ing, be - hold - ing,
O - pen our ears, Thy wis - dom be known; Cleansed and re-
O - pen our ears, Thy
fined in tho't and af-fec-tion, Seal us and make us ev-er Thine own.
Cleansed and re-fined in
rall

442 Somebody Needs Your Love

B. B. McK. B. B. McKinney

1. Out in the dark-ness of sor-row and sin, Some-bod-y needs your love;
2. Man - y are help-less, and wait for your call, Some-bod-y needs your love;
3. Some one is tempt-ed to turn from the right, Some-bod-y needs your love;
4. Some are down-heart-ed, in sor-row they roam, Some-bod-y needs your love;
Led by the Mas-ter, that soul you may win, Some-bod-y needs your love.
Show them that Je-sus is All and in all, Some-bod-y needs your love.
Long-ing for courage and strength for the fight, Some-bod-y needs your love.
Man - y are sigh-ing for heav - en and home, Some-bod-y needs your love.
Chorus
Some-bod - y needs your love, Some-bod - y needs your love, ...
your love,
Some one in sad-ness, yearning for glad-ness, Some-bod-y needs your love.

443 Follow, I Will Follow Thee

Howard L. Brown
Margaret W. Brown
Howard L. Brown
Arr. by Herbert G. Tovey
1. Je - sus calls me, I must fol - low, Fol - low Him to - day (to - day);
2. Je - sus calls me, I must fol - low, Fol - low ev - ery hour (every hour),
3. Je - sus calls me, I must fol - low, Fol - low Him al - way (al - way);
When His ten - der voice is plead - ing How can I de - lay? . . .
Know the bless - ing of His pres - ence, Full - ness of His power. .
When my Sav - iour goes be - fore me I can nev - er stray. . .
Refrain
Fol - low, I will fol - low Thee, my Lord, Fol - - low
Fol-low, fol-low, I will fol - low, Fol-low Thee, my Lord, my Lord, Fol-low, fol - low
ev - ery pass - ing day.............. My to-mor-rows are all
ev - ery pass - ing, Fol-low ev - ery day.
day, pass-ing day.
known to Thee, Thou . . . wilt lead me all the way.
are known to Thee, Thou wilt lead, wilt

444 Christ for the Whole Wide World!

HATTIE BELL ALLEN — B. B. MCKINNEY

1. Christ for the whole wide world! Our task has just be - gun, For mil-lions wait in
2. Christ for the whole wide world! His message must be sent To mil-lions dy - ing
3. Christ for the whole wide world! His her-alds will pro-claim Sal - va - tion for men
ev - ery land The message of God's Son. Shall they be left in sin, To die with-
in their sin To call them to re - pent. Christ Je-sus died to save, But they can
ev-ery-where In Je-sus' bless-ed name. And we who can-not go To bear His
out His Word, With-out the Sav-iour Je-sus Christ, Because they nev-er heard?
nev - er know Un - til we bring our gifts of love And bid His her-alds go!
ti - dings far Will pray for those who take the Word–And witness where we are.
CHORUS
We will give, we will pray, We will wit-ness ev - ery day,
We will glad - ly give, we will hum-bly pray,
ev - ery day,
rit.
That the mil - lions of the whole wide world May know our Sav-iour's love.

445 The Christian Home

Carl J. P. Spitta — B. B. McKinney

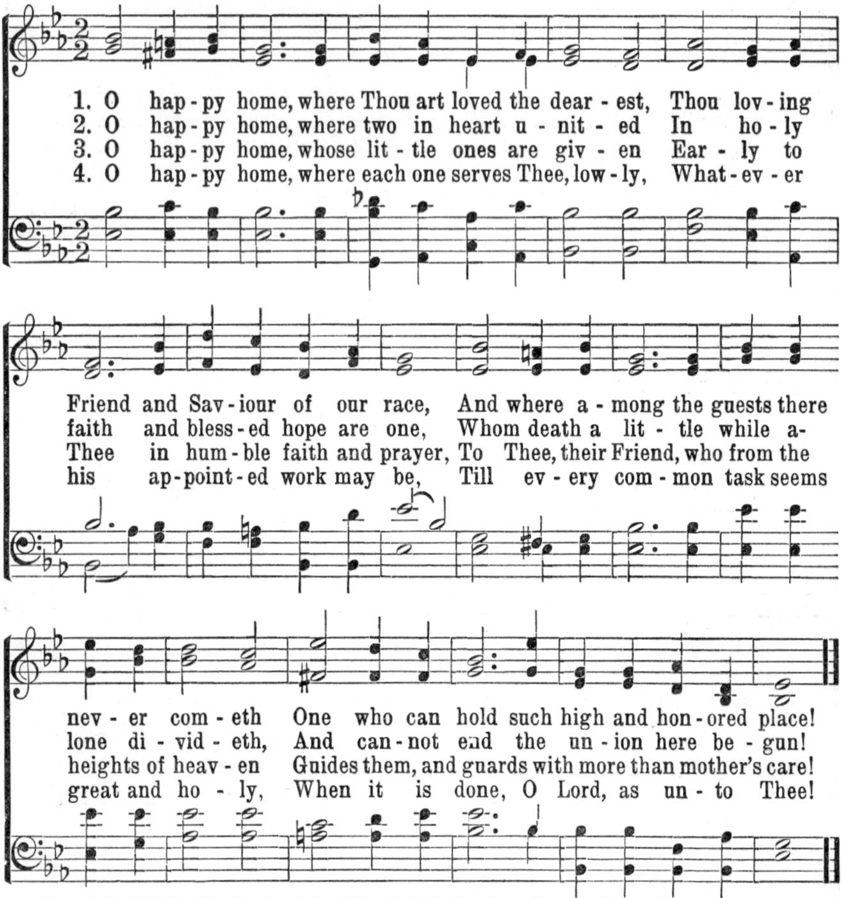

1. O hap-py home, where Thou art loved the dear-est, Thou lov-ing
2. O hap-py home, where two in heart u-nit-ed In ho-ly
3. O hap-py home, whose lit-tle ones are giv-en Ear-ly to
4. O hap-py home, where each one serves Thee, low-ly, What-ev-er

Friend and Sav-iour of our race, And where a-mong the guests there
faith and bless-ed hope are one, Whom death a lit-tle while a-
Thee in hum-ble faith and prayer, To Thee, their Friend, who from the
his ap-point-ed work may be, Till ev-ery com-mon task seems

nev-er com-eth One who can hold such high and hon-ored place!
lone di-vid-eth, And can-not end the un-ion here be-gun!
heights of heav-en Guides them, and guards with more than mother's care!
great and ho-ly, When it is done, O Lord, as un-to Thee!

446 Our Times Are in Thy Hand

W. F. Floyd — Homer Hammontree

1. "Our times are in Thy hand:" Fa-ther, we wish them there;
2. "Our times are in Thy hand," What-ev-er they may be;
3. "Our times are in Thy hand;"—Why should we doubt or fear?
4. "Our times are in Thy hand,"—Je-sus, the Cru-ci-fied!

Our Times Are in Thy Hand

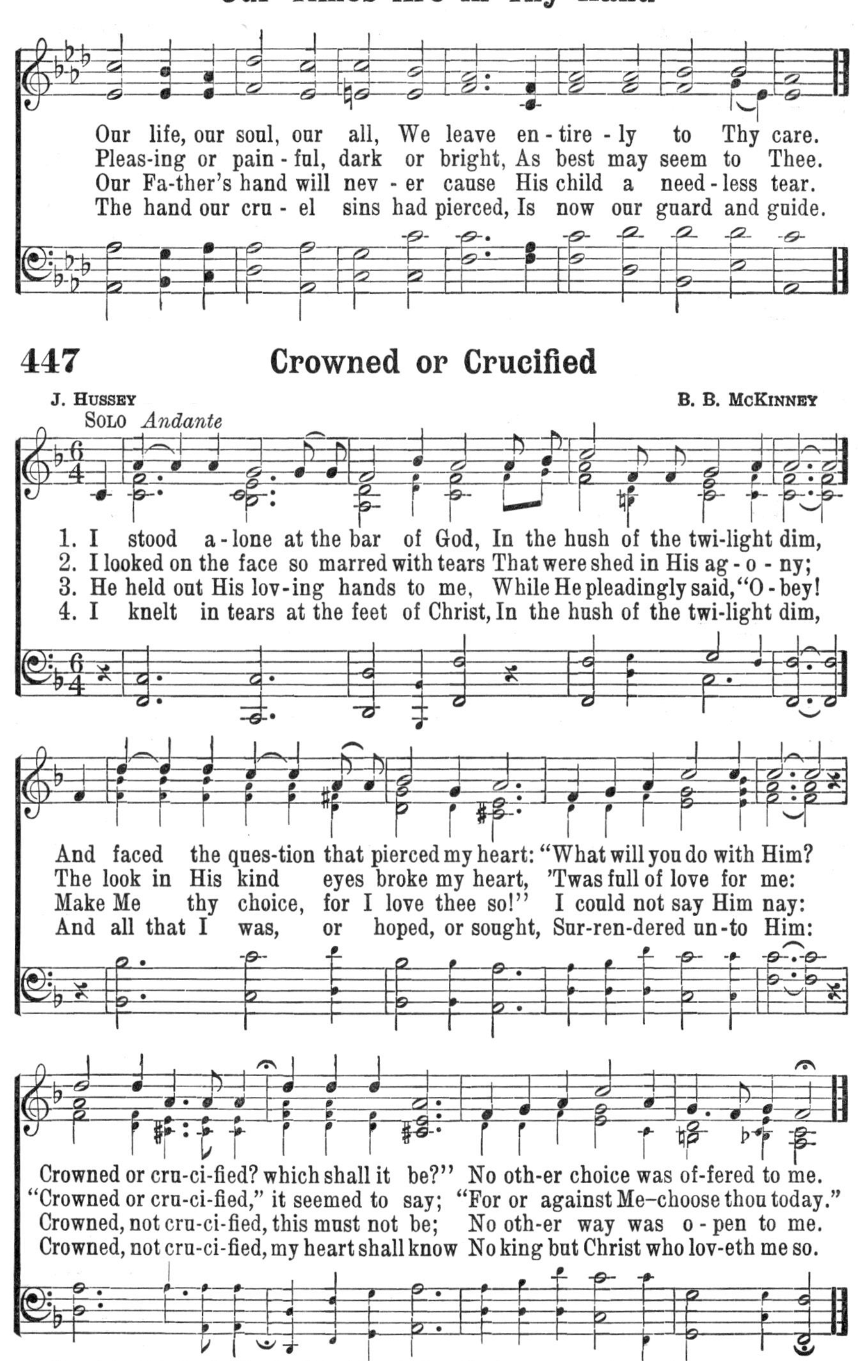
Our life, our soul, our all, We leave en-tire-ly to Thy care.
Pleas-ing or pain-ful, dark or bright, As best may seem to Thee.
Our Fa-ther's hand will nev-er cause His child a need-less tear.
The hand our cru-el sins had pierced, Is now our guard and guide.
447 Crowned or Crucified
J. Hussey
B. B. McKinney
Solo Andante
1. I stood a-lone at the bar of God, In the hush of the twi-light dim,
2. I looked on the face so marred with tears That were shed in His ag-o-ny;
3. He held out His lov-ing hands to me, While He pleadingly said, "O-bey!
4. I knelt in tears at the feet of Christ, In the hush of the twi-light dim,
And faced the ques-tion that pierced my heart: "What will you do with Him?
The look in His kind eyes broke my heart, 'Twas full of love for me:
Make Me thy choice, for I love thee so!" I could not say Him nay:
And all that I was, or hoped, or sought, Sur-ren-dered un-to Him:
Crowned or cru-ci-fied? which shall it be?" No oth-er choice was of-fered to me.
"Crowned or cru-ci-fied," it seemed to say; "For or against Me–choose thou today."
Crowned, not cru-ci-fied, this must not be; No oth-er way was o-pen to me.
Crowned, not cru-ci-fied, my heart shall know No king but Christ who lov-eth me so.

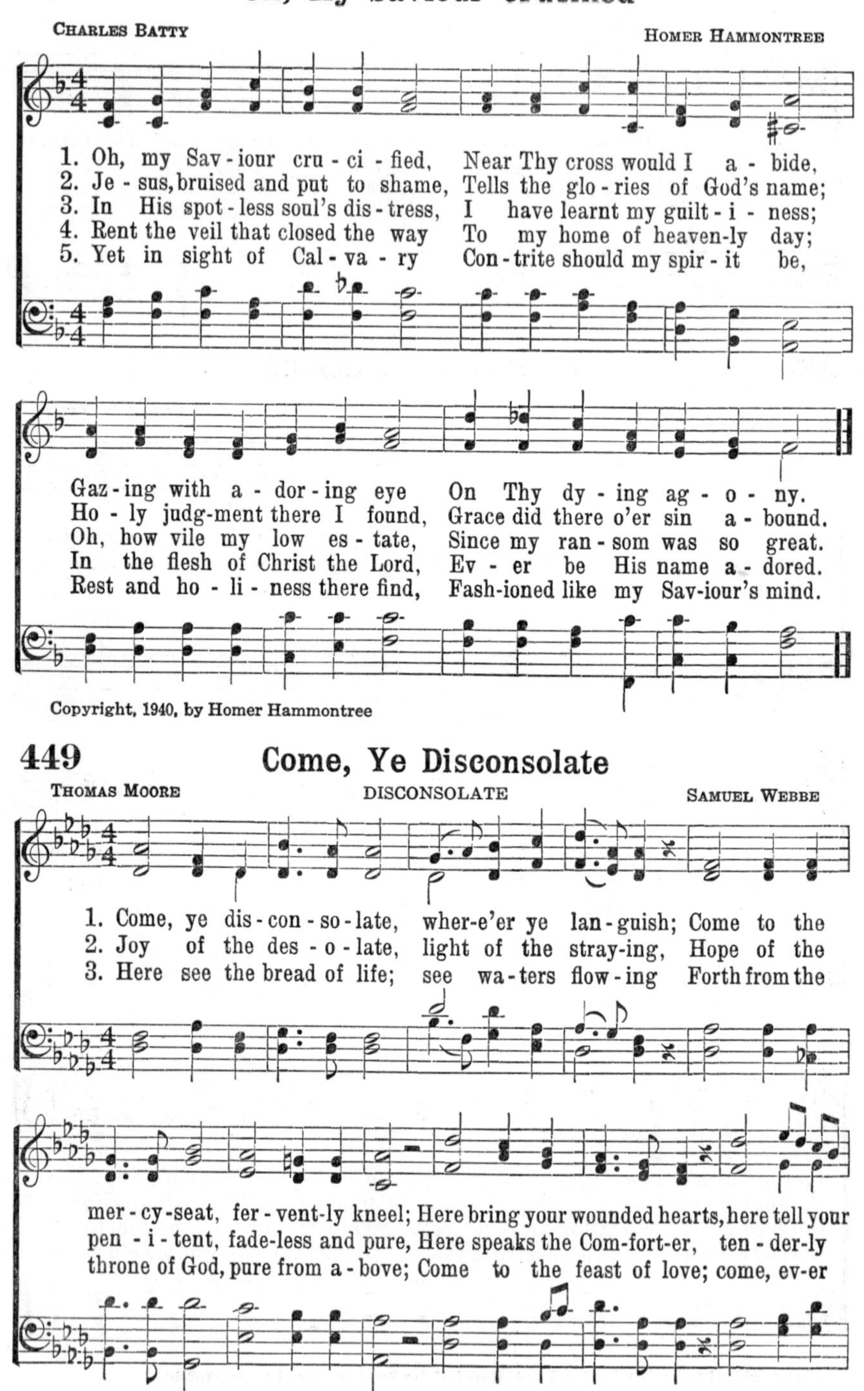
448 Oh, My Saviour Crucified
Charles Batty
Homer Hammontree
1. Oh, my Sav - iour cru - ci - fied, Near Thy cross would I a - bide, Gaz - ing with a - dor - ing eye On Thy dy - ing ag - o - ny.
2. Je - sus, bruised and put to shame, Tells the glo - ries of God's name; Ho - ly judg-ment there I found, Grace did there o'er sin a - bound.
3. In His spot - less soul's dis - tress, I have learnt my guilt - i - ness; Oh, how vile my low es - tate, Since my ran - som was so great.
4. Rent the veil that closed the way To my home of heaven-ly day; In the flesh of Christ the Lord, Ev - er be His name a - dored.
5. Yet in sight of Cal - va - ry Con - trite should my spir - it be, Rest and ho - li - ness there find, Fash-ioned like my Sav-iour's mind.
Copyright, 1940, by Homer Hammontree
449 Come, Ye Disconsolate
Thomas Moore
DISCONSOLATE
Samuel Webbe
1. Come, ye dis - con - so - late, wher-e'er ye lan - guish; Come to the mer - cy - seat, fer - vent - ly kneel; Here bring your wounded hearts, here tell your
2. Joy of the des - o - late, light of the stray-ing, Hope of the pen - i - tent, fade-less and pure, Here speaks the Com-fort-er, ten - der - ly
3. Here see the bread of life; see wa - ters flow - ing Forth from the throne of God, pure from a - bove; Come to the feast of love; come, ev - er

Come, Ye Disconsolate
an - guish; Earth has no sor - row that heaven can - not heal.
say - ing, "Earth has no sor - row that heaven can - not cure."
know - ing Earth has no sor - row but heaven can re - move.
450
Holy Spirit, Lead Us
Claire B. and Richard A. Kelly
Richard A. Kelly
1. O Ho - ly Spir - it, lead us, we pray, We need Thy
2. We need Thy pow - er a - long life's way, Come, gra - cious
3. Com - fort our hearts, hear us, we pray, Give us Thy
guid - ance all through the day; If Thou but teach us to know Thy
Spir - it, a - bide to - day; En - due with love, Thou Might - y
strength from day to day; If we but fol - low, make Thee our
ways, We fol - low glad - ly and sing Thy praise.
One, Oh, help us now to say, "Thy will be done."
Guide, Thy peace will be ours, and joy a - bide.

451 Lord, Lay Some Soul Upon My Heart

First Stanza, Anonymous
2nd and 3rd Stanzas, MACK WEAVER and B. B. MCK.
B. B. MCKINNEY
1. Lord, lay some soul up - on my heart, And love that soul through me;
2. Lord, lead me to some soul in sin, And grant that I may be
3. To win that soul for Thee a - lone, Will be my con - stant prayer;
And may I brave - ly do my part To win that soul for Thee.
En - dued with power and love to win That soul, dear Lord, for Thee.
That when I've reached the great white throne I'll meet that dear one there.
CHORUS
Some soul for Thee, some soul for Thee, This is my ear - nest plea;
Help me each day, on life's high-way, To win some soul for Thee.
Copyright, 1940, by The Sunday School Board of the Southern Baptist Convention
452 My Father Knows
Anonymous
B. B. MCKINNEY
1. He knows the bit-ter, wea-ry way, The end - less striv-ing day by day,
2. He knows when faint and worn we sink, How deep the pain, how near the brink
3. He knows how hard the fight has been, The clouds that come our lives between,
4. He knows! O heart, take up thy cross, And know earth's treasures are but dross,

My Father Knows
rit.
The souls that weep, the souls that pray; My Fa-ther knows, my Fa-ther knows.
Of dark de-spair we pause and shrink; My Fa-ther knows, my Fa-ther knows.
The wounds the world has nev-er seen; My Fa-ther knows, my Fa-ther knows.
And all will prove as gain, not loss; My Fa-ther knows, my Fa-ther knows.
453
Whisper a Prayer
B. B. McK.
B. B. McKinney
1. Come, lin-ger here with the Mas - ter, Come with your bur-den and care;
2. Come to your bless-ed Re - deem - er, He is a Sav - iour in - deed;
3. Wait at the feet of your Mas - ter, Pray that His will may be thine;
Come with your sins and temp-ta - tions, Whis-per, oh, whis-per a prayer.
Call and He sure - ly will an - swer, He will sup - ply ev - ery need.
Wait, calm-ly wait for His pow - er, Won-der-ful pow - er di - vine
Chorus
Whis-per a prayer, Whis-per a prayer, Bring Him your bur-den, Bring Him your care;
rit.
Wait calm-ly here, Je - sus is near; Whis-per a prayer, Whis-per a prayer.

454 Come, Humble Sinner

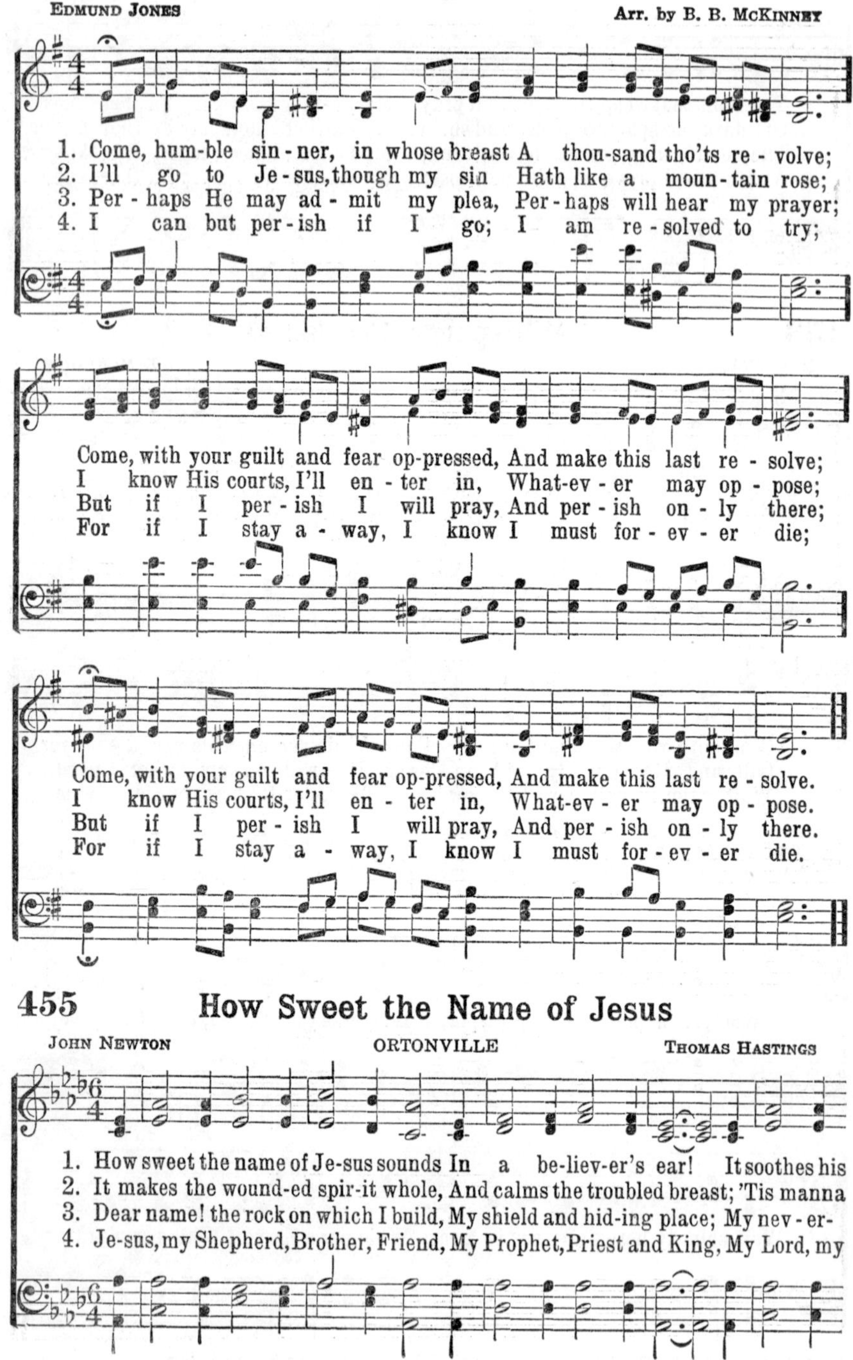
EDMUND JONES
Arr. by B. B. McKINNEY
1. Come, hum-ble sin-ner, in whose breast A thou-sand tho'ts re-volve;
2. I'll go to Je-sus, though my sin Hath like a moun-tain rose;
3. Per-haps He may ad-mit my plea, Per-haps will hear my prayer;
4. I can but per-ish if I go; I am re-solved to try;
Come, with your guilt and fear op-pressed, And make this last re-solve;
I know His courts, I'll en-ter in, What-ev-er may op-pose;
But if I per-ish I will pray, And per-ish on-ly there;
For if I stay a-way, I know I must for-ev-er die;
Come, with your guilt and fear op-pressed, And make this last re-solve.
I know His courts, I'll en-ter in, What-ev-er may op-pose.
But if I per-ish I will pray, And per-ish on-ly there.
For if I stay a-way, I know I must for-ev-er die.
455 How Sweet the Name of Jesus
JOHN NEWTON
ORTONVILLE
THOMAS HASTINGS
1. How sweet the name of Je-sus sounds In a be-liev-er's ear! It soothes his
2. It makes the wound-ed spir-it whole, And calms the troubled breast; 'Tis manna
3. Dear name! the rock on which I build, My shield and hid-ing place; My nev-er-
4. Je-sus, my Shepherd, Brother, Friend, My Prophet, Priest and King, My Lord, my

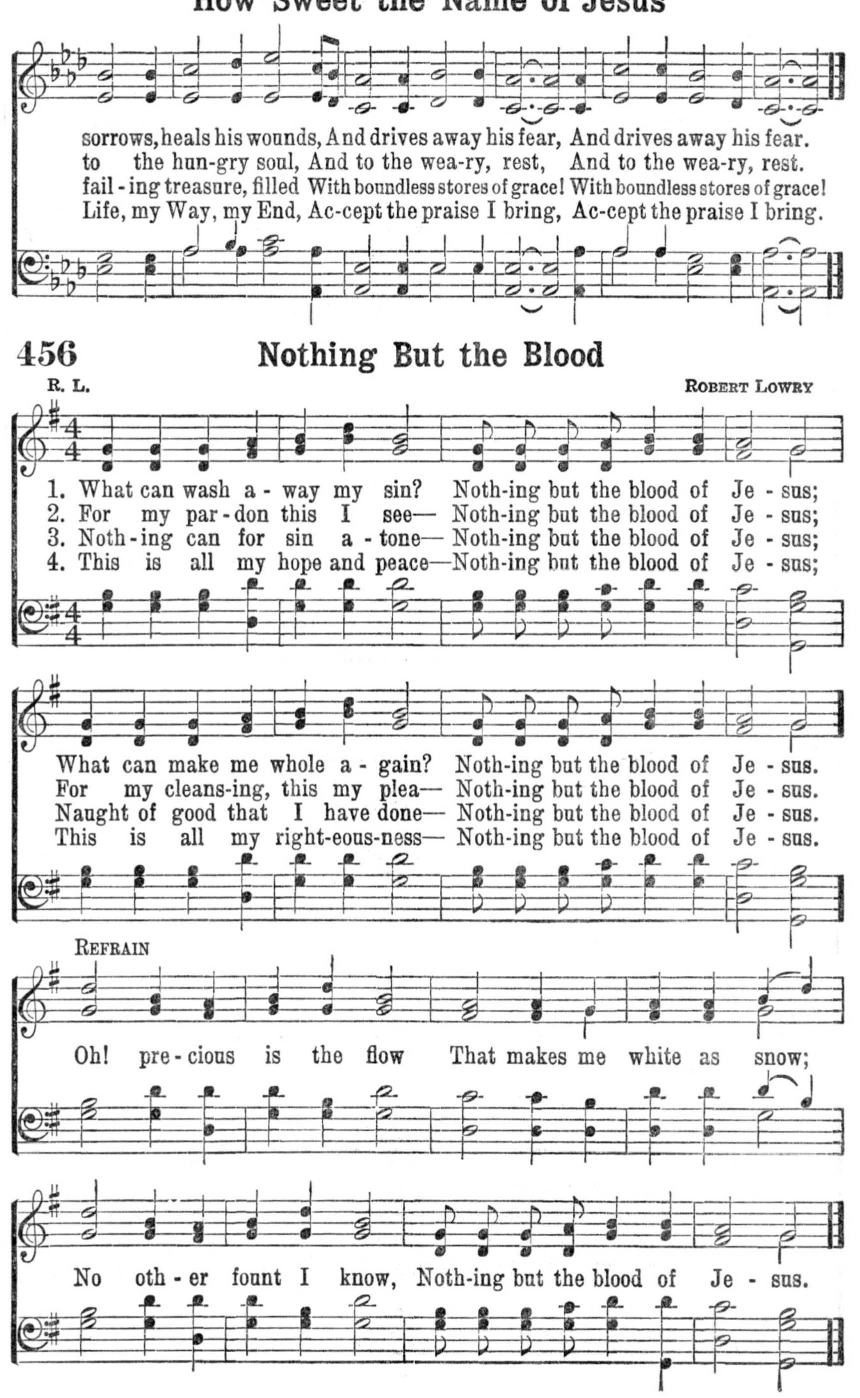
How Sweet the Name of Jesus
sorrows, heals his wounds, And drives away his fear, And drives away his fear.
to the hun-gry soul, And to the wea-ry, rest, And to the wea-ry, rest.
fail - ing treasure, filled With boundless stores of grace! With boundless stores of grace!
Life, my Way, my End, Ac-cept the praise I bring, Ac-cept the praise I bring.
456
Nothing But the Blood
R. L.
Robert Lowry
1. What can wash a - way my sin? Noth-ing but the blood of Je - sus;
2. For my par - don this I see— Noth-ing but the blood of Je - sus;
3. Noth - ing can for sin a - tone— Noth-ing but the blood of Je - sus;
4. This is all my hope and peace—Noth-ing but the blood of Je - sus;
What can make me whole a - gain? Noth-ing but the blood of Je - sus.
For my cleans-ing, this my plea— Noth-ing but the blood of Je - sus.
Naught of good that I have done— Noth-ing but the blood of Je - sus.
This is all my right-eous-ness— Noth-ing but the blood of Je - sus.
Refrain
Oh! pre - cious is the flow That makes me white as snow;
No oth - er fount I know, Noth-ing but the blood of Je - sus.

457 The Star-Spangled Banner

Francis Scott Key

1. Oh, say, can you see, by the dawn's ear-ly light, What so proud-ly we
2. On the shore, dim-ly seen thro' the mists of the deep, Where the foe's haughty
3. And where is that band, who so vaunt-ing-ly swore That the hav-oc of
4. Oh, thus be it ev - er when free-men shall stand Be - tween their loved

hailed at the twilight's last gleaming? Whose broad stripes and bright stars, thro' the
host in dread si - lence re - pos - es, What is that which the breeze, o'er the
war and the bat-tle's con - fu-sion, A home and a coun - try should
homes and the war's des - o - la-tion; Blest with vic - tory and peace, may the

per - il - ous fight, O'er the ramparts we watched, were so gal-lant-ly stream-ing?
tow - er - ing steep, As it fit - ful - ly blows, half conceals, half dis-clos - es?
leave us no more? Their blood has washed out their foul footsteps' pol - lu - tion;
Heaven-rescued land Praise the Power that hath made and preserved us a na-tion!

And the rock-ets' red glare, the bombs bursting in air, Gave proof thro' the
Now it catch-es the gleam of the morning's first beam, In full glo - ry re-
No ref - uge could save the hire-ling and slave From the ter - ror of
Then con-quer we must, when our cause it is just; And this be our

The Star-Spangled Banner

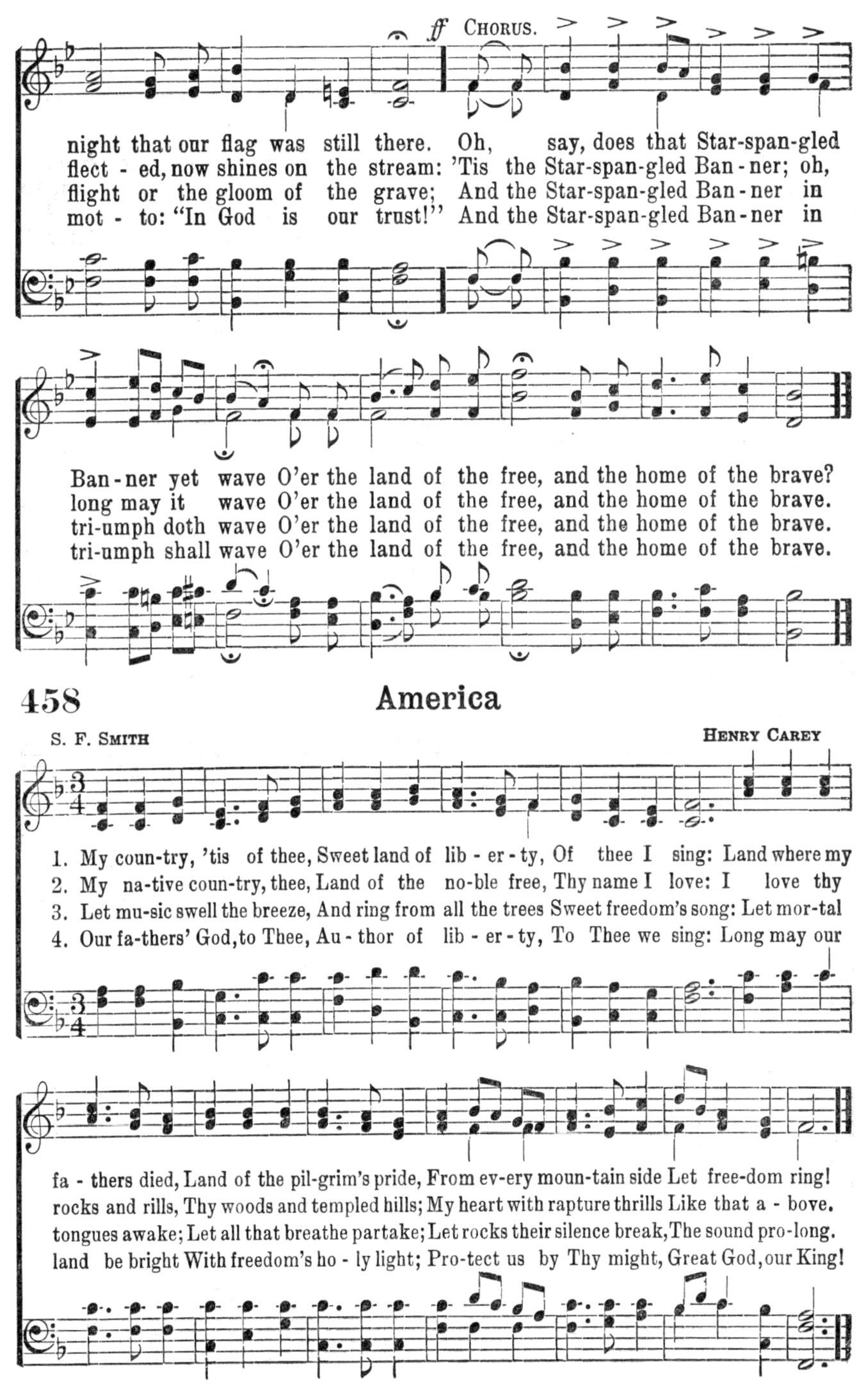
ff CHORUS.
night that our flag was still there. Oh, say, does that Star-spangled
flect - ed, now shines on the stream: 'Tis the Star-span-gled Ban - ner; oh,
flight or the gloom of the grave; And the Star-span-gled Ban - ner in
mot - to: "In God is our trust!" And the Star-span-gled Ban - ner in
Ban-ner yet wave O'er the land of the free, and the home of the brave?
long may it wave O'er the land of the free, and the home of the brave.
tri-umph doth wave O'er the land of the free, and the home of the brave.
tri-umph shall wave O'er the land of the free, and the home of the brave.
458
America
S. F. SMITH
HENRY CAREY
1. My coun-try, 'tis of thee, Sweet land of lib - er - ty, Of thee I sing: Land where my
2. My na-tive coun-try, thee, Land of the no-ble free, Thy name I love: I love thy
3. Let mu-sic swell the breeze, And ring from all the trees Sweet freedom's song: Let mor-tal
4. Our fa-thers' God, to Thee, Au - thor of lib - er - ty, To Thee we sing: Long may our
fa - thers died, Land of the pil-grim's pride, From ev-ery moun-tain side Let free-dom ring!
rocks and rills, Thy woods and templed hills; My heart with rapture thrills Like that a - bove.
tongues awake; Let all that breathe partake; Let rocks their silence break, The sound pro-long.
land be bright With freedom's ho - ly light; Pro-tect us by Thy might, Great God, our King!

459 Flee as a Bird

Mrs. M. S. B. Dana
Mrs. M. S. B. Dana
1. Flee as a bird to your moun - tain, Thou who art wea - ry of sin; . . . . Go to the clear, flow - ing foun - tain, Where you may wash and be clean; Fly, for th' A-veng - er is
2. He is the boun - ti - ful Giv - er, Now un - to Him draw near; . . . Peace then shall flow like a riv - er, Thou shalt be saved from thy fear. Hark! 'tis the Sav - iour
3. He will pro-tect thee for - ev - er, Wipe ev - ery fall - ing tear; . . . . He will for - sake thee, no, nev - er, Shel - tered so ten - der - ly there. Haste, then, the hours are
4. Come, then, to Je - sus, thy Sav - iour, He will re-deem thee from sin; . . . . Blest with a sense of His fa - vor, Make thee all - glo - rious with - in! Call, for the Sav - iour is

Flee as a Bird

near thee; Call, and the Saviour will hear thee; He on His bos-om will
call - ing! Haste! for the twilight is fall - ing! Flee, for the night is ap-
fly - ing, Spend not the moments in sigh - ing, Cease from your sorrow and
near thee, Wait-ing in mer-cy to hear thee; He by His pres-ence will
rall.
bear thee, Thou who art wea-ry of sin, O thou who art wea-ry of
pall - ing! And thou shalt be saved from thy fear, And thou shalt be saved from thy
cry - ing; The Sav-iour will wipe ev-ery tear, The Sav-iour will wipe ev-ery
cheer thee, O thou who art wea-ry of sin, O thou who art wea-ry of
sin.
fear.
tear.
sin.

460 Lead On, Lead On

B. B. McK. B. B. McKinney

Unison

1. Lead on, O King of Glo - ry, We will fol - low, fol - low Thee,
2. Lead on, O King of Glo - ry, We will sing the glad re - frain,
3. Lead on, O King of Glo - ry, Lead on for truth and right,

Thy crim - son ban - ner o - ver us Shall a sign of tri - umph be;
Lead on, O Great De - liv - er - er, O - ver all the world's do - main;
Lift high Thy cross e - ter - nal, Lead on, O Prince of Light;

Thou e - ter - nal Christ of Cal - va - ry, Lead us on from sea to sea,
We have heard Thy call to loy - al - ty, We will strive to set men free,
Let re-deem-ing love per-vade the world, Let its ban-ner be un - furled,

Till the day is done, And the crown is won, Lead on, lead on, lead on!
For the cause of right We will stand and fight, Lead us on, O God of Might.
Till the strife shall cease In a calm re - lease, Lead us on, O Prince of Peace.

Chorus Parts

On, on, on, on, on; On,
Lead on, lead on, Might-y Man of Gal-i - lee; Lead on, lead
Lead on, lead on, lead on; Lead on,

Lead On, Lead On

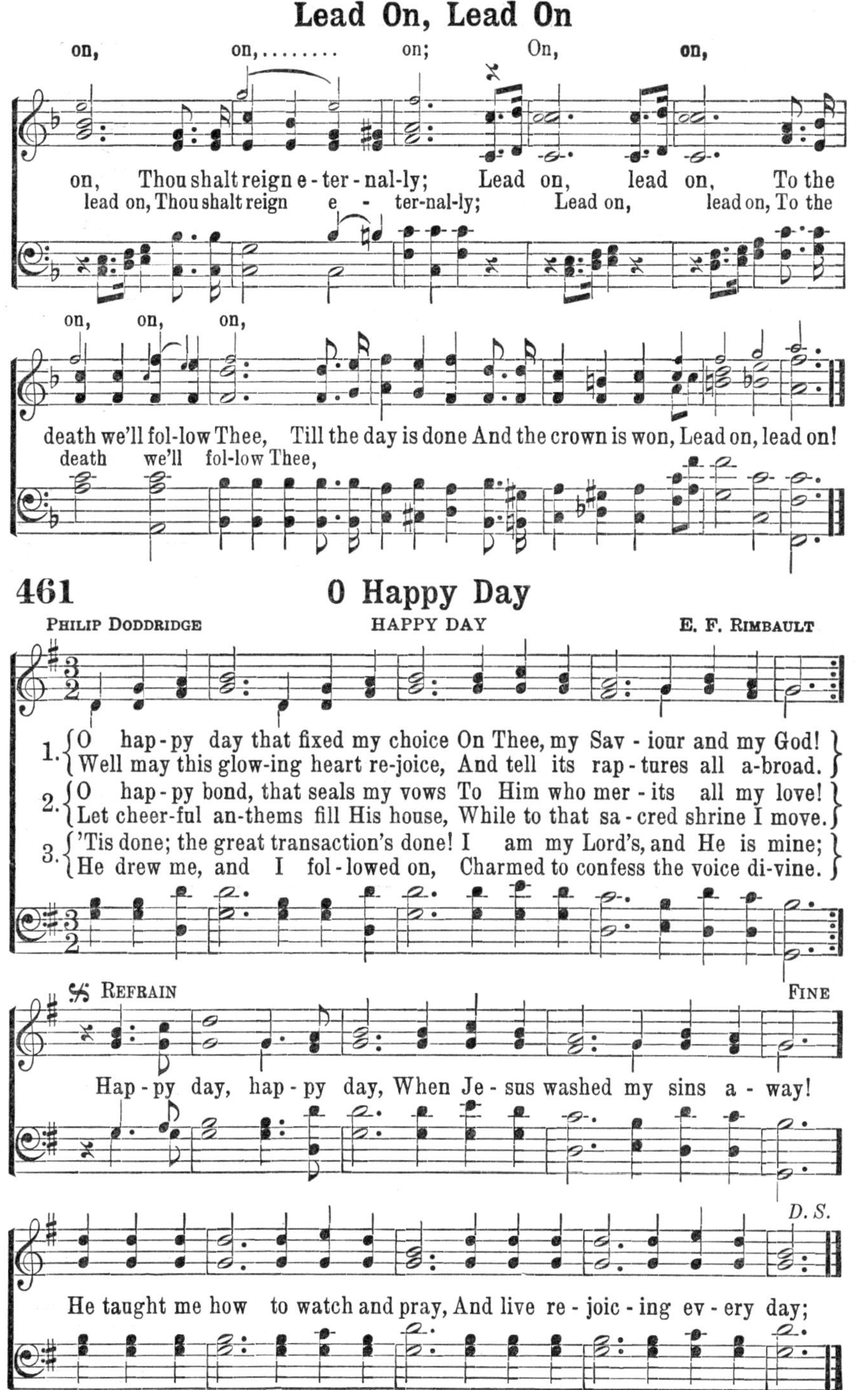

on, on,........ on; On, on,
on, Thou shalt reign e - ter - nal-ly; Lead on, lead on, To the
lead on, Thou shalt reign e - ter-nal-ly; Lead on, lead on, To the
on, on, on,
death we'll fol-low Thee, Till the day is done And the crown is won, Lead on, lead on!
death we'll fol-low Thee,
461
O Happy Day
PHILIP DODDRIDGE
HAPPY DAY
E. F. RIMBAULT
1. {O hap-py day that fixed my choice On Thee, my Sav - iour and my God!
Well may this glow-ing heart re-joice, And tell its rap-tures all a-broad.}
2. {O hap-py bond, that seals my vows To Him who mer - its all my love!
Let cheer-ful an-thems fill His house, While to that sa - cred shrine I move.}
3. {'Tis done; the great transaction's done! I am my Lord's, and He is mine;
He drew me, and I fol-lowed on, Charmed to confess the voice di-vine.}
REFRAIN
FINE
Hap - py day, hap - py day, When Je - sus washed my sins a - way!
D. S.
He taught me how to watch and pray, And live re - joic - ing ev - ery day;

462 Come Unto Him and Rest

B. B. McKinney

From Verdi
Arr. by B. B. McKinney

(DUET AND CHORUS)

Duet Andante
1. Oh, come,........... all ye that la - bor,
2. Oh, soul............. in grief and sor - row,
3. Oh, soul............. in sin and bond - age,
Oh, come,................ ye wea - ry and...... op-prest;
Oh, come,................ on Christ a - lone...... de-pend,
Oh, come,............ ... let Je - sus have...... con-trol,
Come with your bur - den, Come when your heart is dis - trest,
He will not leave you, He will pro - tect, de - fend,
Come to the Sav - iour, He will re - deem and make whole,
Oh, come, oh, come, Come and He'll give you rest, sweet rest.
Oh, come, oh, come, You will find Him your dear - est Friend.
Oh, come, oh, come, Come and find rest un - to your soul.

Come Unto Him and Rest

463 Touch Me, Lord Jesus

Come Unto Him and Rest
CHORUS
Come to the Sav - iour, On Him your bur - den roll, ...
Oh, come, oh, come, Come and find rest un - to your soul.
rit.
463
Touch Me, Lord Jesus
LOUISE CREAMER
B. B. McKINNEY
1. Touch me, Lord Je - sus, With Thy love di - vine; Cleanse my heart, dear Mas - ter, Make me whol - ly Thine.
2. Touch me, Lord Je - sus, Calm the fears in me; Let me know Thy pres - ence In each soul I see.
3. Touch me, Lord Je - sus, With Thy power di - vine; Make each throb-bing heart - beat Sing in tune with Thine.
4. Touch me, Lord Je - sus, Make my heart Thy throne; Mold my life and use me Ev - er as Thine own.
CHORUS
Touch me, bless - ed Je - sus, I would be Thine own; Take my will for - ev - er, Make it Thine a - lone.

464 He Is Not Here, But Is Risen!

D. W. Whittle
James McGranahan
p Andantino
1. Oh, day of awful story— Jesus is dead!
2. A weary night of weeping— Jesus is dead!
3. A day in sorrow dawning— Jesus is dead!
Sad end to hope of glory— Jesus is dead!
A night that knew no sleeping— Jesus is dead!
A sad and gloomy morning— Jesus is dead!
f Chorus Allegretto
Behold the stone is rolled away! And shining ones have come to say:
cres
"He is not here, but is risen! He is not here, but is risen!"
The night of death is past and gone—Arise, and greet the glorious morn!—

He Is Not Here, But Is Risen!
"He is not here, but is ris - en! He is not here, but is ris - en!"
465
O Why Not To-Night?
ELIZABETH REED
J. CALVIN BUSHEY
1. O do not let the Word de - part, And close thine eyes against the light;
2. To - mor-row's sun may nev-er rise To bless thy long-de - lud - ed sight;
3. Our Lord in pit - y lin - gers still, And wilt thou thus His love re - quite?
4. Our bless-ed Lord re - fus - es none Who would to Him their souls u - nite;
Poor sin - ner, hard - en not your heart, Be saved, O to - night.
This is the time, O then be wise, Be saved, O to - night.
Re - nounce at once thy stub - born will, Be saved, O to - night.
Be - lieve on Him, the work is done, Be saved, O to - night.
CHORUS
O why not to-night? O why not to-night?
O why not to-night? why not to-night? Why not to-night? why not to-night?
Wilt thou be saved? Then why not to - night?
Wilt thou be saved, wilt thou be saved? Then why not, O why not to - night?

466 Whispering Hope

A. H. | Arr. from Alice Hawthorne

Duet
1. Soft as the voice of an an - gel, Breath-ing a les-son un - heard,
2. If in the dusk of the twi - light, Dim be the re-gion a - far,
3. Hope, as an an-chor so stead - fast, Rends the dark veil for the soul,
Hope with a gen-tle per-sua - sion Whis-pers her com-fort-ing word:
Will not the deep-en-ing dark - ness Bright-en the glim-mer-ing star?
Whith-er the Mas-ter has en - tered, Rob-bing the grave of its goal;
Wait till the dark-ness is o - ver, Wait till the tem-pest is done,
Then when the night is up - on us, Why should the heart sink a-way?
Come then, O come, glad fru - i - tion, Come to my sad, wea - ry heart;
Hope for the sun-shine to - mor - row, Aft - er the show-er is gone.
When the dark midnight is o - ver, Watch for the breaking of day.
Come, O Thou blest hope of glo - ry, Nev - er, O nev - er de - part.
Chorus
Whis - per-ing hope, . . . O how wel - - come thy voice, . . .
Whis-per-ing hope, whis-per-ing hope, Welcome thy voice, O how welcome thy voice,

Whispering Hope

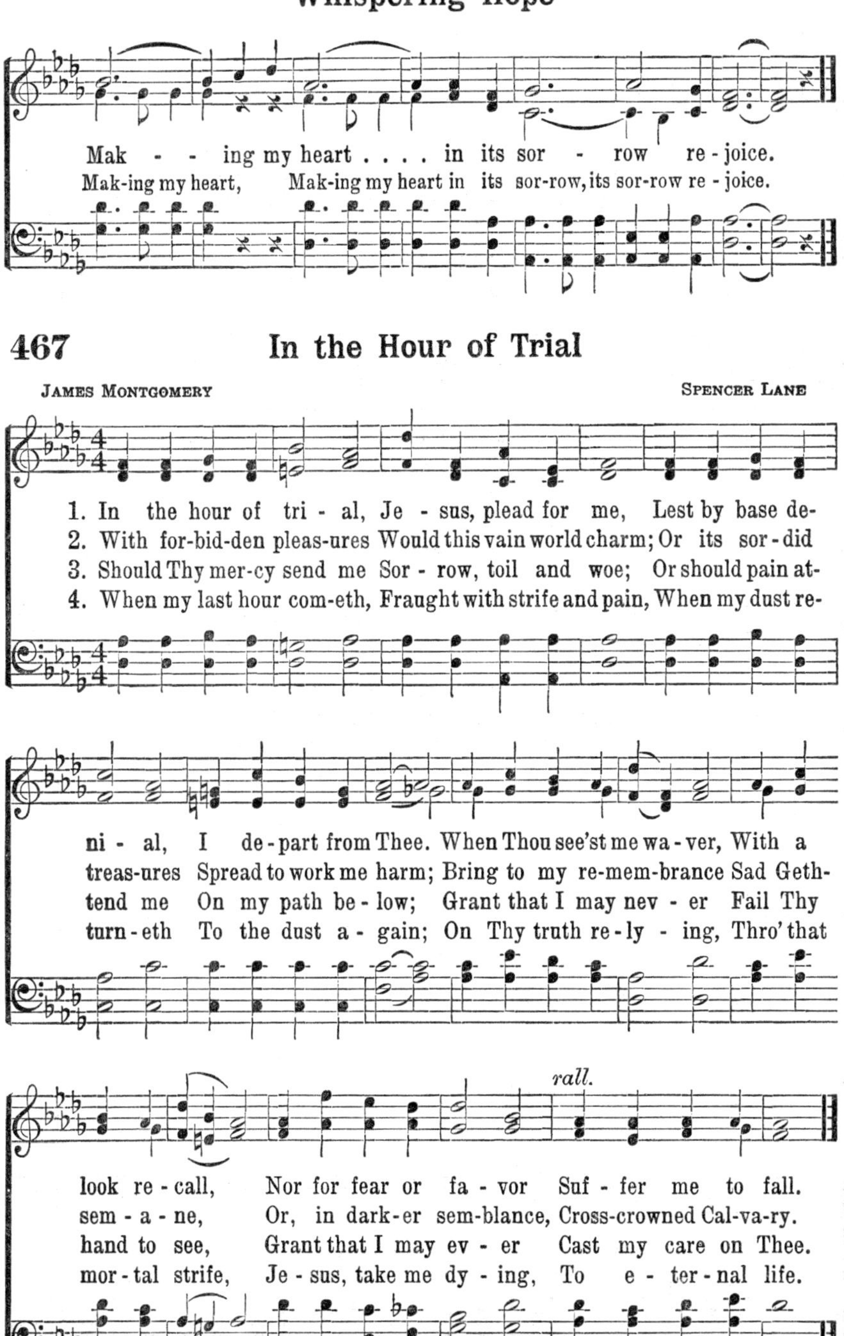
Mak - - ing my heart . . . . in its sor - row re - joice.
Mak-ing my heart, Mak-ing my heart in its sor-row, its sor-row re - joice.
467
In the Hour of Trial
JAMES MONTGOMERY
SPENCER LANE
1. In the hour of tri - al, Je - sus, plead for me, Lest by base de-
2. With for-bid-den pleas-ures Would this vain world charm; Or its sor - did
3. Should Thy mer-cy send me Sor - row, toil and woe; Or should pain at-
4. When my last hour com-eth, Fraught with strife and pain, When my dust re-
ni - al, I de - part from Thee. When Thou see'st me wa - ver, With a
treas-ures Spread to work me harm; Bring to my re-mem-brance Sad Geth-
tend me On my path be - low; Grant that I may nev - er Fail Thy
turn - eth To the dust a - gain; On Thy truth re - ly - ing, Thro' that
rall.
look re - call, Nor for fear or fa - vor Suf - fer me to fall.
sem - a - ne, Or, in dark-er sem-blance, Cross-crowned Cal-va-ry.
hand to see, Grant that I may ev - er Cast my care on Thee.
mor - tal strife, Je - sus, take me dy - ing, To e - ter - nal life.

468 O Holy Night

Adolf Adam
Arr. by B. B. McKinney
Duet Andante
mp
1. O ho - ly night; The stars are bright-ly shin - ing; It is the night of the dear Sav-iour's birth;
2. Led by . . . . the light Of faith se-rene-ly beam - ing, With glow-ing hearts by His cra - dle to stand;
Long lay the world in sin and er - ror pin - - ing, Till He ap-peared, and the soul felt His
Led by the light of the star so bright-ly gleam - ing, Here came the wise men from O - ri - ent

O Holy Night

All Parts in Unison Faster
worth; . . . . A thrill of hope, the wea - ry world re-
land; . . . .
joic - es, For yon - der breaks a new and cloud-less morn!
All Parts in Harmony
ff
Fall on your knees, O hear the an - gel voic - es, O
night di - vine! . . . . O night . . . when Christ was born! O
O night di-vine! O night was born!
night . . . di - vine! . . . . O night, O night di - vine!
O night

469 By Grace Are Ye Saved

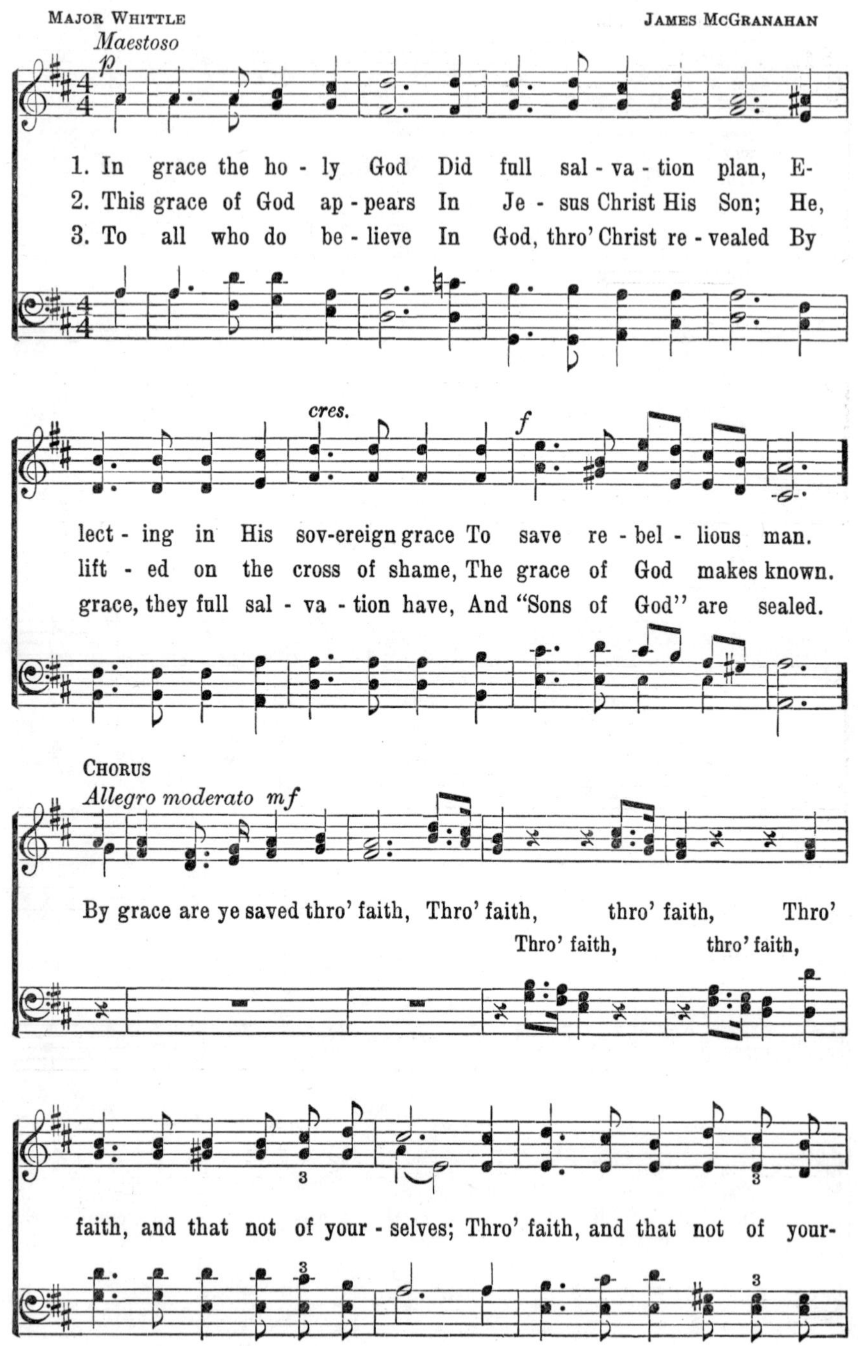
MAJOR WHITTLE
JAMES MCGRANAHAN
Maestoso
p
1. In grace the ho - ly God Did full sal - va - tion plan, E-
2. This grace of God ap - pears In Je - sus Christ His Son; He,
3. To all who do be - lieve In God, thro' Christ re - vealed By
cres.
f
lect - ing in His sov-ereign grace To save re - bel - lious man.
lift - ed on the cross of shame, The grace of God makes known.
grace, they full sal - va - tion have, And "Sons of God" are sealed.
CHORUS
Allegro moderato mf
By grace are ye saved thro' faith, Thro' faith, thro' faith, Thro'
Thro' faith, thro' faith,
faith, and that not of your - selves; Thro' faith, and that not of your-

By Grace Are Ye Saved

Not of works, ... not of works, . . .
cres.
selves; Not of works, ... not of
Not of works, not of works, not of works, not of works, . . .
cres.
works, not of works, not of works, Not of works lest an - y man should
boast; It is the gift of God; Not of works lest an - y man should
cres.
boast; It is the gift of God, It is the gift of God, It
Largo ff
is the gift of God, It is the gift of God, The gift of . . . God.

470 Hallelujah for the Cross

HORATIUS BONAR, ARR. JAMES MCGRANAHAN

1. The cross it stand-eth fast, Hal-le-lu-jah, hal-le-lu-jah! De-fy-ing ev-ery blast, Hal-le-lu-jah, hal-le-lu-jah! The winds of hell have blown, The world its hate hath shown, Yet it is not over-thrown, Hal-le-lu-jah for the cross!
2. It is the old cross still, Hal-le-lu-jah, hal-le-lu-jah! Its tri-umph let us tell, Hal-le-lu-jah, hal-le-lu-jah! The grace of God here shone Thro' Christ the bless-ed Son, Who did for sin a-tone, Hal-le-lu-jah for the cross!
3. 'Twas here the debt was paid, Hal-le-lu-jah, hal-le-lu-jah! Our sins on Je-sus laid, Hal-le-lu-jah, hal-le-lu-jah! So round the cross we sing Of Christ our of-fer-ing, Of Christ our liv-ing King, Hal-le-lu-jah for the cross!

cres.

OBBLIGATO DUET SOP. (or TEN.) and ALTO

Hal-le-lu-jah, hal-le-lu-jah, Hal-le-

SOPRANO & ALTO*

CHORUS *mp* Hal-le-lu-jah, hal-le-lu-jah, Hal-le-

TENOR & BASS

*If desired, the Soprano and Alto may sing the upper staff, omitting the middle staff.

Hallelujah for the Cross!

lu - jah for the cross! Hal - le - lu - jah,
lu - jah for the cross, hal-le - lu-jah for the cross! Hal - le - lu - jah,
hal - le - lu - jah, It shall nev - er suf - fer loss!
hal - le - lu - jah, It shall nev-er suf - fer, nev - er suf - fer loss!
Full Chorus
f
*Hal - le - lu - jah, hal - le - lu - jah, Hal - le - lu - jah for the cross!
cres.
ff
Hal - le - lu - jah, hal - le - lu - jah, It shall nev - er suf - fer loss!

*For a final ending, all the voices may sing the melody in unison through the last eight measures—the instrument playing the harmony.

471 Peace! Be Still!

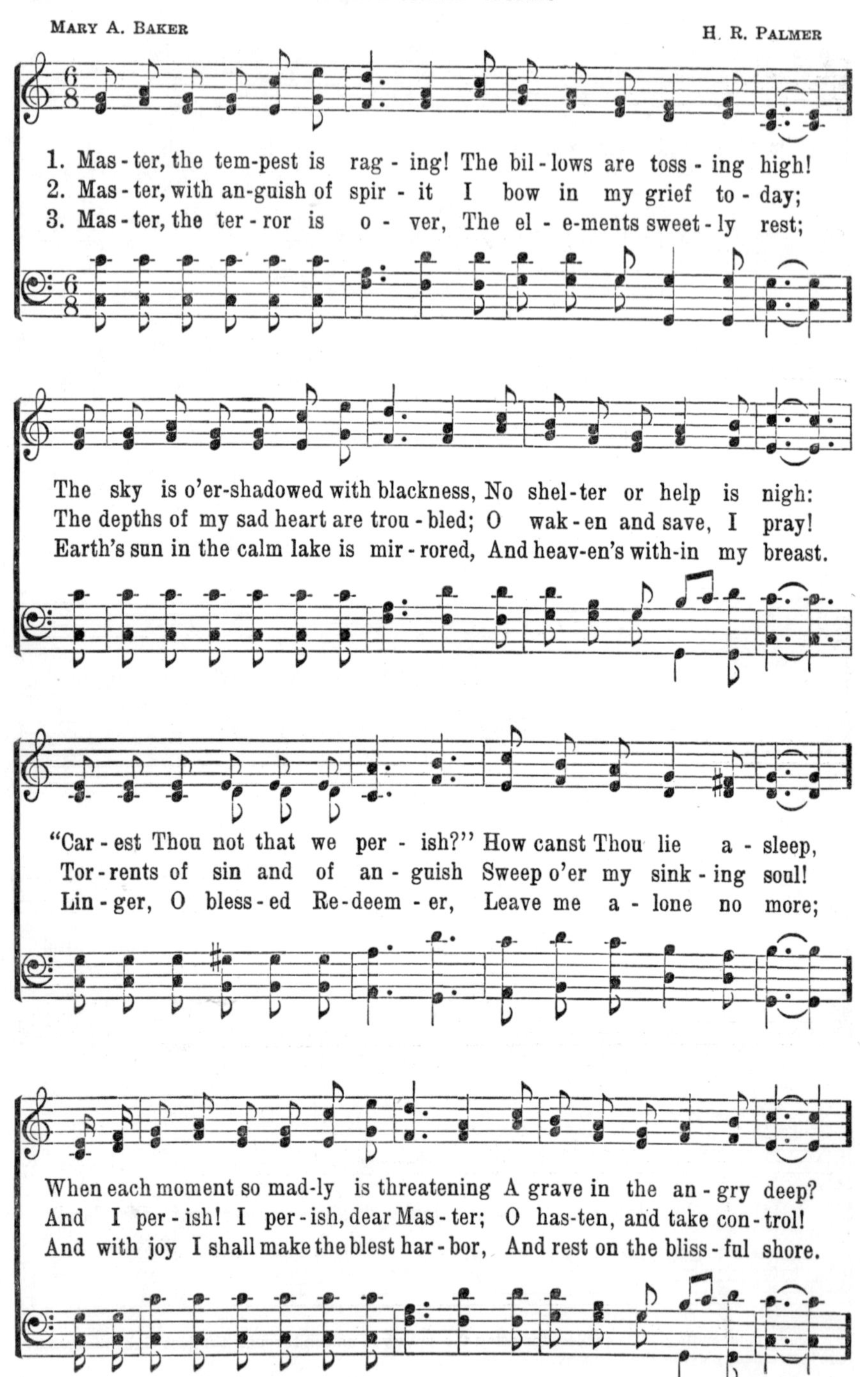
MARY A. BAKER
H. R. PALMER
1. Mas - ter, the tem-pest is rag - ing! The bil - lows are toss - ing high!
2. Mas - ter, with an-guish of spir - it I bow in my grief to - day;
3. Mas - ter, the ter - ror is o - ver, The el - e-ments sweet - ly rest;
The sky is o'er-shadowed with blackness, No shel-ter or help is nigh:
The depths of my sad heart are trou - bled; O wak - en and save, I pray!
Earth's sun in the calm lake is mir - rored, And heav-en's with-in my breast.
"Car - est Thou not that we per - ish?" How canst Thou lie a - sleep,
Tor - rents of sin and of an - guish Sweep o'er my sink - ing soul!
Lin - ger, O bless - ed Re-deem - er, Leave me a - lone no more;
When each moment so mad-ly is threatening A grave in the an - gry deep?
And I per - ish! I per - ish, dear Mas - ter; O has-ten, and take con - trol!
And with joy I shall make the blest har - bor, And rest on the bliss - ful shore.

Peace! Be Still!

REFRAIN
p
pp
"The winds and the waves shall o - bey My will, Peace, be still!"
Peace, be still! peace, be still!
Wheth-er the wrath of the storm-tossed sea, Or de - mons, or men, or what-
cres - - - - - - - - cen - - - - - - - - - - do
ev - er it be, No wa-ter can swal-low the ship where lies The Mas-ter of
ff
o-cean and earth and skies; They all shall sweet-ly o - bey My will; Peace, be still!
p
p
pp
Peace, be still! They all shall sweet-ly o - bey My will; Peace, peace, be still!

472 Praise Ye the Father

Arr. from Chas. Gounod

Praise ye the Fa-ther! Let every heart give thanks to Him! Praise ye the Fa-ther,
Who is ev - er kind and mer-ci - ful! Praise ye the Fa-ther, Who not-eth ev-ery
spar-row's fall! O King of Glo - ry! Let all earth pro-claim Thy maj-es-ty!
Chorus
Sing of the Lord, Every voice proclaim His power! Who bringeth joy to the
Of Him sing praise, and peace
world, And whose mercy endureth for-ev - er! He hath made all the
to all, Our Lord hath made

Praise Ye the Father

world, and the heav'n above us! In His strength, in His love, He ruleth the world; A-
rise, and praise ye the Father! Praise be to the Fa-ther, to the Son, and Ho-ly
Spir-it! Praise Him, ev-ery nation, All the earth shall rejoice in Him! . . . .
Praise the Fa-ther!
Glo - ry to the Lord our King! Glo-ry to His ev - er-last-ing name! Let all
earth be glad, rejoicing in His love, Oh, praise ye the Lord! praise ye the Lord!
1
2

473 **Awake, Put On Thy Strength**

B. B. McKinney

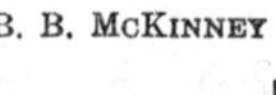

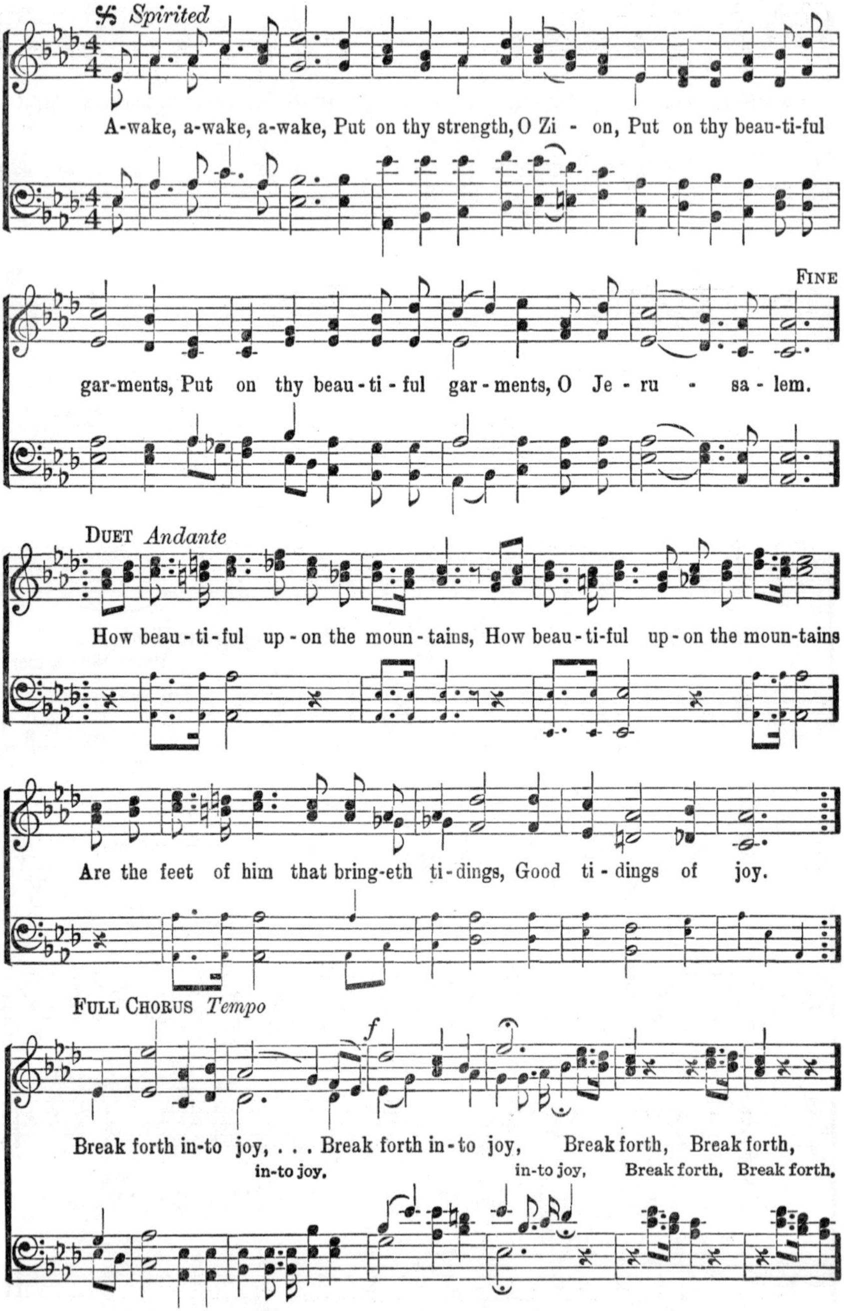

Spirited
A-wake, a-wake, a-wake, Put on thy strength, O Zi - on, Put on thy beau-ti-ful
gar-ments, Put on thy beau-ti-ful gar-ments, O Je - ru - sa - lem.
Fine
Duet Andante
How beau-ti-ful up-on the moun-tains, How beau-ti-ful up-on the moun-tains
Are the feet of him that bring-eth ti-dings, Good ti-dings of joy.
Full Chorus Tempo
Break forth in-to joy, . . . Break forth in-to joy, Break forth, Break forth,
in-to joy. in-to joy, Break forth, Break forth,

Awake, Put On Thy Strength

ff
mf
Break forth in - to joy, Sing to - geth-er, ye waste plac-es of Je - ru - sa - lem;
Sing to - geth-er, ye waste plac-es of Je - ru - sa - lem, For the Lord will bless and
com-fort all His peo - ple, For the Lord will bless and com-fort all His peo - ple.
Allegro
Praise the Lord.... for-ev-er-more,....... Praise the Lord for-ev-er - more, . . .
Praise the Lord for-ev-er-more, Praise the Lord for-ev-er-more,
D. S.
For He is good........ and ev - er kind........ To those who trust in Him.
For He is good and ev-er kind

474 Praise Ye the Lord

Arr. from W. F. SHERWIN
by B. B. McKINNEY
Moderato
INTRODUCTION
f
Praise ye the Lord!
Praise ye the Lord! Praise ye the Lord, praise ye the Lord!
Allegro
Praise Him! Praise Him! O house of Is-rael, praise the Lord! Praise Him!
Praise Him! Sing praise un-to our God.
Moderato
Praise the Lord, Praise the Lord,
Praise the Lord, O Je-
O Je - ru - sa - lem! Praise thy God, Praise thy God,
ru - sa-lem, Je - ru - sa - lem! Praise thy God, thy

Praise Ye the Lord

Praise thy God, O Zi - on; Praise the Lord, O Je - ru - sa - lem,
God, O Zi - on; For He hath strength - ened the
Praise thy God, O Zi - on! He hath bless'd thy chil-dren with-in thee.
bars of thy gates; He hath bless - ed thy chil - dren with - in thee.
Allegro
Praise Him! Praise Him! O house of Is-rael, praise the Lord! Praise Him!
f cres - - cen ff - - do
Praise Him! O Zi - on, praise thy God, O Zi - on praise thy God!
Moderato and majestic
m
f
ff
Praise ye the Lord! Praise ye the Lord! Praise ye the Lord!

475 Onward, Christian Soldiers

Sabine Baring-Gould
W. H. Jude
Unison Tempo di marcia
1. On - ward, Chris-tian sol - - diers! Marching as to war,
2. On - ward, then, ye peo - - ple! Join our hap-py throng,
With the Cross of Je - sus Go - ing on be - fore.
Blend with ours your voic - es In the tri-umph - song;
Christ, the roy - al Mas - ter, Leads a-gainst the foe;
Glo - ry, laud, and hon - or Un - to Christ the King,
For-ward in - to bat - tle, See, His ban-ner go!
This thro' count-less a - ges Men and an-gels sing.
Chorus All Parts
Onward, Christian sol - diers! Marching as to war, With the Cross of Je - sus

Onward, Christian Soldiers

Go-ing on be - fore. Marching, marching, Marching as to
war, With the Cross of Je - sus Go-ing on be - fore. A - MEN.
FINE
Final ending only.
MALE VOICES Unison
At the sign of tri - umph Satan's host doth flee; On, then, Christian
Crowns and thrones may per-ish, Kingdoms rise and wane, But the cross of
mf
ALL VOICES
sol - diers, On to vic-to-ry! Hell's foun-da-tions quiv-er At the
Je - sus Constant will remain; Gates of hell can nev - er 'Gainst the
ff
D.S. to Chorus
shout, at the shout of praise; Brothers, lift your voices, Loud your anthems raise.
cross, 'gainst the cross prevail; We have Christ's own promise, And that cannot fail.

476 God So Loved the World

J. STAINER

Andante ma non lento
p
cresc.
God so loved the world, God so loved the world, that He gave His
world, that He
mf
p
on - ly be - got-ten Son, that who-so be-liev-eth, be-liev-eth in Him should not
cresc.
f
p
per - ish, should not per-ish, but have ev-er-last - ing life. For God sent not His
cresc.
mf
Son in - to the world to con-demn the world, God sent not His Son in - to the
p
world to con-demn the world; But that the world thro' Him might be sav - ed.

God So Loved the World

pp
cresc.
God so loved the world, God so loved the world, that He gave His
world that He
mf
on - ly be - got - ten Son, that who-so be-liev - eth, be - liev-eth in Him
p
cresc.
f
should not per - ish, should not per - ish, but have ev - er - last - ing
cresc.
dim e rall.
life, ev - er - last - ing, ev - er - last - ing life.
ev - er - last - ing life, ev - er - last - ing life.
pp
ppp rall.
God so loved the world, God so loved the world, God so loved the world.

477 Hallelujah Chorus

(The Vocal Score is complete and uniform with the Messiah edition)

George Frederick Handel
Allegro (♩=72)
Intro. f
f
Hal - le - lu-jah! Hal - le - lu-jah! Hal-le-lu-jah! Hal-le-lu-jah! Hal-le - lu-jah!
Hal - le - lu-jah! Hal - le - lu-jah! Hal-le-lu-jah! Hal-le-lu-jah! Hal-le - lu - jah!
for the Lord God om-nip-o-tent reign-eth. Hal-le - lu-jah! Hal-le-lu-jah! Hal-le-
lu - jah! Hal-le - lu - jah! for the Lord God om-nip - o - tent reign-eth. Hal-le-

Hallelujah Chorus

lu-jah! Hal-le-lu-jah! Hal-le-lu-jah! Hal-le-lu-jah! for the Lord
Hal-le-lu-jah! Hal-le-
God om-nip - o-tent reign - eth. Hal-le-lu-jah! Hallelujah! Hallelu-
Hallelujah! Hallelujah! Hallelujah! Hal-le-lu-jah! Hal-le-lu-
lu-jah! Hallelujah! Hal - le - lu - jah! Hallelujah! for the Lord
Hal-le-lu-jah!
jah! Hal-le-lu-jah! Hal-le - lu - jah! Hal-le-lu-jah! Hal-le-lu-jah! Hal-le-lu-jah!
jah! Hal-le-lu-jah! Hal-le - lu - jah! Hal-le-lu-jah! Hal-le-lu-jah!
God om-nip - o-tent reign - eth. Hal-le-lu-jah! Hal-le-lu-jah! Hal-le-lu-jah!
Hal-le-lu-jah! Hal-le-lu-jah!

Hallelujah Chorus

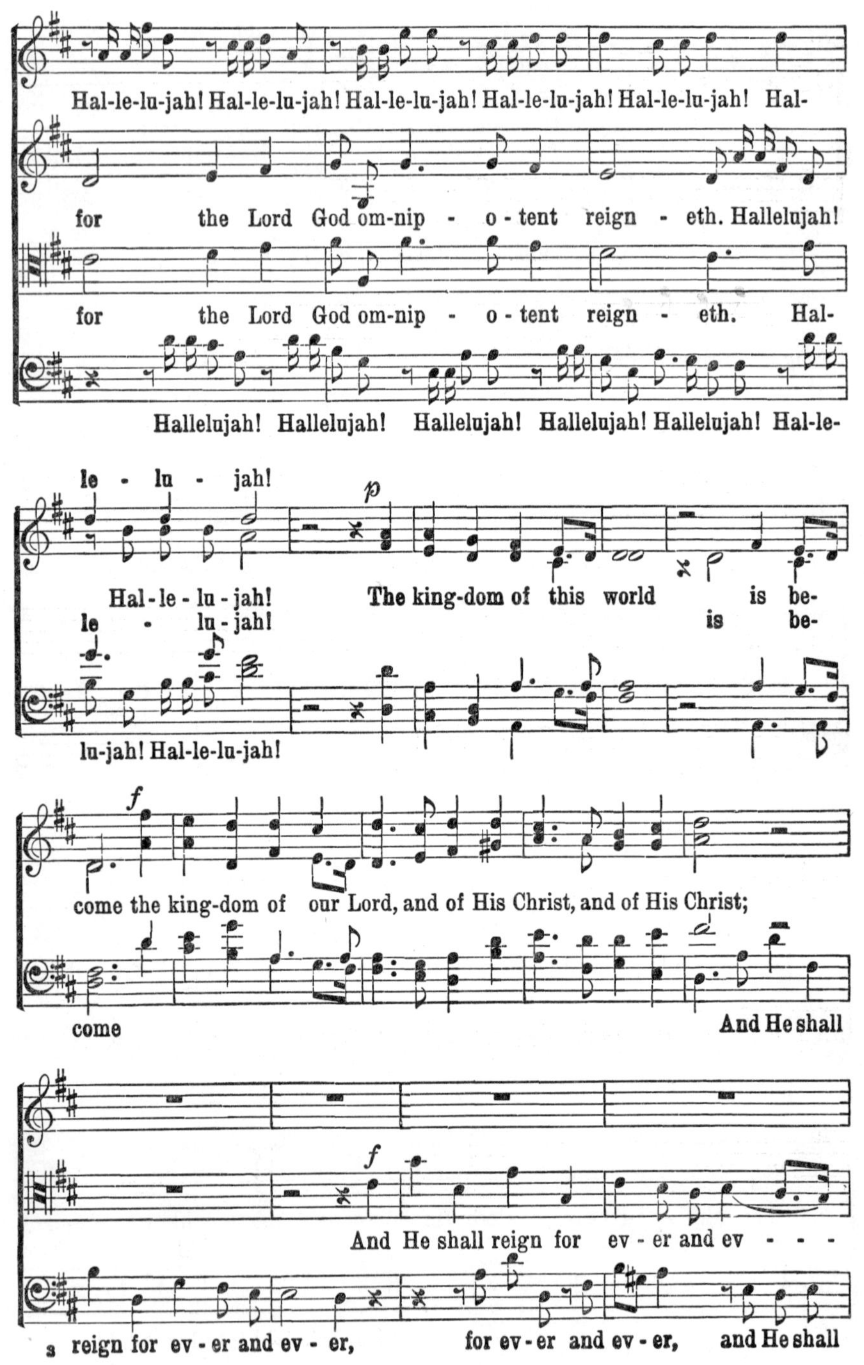

Hal-le-lu-jah! Hal-le-lu-jah! Hal-le-lu-jah! Hal-le-lu-jah! Hal-le-lu-jah! Hal-
for the Lord God om-nip - o-tent reign - eth. Hallelujah!
for the Lord God om-nip - o-tent reign - eth. Hal-
Hallelujah! Hallelujah! Hallelujah! Hallelujah! Hallelujah! Hal-le-
le - lu - jah!
Hal-le-lu-jah! The king-dom of this world is be-
le - lu-jah! is be-
lu-jah! Hal-le-lu-jah!
come the king-dom of our Lord, and of His Christ, and of His Christ;
come
And He shall
And He shall reign for ev-er and ev - - -
reign for ev-er and ev-er, for ev-er and ev-er, and He shall

Hallelujah Chorus

f
And
And He shall reign for ev - er and ev - er, for ev - er
er, And He shall reign for ev - er and ev - - - er,
reign, and He shall reign for ev - er, for ev - er, for ev - er, for
He shall reign for - ev - er and ev - - - er, King of kings, ...
and ev-er, for ev - er and ev-er, King of kings, ...
And He shall reign for ev-er and ev - er, for ev-er and
ev-er and ev-er, for ev - er,
. . . . and Lord of lords, ...
ev - er, Hal-le-lu-jah! Hal-le - lu-jah! for ev - er and
King of kings, ...
. . . .
ev - er, Hal-le-lu - jah! Hal-le - lu - jah! for ev - er and

Hallelujah Chorus
. . . . and Lord of lords, ...
ev - er, Hal-le - lu - jah! Hal-le - lu - jah! for ev - er and
. . . . King of kings, ...
ev - er, Hal-le - lu - jah! Hal-le - lu - jah! for ev - er and
. . . . and Lord of lords, ... and Lord of
ff
ev - er, Hal-le-lu-jah! Hal-le - lu - jah! King of kings, and Lord of
ff
f
lords, and He shall reign,
f
and He shall reign, ... and He shall
lords, and He shall reign for ev - - - - - er,
lords, and He shall reign for ev - er and ev - - - er,
He shall reign for ev - er and ev - - - er,
ff
reign . . . . for ev - er and ev - er, King of kings, for ev-er and
and He shall reign for ev - er and ev - er, King of kings, ...
ff

and He shall reign for ev-er and ev-er, King of kings, for ev-er and

Hallelujah Chorus

And He shall
ev - er, and Lord of lords, Hal-le - lu - jah! Hal-le - lu - jah! And
. . . . . and Lord of lords, ... And He shall
ev - er, and Lord of lords, Hal-le - lu - jah! Hal - le - lu - jah!
reign for ev - er, for ev - er and ev - er,
He shall reign for ev - er and ev - er, King of kings! and Lord of lords!
reign for ev - er, for ev - er and ev - er,
King of kings! and Lord of lords! And He shall reign for ev - er and ev-
And He shall reign for ev-er and ev - er, and ev-
er, King of kings! and Lord of lords! Hal-le - lu - jah!
er, for ev-er, and ev - er, for ev - er, and ev - er,
adagio
Hal-le - lu - jah! Hal - le - lu - jah! Hal - le - lu - jah! Hal - le - lu - jah!

478 Cast Thy Burden Upon the Lord

BIRMINGHAM

PSALM 55: 22; 16: 8

FELIX MENDELSSOHN

Cast thy bur - den up - on the Lord, And He shall sus-
tain thee: He nev - er shall suf - fer the
right - eous to fall; He is at thy right hand. Thy
mer - cy, Lord, is great, and far a - bove the heavens; Let
none be made a - sham - ed, that wait up - on Thee.

479 Be Still, My Soul

KATHARINA VON SCHLEGEL — FINLANDIA — JEAN SIBELIUS
Tr. by JANE L. BORTHWICK

1. Be still, my soul: the Lord is on thy side; . . . Bear pa-tient-ly the cross of grief or pain; Leave to thy God to or-der and pro-vide; . . . In ev-ery change He faith-ful will re-main. Be still, my soul: thy best, thy heaven-ly Friend, . . Thro' thorn-y ways leads to a joy-ful end. . .
2. Be still, my soul: thy God doth un-der-take . . . To guide the fu-ture as He has the past. Thy hope, thy con-fi-dence let noth-ing shake; . . All now mys-te-rious shall be bright at last. Be still, my soul: the waves and winds still know. . . . His voice who ruled them while He dwelt be-low. . .
3. Be still, my soul: the hour is has-tening on . . . . When we shall be for-ev-er with the Lord, When dis-ap-point-ment, grief, and fear are gone, . . . Sor-row for-got, love's pur-est joys re-stored. Be still, my soul: when change and tears are past, . . . All safe and bless-ed we shall meet at last. . .
A-MEN.

480 God Be with You

ENDEAVOR
J. E. Rankin
W. G. Tomer
1. God be with you till we meet a-gain, By His coun-sels guide, up-hold you,
2. God be with you till we meet a-gain, 'Neath His wings pro-tect-ing hide you,
3. God be with you till we meet a-gain; When life's per-ils thick confound you,
4. God be with you till we meet a-gain; Keep love's ban-ner float-ing o'er you;
With His sheep se-cure-ly fold you; God be with you till we meet a-gain.
Dai-ly man-na still pro-vide you; God be with you till we meet a-gain.
Put His arms un-fail-ing round you; God be with you till we meet a-gain.
Smite death's threatening wave before you; God be with you till we meet a-gain.
Chorus
Till we meet, . . . till we meet, Till we meet at Je-sus' feet;
Till we meet, till we meet, Till we meet;
Till we meet, . . . till we meet, God be with you till we meet a-gain.
Till we meet, till we meet,

481 Aids to Worship

Thomas Ken
DOXOLOGY
Louis Bourgeois
Praise God, from whom all blessings flow; Praise Him, all crea-tures here be - low;
Praise Him a - bove, ye heaven-ly host; Praise Fa-ther, Son, and Ho - ly Ghost.
482 The Lord Is In His Holy Temple
QUAM DILECTA
George F. Root
The Lord is in His ho - ly tem - ple, The Lord is in His ho - ly
tem - ple; Let all the earth keep si-lence, Let all the earth keep si-lence be-
fore Him, Keep si - lence, keep si - lence be - fore Him. A-MEN.

483 The Lord Is In His Holy Temple

S. S. Myers

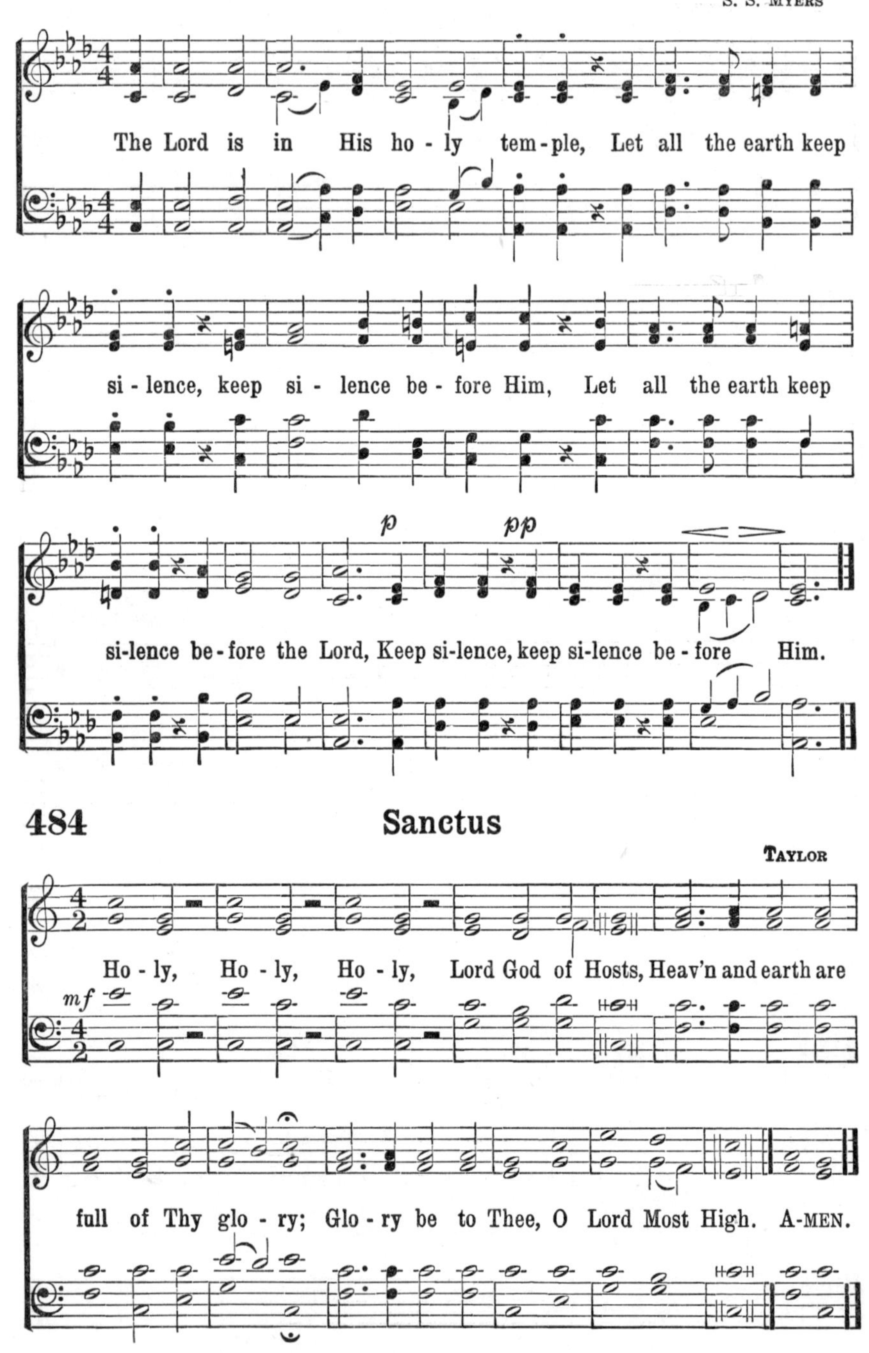
The Lord is in His ho - ly tem-ple, Let all the earth keep
si - lence, keep si - lence be - fore Him, Let all the earth keep
si-lence be-fore the Lord, Keep si-lence, keep si-lence be - fore Him.
p
pp
484
Sanctus
Taylor
mf
Ho - ly, Ho - ly, Ho - ly, Lord God of Hosts, Heav'n and earth are
full of Thy glo - ry; Glo - ry be to Thee, O Lord Most High. A-men.

485 Tread Softly

FANNY J. CROSBY
W. H. DOANE
Gently
p
1. Be si - lent, be si - lent, A whis - per is heard, Be si - lent, and lis - ten, O treas-ure each word!
2. Be si - lent, be si - lent, For ho - ly this place, This al - tar that ech - oes The mes-sage of grace.
3. Be si - lent, be si - lent, Breathe hum-bly our prayer, A fore-taste of E - den This mo-ment we share.
4. Be si - lent, be si - lent, His mer - cy re - cord, Be si - lent, be si - lent And wait on the Lord.
CHORUS
Tread soft - ly, tread soft - ly, The Mas - ter is here, Tread soft - ly, tread soft - ly, He bids us draw near.
Tread soft-ly here, tread soft-ly here,
Tread soft-ly here, tread soft-ly here,
p
p
rit.
486
Bless the Lord, O My Soul
IPPOLITOF-IVANOFF
Bless the Lord, O my soul, Bless-ed art Thou, O Lord. A-MEN.

487 Gracious Father, O Lord, Hear Us

Arr. from BEETHOVEN

Gra - cious Fa - ther, O Lord, hear us, When we call up-
on Thee; O Lord, hear us, Send down Thy love,
O Lord, up - on us; Mer - ci - ful Fa - ther, O Lord,
dim e rit.
pp
hear us; Hear our prayer, hear our prayer. A - MEN.
488 Almighty Father, Hear Our Prayer
MENDELSSOHN
pp
Al-might-y Fa - ther, hear our prayer, and bless all souls that wait before Thee. A-MEN.

489 Hear Our Prayer, O Lord

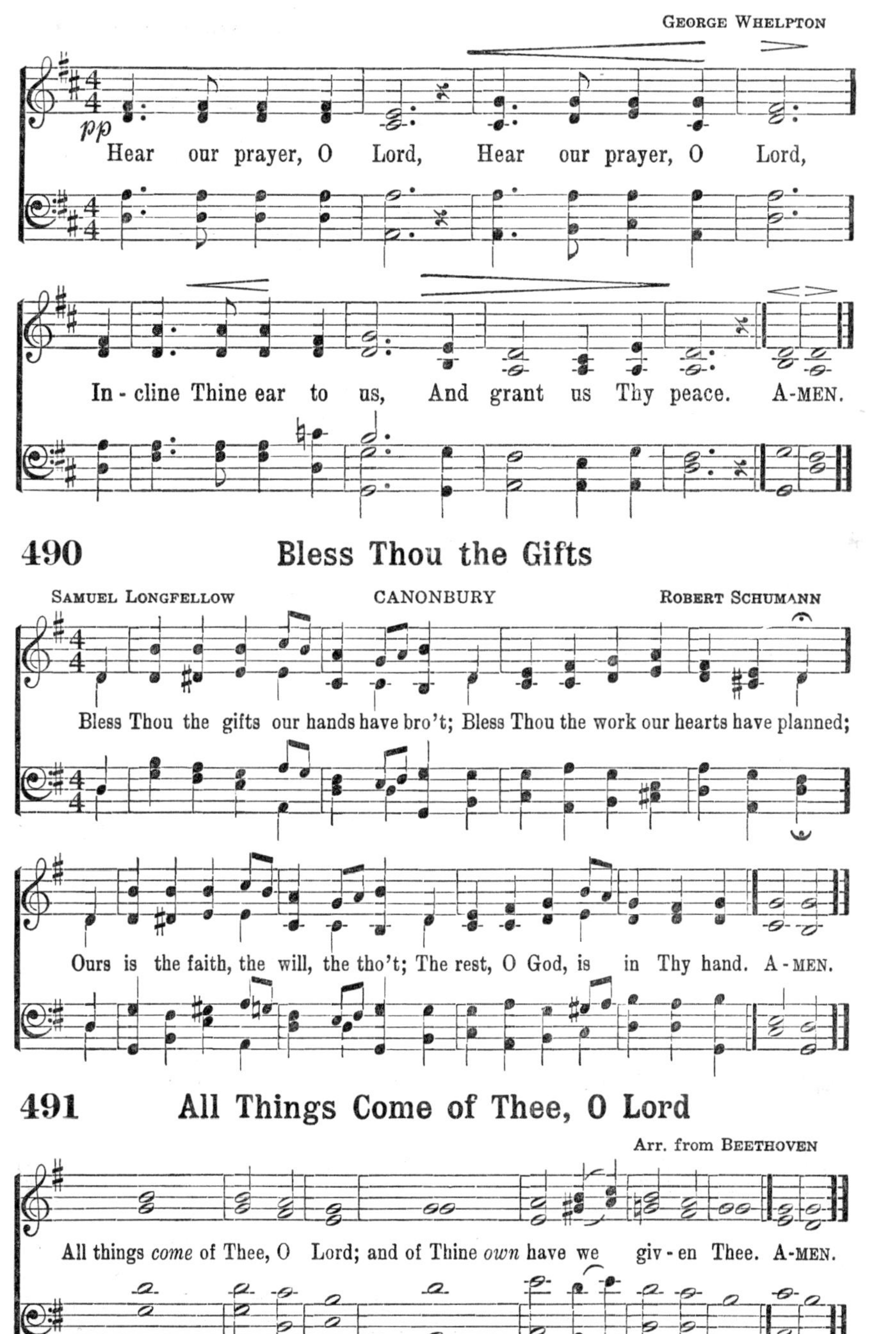
George Whelpton
pp
Hear our prayer, O Lord, Hear our prayer, O Lord,
In-cline Thine ear to us, And grant us Thy peace. A-men.
490 Bless Thou the Gifts
Samuel Longfellow
CANONBURY
Robert Schumann
Bless Thou the gifts our hands have bro't; Bless Thou the work our hearts have planned;
Ours is the faith, the will, the tho't; The rest, O God, is in Thy hand. A-men.
491 All Things Come of Thee, O Lord
Arr. from Beethoven
All things *come* of Thee, O Lord; and of Thine *own* have we giv-en Thee. A-men.

492 We Give Thee But Thine Own

William W. How — ST. ANDREW — Joseph Barnby

We give Thee but Thine own, What-e'er the gift may be; All
that we have is Thine a-lone, A trust, O Lord, from Thee. A-MEN.
493 All Things Are Thine
John G. Whittier
From "Pensum Sacrum"
Arr. by J. S. Bach
In unison
All things are Thine: no gift have we, Lord of all gifts, to
of-fer Thee; And hence with grate-ful hearts to-day,
Thine own be-fore Thy feet we lay. A-MEN.

494 Glory Be to the Father
GLORIA PATRI
Anonymous
First setting
Charles Meineke
Glo-ry be to the Fa-ther, and to the Son, and to the Ho-ly Ghost; As it
was in the be-gin-ning, is now, and ev-er shall be, world with-out end. A-men, A-men.
495 Glory Be to the Father
GLORIA PATRI
Anonymous
Second setting
H. W. Greatorex
Glo-ry be to the Fa-ther, and to the Son, and to the Ho-ly Ghost; As it
was in the be-gin-ning, is now, and ev-er shall be, world with-out end. A-men, A-men.
496 Glory Be to the Father
GLORIA PATRI
Third setting
Old Scottish Chant
Glory be to the Father, and to the Son, and to the Ho-ly Ghost;
As it was in the beginning, is now, and ev-er shall be, world with-out end. A-men.

497 Benediction

JOHN NEWTON B. B. MCKINNEY

May the grace of Christ our Sav-iour, And the Fa-ther's bound-less love,
With the Ho-ly Spir-it's fa-vor, Rest up-on us from a-bove. A-MEN.

498 The Lord Bless Thee and Keep Thee

NUMBERS 6: 24–26 B. B. MCKINNEY

The Lord bless thee and keep thee; The Lord make His face to shine up-

on thee, And be gra-cious un-to thee; The Lord lift up His

coun-te-nance up-on thee, And give thee peace, And give thee peace.

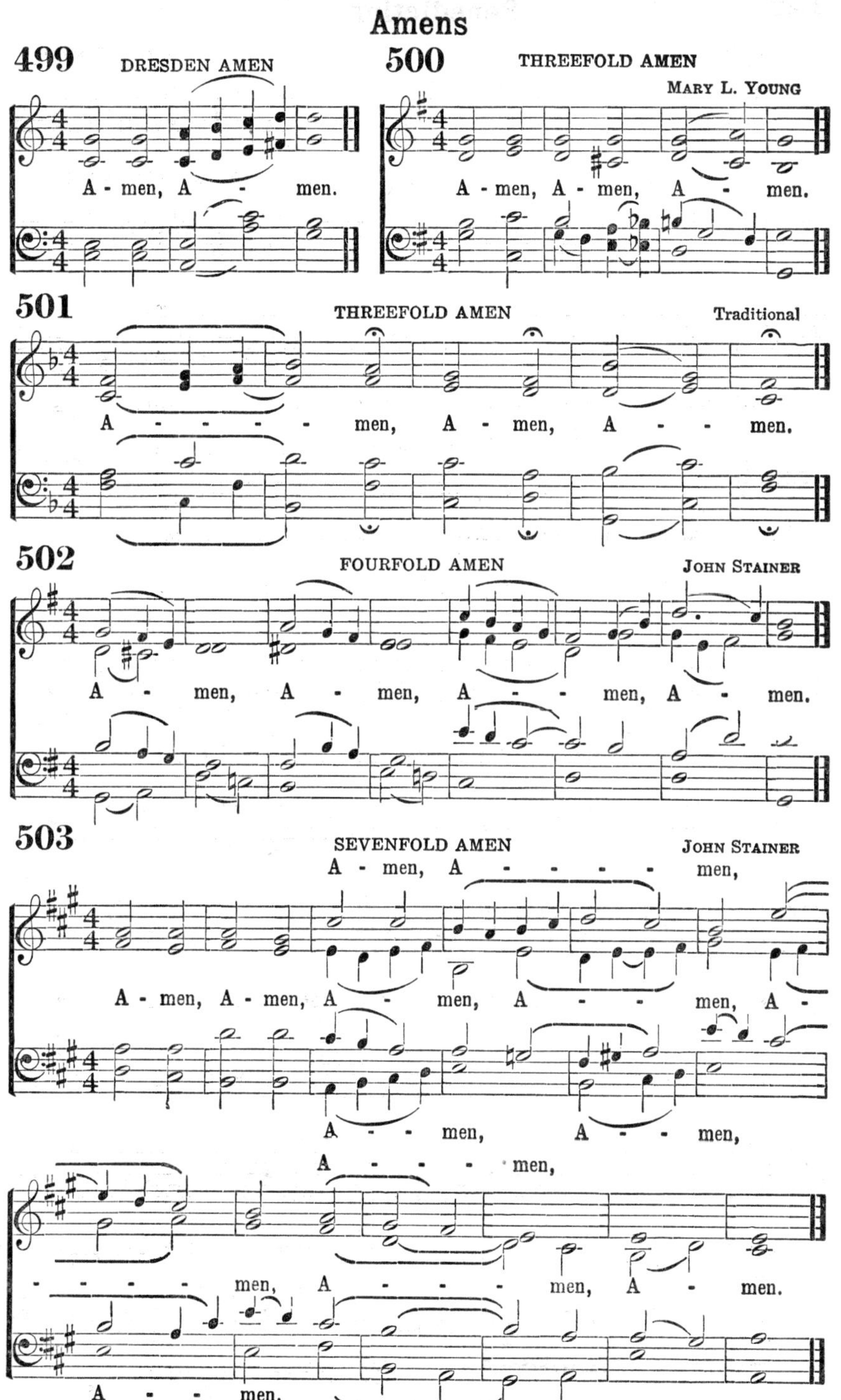
Amens
499
DRESDEN AMEN
A - men, A - men.
500
THREEFOLD AMEN
MARY L. YOUNG
A - men, A - men, A - men.
501
THREEFOLD AMEN
Traditional
A - - - - men, A - men, A - - men.
502
FOURFOLD AMEN
JOHN STAINER
A - men, A - men, A - - men, A - men.
503
SEVENFOLD AMEN
JOHN STAINER
A - men, A - - - - - men,
A - men, A - men, A - men, A - - men, A -
A - - men, A - - men,
A - - - - men,
- - - - men, A - - - - men, A - men.
A - - men,

DRAW NIGH UNTO GOD

Surely the Lord is in this place. This is none other than the house of God, and this is the gate of heaven.

The hour cometh, and now is, when the true worshippers shall worship the Father in spirit and in truth; for the Father seeketh such to worship him.

Serve the Lord with gladness; come before his presence with a song. Know ye that the Lord he is God: it is he that hath made us and not we ourselves; we are his people and the sheep of his pasture.

Know ye that the Lord he is God; it is he that hath made us, and not we ourselves; we are his people, and the sheep of his pasture. Enter into his gates with thanksgiving, and into his courts with praise.

O go your way into his gates with thanksgiving, and into his courts with praise. Be thankful unto him, and speak good of his name. For the Lord is good; his kindness endureth forever, and his faithfulness unto all generations.

Hope in the Lord; for with the Lord there is mercy, and with him is plenteous redemption. Humble yourselves under the mighty hand of God, and he shall lift you up. Draw nigh unto God, and he will draw nigh unto you.

—*From an Old Hymn Book*

RESPONSIVE READINGS

504 Adoration

Psalm 8

O Lord our Lord, how excellent is thy name in all the earth!

Who hast set thy glory above the heavens.

Out of the mouth of babes and sucklings hast thou ordained strength because of thine enemies, that thou mightest still the enemy and the avenger.

When I consider thy heavens, the work of thy fingers, the moon and the stars, which thou hast ordained;

What is man, that thou art mindful of him? and the son of man, that thou visitest him?

For thou hast made him a little lower than the angels, and hast crowned him with glory and honour.

Thou madest him to have dominion over the works of thy hands; thou hast put all things under his feet:

All sheep and oxen, yea, and the beasts of the field;

The fowl of the air, and the fish of the sea, and whatsoever passeth through the paths of the seas.

O Lord our Lord, how excellent is thy name in all the earth!

505 Praise

Psalm 96:1-10

O sing unto the Lord a new song: sing unto the Lord, all the earth.

Sing unto the Lord, bless his name; shew forth his salvation from day to day.

Declare his glory among the heathen, his wonders among all people.

For the Lord is great, and greatly to be praised: he is to be feared above all gods.

For all the gods of the nations are idols: but the Lord made the heavens.

Honour and majesty are before him: strength and beauty are in his sanctuary.

Give unto the Lord, O ye kindreds of the people, give unto the Lord glory and strength.

Give unto the Lord the glory due unto his name: bring an offering, and come into his courts.

O worship the Lord in the beauty of holiness: fear before him, all the earth.

Say among the heathen that the Lord reigneth: the world also shall be established that it shall not be moved: he shall judge the people righteously.

506 My Shepherd

Psalm 23; John 10:11, 14-17

The Lord is my shepherd; I shall not want.

He maketh me to lie down in green pastures: he leadeth me beside the still waters.

He restoreth my soul: he leadeth me in the paths of righteousness for his name's sake.

Yea, though I walk through the valley of the shadow of death, I will fear no evil: for thou art with me; thy rod and thy staff they comfort me.

Thou preparest a table before me in the presence of mine enemies: thou anointest my head with oil; my cup runneth over.

Surely goodness and mercy shall follow me all the days of my life: and I will dwell in the house of the Lord for ever.

I am the good shepherd: the good shepherd giveth his life for the sheep. . . . I am the good shepherd, and know my sheep, and am known of mine.

As the Father knoweth me, even so know I the Father: and I lay down my life for the sheep.

And other sheep I have, which are not of this fold: them also I must bring, and they shall hear my voice; and there shall be one fold, and one shepherd.

Therefore doth my Father love me, because I lay down my life, that I might take it again.

507 My Healer

Psalm 30:1-10, 11b-12

I will extol thee, O Lord; for thou hast lifted me up, and hast not made my foes to rejoice over me.

O Lord my God, I cried unto thee, and thou hast healed me.

O Lord, thou hast brought up my soul from the grave: thou hast kept me alive, that I should not go down to the pit.

Sing unto the Lord, O ye saints of his, and give thanks at the remembrance of his holiness.

For his anger endureth but a moment; in his favour is life: weeping may endure for a night, but joy cometh in the morning.

And in my prosperity I said, I shall never be moved.

Lord, by thy favour thou hast made my mountain to stand strong: thou didst hide thy face, and I was troubled.

I cried to thee, O Lord; and unto the Lord I made supplication.

What profit is there in my blood, when I go down to the pit? Shall the dust praise thee? shall it declare thy truth?

Hear, O Lord, and have mercy upon me: Lord, be thou my helper.

Thou hast put off my sackcloth, and girded me with gladness; to the end that my glory may sing praise to thee, and not be silent.

O Lord my God, I will give thanks unto thee for ever.

508 My Light

Psalm 27:1-11, 13-14

The Lord is my light and my salvation; whom shall I fear? the Lord is the strength of my life; of whom shall I be afraid?

When the wicked, even mine enemies and my foes, came upon me to eat up my flesh, they stumbled and fell.

Though an host should encamp against me, my heart shall not fear: though war should rise against me, in this will I be confident.

One thing have I desired of the Lord, that will I seek after;

That I may dwell in the house of the Lord all the days of my life, to behold the beauty of the Lord, and to enquire in his temple.

For in the time of trouble he shall hide me in his pavilion:

In the secret of his tabernacle shall he hide me; he shall set me up upon a rock.

And now shall mine head be lifted up above mine enemies round about me:

Therefore will I offer in his tabernacle sacrifices of joy; I will sing, yea, I will sing praises unto the Lord.

Hear, O Lord, when I cry with my voice: have mercy also upon me, and answer me.

When thou saidst, Seek ye my face; my heart said unto thee, Thy face, Lord, will I seek.

Hide not thy face far from me; put not thy servant away in anger: thou hast been my help; leave me not, neither forsake me, O God of my salvation.

When my father and my mother forsake me, then the Lord will take me up.

Teach me thy way, O Lord, and lead me in a plain path, because of mine enemies.

I had fainted, unless I had believed to see the goodness of the Lord in the land of the living.

Wait on the Lord: be of good courage, and he shall strengthen thine heart: wait I say, on the Lord.

509 My Help

Psalm 121

I will lift up mine eyes unto the hills, from whence cometh my help.

My help cometh from the Lord, which made heaven and earth.

He will not suffer thy foot to be moved: he that keepeth thee will not slumber.

Behold, he that keepeth Israel shall neither slumber nor sleep.

The Lord is thy keeper: the Lord is thy shade upon thy right hand.

The sun shall not smite thee by day, nor the moon by night.

The Lord shall preserve thee from all evil: he shall preserve thy soul.

The Lord shall preserve thy going out and thy coming in from this time forth, and even for evermore.

510 My Refuge

Psalm 91: 1-12, 15-16

He that dwelleth in the secret place of the most High shall abide under the shadow of the Almighty.

I will say of the Lord, He is my refuge and my fortress: my God; in him will I trust.

Surely he shall deliver thee from the snare of the fowler, and from the noisome pestilence.

He shall cover thee with his feathers, and under his wings shalt thou trust: his truth shall be thy shield and buckler.

Thou shalt not be afraid for the terror by night; nor for the arrow that flieth by day;

Nor for the pestilence that walketh in darkness; nor for the destruction that wasteth at noonday.

A thousand shall fall at thy side, and ten thousand at thy right hand; but it shall not come nigh thee.

Only with thine eyes shalt thou behold and see the reward of the wicked.

Because thou hast made the Lord, which is my refuge, even the most High, thy habitation;

There shall no evil befall thee, neither shall any plague come nigh thy dwelling.

For he shall give his angels charge over thee, to keep thee in all thy ways.

They shall bear thee up in their hands, lest thou dash thy foot against a stone.

He shall call upon me, and I will answer him: I will be with him in trouble; I will deliver him, and honour him.

With long life will I satisfy him, and shew him my salvation.

511 My King

Psalm 24

The earth is the Lord's, and the fulness thereof; the world, and they that dwell therein.

For he hath founded it upon the seas, and established it upon the floods.

Who shall ascend into the hill of the Lord? or who shall stand in his holy place?

He that hath clean hands, and a pure heart; who hath not lifted up his soul unto vanity, nor sworn deceitfully.

He shall receive the blessing from the Lord, and righteousness from the God of his salvation.

This is the generation of them that seek him, that seek thy face, O Jacob. Selah.

Lift up your heads, O ye gates; and be ye lift up, ye everlasting doors; and the King of glory shall come in.

Who is this King of glory? The Lord strong and mighty, the Lord mighty in battle.

Lift up your heads, O ye gates; even lift them up, ye everlasting doors; and the King of glory shall come in.

Who is this King of glory? The Lord of hosts, he is the King of glory.

512 God's Glory

Psalm 19:1-6; Isaiah 40:28-31

The heavens declare the glory of God; and the firmament sheweth his handywork.

Day unto day uttereth speech, and night unto night sheweth knowledge.

There is no speech nor language, where their voice is not heard.

Their line is gone out through all the earth, and their words to the end of the world. In them hath he set a tabernacle for the sun,

Which is as a bridegroom coming out of his chamber, and rejoiceth as a strong man to run a race.

His going forth is from the end of the heaven, and his circuit unto the ends of it: and there is nothing hid from the heat thereof.

Hast thou not known? hast thou not heard, that the everlasting God, the Lord, the Creator of the ends of the earth, fainteth not, neither is weary? there is no searching of his understanding.

He giveth power to the faint; and to them that have no might he increaseth strength.

Even the youths shall faint and be weary, and the young men shall utterly fall:

But they that wait upon the Lord shall renew their strength; they shall mount up with wings as eagles; they shall run, and not be weary; and they shall walk, and not faint.

513 God's Goodness

Psalm 34:8-19, 22

O taste and see that the Lord is good: blessed is the man that trusteth in him.

O fear the Lord, ye his saints: for there is no want to them that fear him.

The young lions do lack, and suffer hunger: but they that seek the Lord shall not want any good thing.

Come, ye children, hearken unto me: I will teach you the fear of the Lord.

What man is he that desireth life, and loveth many days, that he may see good?

Keep thy tongue from evil, and thy lips from speaking guile.

Depart from evil, and do good; seek peace, and pursue it.

The eyes of the Lord are upon the righteous, and his ears are open unto their cry.

The face of the Lord is against them that do evil, to cut off the remembrance of them from the earth.

The righteous cry, and the Lord heareth, and delivereth them out of all their troubles.

The Lord is nigh unto them that are of a broken heart; and saveth such as be of a contrite spirit.

Many are the afflictions of the righteous: but the Lord delivereth him out of them all. . . . The Lord redeemeth the soul of his servants.

514 God's Presence

Psalm 139:1-11, 23-24

O Lord, thou hast searched me, and known me.

Thou knowest my downsitting and mine uprising, thou understandest my thought afar off.

Thou compassest my path and my lying down, and art acquainted with all my ways.

For there is not a word in my tongue, but, lo, O Lord, thou knowest it altogether.

Thou hast beset me behind and before, and laid thine hand upon me.

Such knowledge is too wonderful for me; it is high, I cannot attain unto it.

Whither shall I go from thy spirit? or whither shall I flee from thy presence?

If I ascend up into heaven, thou art there: if I make my bed in hell, behold, thou art there.

If I take the wings of the morning, and dwell in the uttermost parts of the sea;

Even there shall thy hand lead me, and thy right hand shall hold me. If I say, Surely the darkness shall cover me; even the night shall be light about me.

Search me, O God, and know my heart: try me, and know my thoughts:

And see if there be any wicked way in me, and lead me in the way everlasting.

515 God's House

Psalm 84

How amiable are thy tabernacles, O Lord of hosts!

My soul longeth, yea, even fainteth for the courts of the Lord: my heart and my flesh crieth out for the living God.

Yea, the sparrow hath found an house, and the swallow a nest for herself, where she may lay her young, even thine altars, O Lord of hosts, my King, and my God.

Blessed are they that dwell in thy house: they will be still praising thee. Selah.

Blessed is the man whose strength is in thee; in whose heart are the ways of them.

Who passing through the valley of Baca make it a well; the rain also filleth the pools.

They go from strength to strength, every one of them in Zion appeareth before God.

O Lord God of hosts, hear my prayer: give ear, O God of Jacob.

Behold, O God our shield, and look upon the face of thine anointed.

For a day in thy courts is better than a thousand. I had rather be a doorkeeper in the house of my God, than to dwell in the tents of wickedness.

For the Lord God is a sun and shield: the Lord will give grace and glory: no good thing will he withhold from them that walk uprightly.

O Lord of hosts, blessed is the man that trusteth in thee.

516 God's Word

Psalm 19:7-14; 2 Timothy 3:16-17

The law of the Lord is perfect, converting the soul: the testimony of the Lord is sure, making wise the simple.

The statutes of the Lord are right, rejoicing the heart: the commandment of the Lord is pure, enlightening the eyes.

The fear of the Lord is clean, enduring for ever: the judgments of the Lord are true and righteous altogether.

More to be desired are they than gold, yea, than much fine gold: sweeter also than honey and the honeycomb.

Moreover by them is thy servant warned: and in keeping of them there is great reward.

Who can understand his errors? cleanse thou me from secret faults.

Keep back thy servant also from presumptuous sins; let them not have dominion over me: then shall I be upright, and I shall be innocent from the great transgression.

Let the words of my mouth, and the meditation of my heart, be acceptable in thy sight, O Lord, my strength, and my redeemer.

All scripture is given by inspiration of God, and is profitable for doctrine, for reproof, for correction, for instruction in righteousness:

That the man of God may be perfect, throughly furnished unto all good works.

517 God's Works

Psalm 145:3-13, 17

Great is the Lord, and greatly to be praised; and his greatness is unsearchable.

One generation shall praise thy works to another, and shall declare thy mighty acts.

I will speak of the glorious honour of thy majesty, and of thy wondrous works.

And men shall speak of the might of thy terrible acts: and I will declare thy greatness.

They shall abundantly utter the memory of thy great goodness, and shall sing of thy righteousness.

The Lord is gracious, and full of compassion; slow to anger, and of great mercy.

The Lord is good to all: and his tender mercies are over all his works.

All thy works shall praise thee, O Lord; and thy saints shall bless thee.

They shall speak of the glory of thy kingdom, and talk of thy power;

To make known to the sons of men his mighty acts, and the glorious majesty of his kingdom.

Thy kingdom is an everlasting kingdom, and thy dominion endureth throughout all generations.

The Lord is righteous in all his ways, and holy in all his works.

518 Christ Foretold

Isaiah 9:2-7; 7:14

The people that walked in darkness have seen a great light:

They that dwell in the land of the shadow of death, upon them hath the light shined.

Thou hast multiplied the nation, and not increased the joy:

They joy before thee according to the joy in harvest, and as men rejoice when they divide the spoil.

For thou hast broken the yoke of his burden, and the staff of his shoulder, the rod of his oppressor, as in the day of Midian.

For every battle of the warrior is with confused noise, and garments rolled in blood; but this shall be with burning and fuel of fire.

For unto us a child is born, unto us a son is given: and the government shall be upon his shoulder:

And his name shall be called Wonderful, Counsellor, The mighty God, The everlasting Father, The Prince of Peace.

Of the increase of his government and peace there shall be no end, upon the throne of David, and upon his kingdom, to order it, and to establish it with judgment and with justice from henceforth even for ever.

The zeal of the Lord of hosts will perform this.

The Lord himself shall give you a sign;

Behold, a virgin shall conceive, and bear a son, and shall call his name Immanuel.

519 Christ Fulfilling

Luke 2:7-16

And she brought forth her firstborn son, and wrapped him in swaddling clothes, and laid him in a manger; because there was no room for them in the inn.

And there were in the same country shepherds abiding in the field, keeping watch over their flock by night.

And, lo, the angel of the Lord came upon them, and the glory of the Lord shone round about them: and they were sore afraid.

And the angel said unto them, Fear not: for, behold, I bring you good tidings of great joy, which shall be to all people.

For unto you is born this day in the city of David a Saviour, which is Christ the Lord.

And this shall be a sign unto you; Ye shall find the babe wrapped in swaddling clothes, lying in a manger.

And suddenly there was with the angel a multitude of the heavenly host praising God, and saying,

Glory to God in the highest, and on earth peace, good will toward men.

And it came to pass, as the angels were gone away from them into heaven, the shepherds said one to another, Let us now go even unto Bethlehem, and see this thing which is come to pass.

And they came with haste, and found Mary, and Joseph, and the babe lying in a manger.

520 Christ Teaching

Matthew 5:3-14, 16

Blessed are the poor in spirit: for theirs is the kingdom of heaven.

Blessed are they that mourn: for they shall be comforted.

Blessed are the meek: for they shall inherit the earth.

Blessed are they which do hunger and thirst after righteousness: for they shall be filled.

Blessed are the merciful: for they shall obtain mercy.

Blessed are the pure in heart: for they shall see God.

Blessed are the peacemakers: for they shall be called the children of God.

Blessed are they which are persecuted for righteousness' sake: for theirs is the kingdom of heaven.

Blessed are ye, when men shall revile you, and persecute you, and shall say all manner of evil against you falsely, for my sake.

Rejoice, and be exceeding glad: for great is your reward in heaven: for so persecuted they the prophets which were before you.

Ye are the salt of the earth: but if the salt have lost his savour, wherewith shall it be salted? it is thenceforth good for nothing, but to be cast out, and to be trodden under foot of men.

Ye are the light of the world. A city that is set on an hill cannot be hid.

Let your light so shine before men, that they may see your good works, and glorify your Father which is in heaven.

521 Christ Forgiving

Mark 2:3-12

And they come unto him, bringing one sick of the palsy, which was borne of four.

And when they could not come nigh unto him for the press, they uncovered the roof where he was:

And when they had broken it up, they let down the bed wherein the sick of the palsy lay.

When Jesus saw their faith, he said unto the sick of the palsy, Son, thy sins be forgiven thee.

But there were certain of the scribes sitting there, and reasoning in their hearts,

Why doth this man thus speak blasphemies? who can forgive sins but God only?

And immediately when Jesus perceived in his spirit that they so reasoned within themselves, he said unto them, Why reason ye these things in your hearts?

Whether is it easier to say to the sick of the palsy, Thy sins be forgiven thee; or to say, Arise, and take up thy bed, and walk?

But that ye may know that the Son of man hath power on earth to forgive sins, (he saith to the sick of the palsy,)

I say unto thee, Arise, and take up thy bed, and go thy way into thine house.

And immediately he arose, took up the bed, and went forth before them all; insomuch that they were all amazed, and glorified God, saying, We never saw it on this fashion.

522 Christ Healing

Luke 4:38-40; 17:12-17, 19

And he arose out of the synagogue, and entered into Simon's house.

And Simon's wife's mother was taken with a great fever; and they besought him for her.

And he stood over her, and rebuked the fever; and it left her: and immediately she arose and ministered unto them.

Now when the sun was setting, all they that had any sick with divers diseases brought them unto him;

And he laid his hands on every one of them, and healed them.

And as he entered into a certain village, there met him ten men that were lepers, which stood afar off:

And they lifted up their voices, and said, Jesus, Master, have mercy on us.

And when he saw them, he said unto them, Go shew yourselves unto the priests. And it came to pass, that, as they went, they were cleansed.

And one of them, when he saw that he was healed, turned back, and with a loud voice glorified God,

And fell down on his face at his feet, giving him thanks: and he was a Samaritan.

And Jesus answering said, Were there not ten cleansed? but where are the nine?

And he said unto him, Arise, go thy way: thy faith hath made thee whole.

523 Christ Sustaining

John 6:5-14

When Jesus then lifted up his eyes, and saw a great company come unto him, he saith unto Philip, Whence shall we buy bread, that these may eat?

And this he said to prove him: for he himself knew what he would do.

Philip answered him, Two hundred pennyworth of bread is not sufficient for them, that every one of them may take a little.

One of his disciples, Andrew, Simon Peter's brother, saith unto him,

There is a lad here, which hath five barley loaves, and two small fishes: but what are they among so many?

And Jesus said, Make the men sit down. Now there was much grass in the place. So the men sat down, in number about five thousand.

And Jesus took the loaves; and when he had given thanks, he distributed to the disciples, and the disciples to them that were set down; and likewise of the fishes as much as they would.

When they were filled, he said unto his disciples, Gather up the fragments that remain, that nothing be lost.

Therefore they gathered them together, and filled twelve baskets with the fragments of the five barley loaves, which remained over and above unto them that had eaten.

Then those men, when they had seen the miracle that Jesus did, said, This is of a truth that prophet that should come into the world.

524 Christ Inviting

Matthew 11:28-30; Isaiah 55:1-3; John 6:37-38, 40

Come unto me, all ye that labour and are heavy laden, and I will give you rest.

Take my yoke upon you, and learn of me; for I am meek and lowly in heart:

And ye shall find rest unto your souls.

For my yoke is easy, and my burden is light.

Ho, every one that thirsteth, come ye to the waters, and he that hath no money; come ye, buy, and eat; yea, come, buy wine and milk without money and without price.

Wherefore do ye spend money for that which is not bread? and your labour for that which satisfieth not? hearken diligently unto me, and eat ye that which is good, and let your soul delight itself in fatness.

Incline your ear, and come unto me: hear, and your soul shall live; and I will make an everlasting covenant with you, even the sure mercies of David.

All that the Father giveth me shall come to me: and him that cometh to me I will in no wise cast out.

For I came down from heaven, not to do mine own will, but the will of him that sent me.

And this is the will of him that sent me, that every one which seeth the Son, and believeth on him, may have everlasting life: and I will raise him up at the last day.

525 Christ Accepted

Matthew 16:13-18; John 6:66-69; 3:36

When Jesus came into the coasts of Caesarea Philippi, he asked his disciples, saying, Whom do men say that I the Son of man am?

And they said, Some say that thou art John the Baptist: some, Elias; and others, Jeremias, or one of the prophets.

He saith unto them, But whom say ye that I am?

And Simon Peter answered and said, Thou art the Christ, the Son of the living God.

And Jesus answered and said unto him, Blessed art thou, Simon Bar-jona: for flesh and blood hath not revealed it unto thee, but my Father which is in heaven.

And I say also unto thee, That thou art Peter, and upon this rock I will build my church; and the gates of hell shall not prevail against it.

From that time many of his disciples went back, and walked no more with him.

Then said Jesus unto the twelve, Will ye also go away?

Then Simon Peter answered him, Lord, to whom shall we go? thou hast the words of eternal life.

And we believe and are sure that thou art that Christ, the Son of the living God.

He that believeth on the Son hath everlasting life.

526 Christ Saving

John 3:14-21; 20:31

And as Moses lifted up the serpent in the wilderness, even so must the Son of man be lifted up:

That whosoever believeth in him should not perish, but have eternal life.

For God so loved the world, that he gave his only begotten Son, that whosoever believeth in him should not perish, but have everlasting life.

For God sent not his Son into the world to condemn the world; but that the world through him might be saved.

He that believeth on him is not condemned: but he that believeth not is condemned already, because he hath not believed in the name of the only begotten Son of God.

And this is the condemnation, that light is come into the world, and men loved darkness rather than light, because their deeds were evil.

For every one that doeth evil hateth the light, neither cometh to the light, lest his deeds should be reproved.

But he that doeth truth cometh to the light, that his deeds may be made manifest, that they are wrought in God.

These are written, that ye might believe that Jesus is the Christ, the Son of God;

And that believing ye might have life through his name.

527 Christ Commanding

Matthew 28:16-20; Acts 1:8-11

Then the eleven disciples went away into Galilee, into a mountain where Jesus had appointed them.

And when they saw him, they worshipped him: but some doubted.

And Jesus came and spake unto them, saying, All power is given unto me in heaven and in earth.

Go ye therefore, and teach all nations, baptizing them in the name of the Father, and of the Son, and of the Holy Ghost:

Teaching them to observe all things whatsoever I have commanded you:

And, lo, I am with you alway, even unto the end of the world. Amen.

But ye shall receive power, after that the Holy Ghost is come upon you:

And ye shall be witnesses unto me both in Jerusalem, and in all Judaea, and in Samaria, and unto the uttermost part of the earth.

And when he had spoken these things, while they beheld, he was taken up; and a cloud received him out of their sight.

And while they looked stedfastly toward heaven as he went up, behold, two men stood by them in white apparel;

Which also said, Ye men of Galilee, why stand ye gazing up into heaven?

This same Jesus, which is taken up from you into heaven, shall so come in like manner as ye have seen him go into heaven.

528 Christ Reigning

1 Corinthians 15:3-4, 19-28

For I delivered unto you first of all that which I also received, how that Christ died for our sins according to the scriptures;

And that he was buried, and that he rose again the third day according to the scriptures:

If in this life only we have hope in Christ, we are of all men most miserable.

But now is Christ risen from the dead, and become the firstfruits of them that slept.

For since by man came death, by man came also the resurrection of the dead.

For as in Adam all die, even so in Christ shall all be made alive.

But every man in his own order: Christ the firstfruits; afterward they that are Christ's at his coming.

Then cometh the end, when he shall have delivered up the kingdom to God, even the Father; when he shall have put down all rule and all authority and power.

For he must reign, till he hath put all enemies under his feet.

The last enemy that shall be destroyed is death.

For he hath put all things under his feet.

And when all things shall be subdued unto him, then shall the Son also himself be subject unto him that put all things under him, that God may be all in all.

529 Christ Returning

Daniel 7:13-14; 1 Thessalonians 4:13-18

I saw in the night visions, and, behold, one like the Son of man came with the clouds of heaven, and came to the Ancient of days, and they brought him near before him.

And there was given him dominion, and glory, and a kingdom, that all people, nations, and languages, should serve him:

His dominion is an everlasting dominion, which shall not pass away, and his kingdom that which shall not be destroyed.

But I would not have you to be ignorant, brethren, concerning them which are asleep, that ye sorrow not, even as others which have no hope.

For if we believe that Jesus died and rose again, even so them also which sleep in Jesus will God bring with him.

For this we say unto you by the word of the Lord, that we which are alive and remain unto the coming of the Lord shall not prevent them which are asleep.

For the Lord himself shall descend from heaven with a shout, with the voice of the archangel, and with the trump of God: and the dead in Christ shall rise first:

Then we which are alive and remain shall be caught up together with them in the clouds, to meet the Lord in the air: and so shall we ever be with the Lord.

Wherefore comfort one another with these words.

530 Christ All and in All

Colossians 3:1-11, 16

If ye then be risen with Christ, seek those things which are above, where Christ sitteth on the right hand of God.

Set your affection on things above, not on things on the earth.

For ye are dead, and your life is hid with Christ in God.

When Christ, who is our life, shall appear, then shall ye also appear with him in glory.

Mortify therefore your members which are upon the earth; fornication, uncleanness, inordinate affection, evil concupiscence, and covetousness, which is idolatry:

For which things' sake the wrath of God cometh on the children of disobedience:

In the which ye also walked some time, when ye lived in them.

But now ye also put off all these; anger, wrath, malice, blasphemy, filthy communication out of your mouth.

Lie not one to another, seeing that ye have put off the old man with his deeds;

And have put on the new man, which is renewed in knowledge after the image of him that created him:

Where there is neither Greek nor Jew, circumcision nor uncircumcision, Barbarian, Scythian, bond nor free: but Christ is all, and in all.

Let the word of Christ dwell in you richly in all wisdom.

531 The Holy Spirit

John 14:16-17, 26; 16:7-14

And I will pray the Father, and he shall give you another Comforter, that he may abide with you for ever;

Even the Spirit of truth; whom the world cannot receive, because it seeth him not, neither knoweth him: but ye know him; for he dwelleth with you, and shall be in you.

But the Comforter, which is the Holy Ghost, whom the Father will send in my name, he shall teach you all things, and bring all things to your remembrance, whatsoever I have said unto you.

Nevertheless I tell you the truth; It is expedient for you that I go away: for if I go not away, the Comforter will not come unto you; but if I depart, I will send him unto you.

And when he is come, he will reprove the world of sin, and of righteousness, and of judgment:

Of sin, because they believe not on me;

Of righteousness, because I go to my Father, and ye see me no more;

Of judgment, because the prince of this world is judged.

I have yet many things to say unto you, but ye cannot bear them now.

Howbeit when he, the Spirit of truth, is come, he will guide you into all truth: for he shall not speak of himself; but whatsoever he shall hear, that shall he speak: and he will shew you things to come.

He shall glorify me: for he shall receive of mine, and shall shew it unto you.

532 Church Ordinances

Matthew 3:13-17; 26:26-30

Then cometh Jesus from Galilee to Jordan unto John, to be baptized of him.

But John forbad him, saying, I have need to be baptized of thee, and comest thou to me?

And Jesus answering said unto him, Suffer it to be so now: for thus it becometh us to fulfil all righteousness. Then he suffered him.

And Jesus, when he was baptized, went up straightway out of the water: and, lo, the heavens were opened unto him, and he saw the Spirit of God descending like a dove, and lighting upon him:

And lo a voice from heaven, saying, This is my beloved Son, in whom I am well pleased.

And as they were eating, Jesus took bread, and blessed it, and brake it, and gave it to the disciples, and said, Take, eat; this is my body.

And he took the cup, and gave thanks, and gave it to them, saying, Drink ye all of it;

For this is my blood of the new testament, which is shed for many for the remission of sins.

But I say unto you, I will not drink henceforth of this fruit of the vine, until that day when I drink it new with you in my Father's kingdom.

And when they had sung an hymn, they went out into the mount of Olives.

533 Church Officers

1 Timothy 3:1-10, 13

This is a true saying, If a man desire the office of a bishop, he desireth a good work.

A bishop then must be blameless, the husband of one wife, vigilant, sober, of good behaviour, given to hospitality, apt to teach;

Not given to wine, no striker, not greedy of filthy lucre; but patient, not a brawler, not covetous;

One that ruleth well his own house, having his children in subjection with all gravity;

(For if a man know not how to rule his own house, how shall he take care of the church of God?)

Not a novice, lest being lifted up with pride he fall into the condemnation of the devil.

Moreover he must have a good report of them which are without; lest he fall into reproach and the snare of the devil.

Likewise must the deacons be grave, not doubletongued, not given to much wine, not greedy of filthy lucre;

Holding the mystery of the faith in a pure conscience.

And let these also first be proved; then let them use the office of a deacon, being found blameless.

For they that have used the office of a deacon well purchase to themselves a good degree, and great boldness in the faith which is in Christ Jesus.

534 The Commandments

Exodus 20:3-5a, 7-8, 12-17; Matthew 22:36-39

Thou shalt have no other gods before me.

Thou shalt not make unto thee any graven image, or any likeness of any thing that is in heaven above, or that is in the earth beneath, or that is in the water under the earth: Thou shalt not bow down thyself to them, nor serve them:

Thou shalt not take the name of the Lord thy God in vain; for the Lord will not hold him guiltless that taketh his name in vain.

Remember the sabbath day, to keep it holy.

Honour thy father and thy mother: that thy days may be long upon the land which the Lord thy God giveth thee.

Thou shalt not kill.

Thou shalt not commit adultery.

Thou shalt not steal.

Thou shalt not bear false witness against thy neighbour.

Thou shalt not covet.

Master, which is the great commandment in the law?

Jesus said unto him, Thou shalt love the Lord thy God with all thy heart, and with all thy soul, and with all thy mind.

This is the first and great commandment.

And the second is like unto it, Thou shalt love thy neighbour as thyself.

535 Faithfulness

Matthew 24:45-47; Luke 16:10-13; Revelation 2:10b; 1 Corinthians 15:57-58

Who then is a faithful and wise servant, whom his lord hath made ruler over his household, to give them meat in due season?

Blessed is that servant, whom his lord when he cometh shall find so doing.

Verily I say unto you, That he shall make him ruler over all his goods.

He that is faithful in that which is least is faithful also in much: and he that is unjust in the least is unjust also in much.

If therefore ye have not been faithful in the unrighteous mammon, who will commit to your trust the true riches?

And if ye have not been faithful in that which is another man's, who shall give you that which is your own?

No servant can serve two masters: for either he will hate the one, and love the other; or else he will hold to the one, and despise the other. Ye cannot serve God and mammon.

Be thou faithful unto death, and I will give thee a crown of life.

Thanks be to God, which giveth us the victory through our Lord Jesus Christ.

Therefore, my beloved brethren, be ye stedfast, unmoveable, always abounding in the work of the Lord, forasmuch as ye know that your labour is not in vain in the Lord.

536 Obedience

John 15:10, 14; 1 John 2:3-6
Revelation 22:7-14

If ye keep my commandments, ye shall abide in my love; even as I have kept my Father's commandments, and abide in his love.

Ye are my friends, if ye do whatsoever I command you.

And hereby we do know that we know him, if we keep his commandments.

He that saith, I know him, and keepeth not his commandments, is a liar, and the truth is not in him.

But whoso keepeth his word, in him verily is the love of God perfected: hereby know we that we are in him.

He that saith he abideth in him ought himself also so to walk, even as he walked.

Behold, I come quickly: blessed is he that keepeth the sayings of the prophecy of this book.

And I John saw these things and heard them. And when I had heard and seen, I fell down to worship before the feet of the angel which shewed me these things.

Then saith he unto me, See thou do it not: for I am thy fellowservant, and of thy brethren the prophets, and of them which keep the sayings of this book: worship God.

And he saith unto me, Seal not the sayings of the prophecy of this book: for the time is at hand.

He that is unjust, let him be unjust still: and he which is filthy, let him be filthy still: and he that is righteous, let him be righteous still: and he that is holy, let him be holy still.

And, behold, I come quickly; and my reward is with me, to give every man according as his work shall be.

I am Alpha and Omega, the beginning and the end, the first and the last.

Blessed are they that do his commandments, that they may have right to the tree of life.

537 Patience

James 1:3-4; 5:7-8; 2 Peter 1:4-7

Knowing this, that the trying of your faith worketh patience.

But let patience have her perfect work, that ye may be perfect and entire, wanting nothing.

Be patient therefore, brethren, unto the coming of the Lord. Behold, the husbandman waiteth for the precious fruit of the earth, and hath long patience for it, until he receive the early and latter rain.

Be ye also patient; stablish your hearts: for the coming of the Lord draweth nigh.

Whereby are given unto us exceeding great and precious promises: that by these ye might be partakers of the divine nature, having escaped the corruption that is in the world through lust.

And beside this, giving all diligence, add to your faith virtue; and to virtue knowledge;

And to knowledge temperance; and to temperance patience; and to patience godliness;

And to godliness brotherly kindness; and to brotherly kindness charity.

538 Liberality

Psalm 41:1-3; Mark 12:41-44; 2 Corinthians 8:1-5

Blessed is he that considereth the poor: the Lord will deliver him in time of trouble.

The Lord will preserve him, and keep him alive; and he shall be blessed upon the earth: and thou wilt not deliver him unto the will of his enemies.

The Lord will strengthen him upon the bed of languishing: thou wilt make all his bed in his sickness.

And Jesus sat over against the treasury, and beheld how the people cast money into the treasury: and many that were rich cast in much.

And there came a certain poor widow, and she threw in two mites, which make a farthing.

And he called unto him his disciples, and saith unto them, Verily I say unto you, That this poor widow hath cast more in, than all they which have cast into the treasury:

For all they did cast in of their abundance; but she of her want did cast in all that she had, even all her living.

Moreover, brethren, we do you to wit of the grace of God bestowed on the churches of Macedonia;

How that in a great trial of affliction the abundance of their joy and their deep poverty abounded unto the riches of their liberality.

For to their power, I bear record, yea, and beyond their power they were willing of themselves;

Praying us with much intreaty that we would receive the gift, and take upon us the fellowship of the ministering to the saints.

And this they did, not as we hoped, but first gave their own selves to the Lord, and unto us by the will of God.

539 Missions

Mark 16:15; Romans 10:8-15

And he said unto them, Go ye into all the world, and preach the gospel to every creature.

But what saith it? The word is nigh thee, even in thy mouth, and in thy heart: that is, the word of faith, which we preach;

That if thou shalt confess with thy mouth the Lord Jesus, and shalt believe in thine heart that God hath raised him from the dead, thou shalt be saved.

For with the heart man believeth unto righteousness; and with the mouth confession is made unto salvation.

For the scripture saith, Whosoever believeth on him shall not be ashamed.

For there is no difference between the Jew and the Greek: for the same Lord over all is rich unto all that call upon him.

For whosoever shall call upon the name of the Lord shall be saved.

How then shall they call on him in whom they have not believed? and how shall they believe in him of whom they have not heard?

And how shall they hear without a preacher?

And how shall they preach, except they be sent?

540 Revival

Psalm 85

Lord, thou hast been favourable unto thy land: thou hast brought back the captivity of Jacob.

Thou hast forgiven the iniquity of thy people, thou hast covered all their sin. Selah.

Thou hast taken away all thy wrath: thou hast turned thyself from the fierceness of thine anger.

Turn us, O God of our salvation, and cause thine anger toward us to cease.

Wilt thou be angry with us for ever? wilt thou draw out thine anger to all generations?

Wilt thou not revive us again: that thy people may rejoice in thee?

Shew us thy mercy, O Lord, and grant us thy salvation.

I will hear what God the Lord will speak: for he will speak peace unto his people, and to his saints: but let them not turn again to folly.

Surely his salvation is nigh them that fear him; that glory may dwell in our land.

Mercy and truth are met together; righteousness and peace have kissed each other.

Truth shall spring out of the earth; and righteousness shall look down from heaven.

Yea, the Lord shall give that which is good; and our land shall yield her increase.

Righteousness shall go before him; and shall set us in the way of his steps.

541 Repentance

Psalm 51:1-4, 7-13, 16-17

Have mercy upon me, O God, according to thy lovingkindness: according unto the multitude of thy tender mercies blot out my transgressions.

Wash me throughly from mine iniquity, and cleanse me from my sin.

For I acknowledge my transgressions: and my sin is ever before me.

Against thee, thee only, have I sinned, and done this evil in thy sight: that thou mightest be justified when thou speakest, and be clear when thou judgest.

Purge me with hyssop, and I shall be clean: wash me, and I shall be whiter than snow.

Make me to hear joy and gladness; that the bones which thou hast broken may rejoice.

Hide thy face from my sins, and blot out all mine iniquities.

Create in me a clean heart, O God; and renew a right spirit within me.

Cast me not away from thy presence; and take not thy holy spirit from me.

Restore unto me the joy of thy salvation; and uphold me with thy free spirit.

Then will I teach transgressors thy ways: and sinners shall be converted unto thee.

For thou desirest not sacrifice; else would I give it: thou delightest not in burnt offering.

The sacrifices of God are a broken spirit: a broken and a contrite heart, O God, thou wilt not despise.

542 Gospel

Isaiah 52:7-10; Matthew 4:23; Luke 4:18-19; Romans 1:16

How beautiful upon the mountains are the feet of him that bringeth good tidings, that publisheth peace;

That bringeth good tidings of good, that publisheth salvation; that saith unto Zion, Thy God reigneth!

Thy watchmen shall lift up the voice; with the voice together shall they sing:

For they shall see eye to eye, when the Lord shall bring again Zion.

Break forth into joy, sing together, ye waste places of Jerusalem:

For the Lord hath comforted his people, he hath redeemed Jerusalem.

The Lord hath made bare his holy arm in the eyes of all the nations; and all the ends of the earth shall see the salvation of our God.

And Jesus went about all Galilee, teaching in their synagogues, and preaching the gospel of the kingdom, and healing all manner of sickness.

The Spirit of the Lord is upon me, because he hath anointed me to preach the gospel to the poor;

He hath sent me to heal the brokenhearted, to preach deliverance to the captives, and recovering of sight to the blind, to set at liberty them that are bruised,

To preach the acceptable year of the Lord.

For I am not ashamed of the gospel of Christ: for it is the power of God unto salvation to every one that believeth.

543 Grace

Ephesians 2:4-8; Titus 2:11-14; 3:5-7

But God, who is rich in mercy, for his great love wherewith he loved us,

Even when we were dead in sins, hath quickened us together with Christ, (by grace ye are saved;)

And hath raised us up together, and made us sit together in heavenly places in Christ Jesus:

That in the ages to come he might shew the exceeding riches of his grace in his kindness toward us through Christ Jesus.

For by grace are ye saved through faith; and that not of yourselves: it is the gift of God:

For the grace of God that bringeth salvation hath appeared to all men,

Teaching us that, denying ungodliness and worldly lusts, we should live soberly, righteously, and godly, in this present world;

Looking for that blessed hope, and the glorious appearing of the great God and our Saviour Jesus Christ;

Who gave himself for us, that he might redeem us from all iniquity, and purify unto himself a peculiar people, zealous of good works.

Not by works of righteousness which we have done, but according to his mercy he saved us, by the washing of regeneration, and renewing of the Holy Ghost;

Which he shed on us abundantly through Jesus Christ our Saviour;

That being justified by his grace, we should be made heirs according to the hope of eternal life.

544 Justification

Romans 5:1-11

Therefore being justified by faith, we have peace with God through our Lord Jesus Christ:

By whom also we have access by faith into this grace wherein we stand, and rejoice in hope of the glory of God.

And not only so, but we glory in tribulations also: knowing that tribulation worketh patience;

And patience, experience; and experience, hope:

And hope maketh not ashamed; because the love of God is shed abroad in our hearts by the Holy Ghost which is given unto us.

For when we were yet without strength, in due time Christ died for the ungodly.

For scarcely for a righteous man will one die: yet peradventure for a good man some would even dare to die.

But God commendeth his love toward us, in that, while we were yet sinners, Christ died for us.

Much more then, being now justified by his blood, we shall be saved from wrath through him.

For if, when we were enemies, we were reconciled to God by the death of his Son, much more, being reconciled, we shall be saved by his life.

And not only so, but we also joy in God through our Lord Jesus Christ, by whom we have now received the atonement.

545 Restoration

Galatians 6:1-10, 14

Brethren, if a man be overtaken in a fault, ye which are spiritual, restore such an one in the spirit of meekness; considering thyself, lest thou also be tempted.

Bear ye one another's burdens, and so fulfil the law of Christ.

For if a man think himself to be something, when he is nothing, he deceiveth himself.

But let every man prove his own work, and then shall he have rejoicing in himself alone, and not in another.

For every man shall bear his own burden.

Let him that is taught in the word communicate unto him that teacheth in all good things.

Be not deceived; God is not mocked: for whatsoever a man soweth, that shall he also reap.

For he that soweth to his flesh shall of the flesh reap corruption; but he that soweth to the Spirit shall of the Spirit reap life everlasting.

And let us not be weary in well doing: for in due season we shall reap, if we faint not.

As we have therefore opportunity, let us do good unto all men, especially unto them who are of the household of faith.

But God forbid that I should glory, save in the cross of our Lord Jesus Christ, by whom the world is crucified unto me, and I unto the world.

546 Works

James 2:14-24

What doth it profit, my brethren, though a man say he hath faith, and have not works? can faith save him?

If a brother or sister be naked, and destitute of daily food,

And one of you say unto them, Depart in peace, be ye warmed and filled; notwithstandnig ye give them not those things which are needful to the body; what doth it profit?

Even so faith, if it hath not works, is dead, being alone.

Yea, a man may say, Thou hast faith, and I have works: shew me thy faith without thy works, and I will shew thee my faith by my works.

Thou believest that there is one God; thou doest well: the devils also believe, and tremble.

But wilt thou know, O vain man, that faith without works is dead?

Was not Abraham our father justified by works, when he had offered Isaac his son upon the altar?

Seest thou how faith wrought with his works, and by works was faith made perfect?

And the scripture was fulfilled which saith, Abraham believed God, and it was imputed unto him for righteousness: and he was called the Friend of God.

Ye see then how that by works a man is justified, and not by faith only.

547 Wisdom

Proverbs 3:13-23; James 1:5

Happy is the man that findeth wisdom, and the man that getteth understanding.

For the merchandise of it is better than the merchandise of silver, and the gain thereof than fine gold.

She is more precious than rubies: and all the things thou canst desire are not to be compared unto her.

Length of days is in her right hand; and in her left hand riches and honour.

Her ways are ways of pleasantness, and all her paths are peace.

She is a tree of life to them that lay hold upon her: and happy is every one that retaineth her.

The Lord by wisdom hath founded the earth; by understanding hath he established the heavens.

By his knowledge the depths are broken up, and the clouds drop down the dew.

My son, let not them depart from thine eyes: keep sound wisdom and discretion:

So shall they be life unto thy soul, and grace to thy neck.

Then shalt thou walk in thy way safely, and thy foot shall not stumble.

If any of you lack wisdom, let him ask of God, that giveth to all men liberally, and upbraideth not; and it shall be given him.

548 Prayer

Matthew 6:9-15; 7:7-11; James 5:16b

After this manner therefore pray ye: Our Father which art in heaven, Hallowed be thy name.

Thy kingdom come. Thy will be done in earth, as it is in heaven.

Give us this day our daily bread.

And forgive us our debts, as we forgive our debtors.

And lead us not into temptation, but deliver us from evil: For thine is the kingdom, and the power, and the glory, for ever. Amen.

For if ye forgive men their trespasses, your heavenly Father will also forgive you:

But if ye forgive not men their trespasses, neither will your Father forgive your trespasses.

Ask, and it shall be given you; seek, and ye shall find; knock, and it shall be opened unto you:

For every one that asketh receiveth; and he that seeketh findeth; and to him that knocketh it shall be opened.

Or what man is there of you, whom if his son ask bread, will he give him a stone? Or if he ask a fish, will he give him a serpent?

If ye then, being evil, know how to give good gifts unto your children, how much more shall your Father which is in heaven give good things to them that ask him?

The effectual fervent prayer of a righteous man availeth much.

549 Childlikeness

Matthew 18:1-6; 19:13-14; Psalm 103:13; 1 Corinthians 14:20

At the same time came the disciples unto Jesus, saying, Who is the greatest in the kingdom of heaven?

And Jesus called a little child unto him, and set him in the midst of them,

And said, Verily I say unto you, Except ye be converted, and become as little children, ye shall not enter into the kingdom of heaven.

Whosoever therefore shall humble himself as this little child, the same is greatest in the kingdom of heaven.

And whoso shall receive one such little child in my name receiveth me.

But whoso shall offend one of these little ones which believe in me, it were better for him that a millstone were hanged about his neck, and that he were drowned in the depth of the sea.

Then were there brought unto him little children, that he should put his hands on them, and pray: and the disciples rebuked them.

But Jesus said, Suffer little children, and forbid them not, to come unto me: for of such is the kingdom of heaven.

Like as a father pitieth his children, so the Lord pitieth them that fear him.

Brethren, be not children in understanding: howbeit in malice be ye children, but in understanding be men.

550 Faith

Hebrews 11:1, 4-10

Now faith is the substance of things hoped for, the evidence of things not seen.

By faith Abel offered unto God a more excellent sacrifice than Cain, by which he obtained witness that he was righteous, God testifying of his gifts: and by it he being dead yet speaketh.

By faith Enoch was translated that he should not see death; and was not found, because God had translated him: for before his translation he had this testimony, that he pleased God.

But without faith it is impossible to please him: for he that cometh to God must believe that he is, and that he is a rewarder of them that diligently seek him.

By faith Noah, being warned of God of things not seen as yet, moved with fear, prepared an ark to the saving of his house; by the which he condemned the world, and became heir of the righteousness which is by faith.

By faith Abraham, when he was called to go out into a place which he should after receive for an inheritance, obeyed; and he went out, not knowing whither he went.

By faith he sojourned in the land of promise, as in a strange country, dwelling in tabernacles with Isaac and Jacob, the heirs with him of the same promise:

For he looked for a city which hath foundations, whose builder and maker is God.

551 Fellowship

Romans 12:9-21

Let love be without dissimulation. Abhor that which is evil; cleave to that which is good.

Be kindly affectioned one to another with brotherly love; in honour preferring one another;

Not slothful in business; fervent in spirit; serving the Lord;

Rejoicing in hope; patient in tribulation; continuing instant in prayer;

Distributing to the necessity of saints; given to hospitality.

Bless them which persecute you: bless, and curse not.

Rejoice with them that do rejoice, and weep with them that weep.

Be of the same mind one toward another. Mind not high things, but condescend to men of low estate. Be not wise in your own conceits.

Recompense to no man evil for evil. Provide things honest in the sight of all men.

If it be possible, as much as lieth in you, live peaceably with all men.

Dearly beloved, avenge not yourselves, but rather give place unto wrath: for it is written, Vengeance is mine; I will repay, saith the Lord.

Therefore if thine enemy hunger, feed him; if he thirst, give him drink: for in so doing thou shalt heap coals of fire on his head.

Be not overcome of evil, but overcome evil with good.

552 Greatness

Mark 10:35-44

And James and John, the sons of Zebedee, come unto him, saying, Master, we would that thou shouldest do for us whatsoever we shall desire.

And he said unto them, What would ye that I should do for you?

They said unto him, Grant unto us that we may sit, one on thy right hand, and the other on thy left hand, in thy glory.

But Jesus said unto them, Ye know not what ye ask: can ye drink of the cup that I drink of? and be baptized with the baptism that I am baptized with?

And they said unto him, We can. And Jesus said unto them, Ye shall indeed drink of the cup that I drink of; and with the baptism that I am baptized withal shall ye be baptized:

But to sit on my right hand and on my left hand is not mine to give; but it shall be given to them for whom it is prepared.

And when the ten heard it, they began to be much displeased with James and John.

But Jesus called them to him, and saith unto them, Ye know that they which are accounted to rule over the Gentiles exercise lordship over them; and their great ones exercise authority upon them.

But so shall it not be among you: but whosoever will be great among you, shall be your minister:

And whosoever of you will be the chiefest, shall be servant of all.

553 Victory

1 John 5:1-5; Romans 8:35-39

Whosoever believeth that Jesus is the Christ is born of God: and every one that loveth him that begat loveth him also that is begotten of him.

By this we know that we love the children of God, when we love God, and keep his commandments.

For this is the love of God, that we keep his commandments: and his commandments are not grievous.

For whatsoever is born of God overcometh the world: and this is the victory that overcometh the world, even our faith.

Who is he that overcometh the world, but he that believeth that Jesus is the Son of God?

Who shall separate us from the love of Christ? shall tribulation, or distress, or persecution, or famine, or nakedness, or peril, or sword?

As it is written, For thy sake we are killed all the day long; we are accounted as sheep for the slaughter.

Nay, in all these things we are more than conquerors through him that loved us.

For I am persuaded, that neither death, nor life, nor angels, nor principalities, nor powers, nor things present, nor things to come,

Nor height, nor depth, nor any other creature, shall be able to separate us from the love of God, which is in Christ Jesus our Lord.

554 Patriotism

Romans 13:1-10

Let every soul be subject unto the higher powers, For there is no power but of God: the powers that be are ordained of God.

Whosoever therefore resisteth the power, resisteth the ordinance of God: and they that resist shall receive to themselves damnation.

For rulers are not a terror to good works, but to the evil. Wilt thou then not be afraid of the power? do that which is good, and thou shalt have praise of the same:

For he is the minister of God to thee for good. But if thou do that which is evil, be afraid; for he beareth not the sword in vain: for he is the minister of God, a revenger to execute wrath upon him that doeth evil.

Wherefore ye must needs be subject, not only for wrath, but also for conscience sake.

For for this cause pay ye tribute also: for they are God's ministers, attending continually upon this very thing.

Render therefore to all their dues: tribute to whom tribute is due; custom to whom custom; fear to whom fear; honour to whom honour.

Owe no man any thing, but to love one another: for he that loveth another hath fulfilled the law.

For this, Thou shalt not commit adultery, Thou shalt not kill, Thou shalt not steal, Thou shalt not bear false witness, Thou shalt not covet; and if there be any other commandment, it is briefly comprehended in this saying, namely, Thou shalt love thy neighbour as thyself.

Love worketh no ill to his neighbour: therefore love is the fulfilling of the law.

555 Abstinence

Proverbs 20: 1; 23: 1-2, 20-21, 29-32; 1 Corinthians 8:13

Wine is a mocker, strong drink is raging: and whosoever is deceived thereby is not wise.

When thou sittest to eat with a ruler, consider diligently what is before thee:

And put a knife to thy throat, if thou be a man given to appetite.

Be not among winebibbers; among riotous eaters of flesh:

For the drunkard and the glutton shall come to poverty: and drowsiness shall clothe a man with rags.

Who hath woe? who hath sorrow? who hath contentions? who hath babbling? who hath wounds without cause? who hath redness of eyes?

They that tarry long at the wine; they that go to seek mixed wine.

Look not thou upon the wine when it is red, when it giveth his colour in the cup, when it moveth itself aright.

At the last it biteth like a serpent, and stingeth like an adder.

Wherefore, if meat make my brother to offend, I will eat no flesh while the world standeth, lest I make my brother to offend.

556 Reign of Peace

Isaiah 11:1-7, 9

And there shall come forth a rod out of the stem of Jesse, and a Branch shall grow out of his roots:

And the spirit of the Lord shall rest upon him, the spirit of wisdom and understanding, the spirit of counsel and might, the spirit of knowledge and of the fear of the Lord;

And shall make him of quick understanding in the fear of the Lord: and he shall not judge after the sight of his eyes, neither reprove after the hearing of his ears:

But with righteousness shall he judge the poor, and reprove with equity for the meek of the earth: and he shall smite the earth with the rod of his mouth, and with the breath of his lips shall he slay the wicked.

And righteousness shall be the girdle of his loins, and faithfulness the girdle of his reins.

The wolf also shall dwell with the lamb, and the leopard shall lie down with the kid; and the calf and the young lion and the fatling together; and a little child shall lead them.

And the cow and the bear shall feed; their young ones shall lie down together: and the lion shall eat straw like the ox.

They shall not hurt nor destroy in all my holy mountain: for the earth shall be full of the knowledge of the Lord, as the waters cover the sea.

557 The Golden Rule

Luke 6:27-37

But I say unto you which hear, Love your enemies, do good to them which hate you,

Bless them that curse you, and pray for them which despitefully use you.

And unto him that smiteth thee on the one cheek offer also the other; and him that taketh away thy cloke forbid not to take thy coat also.

Give to every man that asketh of thee; and of him that taketh away thy goods ask them not again.

And as ye would that men should do to you, do ye also to them likewise.

For if ye love them which love you, what thank have ye? for sinners also love those that love them.

And if ye do good to them which do good to you, what thank have ye? for sinners also do even the same.

And if ye lend to them of whom ye hope to receive, what thank have ye? for sinners also lend to sinners, to receive as much again.

But love ye your enemies, and do good, and lend, hoping for nothing again; and your reward shall be great, and ye shall be the children of the Highest: for he is kind unto the unthankful and to the evil.

Be ye therefore merciful, as your Father also is merciful.

Judge not, and ye shall not be judged: condemn not, and ye shall not be condemned: forgive, and ye shall be forgiven.

558 Comfort

Isaiah 40:1-5, 9-11

Comfort ye, comfort ye my people, saith your God.

Speak ye comfortably to Jerusalem, and cry unto her, that her warfare is accomplished, that her iniquity is pardoned:

For she hath received of the Lord's hand double for all her sins.

The voice of him that crieth in the wilderness, Prepare ye the way of the Lord, make straight in the desert a highway for our God.

Every valley shall be exalted, and every mountain and hill shall be made low: and the crooked shall be made straight, and the rough places plain:

And the glory of the Lord shall be revealed, and all flesh shall see it together: for the mouth of the Lord hath spoken it.

O Zion, that bringest good tidings, get thee up into the high mountain; O Jerusalem, that bringest good tidings, lift up thy voice with strength;

Lift it up, be not afraid; say unto the cities of Judah, Behold your God!

Behold, the Lord God will come with strong hand, and his arm shall rule for him: behold, his reward is with him, and his work before him.

He shall feed his flock like a shepherd: he shall gather the lambs with his arm, and carry them in his bosom, and shall gently lead those that are with young.

559 Hope

John 14:1-3; 2 Corinthians 5:1-8

Let not your heart be troubled: ye believe in God, believe also in me.

In my Father's house are many mansions: if it were not so, I would have told you. I go to prepare a place for you.

And if I go and prepare a place for you, I will come again, and receive you unto myself; that where I am, there ye may be also.

For we know that if our earthly house of this tabernacle were dissolved, we have a building of God, an house not made with hands, eternal in the heavens.

For in this we groan, earnestly desiring to be clothed upon with our house which is from heaven:

If so be that being clothed we shall not be found naked.

For we that are in this tabernacle do groan, being burdened: not for that we would be unclothed, but clothed upon, that mortality might be swallowed up of life.

Now he that hath wrought us for the selfsame thing is God, who also hath given unto us the earnest of the Spirit.

Therefore we are always confident, knowing that, whilst we are at home in the body, we are absent from the Lord: (For we walk by faith, not by sight:)

We are confident, I say, and willing rather to be absent from the body, and to be present with the Lord.

560 Ready

2 Timothy 4:6-8; 2 Peter 3:9-12; Matthew 24:42, 44

For I am now ready to be offered, and the time of my departure is at hand.

I have fought a good fight, I have finished my course, I have kept the faith:

Henceforth there is laid up for me a crown of righteousness, which the Lord, the righteous judge, shall give me at that day: and not to me only, but unto all them also that love his appearing.

The Lord is not slack concerning his promise, as some men count slackness; but is longsuffering to us-ward, not willing that any should perish, but that all should come to repentance.

But the day of the Lord will come as a thief in the night; in the which the heavens shall pass away with a great noise, and the elements shall melt with fervent heat, the earth also and the works that are therein shall be burned up.

Seeing then that all these things shall be dissolved, what manner of persons ought ye to be in all holy conversation and godliness,

Looking for and hasting unto the coming of the day of God, wherein the heavens being on fire shall be dissolved, and the elements shall melt with fervent heat?

Watch therefore: for ye know not what hour your Lord doth come. . . , Therefore be ye also ready: for in such an hour as ye think not the Son of man cometh.

561 "Quickly"

Revelation 22:12-20

And, behold, I come quickly; and my reward is with me, to give every man according as his work shall be.

I am Alpha and Omega, the beginning and the end, the first and the last.

Blessed are they that do his commandments, that they may have right to the tree of life, and may enter in through the gates into the city.

For without are dogs, and sorcerers, and whoremongers, and murderers, and idolaters, and whosoever loveth and maketh a lie.

I Jesus have sent mine angel to testify unto you these things in the churches. I am the root and the offspring of David, and the bright and morning star.

And the Spirit and the bride say, Come. And let him that heareth say, Come. And let him that is athirst come. And whosoever will, let him take the water of life freely.

For I testify unto every man that heareth the words of the prophecy of this book, If any man shall add unto these things, God shall add unto him the plagues that are written in this book:

And if any man shall take away from the words of the book of this prophecy, God shall take away his part out of the book of life, and out of the holy city, and from the things which are written in this book.

He which testifieth these things saith, Surely I come quickly.

Amen. Even so, come, Lord Jesus.

562 Heaven

Revelation 7:9-15, 17

After this I beheld, and, lo, a great multitude, which no man could number, of all nations, and kindreds, and people, and tongues, stood before the throne, and before the Lamb, clothed with white robes, and palms in their hands;

And cried with a loud voice, saying, Salvation to our God which sitteth upon the throne, and unto the Lamb.

And all the angels stood round about the throne, and about the elders and the four beasts, and fell before the throne on their faces, and worshipped God,

Saying, Amen: Blessing, and glory, and wisdom, and thanksgiving, and honour, and power, and might, be unto our God for ever and ever. Amen.

And one of the elders answered, saying unto me, What are these which are arrayed in white robes? and whence came they?

And I said unto him, Sir, thou knowest. And he said to me, These are they which came out of great tribulation, and have washed their robes, and made them white in the blood of the Lamb.

Therefore are they before the throne of God, and serve him day and night in his temple: and he that sitteth on the throne shall dwell among them.

For the Lamb which is in the midst of the throne shall feed them, and shall lead them unto living fountains of waters: and God shall wipe away all tears from their eyes.

563 Benedictions

Numbers 6:24-26; 2 Corinthians 13:14; Hebrews 13:20-21; 1 Peter 5:10-11; Jude 24-25; Revelation 22:21

The Lord bless thee, and keep thee:

The Lord make his face shine upon thee, and be gracious unto thee:

The Lord lift up his countenance upon thee, and give thee peace.

The grace of the Lord Jesus Christ, and the love of God, and the communion of the Holy Ghost, be with you all. Amen.

Now the God of peace, that brought again from the dead our Lord Jesus, that great shepherd of the sheep, through the blood of the everlasting covenant,

Make you perfect in every good work to do his will, working in you that which is wellpleasing in his sight, through Jesus Christ; to whom be glory for ever and ever. Amen.

But the God of all grace, who hath called us unto his eternal glory by Christ Jesus, after that ye have suffered a while, make you perfect, stablish, strengthen, settle you.

To him be glory and dominion for ever and ever. Amen.

Now unto him that is able to keep you from falling, and to present you faultless before the presence of his glory with exceeding joy,

To the only wise God our Saviour, be glory and majesty, dominion and power, both now and ever. Amen.

The grace of our Lord Jesus Christ be with you all. Amen.

RESPONSIVE READINGS

INDEX OF TUNES

INDEX

Titles are in SMALL CAPS; first lines in lower case type

TOPICAL INDEX

Choruses

(Short)

Church

Closing Hymns

Comfort

Confession

Conflict

Consecration

Cross

Devotional

Duets

Evening Hymns

Faith

Fellowship

Funeral Hymns

God

Grace

Guidance

Heaven

Holy Spirit

Invitation

Jesus

Joy

Lord's Day

Lord's Supper

Love

Missionary Hymns

Morning Hymns

Mother's Day Hymns

Opening Hymns

Patriotic

Praise

Prayer

Quartets

Repentance

Resurrection

Saviour

Second Coming

(See Christ's Return)

Security

Social Service

Solos

Glory Be to the Father
GLORIA PATRI
H. W. GREATOREX
Glo-ry be to the Fa-ther, and to the Son, and to the Ho-ly Ghost; As it
was in the beginning, is now, and ever shall be, world without end. A-men, A-men.
Glory Be to the Father
[Second Tune]
GLORIA PATRI
CHARLES MEINEKE
Glo-ry be to the Fa-ther, and to the Son, and to the Ho-ly Ghost; As it
was in the beginning, is now, and ever shall be, world without end. A-men, A-men.
Holy, Holy, Holy
Theme from the "Holy City"
ALFRED R. GAUL
Ho-ly, Ho-ly, Ho-ly, Lord of Hosts; Holy, Holy, Holy is the Lord of Hosts. A-men.